Modern Factor Analysis

Modern Factor Analysis

HARRY H. HARMAN

Second Edition, Revised

THE UNIVERSITY OF CHICAGO PRESS

Chicago and London

Library of Congress Catalog Card Number : 67–20572

The University of Chicago Press, Chicago and London

The University of Toronto Press, Toronto 5, Canada

© 1960, 1967 by The University of Chicago

Revised Edition published 1967

Printed in the United States of America

Dedicated to the memory of

Professor Karl John Holzinger

Preface to Second Edition

The author has been very gratified with the reception of *Modern Factor Analysis* over the past seven years. During this time he listened intently to reviewers, correspondents, and colleagues. This revised edition takes cognizance of such suggestions and criticisms—improving, it is hoped, the presentation of the original material— and also introduces much new material.

Since the first edition of this text was published, factor analysis has made considerable progress in several directions. Continued research has led to new techniques for coping with long-standing problems in factor analysis as well as for pushing into areas previously unexplored. Largely responsible were the advances made in electronic computers and their associated programs. Not only have the computers suggested new avenues of research, but because of their greater availability and at reduced costs, factor analysis has been applied in many new areas and by many new workers. All this is reflected in the revised edition, but always with emphasis on the methodological aspects rather than the applications.

The organization of the text remains unchanged—consisting of five major parts covering the basic foundation of factor analysis, direct solutions, derived solutions, factor measurements, and problem material. Within this structure, however, many changes have been introduced. Thus, the original chapter 17 has become the new chapter 10 (properly placed in part ii); the old chapters 7 and 8 have been consolidated into new chapter 7; the old chapter 10 has been condensed and has become a section of the new chapter 8; while entirely new material will be found in chapter 9 and sections **8.2**, **8.8**, **15.5**, and **16.3**. In addition, many other sections of the book were changed to bring them in line with present-day theory and practice. The net result is that the new edition, although totally revised, is about the same length as the first edition.

Important changes were introduced as a direct result of the impact of computers: certain classical methods of factor analysis are now obsolete. For example, the centroid method, for all its historical interest and importance, is a technique that has given way to the more mathematically sound principal-factor method made possible by the modern-day computer. By the same token, hand-computing techniques such as those covered in sections **3.3** and **3.4** assume less importance in the present computer era, but their study has considerable heuristic value. In general, the author still favors an eclectic approach, but more attention is paid to the present-day relevance of the various methods and recommendations are made among the several alternatives.

The author has drawn upon many published researches to enhance the text, and the acknowledgments made in the preface of the first edition are implied once again. In addition, I especially want to extend my thanks to Professor Robert I. Jennrich and my son, Alvin J. Harman, both of whom suggested a more consistent use of matrix notation and critically reviewed portions of the revised manuscript. Also, Dr. Jennrich made available to me draft copies of his paper and computer program, upon which the direct oblimin method of section **15.5** is based.

In the attempt to keep up to date on the new developments in factor analysis, I have been aided materially by the stimulating and provocative discussions of the Factor Analysis Work Group, sponsored in part by the U.S. Office of Naval Research, during 1962–66. The regular members at the semiannual meetings of this group included L. R. Tucker, chairman, R. Bargmann, H. H. Harman, C. W. Harris, P. Horst, L. G. Humphreys, H. F. Kaiser, W. Meredith, and C. Wrigley, and visitors at specific meetings included L. Guttman, K. Jöreskog, and A. Madansky.

Once again, I am pleased to express my gratitude to Margot von Mendelssohn for her continued assistance in updating the bibliography and in the preparation of the manuscript for the revised edition.

HARRY H. HARMAN

Princeton, New Jersey

Preface to First Edition

Modern Factor Analysis reflects the progress made in the nineteen years since my publication with Professor Karl. J. Holzinger of *Factor Analysis*, and includes the advances that have taken place in the computing art. Many new concepts and procedures have been developed in these years while some unwieldy methods are now obsolete.

A revised edition of Holzinger and Harman's *Factor Analysis* might have appeared several years ago were it not for the untimely death of Dr. Holzinger in 1954. We were just laying the groundwork for the revision of our original work, and were anticipating the actual start in the late summer of that year, following his appointment as visiting professor at the University of California at Berkeley. In addition to the deep personal loss, Dr. Holzinger's death ended a professional partnership of twenty years which the writer held in highest esteem.

In the light of the vast and broad advances that have occurred in factor analysis due largely to the advent of electronic computers, a revision alone would have been insufficient to include the new material covered in the present text. Among the more important features of *Modern Factor Analysis* are the following: (1) the treatment of "simple structure" concepts and methods, usually associated with the Thurstone school of factor analysis; (2) the introduction of analytical methods of rotation to desired final solutions; (3) the use of high-speed electronic computers in factor analysis; (4) the use of the square root method for desk calculator operations; (5) the introduction of statistical tests of hypotheses in factor analysis; (6) the presentation of problems and exercises, and answers to go with them; and (7) the very extensive, pertinent bibliography on the theory and methods of factor analysis. This book is intended to serve as a reference treatise on factor analysis in the current stage of advancement of the subject. Furthermore, it is hoped that its utility as a text book will be enhanced by the many problems and exercises, as well as the computing algorithms and summaries of concepts and notation.

The text is organized into five major parts, covering the foundation of factor analysis, direct solutions, derived solutions, some special topics, and problem material. The six chapters of part I provide the historical background and basic notions of factor analysis, introducing the fundamental mathematics necessary for a proper understanding of the subject, and concluding with an enumeration and general description of the principal forms of factor solutions. Part II develops several of these solutions directly from the observed data (the correlations among the variables). This is accomplished in five chapters where computing procedures and illustrative examples are presented as well as the theoretical developments. The notion of derived solutions is introduced in part III by considering the relationships among the arbitrary choices of factor solutions. Then follows an elaboration of the simple structure principles, the distinction between primary and reference coordinate systems, and the analytical methods of arriving at either orthogonal or oblique multiple-factor solutions from some arbitrary initial solution. In part IV two broad special topics are considered. While most of the text is concerned with the resolution of the observed variables in terms of the factors, here a chapter is devoted in the inverse problem of measuring the factors in terms of the variables. Some very effective computing procedures are presented for this purpose. The final chapter is concerned with formal statistical tests in factor analysis, in contradistinction to the implicit mathematical basis assumed in standard factor analysis methods.

Following the text proper there are several additional items. In part V a large group of problems and exercises not only provides useful material for classroom use, but is intended to support and supplement the formal presentation. Of the statistical tables presented in the Appendix, some are standard and are provided simply for the convenience of the reader while some are unique to factor analysis. The Bibliography has been carefully culled from the vast literature to include only those specific papers and treatises that are relevant to the theory and methods of factor analysis. A myriad of applications has purposefully been excluded. Finally, a very detailed Index is included.

Throughout the text the theoretical developments are elucidated both by the detailed computing procedures and the numerical illustrations. The particular content area of these data has no special significance since they are employed merely to exemplify the techniques. For this reason, many of the numerical examples that were first employed by Holzinger and Harman, and have since become classics in the literature, are used in *Modern Factor Analysis* to illustrate the new techniques and make possible comparisons with the old.

While factor analysis was created and developed largely by psychologists, its usefulness as a statistical tool has much broader implications. It is in the latter sense that the subject is presented in this text. Psychological data are used for illustrative purposes, but no attempt is made to formulate new psychological theories. This book is intended to provide the student with the basis for a clear understanding of the concepts and techniques of factor analysis. He is then in a position to employ factor analysis as a statistical tool in developing theories in psychology or other disciplines.

Mathematical language is employed in order to present a precise, unambiguous picture—not for the sake of mere elegance, nor even for rigorous proof. Some proofs are given, some roughly indicated, some omitted entirely. Primarily, the work is an exposition and not a formal mathematical development. However, the mathematical language represents careful selection and is precise. It is the author's firm belief that a little effort on the part of the reader to grasp and to follow the notation will yield immeasurable rewards in understanding the subject.

The author gratefully renders due homage to the many individuals whose published researches have been drawn upon for the enrichment of these pages. I wish it were possible in every instance to assign credit where it is due, but in any event, I want to avoid claiming credit to myself for any development first made by another. It is a particular pleasure for me to acknowledge my debt to both Professor Holzinger and Professor Thurstone for my early development in the field of factor analysis.

Of course many of the author's thoughts on the foundation and basic mode of presenting the factor problem were incorporated in his joint work with Dr. Holzinger. He is indebted to the University of Chicago Press for permission to use portions of such work which first appeared in Holzinger and Harman, *Factor Analysis*.

Permission from John Wiley and Sons, Inc., to reprint material from the author's chapter, "Factor Analysis," in *Mathematical Methods for Digital Computers*, edited by Anthony Ralston and Herbert S. Wilf, is gratefully acknowledged. I am indebted to Professor Sir Ronald A. Fisher, F.R.S., Cambridge, and to Dr. Frank Yates, F.R.S., Rothamsted, also to Messrs. Oliver & Boyd Ltd., Edinburgh, for permission to reprint Table D in the Appendix, taken from their book *Statistical Tables for Biological, Agricultural and Medical Research*.

Portions of the manuscript have been read, and helpful suggestions made, by Dr. Edith S. Jay and Dr. John M. Leiman. Invaluable assistance was provided by Mr. Leonard W. Staugas in the application of electronic computers to the solution of many problems in the text. The drafting of the illustrations is largely due to Mr. Toshio Odano. Mr. Wayne H. Jones offered critical assistance and wise counsel on many occasions during the final preparation of this book, and was especially helpful in regard to the final draft of chapter 17. All of the foregoing are my colleagues at the System Development Corporation, and to each one I acknowledge indebtedness and deep appreciation.

The author had the benefit of consultation with Professor John B. Carroll, Harvard University, Professor Henry F. Kaiser, University of Illinois, and Dr. David R. Saunders, Educational Testing Service, in regard to the analytical methods for the multiple-factor solution. In addition, Professor Kaiser gave me a critical appraisal of the first drafts of chapters 14 and 15, and arranged for the calculation of several complex problems on the Illiac. Professor Carroll also read these chapters and provided me with the computer programs and his draft of the oblimin methods as soon as they were available in late 1958. It is a pleasure to acknowledge appreciation for this generous assistance.

Dr. Ardie Lubin, Walter Reed Army Institute of Research, provided stimulation and encouragement at the initiation of the work, and had a major part in preparing the first draft of chapter 17. While I may not have written the text along the lines of compact matrix algebra and precise statistical terms as Dr. Lubin would have liked to see it, nonetheless I am grateful for the many incisive discussions with him.

My sincere thanks are due Mr. Harry A. Liff for suggesting that the present work be undertaken and for his constant encouragement during the last two years of preparation of the manuscript.

Finally, I owe a special debt of gratitude to Margot von Mendelssohn for her tireless assistance in all phases of the book's preparation.

H.H.H.

Pacific Palisades, California
1960

Contents

Part II

Direct Solutions

Part III

Derived Solutions

Part IV

Factor Measurements

Part V

Problems and Exercises

Appendix

List of Illustrations

Guide to Notation

The text is organized to assist the reader in quickly locating any topic or displayed material. All items are tied to the chapter number. The primary subdivisions of chapters are sections—printed in boldface type and consisting of chapter number, period, and serial number of section within chapter, e.g., **10.4** for the fourth section in chapter 10. The mathematical equations, tables, and figures are similarly numbered within each chapter, but in ordinary type and with the equation number enclosed in parentheses. Examples of these are: equation (11.6), Table 11.2, Figure 5.1. In referring to a table or figure, the identifying word is always employed; but since equations are distinguished by parentheses, frequently the equation number is given without the words "equation" or "formula". References to bibliographical entries are enclosed in square brackets, e.g., Gibson [150].

Definitions and symbols are introduced as necessary to clarify the presentation. For convenience, the locations of the principal sources of notation are indicated in the following table.

SUMMARIES OF NOTATION

Item	Page	Description
Eq. (2.20)	19	Symbols for composition of variance
Sec. **3.2**	30	Definitions of determinants and matrices
Sec. **3.2**, par. **8**	32	Notation for vectors, matrices, and determinants
Table 3.3	43	Square root method for calculating inverse of a matrix
Table 4.1	66	Geometric concepts
Table 6.1	108	Summary of types of factor solutions
Eq. (7.11)	118	Set-theory notations
Table 10.1	215	Notation for matrices in statistical estimation of factor weights
Table 11.1	235	Concepts and notation for multiple-group solution
Table 13.4	290	Notation in oblique solutions
Table 15.1	315	Concepts and notation for analytical multiple-factor solutions
Table 16.1	347	Notation for matrices frequently used
Table 16.8	364	Computing algorithm for measurement of factors
Table 16.9	366	Computing algorithm for inverse of correlation matrix from factor solution

PART I

FOUNDATIONS OF FACTOR ANALYSIS

1
Introduction

1.1. *Brief History of Factor Analysis*

Factor analysis is a branch of statistical science, but because of its development and extensive use in psychology the technique itself is often mistakenly considered as psychological theory. The method came into being specifically to provide mathematical models for the explanation of psychological theories of human ability and behavior. Among the more famous of such theories are those proposed by Spearman, Burt, Kelley, Thurstone, Holzinger, and Thomson.

The birth of factor analysis is generally ascribed to Charles Spearman. His monumental work in developing a psychological theory involving a single general factor and a number of specific factors goes back to 1904 when his paper "General Intelligence, Objectively Determined and Measured" was published in the *American Journal of Psychology*. Of course, his 1904 investigation was only the beginning of his work in developing the Two-Factor Theory, and his early work is not explicitly in terms of "factors." Perhaps a more crucial article, certainly insofar as the statistical aspects are concerned, is the 1901 paper by Karl Pearson [386] in which he sets forth "the method of principal axes." Nevertheless, Spearman, who devoted the remaining forty years of his life to the development of factor analysis, is regarded as the father of the subject.

A considerable amount of work on the psychological theories and mathematical foundations of factor analysis followed in the next twenty years. The principal contributors during this period included Charles Spearman, Cyril Burt, Karl Pearson, Godfrey H. Thomson, J. C. Maxwell Garnett, and Karl Holzinger; the topics receiving the greatest attention were attempts to prove or disprove the existence of general ability, the study of sampling errors of tetrad differences, and computational methods for a single general factor which included the fundamental formula of the centroid solution.

3

The early modern period, including the bulk of the active and published controversy on factor analysis, came after 1925, with a real spurt of activity in the 1930's. By this time it had become quite apparent that Spearman's Two-Factor Theory was not always adequate to describe a battery of psychological tests. So group factors found their way into factor analysis; although the experimenters, at first, were very reluctant to admit such deviation from the basic theory and restricted the group factors to as small a number as possible. What actually happened was that the *theory* of a general and specific factors in Spearman's original form was superseded by theories of many group factors, but the early *method* continued to be employed to determine these many factors. Then it naturally followed that some workers explored the possibility of extracting several factors directly from a matrix of correlations among tests, and thus arose the concept of multiple-factor analysis in the work of Garnett [140].

While the actual term may be attributed to L. L. Thurstone, and while he undoubtedly has done most to popularize the method of multiple-factor analysis, he certainly was not the first to take exception to Spearman's Two-Factor Theory and was not the first to develop a theory of many factors. It is not even the centroid method of analysis (see sec. **8.9**) for which Thurstone deserves a place of prominence in factor analysis. The centroid method is clearly admitted by Thurstone to be a computational compromise for the principal-factor solution. The truly remarkable contribution of Thurstone was the generalization of Spearman's tetrad-difference criterion to the *rank* of the correlation matrix as the basis for determining the number of common factors (see **4.10** and chap. 5). He saw that a zero tetrad-difference corresponded to the vanishing of a second-order determinant, and extended this notion to the vanishing of higher order determinants as the condition for more than a single factor. The matrix formulation of the problem has greatly facilitated further advances in factor analysis.

The mathematical techniques inherent in factor analysis certainly are not limited to psychological applications. The principal concern of factor analysis is the resolution of a set of variables linearly in terms of (usually) a small number of categories or "factors". This resolution can be accomplished by the analysis of the correlations among the variables. A satisfactory solution will yield factors which convey all the essential information of the original set of variables. Thus, the chief aim is to attain scientific parsimony or economy of description.

As will become evident in the course of this text, a given matrix of correlations can be factored in an infinite number of ways. (It is not entirely clear whether this well-known fact was truly appreciated in the earlier days of factor analysis; and if, in fact, the failure to recognize this mathematical truism may not have been the cause of the many controversies regarding the "true", the "best", or the "invariant" solution for a set of variables.) When an infinite number of equally accurate solutions are available, the question arises: How shall a choice be made among these possibilities? The preferred types of factor solutions are determined on the basis of two general principles: (1) statistical simplicity, and (2) psychological meaningfulness (if the content area is psychology). In turn, each of these requires interpretation, and each has been applied variously to yield several distinct schools of factor analysts.

If one were to make his choice entirely upon statistical considerations, a rather natural approach would be to represent the original set of variables in terms of a number of factors, determined in sequence so that at each successive stage the factor would account for a maximum of the variance. This statistically optimal solution—the method of principal axes discussed in chapter 8—was first proposed by Pearson at the turn of the century, and in the 1930's Hotelling provided the full development of the method. While this procedure is perfectly straightforward, it entails a very considerable amount of computation, and becomes impractical with ordinary computing facilities when the matrix is of order 10 or greater. In recent years, however, this difficulty has been overcome by the use of high-speed electronic computers.

Another choice based upon statistical considerations is the centroid solution. As indicated above, this method was introduced only as a computational expedient when it became apparent that the principal-factor solution was too laborious. All that can be said for the centroid method is that it produces without much arithmetic one of many possible sets of axes which account for the variance in a manner approximating the optimal situation of the principal axes.

The end product of these solutions—principal or centroid—generally is not acceptable to psychologists (although Burt sometimes prefers the principal-factor solution). In quest of "meaningful" factor solutions, psychologists have introduced various theories in the hope of arriving at a form of solution which would be unique and apply equally well to intelligence, personality, physical measurements, and any other variables with which they might be concerned. Holzinger's Bi-Factor Theory and Thurstone's Simple Structure Theory are in this class. On the other hand, Thomson's Sampling Theory ([465], chaps. 3 and 20) is primarily a psychological theory of the mind. There is no preferred type of factor solution obtainable uniquely on grounds of psychological significance (see **6.2**). If psychological meaningfulness rather than a mathematical standard is imposed, then the judgment of the investigator must be involved. The recent progress toward objective solutions to this problem is presented in chapters 14 and 15.

As pointed out above, a principal objective of factor analysis is to attain a parsimonious description of observed data. This aim should not be construed to mean that factor analysis necessarily attempts to discover the "fundamental" or "basic" categories in a given field of investigation such as psychology. It might be desirable to base such an analysis upon a set of variables which measures all possible mental aspects of a given population as completely and accurately as possible. Even in such a case, however, the factors would not be completely fundamental because of the omission of important measures which were not yet devised. While the goal of complete description cannot be reached theoretically, it may be approached practically in a limited field of investigation where a relatively small number of variables is considered exhaustive. In all cases, however, factor analysis does give a simple interpretation of a given body of data and thus affords a fundamental description of the particular set of variables analyzed.

The essential purpose of factor analysis has been well expressed by Kelley [306, p. 120]: "There is no search for timeless, spaceless, populationless truth in factor analysis; rather, it represents a simple, straightforward problem of description in several dimensions of a definite group functioning in definite manners, and he who assumes to read more remote verities into the factorial outcome is certainly doomed to disappointment."

1.2. *Applications of Factor Analysis*

The application of factor-analysis techniques has been chiefly in the field of psychology. This limitation has no foundation other than the fact that it had its origin in psychology and that accounts of the subject have tended to be "... so bound up with the psychological conception of mental factors that an ordinary statistician has difficulty in seeing it in a proper setting in relation to the general body of statistical method" [312, p. 60]. One objective of this book is to correct this situation.

The methods of factor analysis may lead to some theory suggested by the form of the solution, and conversely one may formulate a theory and verify it by an appropriate form of factorial solution. The latter approach is illustrated by Spearman's theory *"all branches of intellectual activity have in common one fundamental function (or group of functions) whereas the remaining or specific elements of the activity seem in every case to be wholly different from that in all others"* [438, p. 202]. He showed that if certain relationships (the tetrads defined in **5.3**) exist among the correlations, all the variables can be resolved into linear expressions involving only one general factor and an additional factor unique to each variable. These relationships furnish the statistical verification of the "Two-Factor Theory." If a set of psychological variables yields correlation coefficients which do not satisfy the preceding relationships, then a more complex theory may be postulated. This may require several common factors in the statistical description of the variables.

One of the earliest proposals for broadening the psychological uses of factor analysis was made in 1940 by Truman L. Kelley [307], when he gave a method for attaining the greatest social utility while at the same time preserving individual liberties and rights. Then during World War II, with the large-scale testing, classification, and assignment problems, factor analysis was employed widely throughout the several branches of the military services of the United States. Psychologists, of course, have continued to develop and exploit the technique to the present day.

Many psychologists have engaged in extensive testing programs, employing factor analysis to determine a relatively small number of tests to describe the human mind as completely as possible. The usual approach includes the factor analysis of a large battery of tests in order to identify a few common factors. Then the tests which best measure these factors, or, preferably, revised tests based upon these, may be selected as direct measures of the "factors of mind." However, only to the extent to which psychologists agree that the tests selected are the "right tests" can they be said to be actual measures of the factors. Such "factor tests" should be of a "pure" nature, differing widely from one another so as to cover the entire range of mental activity. Several major studies have been undertaken to identify factors from large sets of tests. Among the early studies of this type are the Spearman–Holzinger [234] unitary trait investigation and Thurstone's [472] primary mental abilities study. More recent studies concerned with the isolation of specific psychological factors are very numerous, e.g., J. P. Guilford [167], Raymond B. Cattell [76], and John French [135].

Almost as numerous are the applications to fields of psychology other than intelligence. Again, by way of illustration, can be included: a study of temperament [169]; an investigation of executive morale [425]; uses in clinical therapy [346, 361]; analysis of perceptual bases of speaker identity [502]; and determination of the voting behavior of justices of the Supreme Court [424, 480].

In recent years there has been an ever increasing application of factor analysis to fields other than psychology—fields as varied as sociology and meteorology, political science and medicine, geography and business. While it is not the intent of this book to go into any detail on the many content applications of factor analysis, it is fitting to note some of the newer areas where it is being used. A sampling from about 200 such applications into a dozen distinct fields discloses some of the exciting uses of factor analysis. The following are illustrative of these applied studies:

International relations [10, 410, 411, 453];

Urbanization and economic development [37, 38, 48, 154, 157, 163, 220, 393, 421];

Sociology [78, 170, 350, 389];

Economics [13, 124, 310, 315, 316, 532];

Man-machine systems [412, 481];

Accident research [165, 500];

Communications [509, 510];

Taxonomy, from such varied fields as entomology and classification of publications [45, 46, 406, 407, 431, 434];

Biology [433, 533];

Physiology and medicine [15, 247, 282, 382, 384, 390], with special reference to cardio-vascular diseases [66, 67, 82, 92, 419];

Geology [273, 317];

Meteorology [17, 517].

From the foregoing brief enumeration of some of the studies employing factor analysis, it can be seen that many investigators have come to appreciate the power and benefits to be reaped from this multivariate statistical technique.

The applications of factor analysis indicated above are concerned primarily with classification and verification of scientific hypotheses in the particular field of investigation. Quite a different use—regarded by some to be the chief value of factor analysis—is to supplement, and perhaps simplify, conventional statistical techniques and computations. Typical of this kind of application is the use of factor analysis in expediting the computation of multiple regression statistics (see e.g., [108], [90]), the savings being especially noticeable when the number of variables is large and the number of factors small. This comes about from the fact that the task of inverting a correlation matrix is reduced essentially from the order of the number of variables to the order of the number of factors (see chap. 16). In the problem of studying the relationship between two sets of variables factor analysis can again be employed. The best linear function of the variables in each set is obtained by factorial methods, and then the correlation between these composites gives what is known as the *canonical correlation* [262]. Such a correlation is the maximum possible between the two sets of variables.

While the present text is concerned primarily with the exposition of various procedures in factor analysis, numerous examples are employed for illustrative purposes. Some examples are hypothetical, but most of them are taken from psychology and the social sciences. These examples serve to clarify the theoretical treatment only, not to exhibit the practical usefulness of factor analysis.

1.3. *Scientific Explanation and Choice*

Factor analysis, like all statistics, is a branch of applied mathematics. Thus, it is used as a tool in the empirical sciences. In dealing with observed data, of course, there are inherent discrepancies. One of the objectives of statistical theory is to provide a scientific law, or mathematical model, to explain the underlying behavior of the data. Some simple examples include: (1) a linear regression for the prediction of school success from three entrance examinations; (2) a mathematical curve, such as the normal distribution or one of the Pearson family of curves, for the explanation of an observed frequency distribution; (3) a chi-square test of significance for the independence of such classifications as "treated or not treated with a certain serum," and "cured or not cured". Such laws make allowance for random variations of the observed data from the theoretically expected values. It is conceivable that any one of several, quite different, mathematical models may provide an equally good fit or explanation of a set of data.

In general, science is concerned with the establishment of laws regarding the behavior of empirical events or elements in the particular field. Such laws—usually expressed as mathematical functions—serve to relate the knowledge about the known elements and to provide reliable predictions about future elements. The standard procedure in developing a scientific theory involves the formulation of a mathematical law on the basis of some observations (with discrepancies), followed by the verification of the particular mathematical model with new observations. For any problem in an applied science there may be a number of mathematical theories which explain the phenomena in a satisfactory manner. A misunderstanding of the relationship between a mathematical model and observed data is frequently encountered. When a theory has been successfully employed in describing a set of data, there is a tendency to accept this law as the only correct one for describing the observations.

> Furthermore, it is sometimes inferred that nature behaves in precisely the way which the mathematics indicates. As a matter of fact, nature never does behave in this way, and there are *always more mathematical theories than one* whose results depart from a given set of data by less than the errors of observation.
> . . . .
> The danger is always when a theory has been found to be convenient and effective over a long period of time, that people begin to think that nature herself behaves precisely in the way which is indicated by the theory. This is never the case, and the belief that it is so may close our minds to other possible theories and be a serious impedence to progress in the development of our interpretations of the world around us [41, pp. 472, 477, author's italics].

The above observations apply equally well in different fields. One of the simplest cases arises in the problem of surveying a small tract of land. For this purpose either of two mathematical theories, plane or spherical trigonometry, may be applied. Thus, in surveying a city lot the result by either theory would be equally satisfactory, and the engineer would prefer the plane theory because of its greater simplicity. In this instance, however, there is no doubt as to the greater accuracy of the spherical theory since the earth is essentially spherical.

In the field of astronomy there are two common theories describing the solar system. The Ptolemaic and Copernican theories, with suitable modification of the former, describe the motions of the planets with equal accuracy. "There is really no advantage for either of these theories as compared with the other, as far as their adaptability to explain numerically the facts of the solar system is concerned. The Copernican theory is, however, much the simpler geometrically and mathematically. For this reason it has been adapted and developed until astronomers can predict coming celestial events with most surprising accuracy" [41, pp. 477–8].

Even the subject of geometry, which might seem to depend on a unique mathematical theory, can be described by means of many different theories. Thus, the physical configurations in a plane can be interpreted in the light of Euclidean geometry, Riemannian geometry, or various other types of non-Euclidean geometry. Therefore, the applied science of geometry can have several alternative theories as its basis.

As in the foregoing illustrations there are different models, or forms of solution, which may arise in the factorial analysis of a particular set of data. The usefulness of factor analysis as a scientific tool has been questioned by some workers because of this indeterminacy. It should be evident, however, that this is tantamount to indicting all applied sciences because they do not depend upon unique theories.

Since the beginning of this century, psychologists and statisticans have developed several types of factorial solutions. The proponent of each system of analysis has urged its suitability for the interpretation of psychological data. The strong feelings and emotions that characterized one period in the development of factor analysis have been described with both sarcasm and wit by Cureton [91, p. 287]:

> Factor theory may be defined as a mathematical rationalization. A factor-analyst is an individual with a peculiar obsession regarding the nature of mental ability or personality. By the application of higher mathematics to wishful thinking, he always proves that his original fixed idea or compulsion was right or necessary. In the process he usually proves that all other factor-analysts are dangerously insane, and that the only salvation for them is to undergo his own brand of analysis in order that the true essence of their several maladies may be discovered. Since they never submit to this indignity, he classes them all as hopeless cases, and searches about for some branch of mathematics which none of them is likely to have studied in order to prove that their incurability is not only necessary but also sufficient.

The heated and inspired controversies about the "best" method of factor analysis are over—Charles Spearman (1863–1945), L. L. Thurstone (1887–1955), Karl J. Holzinger (1893–1954) have all passed from the scene. It is not a personal controversy that is implied here, but rather the strong conviction of each individual who had devoted a major part of his life to the development of a particular school of thought in factor analysis. The many papers that appeared during the thirties and forties urging "this method" rather than "that method" had their place in the growth of the subject. However, with a fuller understanding of the salient features of each method, and with the increased efficiency of computations, the differences among the various methods no longer loom so ominously, and the followers of a particular approach are much more tolerant of the adherents of an alternative scheme.

It should be evident that the different types of factorial solutions correspond to the different mathematical theories in the description of a particular scientific problem. Several preferred forms of solution are enumerated (see chap. 6), before the detailed presentation of the factor analysis theory and computing procedures. From such statements of the salient features of the preferred solutions, the researcher may weigh the advantages and limitations of any particular type of solution for his particular data.

It is the sincere hope of the author that the present book will provide a better understanding of apparently competing methods of factor analysis. By bringing the several methods under proper focus, an unbiased decision regarding the appropriateness of any one of them should be possible.

2
Factor Analysis Model

2.1. *Introduction*

As noted in the preceding section, one of the first tasks confronting the researcher who is concerned with the analysis of a body of observed data is the formulation of some kind of theoretical statistical model. Sometimes this fundamental step is overlooked or only tacitly implied. In any event, a particular model must be acknowledged if any inference is to be made about the observed data. Of course, there are many different models for observed data depending on the purpose of the analysis. Because of the inherent desire of scientists to explain observed phenomena in terms of elegant (i.e., simple) theories, and because the mathematical development might otherwise become frightfully complex, a linear model is frequently assumed. That is a basic assumption made throughout this book. The generalizations that might ensue from a removal of the linear constraint are indicated by Bartlett [31, pp. 32–34], McDonald [359], and Wood [531].

The fundamental statistical concepts and notation required in factor analysis are set forth in **2.2**. This is followed by the linear models employed in factor analysis. The variance composition of a variable, attributable to the different types of factors postulated in the model, is presented in **2.4**. Again, some of the basic terms are delineated and clearly defined. The factor problem is then presented in **2.5**, where the elements to be determined by the analysis are identified. Then the degree of fit of the factor model to the observed data is considered in **2.6**, and the indeterminacy of factor solutions is explained in **2.7**. Finally, in **2.8** many of the preceding concepts are put in much more compact form by the use of matrix notation.

2.2. *Basic Statistics*

A statistical study typically involves a group of individuals with some common attributes. The term "individual" is used here in a generic sense to stand for such objects or entities as persons, census tracts, businesses, etc. Measurements made on such individuals, or attributes of these entities, are designated simply as *variables*. Throughout this text the letter N is used for the total number of individuals, and the letter n for the number of variables. A particular variable is denoted by X_j, or simply j, which may be any one of the n variables: 1, 2, 3, ..., n. The index i is employed to designate any one of the N individuals: 1, 2, 3, ..., N. Then, the value of a variable X_j for individual i is represented by X_{ji}, the order of the subscripts being of importance. A particular X_{ji} is called an *observed value* which is measured from an arbitrary origin and by an arbitrary unit.

It is customary in statistical literature to employ Greek letters to denote population parameters (and hypothetical or latent variables) and corresponding Latin letters to indicate simple observations of these variables. Also, to indicate a sample *estimate* of a population parameter, the latter symbol is modified by placing a caret ($\widehat{\ }$) over it. To the extent that it is convenient, and does not violate long established practice in factor analysis, such notation will be followed in this text.

Some simple statistical concepts are presented here for ready reference. Frequent use is made of the sum of the N values for a variable X_j, namely:

$$(2.1) \qquad \sum_{i=1}^{N} X_{ji} \quad \text{or} \quad \sum X_{ji},$$

where, in the second expression, the summation is understood to be over all values of the variable. This convention for the summation with respect to the number of observations of a particular variable will be observed throughout the text. Furthermore, the index i will be reserved explicitly to refer to the individuals, that is, for the range 1 to N.

For a sample of N observations, the *mean* of any variable is defined by

$$(2.2) \qquad \overline{X}_j = \sum X_{ji}/N.$$

The n population means would be designated μ_j if they were required in any theoretical development. The observed values of the variables may be transformed to more convenient form by fixing the origin and the unit of measurement. When the origin is placed at the sample mean, a particular value

$$(2.3) \qquad x_{ji} = X_{ji} - \overline{X}_j$$

is called a *deviate*.

The *sample* variance* of variable X_j is defined by

$$(2.4) \qquad s_j^2 = \sum x_{ji}^2/N.$$

The population variances are denoted by σ_j^2. Now, taking the sample standard deviation as the unit of measurement, the *standardized value* of variable j for individual i

---

* It should be noted that the sample value of the variance is a biased estimate of the population variance from a normal distribution, but multiplication by $N/(N - 1)$ makes it unbiased.

is given by

$$(2.5) \qquad z_{ji} = x_{ji}/s_j.$$

The set of all values z_{ji} $(i = 1, 2, \ldots, N)$ is called a variable z_j in *standard form*. Obviously the variance of z_j is unity.

For any two variables j and k the sample *covariance* is defined by

$$(2.6) \qquad s_{jk} = \sum x_{ji} x_{ki}/N,$$

and the corresponding population parameter is designated σ_{jk}. The *correlation coefficient* in the universe is ρ_{jk} and in the sample is defined by

$$(2.7) \qquad r_{jk} = s_{jk}/s_j s_k = \sum z_{ji} z_{ki}/N = \sum x_{ji} x_{ki} \left/ \sqrt{\sum x_{ji}^2 \sum x_{ki}^2} \right..$$

The correlations among all the variables of a study are usually computed as the initial step in a factor analysis.

In order to provide concrete illustrations of some of the basic statistics, a very simple numerical example is now introduced. The same example will be used throughout the text to demonstrate the various features of factor analysis. Only $N = 12$ individuals and $n = 5$ variables are considered in order to bring out all aspects of factor analysis, while at the same time keeping the computation at a minimum. While artificial data might have been contrived to yield exact mathematical solutions, it was deemed more advisable to use objective, fallible data, even though most of the standards regarding experimental design, sampling, and reliability are obviously ignored. So, while the data are "real," the results are not intended to have any real substantive value but merely to illustrate the methods, and perhaps to provide a convenient numerical problem for checking of computer programs.

With this understanding, the data in Table 2.1 were taken (not entirely arbitrarily) from a study of the Los Angeles Standard Metropolitan Statistical Area. The twelve individuals used in the example are census tracts—small areal subdivisions of Los Angeles. A full-scale factor analysis of 67 variables (in percentage form rather than actual values to allow for greater comparability) and 1,169 census tracts is reported by Burns and Harman [48]. The study was designed to include groups of variables involving population, employment, income, and housing characteristics, and these are represented in the little example. From the raw data, the correlations among the five variables were computed as the initial step toward subsequent factor analysis work. These correlations are shown in Table 2.2.* While the calculation of the correlations is singled out as a separate step, it is done so only for ease of presentation. Nowadays, when large electronic computers are quite readily available for factor analysis work, the determination of the correlations is a trivial step in the computer process going from the raw data to the final solution. As this example is used again and again in the text, the thread will be picked up from the correlations to the next phase and subsequent ones.

---

* The only reason for showing five decimal places (as output from an IBM 7094) is to provide a means for checking numerical calculations.

Table 2.1

Raw Data for Five Socio-Economic Variables

Individual (Tract No.) *i*	Variable				
	Total Popula- tion 1	Median School Years 2	Total Employ- ment 3	Misc. Professional Services 4	Median Value House 5
1 (1439)	5,700	12.8	2,500	270	25,000
2 (2078)	1,000	10.9	600	10	10,000
3 (2408)	3,400	8.8	1,000	10	9,000
4 (2621)	3,800	13.6	1,700	140	25,000
5 (7007)	4,000	12.8	1,600	140	25,000
6 (5312)	8,200	8.3	2,600	60	12,000
7 (6032)	1,200	11.4	400	10	16,000
8 (6206)	9,100	11.5	3,300	60	14,000
9 (4037)	9,900	12.5	3,400	180	18,000
10 (4605)	9,600	13.7	3,600	390	25,000
11 (5323)	9,600	9.6	3,300	80	12,000
12 (5416)	9,400	11.4	4,000	100	13,000
Mean	6,242	11.4	2,333	121	17,000
Standard deviation	3,440	1.8	1,241	115	6,368

Table 2.2

Correlations among Five Socio-Economic Variables

Variable *j*	1	2	3	4	5
1. Total population	1.00000	.00975	.97245	.43887	.02241
2. Median school years	.00975	1.00000	.15428	.69141	.86307
3. Total employment	.97245	.15428	1.00000	.51472	.12193
4. Misc. profess. services	.43887	.69141	.51472	1.00000	.77765
5. Median value house	.02241	.86307	.12193	.77765	1.00000

2.3. *Linear Models*

It is the object of factor analysis to represent a variable z_j in terms of several under-lying *factors*, or hypothetical constructs. The simplest mathematical model for describing a variable in terms of several others is a linear one, and that is the form of representation employed here. However, there are still several alternatives within the linear framework, depending on the objective of the analysis. A distinction between two objectives can be made immediately, namely: (1) to extract the maximum variance; and (2) to "best" reproduce the observed correlations.

An empirical method for the reduction of a large body of data so that a maximum of the variance is extracted was first proposed by Karl Pearson [386] and fully developed as the method of *principal components,* or *component analysis,* by Harold Hotelling [259]. The model for component analysis is simply:

$$(2.8) \qquad z_j = a_{j1}F_1 + a_{j2}F_2 + \cdots + a_{jn}F_n \qquad (j = 1, 2, \cdots, n),$$

where each of the n observed variables is described linearly in terms of n new uncorrelated components $F_1, F_2, \cdots, F_n$. An important property of this method, insofar as the summarization of data is concerned, is that each component, in turn, makes a maximum contribution to the sum of the variances of the n variables. For a practical problem only a few components may be retained, especially if they account for a large percentage of the total variance. However, all the components are required to reproduce the correlations among the variables.

In contrast to the maximum variance approach, the *classical factor analysis* model is designed to maximally reproduce the correlations (various methods for accomplishing this are the subject of a large portion of this book). The basic factor analysis model may be put in the form:

$$(2.9) \qquad z_j = a_{j1}F_1 + a_{j2}F_2 + \cdots + a_{jm}F_m + d_jU_j \qquad (j = 1, 2, \cdots, n),$$

where each of the n observed variables is described linearly in terms of m (usually much smaller than n) *common factors* and a *unique factor.* The common factors account for the correlations among the variables, while each unique factor accounts for the remaining variance (including error) of that variable. The coefficients of the factors are frequently referred to as "loadings."

To call attention to the fact that the expression (2.9) is a mathematical model of the observed variable, it is sometimes designated by z'_j. For simplicity the prime will usually be omitted in the theoretical expression for the variable. Furthermore, if one wanted to be precise, as regards statistical notation, the symbols for the factors and their coefficients should be Greek letters since they are in the nature of population parameters and can only be inferred from the observed data. However, the notation of (2.9) is so well established in the factor analysis literature* that it was deemed wiser not to change it. Of course, the a's and F's are generally used symbols and imply no relationships between the two models (2.8) and (2.9).

The classical factor analysis model (2.9) may be written explicitly for the value of variable j for individual i as follows:

$$(2.10) \qquad z_{ji} = \sum_{p=1}^{m} a_{jp}F_{pi} + d_jU_{ji} \qquad (i = 1, 2, \cdots, N; j = 1, 2, \cdots, n).$$

In this expression F_{pi} is the value of a common factor p for an individual i, and each of the m terms $a_{jp}F_{pi}$ represents the contribution of the corresponding factor to the linear composite, while d_jU_{ji} is the "residual error" in the theoretical representation of the observed measurement z_{ji}.

---

* The only exception occurs in the mathematical-statistical contributions to factor analysis.

Without any loss of generality, it can be assumed that the F's and U's have zero means and unit variances, since they are unknown in practice. Furthermore, the n unique factors are supposed to be independent of one another and also independent of the m common factors. In model (2.9) the F's are considered statistical variates or random variables, defined by a probability density function which, for certain purposes, is taken to be normal. When the factors are assumed to be independent normal variates, it follows that the z's have a multivariate normal distribution (discussed further in chap. 10).

While the statement of the factor analysis model in (2.10) makes explicit the values of the factors, they must actually be estimated indirectly, as explained in chapter 16. There is another model which overtly is like (2.10), but with the important difference that the factor values F_{pi} are treated as parameters to be estimated directly, along with the factor loadings. It appears to have certain desirable features, but also many unresolved problems. This model, which is investigated by Anderson and Rubin [14], Whittle [519], and Jöreskog [285] will not be developed in this text.

The model of primary interest is (2.9), with the basic problem of factor analysis being the estimation of the nm loadings of the common factors. Various methods are available for accomplishing this and are developed in detail in the chapters following the foundations set forth in part i. Throughout this text, the variables are standardized and the correlations among them are employed in the calculations of the factor loadings. Some attempts have been made to estimate the factor loadings directly from the observed values of the variables rather than their covariances or correlations (see, for example, [236], [414], [519], [545]), but such procedures are not considered here. It should be apparent that the factor analysis model bears a strong resemblance to that of regression analysis insofar as a variable is described as a linear combination of another set of variables plus a residual. However, in regression analysis the set of independent variables are observable while in factor analysis they are hypothetical constructs which can only be estimated from the observed data. Finally, the factors themselves are estimated in a subsequent stage of the analysis (see chap. 16).

For most of the exposition in this text, no assumptions are made about the statistical distributions of the variables. More precisely, the correlations among the variables for a given sample are treated as if they were the true correlations in the population, ignoring statistical variation. Alternatively, various procedures are developed which operate on the correlations among a set of variables to produce solutions in the sense of model (2.9), accepting these correlations as mathematical rather than statistical entities. However, when questions of statistical inference arise—regarding the number of common factors or the significance of factor loadings—then specific assumptions on the distribution functions of the factors and the observed variables are introduced (see, chaps. 9 and 10).

2.4. *Composition of Variance*

The variance of a variable may be expressed in terms of the factors according to the model of the preceding section. Thus, applying the definition (2.4) to the model

(2.10) of z_j yields:

$$s_j^2 = \sum z_{ji}^2/N = \sum_{p=1}^{m} a_{jp}^2 \left(\sum F_{pi}^2/N \right) + d_j^2 \sum U_{ji}^2/N$$

$$+ 2 \sum_{p<q=1}^{m} a_{jp}a_{jq}\left(\sum F_{pi}F_{qi}/N \right) + 2d_j \sum_{p=1}^{m} a_{jp}\left(\sum F_{pi}U_{ji}/N \right),$$

where, it will be remembered, the sums without an indicated index are on i from 1 to N. Now, since the variance of a variable in standard form is equal to unity, and all variables (including the factors) are assumed to be in standard form for any sample, the last equation may be written

(2.11) $$s_j^2 = 1 = \sum_{p=1}^{m} a_{jp}^2 + d_j^2 + 2 \sum_{p<q=1}^{m} a_{jp}a_{jq}r_{F_pF_q} + 2d_j \sum_{p=1}^{m} a_{jp}r_{F_pU_j}.$$

The unique factors are always uncorrelated with the common factors, and if the common factors are uncorrelated* among themselves, then the expression (2.11) simplifies to

(2.12) $$s_j^2 = 1 = a_{j1}^2 + a_{j2}^2 + \cdots + a_{jm}^2 + d_j^2.$$

The terms on the right represent the portions of the unit variance of z_j ascribable to the respective factors. For example, a_{j2}^2 is the contribution of the factor F_2 to the variance of z_j. The *total contribution* of a factor F_p to the variances of all the variables is defined to be

(2.13) $$V_p = \sum_{j=1}^{n} a_{jp}^2 \qquad\qquad (p = 1, 2, \cdots, m),$$

and the total contribution of all the common factors to the total variance of all the variables is given by

(2.14) $$V = \sum_{p=1}^{m} V_p.$$

The ratio V/n is sometimes employed as an indicator of the completeness of the factor analysis.

From the composition of the total unit variance as expressed by (2.12), two important concepts in factor analysis follow: (1) the *communality* of a variable z_j, which is given by the sum of the squares of the common-factor coefficients, viz.,

(2.15) $$h_j^2 = a_{j1}^2 + a_{j2}^2 + \cdots + a_{jm}^2 \qquad\qquad (j = 1, 2, \cdots, n),$$

and (2) the *uniqueness*, which is the contribution of the unique factor. The latter indicates the extent to which the common factors fail to account for the total unit variance of the variable. Sometimes it is convenient to separate the uniqueness of a

---

* The case of correlated factors is treated in detail in chaps. 13 and 15.

variable into two portions of variance—that due to the particular selection of variables in the study and that due to unreliability of measurement. If additional variables were added to a given set, their correlations with the original variables might necessitate the postulation of further common factors. However, any such potential linkages of a given variable can only be expressed as a portion of its uniqueness in the study with the original set of variables. This portion of the uniqueness is termed the *specificity* of the variable. The remaining portion, due to imperfections of measurement, is the *error variance* or *unreliability* of the variable. The complement of the error variance is sometimes called the "reliability" of the variable. In psychology, this systematic component of the variable (as distinguished from error components) is usually measured by the correlation between two separate administrations of the same test, or parallel forms of the test. Two such representations of a variable may be denoted z_j and z_J, and their correlation r_{jJ} is then the measure of the reliability of the variable.

When the unique factors are decomposed into the two types described above, the linear model (2.9) for any variable may be written in the form

$$(2.16) \qquad z_j = a_{j1}F_1 + a_{j2}F_2 + \cdots + a_{jm}F_m + b_jS_j + e_jE_j \qquad (j = 1, 2, \cdots, n).$$

Here S_j and E_j are the *specific* and *error factors*, respectively, and b_j and e_j their coefficients. Since the specific and error factors are uncorrelated, the following relationship between the uniqueness and its component parts is immediately found:

$$(2.17) \qquad\qquad d_j^2 = b_j^2 + e_j^2.$$

Hence, the total variance may be expressed in the following alternative way:

$$(2.18) \qquad\qquad s_j^2 = 1 = h_j^2 + d_j^2 = h_j^2 + b_j^2 + e_j^2.$$

Thus, the total variance of a variable may be said to be made up of the communality (attributable to the F's) and the uniqueness; or, alternatively, the total variance is made up of the communality, the specificity (attributable to the S's), and the un-reliability (attributable to the E's).

By factorial methods the communality h_j^2 and the uniqueness d_j^2 of each variable in a set are obtained. The uniqueness of each variable may then be split into the specificity and unreliability, but this is independent of the factorial solution. If the reliability r_{jJ} of a variable z_j is known (it may be obtained by experimental methods), then the error variance may be obtained by means of the equation

$$e_j^2 = 1 - r_{jJ}.$$

Then, knowing the unreliability, the specificity follows from (2.17), viz.,

$$b_j^2 = d_j^2 - e_j^2,$$

where the uniqueness d_j^2 is known from the factorial solution. Since the reliability is the complement of the unreliability e_j^2, it follows from (2.18) that

$$r_{jJ} = h_j^2 + b_j^2$$

and hence:

(2.19)
$$h_j^2 = r_{jJ} - b_j^2 \leqq r_{jJ}.$$

In other words, the communality of any variable is less than or equal to the reliability of the variable, and equals the reliability only when the specificity vanishes.

Employing the model (2.16) for the expression of a variable z_j in terms of factors, the composition of variance of such a variable (in decreasing order of magnitude, generally) is given by:

(2.20)

	Total variance	(1)	$= h_j^2 + b_j^2 + e_j^2 = h_j^2 + d_j^2,$
	Reliability	$(r_{jJ}) = h_j^2 + b_j^2$	$= 1 - e_j^2,$
	Communality	$(h_j^2) = h_j^2$	$= 1 - d_j^2,$
	Uniqueness	$(d_j^2) =$	$b_j^2 + e_j^2 = 1 - h_j^2,$
	Specificity	$(b_j^2) =$	$b_j^2 \quad = d_j^2 - e_j^2,$
	Error variance	$(e_j^2) =$	$e_j^2 = 1 - r_{jJ}.$

An index of *completeness of factorization* may be expressed in the form:

(2.21)
$$C_j = 100 h_j^2 / (h_j^2 + b_j^2) = 100 \text{ communality/reliability}.$$

This index shows the percentage of the reliability variance of a variable accounted for by the common factors. The index C_j is always less than 100 and approaches 100 only when the specificity b_j^2 vanishes. Obviously the analysis for determining the coefficients a_{jp} should not be carried to the point where no specificity is present when dealing with a finite set of variables.

Some workers may not care to assume specific or even error factors as indicated by (2.16). Then the factors S_j and E_j are not postulated, and the number of common factors m may be less than, or equal to, the number of variables n. However, the hypothesis of factors indicated by (2.16) appears tenable even for variables which appear to describe a set of objects very completely and with great precision.

2.5. *Factor Patterns and Structures*

Having described the composition of variables in terms of factors, it is now possible to consider in broad outline the objectives of a factor analysis of data. For a set of n variables, the linear model (2.9) expressing any variable z_j in terms of m common factors and its unique factor may be written in a slightly expanded form as follows:

$$z_1 = a_{11}F_1 + a_{12}F_2 + \cdots + a_{1m}F_m + d_1U_1$$

$$z_2 = a_{21}F_1 + a_{22}F_2 + \cdots + a_{2n}F_m \qquad\qquad + d_2U_2$$

(2.22)

$$\cdot \quad \cdot \quad \cdot \quad \cdot \quad \cdot \quad \cdot \quad \cdots \quad \cdot \quad \cdot \quad \cdot \qquad\qquad\qquad \cdot$$

$$z_n = a_{n1}F_1 + a_{n2}F_2 + \cdots + a_{nm}F_m \qquad\qquad + d_nU_n.$$

Such a set of equations is called a *factor pattern*, or more briefly, *pattern*. For simplicity a pattern may be presented in tabular form in which only the coefficients of the factors are listed, with the factor designations at the head of the columns. Sometimes a table including only the coefficients of the common factors may be referred to as the pattern. In a pattern (2.22), the common factors F_p ($p = 1, 2, \cdots, m$) may be either correlated or uncorrelated, but the unique factors U_j ($j = 1, 2, \cdots, n$) are always assumed to be uncorrelated among themselves and with all common factors. In the linear description of a particular variable, the actual number of common factors involved may be less than m, some of the coefficients being zero. The number of common factors involved in the description of a variable is called its *complexity*.

Factor analysis yields not only patterns but also correlations between the variables and the factors. A table of such correlations is called a *factor structure*, or merely a *structure*. Both a structure and a pattern are necessary in order to furnish a complete solution. The functional relationships between the elements of a structure and the coefficients of a pattern will now be shown.

Multiplying any one of equations (2.22) by the respective factors, summing over the number of observations N, and dividing by N, produces

$$r_{z_jF_1} = a_{j1} \qquad + a_{j2}r_{F_1F_2} + \cdots + a_{jp}r_{F_1F_p} + \cdots + a_{jm}r_{F_1F_m},$$

$$\cdot \quad \cdot \quad \cdot \quad \cdot \quad \cdot \quad \cdot \quad \cdot \quad \cdots \quad \cdot \quad \cdot \quad \cdot \quad \cdots \quad \cdot \quad \cdot \quad \cdot$$

(2.23) $\quad r_{z_jF_p} = a_{j1}r_{F_pF_1} + a_{j2}r_{F_pF_2} + \cdots + a_{jp} \qquad + \cdots + a_{jm}r_{F_pF_m},$

$$\cdot \quad \cdot \quad \cdot \quad \cdot \quad \cdot \quad \cdot \quad \cdot \quad \cdots \quad \cdot \quad \cdot \quad \cdot \quad \cdots \quad \cdot \quad \cdot \quad \cdot$$

$$r_{z_jF_m} = a_{ji}r_{F_mF_1} + a_{j2}r_{F_mF_2} + \cdots + a_{jp}r_{F_mF_p} + \cdots + a_{jm},$$

and

(2.24) $$r_{z_jU_j} = d_j.$$

Equation (2.24) shows that the correlations with the unique factors (the elements $r_{z_jU_j}$ of a factor structure) are always identical with the coefficients of the unique factors in the pattern. When no confusion can arise, the table of correlations of variables with common factors only, i.e., the table of $r_{z_jF_p}$, will be referred to as the factor structure.

While it might appear that equations (2.23) are to be used to evaluate the structure elements, more frequently these equations are used to obtain the values of the pattern coefficients when the correlations between variables and factors and the correlations among the factors themselves are known. Formally, (2.23) may be considered as n sets of m linear equations in the unknown a_{jp} $(j = 1, \cdots, n; p = 1, \cdots, m)$, with the left-hand members as known quantities. It is then possible to solve these systems of equations for the unknown coefficients a_{jp}. Computing procedures for such formal solutions are developed in chapter 3 and applied in chapter 13, while the entire part ii is devoted to the direct analyses for the factor patterns.

From equations (2.23) it is apparent that the elements $r_{z_j F_p}$ of a structure are generally different from the coefficients a_{jp} of a pattern. In case the common factors F_p are uncorrelated, that is, $r_{F_p F_q} = 0$ $(p \neq q)$, then equations (2.23) reduce to

(2.25) $$r_{z_j F_p} = a_{jp} \qquad (j = 1, 2, \cdots, n; \quad p = 1, 2, \cdots, m).$$

Thus, *only in the case of uncorrelated factors are the elements of a structure identical with the corresponding coefficients of a pattern.* In an analysis involving uncorrelated factors, a complete solution is furnished merely by a factor pattern inasmuch as the correlations of the variables with the factors are given by the respective coefficients.

As already indicated, both structure and pattern should be produced in making a complete factor analysis. The structure reveals the correlations of variables and factors, which are useful for the identification of factors and for subsequent estimates of the latter (see chap. 16). The pattern shows the linear composition of variables in terms of factors in the form of regression equations. It may also be used for reproducing the correlations between variables to determine the adequacy of the solution, which is discussed in **2.6**. In comparing different systems of factors for a given set of variables, again patterns are useful.

2.6. *Statistical Fit of the Factor Model*

In the preceding sections a model was developed as the mathematical theory underlying the observed data. This model—the set of equations (2.22)—makes the assumption that the variables are composed linearly of the factors. In what sense does a set of factors explain the relationships among the variables? That is the subject of the present section.

The observed correlations among the variables constitute the primary data. What happens to the correlation between two variables which are approximated by the linear model? If, in general, such correlations derived from the factor model are little different from the observed correlations, the model is said to fit the empirical data well; otherwise, the approximation is poor and the hypothesis should be altered. The correlation between two variables may be reproduced from the factor pattern (2.22) by the following procedure: multiply any two such equations, sum over the number of individuals N, and divide by N. Remembering that the factors are in standard form, the correlation between variables z_j and z_k $(j, k = 1, 2, \cdots, n)$ can be

21

expressed as follows:

$$(2.26) \quad \begin{cases} r'_{jk} = a_{j1}a_{k1} + a_{j2}a_{k2} + a_{j3}a_{k3} + \cdots + a_{jm}a_{km} \\ \quad + (a_{j1}a_{k2} + a_{k1}a_{j2})r_{F_1F_2} + \cdots + (a_{j1}a_{km} + a_{k1}a_{jm})r_{F_1F_m} \\ \quad + (a_{j2}a_{k3} + a_{k2}a_{j3})r_{F_2F_3} + \cdots + (a_{j2}a_{km} + a_{k2}a_{jm})r_{F_2F_m} \\ \quad + \cdots + a_{j1}d_k r_{F_1U_k} + a_{k1}d_j r_{F_1U_j} + \cdots + a_{jm}d_k r_{F_mU_k} + a_{km}d_j r_{F_mU_j} \\ \quad + d_j d_k r_{U_jU_k}, \end{cases}$$

where the *reproduced correlation* (computed from the pattern) is written r'_{jk} to distinguish it from the observed correlation r_{jk}. This distinction is made throughout the text.

The unique factors have been assumed to be uncorrelated with the common factors and among themselves, hence $r_{F_pU_j} = r_{F_pU_k} = r_{U_jU_k} = 0$. If the common factors are uncorrelated, equation (2.26) simplifies still further. The correlations $r_{F_pF_q}$ ($p \neq q$; $p, q = 1, 2, \cdots, m$) are then zero, and everything below the first line of the equation vanishes. For the case of uncorrelated common factors, the correlation between any two variables is reproduced from the factor pattern by an equation of the following form:

$$(2.27) \quad r'_{jk} = a_{j1}a_{k1} + a_{j2}a_{k2} + \cdots + a_{jm}a_{km} \quad (j \neq k; \; j, k = 1, 2, \cdots, n).$$

This expression is merely the sum of the products of corresponding pattern coefficients of the two variables correlated. Of course, the self correlation of a variable is unity. The factor analysis model preserves this property through the unique factor for each variable. Thus, the reproduced self correlation for variable j can be obtained from (2.26) by setting $k = j$, and, again assuming uncorrelated factors, it can readily be seen that its value is simply the sum of the communality and the uniqueness of the variable.

Now that the distinction between the observed and the reproduced correlations has been made, what should be the extent of their agreement? The correlations reproduced by the factor pattern, as given most generally in (2.26) or for the case of uncorrelated factors in (2.27), should not agree exactly with the observed correlations because allowance must be made for sampling and experimental errors. It is a commonly accepted scientific principle that a theoretical law should be simpler than the observed data upon which it is based, and hence discrepancies between the law and the data are to be expected. In the case of factor analysis, functions (the correlations r'_{jk}) of the assumed linear composition of variables should be expected to vary somewhat from the observed values.

After a factor pattern has been obtained, its adequacy as a description of the variables is determined from the extent to which it explains the correlations among the variables. This is done by forming the reproduced correlations from the pattern and subtracting them from the corresponding observed correlations. The resulting differences are known as *residual correlations*, and are defined by

$$(2.28) \quad \bar{r}_{jk} = r_{jk} - r'_{jk},$$

where r_{jk} is the observed correlation and r'_{jk} is the correlation reproduced from the pattern. In case the common factors are uncorrelated, the residuals then reduce to the form:

$$(2.29) \qquad \bar{r}_{jk} = r_{jk} - (a_{j1}a_{k1} + a_{j2}a_{k2} + \cdots + a_{jm}a_{km}).$$

The question then arises as to how nearly the correlations reproduced from a factor pattern should fit the observed ones.* The agreement may be judged by the size and distribution of the residuals $\bar{r}_{jk}$. The magnitude of the residuals should, of course, be approximately zero. When all common factors have been removed in forming the residuals, then no further linkages between variables exist. It might, therefore, be expected that the distribution of residuals would be similar to that of a zero correlation in a sample of equal size. The standard error of such a zero correlation is given by the formula

$$\sigma_{r=0} = 1/\sqrt{N-1},$$

and, since N is usually large, a standard for judging adequacy of fit may be taken to be:

$$(2.30) \qquad \sigma_{\bar{r}} \leqq 1/\sqrt{N},$$

where $\sigma_{\bar{r}}$ is the standard deviation of the series of residuals. This standard is a crude one since it depends only on the size of the sample, whereas the briefest reflection would suggest that the size of residuals must depend also on other characteristics, especially the number of variables.

On the basis of the size of the sample alone, the following conclusions from the criterion (2.30) may be drawn. If $\sigma_{\bar{r}}$ is appreciably greater than $1/\sqrt{N}$, it may be concluded that there are further significant linkages between variables, and a modification of the form of solution is required. In case $\sigma_{\bar{r}}$ is considerably less than $1/\sqrt{N}$, it would appear that unjustified linkages between variables have been included in the solution. When the standard deviation of the residuals is just below that of a zero correlation, the solution may be regarded as acceptable in the light of the above standard. This statistical test was recommended by Kelley [305, p. 12] and Thurstone [468, p. 147] in the 1930's. More exact statistical tests are discussed in chapters 9 and 10.

2.7. *Indeterminacy of Factor Solutions*

In any scientific field the observed phenomena can be described in a great variety of ways which are mutually consistent. The choice of a particular interpretation must then depend upon its utility. This arbitrariness or indeterminacy, which has been recognized by philosophers of science for a long time, is put succinctly by F. R. Moulton [373, p. 484]:

> ...every set of phenomena can be interpreted consistently in various ways, in fact, in infinitely many ways. It is our privilege to choose among the possible interpretations the ones that appear to us most satisfactory, whatever may be the reasons for our choice. If scientists

---

* A simple standard for "when to stop factoring" has not been developed. This problem is discussed in chaps. 8, 9, and 10.

would remember that various equally consistent interpretations of every set of observational data can be made, they would be much less dogmatic than they often are, and their beliefs in a possible ultimate finality of scientific theories would vanish.

The factor problem, likewise, is indeterminate in the sense that, given the correlations of a set of variables, the coefficients of a factor pattern are not uniquely determined. That is, systems of orthogonal, or uncorrelated, factors may be chosen, *consistent with the observed correlations,* in an infinity of ways. This property has been known by mathematicians and statisticians from the time they had become interested in factor analysis, and one of the first formal demonstrations was given by Hotelling [259, pp. 417–22] for the case of principal components. More recently, with the use of matrix algebra, a succinct proof was given by Anderson and Rubin [14, pp. 112–13].

In essence, the indeterminacy in the model—the factor loadings a_{jp} are not unique —arises from the fact that a solution determines the m-dimensional space containing the common factors, but it does not determine the basis or frame of reference or the exact position of these factors. The indeterminacy occurs at two stages: in getting an (arbitrary) solution which satisfies the model in a statistical sense, and in getting the solution in a form most amenable to interpretation. In general the computational methods do not yield unique values for the factor loadings, an exception being the principal-factor solution (chap. 8). However, any solution may be put in a "canonical form" (see **8.8**). The indeterminacy at the second stage still exists (see part iii). After a factor solution has been found that fits the empirical data (to within a given degree of accuracy), it may be transformed or "rotated" to another solution (fitting the data equally well) which may have greater meaning to investigators in a particular field.

2.8.   *The Factor Model in Matrix Notation**

Before leaving the general overview of factor analysis, it is desirable to set forth the ideas developed earlier in this chapter in compact matrix notation. The advantages go beyond mere simplification; frequently, certain properties and proofs can be derived by the use of matrix language which might otherwise be hidden from view. In this section some of the fundamental properties of factor patterns and structures are put in matrix form, while in subsequent chapters many of the methods of factor analysis are developed by the use of matrix algebra.

First, some of the very basic concepts involved in factor analysis will be expressed in matrix notation. The n variables of a study may be designated by a column vector, as follows:

$$(2.31) \qquad \mathbf{z} = \begin{bmatrix} z_1 \\ z_2 \\ \cdot \\ \cdot \\ \cdot \\ z_n \end{bmatrix},$$

* The reader who wishes a review of the basic concepts of matrix algebra may want to turn to chap. 3 before reading this section.

while the complete set of N values for each of the n variables will be represented by the $n \times N$ matrix:

$$(2.32) \qquad \mathbf{Z} = \begin{bmatrix} z_{11} & z_{12} & \cdots & z_{1N} \\ z_{21} & z_{22} & \cdots & z_{2N} \\ \cdot & \cdot & \cdots & \cdot \\ z_{n1} & z_{n2} & \cdots & z_{nN} \end{bmatrix}.$$

Similarly, the factors may be represented as follows:

$$\mathbf{f} = \begin{bmatrix} F_1 \\ \cdot \\ \cdot \\ \cdot \\ F_m \end{bmatrix}, \quad \mathbf{F} = \begin{bmatrix} F_{11} & F_{12} & \cdots & F_{1N} \\ \cdot & \cdot & \cdot & \cdots & \cdot \\ F_{m1} & F_{m2} & \cdots & F_{mN} \end{bmatrix}.$$

$$(2.33)$$

$$\mathbf{u} = \begin{bmatrix} U_1 \\ \cdot \\ \cdot \\ \cdot \\ U_n \end{bmatrix}, \quad \mathbf{U} = \begin{bmatrix} U_{11} & U_{12} & \cdots & U_{1N} \\ \cdot & \cdot & \cdot & \cdots & \cdot \\ U_{n1} & U_{n2} & \cdots & U_{nN} \end{bmatrix}.$$

The coefficients of the factors in a factor pattern may be represented by the following matrix:

$$(2.34) \qquad \mathbf{M} = \begin{bmatrix} a_{11} & a_{12} & \cdots & a_{1m} & d_1 & 0 & \cdots & 0 \\ a_{21} & a_{22} & \cdots & a_{2m} & 0 & d_2 & \cdots & 0 \\ \cdot & \cdot & \cdots & \cdot & \cdot & \cdot & \cdots & \cdot \\ a_{n1} & a_{n2} & \cdots & a_{nm} & 0 & 0 & \cdots & d_n \end{bmatrix} = (\mathbf{A}|\mathbf{D}),$$

wherein the total pattern matrix $\mathbf{M}$ is made up of the matrix $\mathbf{A}$ of common-factor coefficients and the diagonal matrix $\mathbf{D}$ of unique-factor coefficients. Usually, the matrix $\mathbf{A}$ is referred to as the *pattern matrix*. In general, the elements a_{jp} of the matrix $\mathbf{A}$ are to be considered as coefficients in an oblique-factor pattern, i.e., a pattern based upon correlated factors. In the course of a factor analysis, sometimes both an (initial) orthogonal pattern $\mathbf{A}$ and a (final) oblique pattern $\mathbf{P}$ are determined. When there are two distinct pattern matrices in the same context, then it is necessary to use distinguishing notation.

Employing the foregoing definitions, the factor pattern (2.22) may be written.

$$(2.35) \qquad \mathbf{z} = \mathbf{M}\{\mathbf{f}|\mathbf{u}\} = (\mathbf{A}|\mathbf{D})\{\mathbf{f}|\mathbf{u}\} = \mathbf{Af} + \mathbf{Du},$$

or, for the common-factor portion alone:

$$(2.36) \qquad \mathbf{z} = \mathbf{Af}.$$

25

No new notation is used to designate the variables since the context would make it perfectly clear whether the complete or the common-factor portion was involved.

In addition to a pattern, a factor analysis also yields a structure, i.e., a table of correlations of the variables with the factors (the latter being identical with the pattern only if the common factors are uncorrelated). Of course, the correlations of the variables with the unique factors are identical with the unique factor coefficients according to (2.24), and the diagonal matrix of these values has been designated **D**. Now, defining the correlations with the common factors by

$$(2.37) \qquad\qquad s_{jp} = r_{z_j F_p}, \qquad (j = 1, 2, \cdots, n; \quad p = 1, 2, \cdots, m)$$

the factor structure may be represented by:

$$(2.38) \qquad\qquad \mathbf{S} = \begin{bmatrix} s_{11} & s_{12} & \cdots & s_{1m} \\ s_{21} & s_{22} & \cdots & s_{2m} \\ \cdot & \cdot & \cdots & \cdot \\ s_{n1} & s_{n2} & \cdots & s_{nm} \end{bmatrix}.$$

The notation for the elements of a factor structure should not be confused with the definition (2.6) of a sample covariance. The context will make it perfectly clear which is implied.

Having expressed a pattern and a structure of a given factor analysis in matrix form, it is possible to develop certain relationships between them. As the first step toward this end, consider the factor pattern (2.36) written explicitly for the N entities, namely,

$$(2.39) \qquad\qquad \mathbf{Z} = \mathbf{AF},$$

and postmultiply both sides of this expression by the transpose of the matrix of factor values and divide by the scalar N to obtain:

$$(2.40) \qquad\qquad \mathbf{ZF'}/N = \mathbf{A}(\mathbf{FF'}/N).$$

The left-hand member of this equation simplifies as follows:

$$(2.41) \qquad\qquad \mathbf{ZF'}/N = \mathbf{S},$$

since each element is a correlation coefficient according to the basic definition (2.7). The expression within the parentheses in the right-hand member of (2.40) is also a matrix of correlation coefficients—among the factors— since all the factors are in standard form. This matrix of correlations among the common factors is defined by

$$(2.42) \qquad\qquad \mathbf{\Phi} = \mathbf{FF'}/N = \begin{bmatrix} 1 & r_{F_1 F_2} & \cdots & r_{F_1 F_m} \\ r_{F_2 F_1} & 1 & \cdots & r_{F_2 F_m} \\ \cdot & \cdot & \cdots & \cdot \\ r_{F_m F_1} & r_{F_m F_2} & \cdots & 1 \end{bmatrix}.$$

Upon substituting (2.41) and (2.42) into (2.40), the latter expression reduces to:

$$\text{(2.43)} \qquad \mathbf{S} = \mathbf{A\Phi}.$$

This is the fundamental relationship between a factor pattern **A** and a factor structure **S**—the structure matrix is equal to the pattern matrix postmultiplied by the matrix of correlations among the factors. From this relationship it is clear that if the factors are uncorrelated (i.e., **Φ** is an identity matrix), the elements of the structure are equal to the corresponding elements of the pattern. The explicit expression for the pattern matrix can be obtained from (2.43) by postmultiplying both sides by $\mathbf{\Phi}^{-1}$. The result is

$$\text{(2.44)} \qquad \mathbf{A} = \mathbf{S\Phi}^{-1}.$$

It is possible to express the matrix $\mathbf{R}^{\dagger}$ of reproduced correlations (with communalities in the diagonal) in several alternative forms, employing the foregoing relationship between a pattern and a structure. By definition, the matrix of observed correlations is given by

$$\text{(2.45)} \qquad \mathbf{R} = \mathbf{ZZ'}/N.$$

If (2.39) is substituted into this equation, and the observed correlation matrix is replaced by the matrix of reproduced correlations, there results:*

$$\text{(2.46)} \qquad \mathbf{R}^{\dagger} = \mathbf{AFF'A'}/N = \mathbf{A(FF'}/N)\mathbf{A'} = \mathbf{A\Phi A'},$$

where the last equality follows from (2.42).

Sometimes it is desirable to consider the reproduced correlation matrix with ones in the diagonal, i.e., adding the uniqueness d_j^2 to the communality h_j^2 of each variable. This matrix is represented by $(\mathbf{R}^{\dagger} + \mathbf{D}^2)$, and equation (2.46) becomes:

$$\text{(2.47)} \qquad (\mathbf{R}^{\dagger} + \mathbf{D}^2) = \mathbf{M}\begin{pmatrix} \mathbf{\Phi} & \mathbf{O} \\ \mathbf{O} & \mathbf{I} \end{pmatrix}\mathbf{M'},$$

in which the composite square matrix (of order $m + n$) includes the identity matrix (of order n) of correlations among the unique factors as well as the correlation matrix (of order m) among the common factors.

From the relationship between a pattern and a structure, alternative formulas can be derived which obviate the explicit use of the matrix **Φ**. Thus, substituting (2.43) into (2.46) produces

$$\text{(2.48)} \qquad \mathbf{R}^{\dagger} = \mathbf{SA'},$$

---

* In replacing observed by computed correlations, the tacit assumption is made that the residuals vanish. To avoid additional symbolism, **R** is employed sometimes for both matrices, but it should be clear when it is computed from the observed variables and when it is computed from the factor pattern.

or

(2.49) $$\mathbf{R}^{\dagger} = \mathbf{A}\mathbf{S'},$$

since $\mathbf{\Phi}$ is symmetric.

Of course, when the factors are uncorrelated, the matrix $\mathbf{\Phi}$ reduces to an identity matrix and formula (2.46) simplifies to the following expression for the reproduced correlations:

(2.50) $$\mathbf{R}^{\dagger} = \mathbf{A}\mathbf{A'}.$$

This equation has been called "the fundamental factor theorem" by Thurstone [468, p. 70].

An important observation can be made at this point. The factor problem is concerned with fitting a set of data (the observed correlations) with a model—the factor pattern (2.22), or (2.35) in matrix notation. Under the assumption of such a pattern, the correlations are reproduced by means of the common-factor coefficients alone, as may be seen from (2.50).* For the reproduced correlation matrix $\mathbf{R}^{\dagger}$ to be an appropriate fit to the observed correlation matrix $\mathbf{R}$, the diagonal elements must also be reproduced from the common-factor portion of the pattern. Thus, if numbers approximating the communalities are put in the diagonal of the matrix of observed correlations, the factor solution will involve both common and unique factors and the foregoing formulas will appropriately reproduce all the elements comparable to the observed data. On the other hand, if unities are placed in the principal diagonal of the observed correlation matrix then the factor solution must necessarily involve *only* common factors in order for equation (2.50) to reproduce the unities. In this case no provision is made for unique factors, implying the component analysis model (2.8). If such values between communalities and unities as the reliabilities are employed, then the factor solution would involve common and error factors, but the specificity would be included in the "common-factor" variance. From these considerations it should be clear that the *values put in the diagonal of the observed correlation matrix determine what portions of the unit variances are factored into common factors.*

---

* In the discussion of this paragraph, there is no loss in generality to assume that the factors are uncorrelated.

3
Matrix Concepts Essential to Factor Analysis

3.1. *Introduction*

The solution of systems of linear equations provided the impetus for the development of the theory of determinants, and from the latter grew the theory of matrices. In modern mathematical thinking it is generally accepted that "the idea of matrix precedes that of determinant." Furthermore, it is now recognized that the importance of the concept of determinant is over-rated. While determinants are quite useful, systems of equations certainly can be solved efficiently without them. Also, the bulk of the mathematical theory of matrices can be developed without the explicit use of determinants. Nonetheless, because of historical precedent that has been established, the basic concepts of determinants are enumerated before matrices and introduced in **3.2**.

Many problems arising in applied mathematics can be formulated in terms of systems of linear equations. While this fact has long been recognized, the advent of high-speed digital electronic computers has provided a special impetus to the problem of solving a system of linear equations and the associated problem of finding the eigenvalues of a matrix (see chap. 8). Considerable research in these areas has been conducted in recent years, and there are many excellent expositions of the theory and numerical methods especially amenable to high-speed computers. Examples of such works include the reports of the National Bureau of Standards [376], Faddeev [123], and White [516]. On the other hand, Dwyer [111] presents an excellent treatment of systems of linear equations for use with a desk calculator.

Many phases of factor analysis involve the solution of a set of simultaneous linear equations, either explicitly or implied in the work. Two general methods for solving such sets of equations are presented in **3.3** and **3.4**. Then an application of these methods to the calculation of the inverse of a matrix is developed in **3.5**.

3.2. *Basic Concepts of Determinants and Matrices*

For a full and proper understanding of factor analysis it is almost imperative that the student have a basic knowledge of matrix algebra. In the development of the text, it is presupposed that the reader has had some exposure to this subject. The aim of this section is to assist him in recalling this knowledge, and to make the fundamental definitions and theorems on matrices immediately available.* For purposes of reference, the classical or more traditional notation and properties of determinants are presented.

1. Definition of a determinant of order 2.—A sum of product terms, with alternating algebraic signs, frequently occurs in mathematical work and has been given a special name and notation. For example, the expression

$$ad - bc$$

is denoted by the symbol

$$\begin{vmatrix} a & b \\ c & d \end{vmatrix},$$

which is called a *determinant of the second order*, since it contains two rows and two columns.

2. Definition of a determinant of order 3.—The symbol

$$\begin{vmatrix} a_1 & b_1 & c_1 \\ a_2 & b_2 & c_2 \\ a_3 & b_3 & c_3 \end{vmatrix}$$

is called a *determinant of the third order* and stands for

$$a_1 b_2 c_3 - a_1 b_3 c_2 + a_2 b_3 c_1 - a_2 b_1 c_3 + a_3 b_1 c_2 - a_3 b_2 c_1.$$

The nine numbers $a_1, \cdots, c_3$ are called the *elements* of the determinant. In the symbol these elements lie in three (horizontal) *rows* and also in three (vertical) *columns*. For example, a_3, b_3, c_3 are the elements of the third row, while the three b's are the elements of the second column. The diagonal from the upper left-hand corner to the lower right-hand corner is called the *principal diagonal*.

3. Definition of a determinant of order n.—A determinant of the nth order is defined by:

$$(3.1) \qquad \det A = \begin{vmatrix} a_{11} & a_{12} & \cdots & a_{1n} \\ a_{21} & a_{22} & \cdots & a_{2n} \\ \cdot & \cdot & \cdots & \cdot \\ a_{n1} & a_{n2} & \cdots & a_{nn} \end{vmatrix},$$

* For detailed treatment of these subjects the reader is referred to such excellent texts as Bodewig [43], Hadley [190], and Paige and Swift [385].

where the n^2 elements are denoted by a's with two subscripts, the first representing the number of the row and the second the number of the column in which the element appears. By definition the determinant A stands for the sum of $n!$ terms, each of which is (apart from sign) the product of n elements, one and only one from each column, and one and only one from each row. The algebraic signs are determined most easily by the method of expanding the determinant which is explained in **5** below.

4. Minors and cofactors.—The determinant of order $n - 1$ obtained by striking out the row and column crossing at a given element of a determinant of order n is called the *minor* of that element. Thus, corresponding to the element a_{jk}, in the jth row and the kth column of the determinant A, there exists the minor M_{jk} which is obtained upon crossing out the given row and column. Frequently there is occasion to consider not this minor M_{jk} but the *cofactor* A_{jk} of a_{jk} defined by

(3.2)
$$A_{jk} = (-1)^{j+k} M_{jk}.$$

The algebraic signs attached to the minors to obtain the corresponding cofactors are alternately $+$ and $-$, as indicated by the following diagram which is associated with the elements of a determinant:

$$
\begin{array}{cccc}
+ & - & + & - \\
- & + & - & + \\
+ & - & + & - \\
- & + & - & +
\end{array}
$$

5. Expansion of a determinant.—Any determinant A may be expanded according to the elements of any row j:

(3.3)
$$\det A = \sum_{k=1}^{n} a_{jk} A_{jk} \qquad (j = 1, 2, \cdots, n),$$

or, in terms of any column k:

(3.4)
$$\det A = \sum_{j=1}^{n} a_{jk} A_{jk} \qquad (k = 1, 2, \cdots, n).$$

Thus, for the third-order determinant

$$\det A = \begin{vmatrix} a_{11} & a_{12} & a_{13} \\ a_{21} & a_{22} & a_{23} \\ a_{31} & a_{32} & a_{33} \end{vmatrix},$$

the expansion according to the elements of the second column becomes, according to (3.4) with $k = 2$:

$$\det A = a_{12} A_{12} \qquad + a_{22} A_{22} \qquad + a_{32} A_{32}$$
$$= -a_{12} M_{12} \qquad + a_{22} M_{22} \qquad - a_{32} M_{32}$$
$$= -a_{12}(a_{21}a_{33} - a_{31}a_{23}) + a_{22}(a_{11}a_{33} - a_{31}a_{13}) - a_{32}(a_{11}a_{23} - a_{21}a_{13}),$$

31

which, upon rearranging of terms, may be written as follows:

$$\det A = a_{11}a_{22}a_{33} + a_{12}a_{23}a_{31} + a_{13}a_{32}a_{21} - a_{13}a_{22}a_{31} - a_{23}a_{32}a_{11} - a_{33}a_{21}a_{12}.$$

By successively applying the foregoing method, a determinant of any order eventually can be reduced to the explicit expansion of determinants of the second order.

6. Definition of a matrix.—A system of mn numbers a_{jk} arranged in a rectangular array of m rows and n columns is called an $m \times n$ *matrix*. If $m = n$, the array is called a square matrix of order n. A matrix will be represented by any of the following:

(3.5)
$$\mathbf{A} = (a_{jk}) = \begin{bmatrix} a_{11} & a_{12} & \cdots & a_{1n} \\ a_{21} & a_{22} & \cdots & a_{2n} \\ \cdot & \cdot & \cdots & \cdot \\ a_{m1} & a_{m2} & \cdots & a_{mn} \end{bmatrix},$$

7. Definition of a vector.—Two special instances of a matrix occur frequently, namely, a single row or a single column. Any such array of $1 \times n$ or $n \times 1$ elements is called a *vector*, or more specifically, a *row vector* or a *column vector*, respectively. Simple examples of a row vector are the notations (x, y) and (x, y, z) for points in a plane and in space, the elements of these vectors being the coordinates of the points. Similarly, the coordinates of a point in space might be represented by a column vector in any one of the forms:

$$\mathbf{x} = \begin{bmatrix} x_1 \\ x_2 \\ x_3 \end{bmatrix} = \{x_1 \, x_2 \, x_3\},$$

where the last expression may be used to conserve space.

8. Notation for vectors, matrices, and determinants.—It should be noted that even when a matrix is square it is not a determinant. A determinant whose elements are real numbers, represents a real number, while a matrix does not have a value in the ordinary sense. The difference between a square matrix and a determinant is clearly seen upon interchanging the rows and columns; the determinant has the same value, but the matrix is generally different from the original one.

Throughout this text, capital **boldface** letters are used to denote matrices other than row or column vectors, while lower case **boldface** letters are used for vectors. A determinant, when represented by a single letter, is printed in *italic* (usually preceded by "det"). The determinant of a matrix $\mathbf{A}$ (see **10** below) is indicated by $|\mathbf{A}|$.

9. Transpose of a matrix.—A matrix which is derived from another by interchanging the rows and columns is called the *transpose* of the original *matrix*. Thus, if

$$\mathbf{A} = \begin{bmatrix} a_{11} & a_{12} & a_{13} \\ a_{21} & a_{22} & a_{23} \\ a_{31} & a_{32} & a_{33} \end{bmatrix},$$

then the transpose of **A** is the matrix

$$\mathbf{A'} = \begin{bmatrix} a_{11} & a_{21} & a_{31} \\ a_{12} & a_{22} & a_{32} \\ a_{13} & a_{23} & a_{33} \end{bmatrix}.$$

The prime notation for the transpose is followed throughout the text. The transpose of a row vector is a column vector, and vice versa. Thus, in the example of **7** above, the transpose of the column vector **x** is the row vector $\mathbf{x'} = (x_1\ x_2\ x_3)$.

10. Determinants of a matrix.—Although square matrices and determinants are wholly different things, it is possible to form from the elements of a square matrix a determinant which is called the *determinant of the matrix*. The notation employed is bold-face type for the matrix and vertical lines for the determinant of the matrix. Thus the determinant of a square matrix **A** is denoted by $|\mathbf{A}|$. Other determinants, of lower order, can be formed from any rectangular matrix by striking out certain rows and columns. For many problems it is important to know the order of the highest nonvanishing determinant of a matrix.

11. Rank of a matrix.—A matrix **A** is said to be of *rank r* if it contains at least one *r*-rowed determinant which is not zero, whereas all determinants of **A** of order higher than *r* are zero. In other words, the rank of a matrix is the order of the largest non-vanishing determinant.

By the rank of a determinant is meant the rank of its matrix.

12. Singular matrix.—A square matrix is said to be *singular* if its determinant is zero. Otherwise, it is called *nonsingular*.

13. Matrix equations.—Any two matrices **A** and **B** are said to be equal if and only if every element of **A** is equal to the corresponding element of **B**. Thus, if $\mathbf{A} = (a_{jk})$ and $\mathbf{B} = (b_{jk})$ then the equation

$$\mathbf{A} = \mathbf{B}$$

implies that $a_{jk} = b_{jk}$ for every *j* and *k*. Thus it is evident that a single matrix equation stands for as many algebraic equations as there are elements in either of the matrices which are equated.

14. Symmetric matrix.—A matrix **A** is *symmetric* if and only if it is equal to its transpose **A'**. In other words, the matrix $\mathbf{A} = (a_{jk})$ is symmetric in case it remains unaltered by the interchange of its rows and columns, i.e.,

$$a_{jk} = a_{kj} \qquad\qquad (j, k = 1, 2, \cdots, n).$$

The following is an example of a symmetric matrix:

$$\begin{bmatrix} .78 & -.16 & .23 & .04 \\ -.16 & .59 & -.34 & -.21 \\ .23 & -.34 & .86 & .40 \\ .04 & -.21 & .40 & .65 \end{bmatrix}.$$

All correlation matrices are symmetric.

15. Gramian matrix.—A matrix of special interest to factor analysis is frequently referred to in psychological literature as a "Gramian" matrix, or a matrix with Gramian properties. These properties include symmetry and positive semidefiniteness. The symmetric characteristic of a matrix is defined in **14** above. A matrix is said to be *positive semidefinite* if all its principal minors are greater than or equal to zero.* All correlation matrices with unities in the principal diagonal are Gramian matrices (see Theorem 4.5); and communality estimates as replacements for the diagonal values are considered "proper" only if the Gramian properties are preserved (see chap. 5).

16. Sum or difference of matrices.—The sum (or difference) of two matrices each of m rows and n columns is defined to be an $m \times n$ matrix each of whose elements is the sum (or difference) of the corresponding elements of the given matrices. All the laws of ordinary algebra hold for the addition or subtraction of matrices.

17. Multiplication of matrices.—The element in the jth row and the kth column of the product of a matrix **A** with n columns by a matrix **B** with n rows is the sum of the products of the successive elements of the jth row of **A** by the corresponding elements of the kth column of **B**.

For example, if

$$
\mathbf{A} = \begin{bmatrix} a_{11} & a_{12} & a_{13} \\ a_{21} & a_{22} & a_{23} \end{bmatrix}, \qquad \mathbf{B} = \begin{bmatrix} b_{11} & b_{12} \\ b_{21} & b_{22} \\ b_{31} & b_{32} \end{bmatrix},
$$

then the product **C** of these matrices is

$$
\mathbf{C} = \mathbf{A} \cdot \mathbf{B} = \begin{bmatrix} a_{11}b_{11} + a_{12}b_{21} + a_{13}b_{31} & a_{11}b_{12} + a_{12}b_{22} + a_{13}b_{32} \\ a_{21}b_{11} + a_{22}b_{21} + a_{23}b_{31} & a_{21}b_{12} + a_{22}b_{22} + a_{23}b_{32} \end{bmatrix}.
$$

It should be noted that in this *row-by-column multiplication* of matrices the number of columns in the first matrix must be equal to the number of rows in the second. The product matrix then contains the number of rows of the first matrix and the number of columns of the second. Thus, in the example, the product of the 2×3 matrix by the 3×2 matrix is a 2×2 matrix. This may be conveniently noted by writing the order of each matrix as superscripts, namely,

$$
\mathbf{A}^{2 \times 3} \cdot \mathbf{B}^{3 \times 2} = \mathbf{C}^{2 \times 2}.
$$

In general,

(3.6)
$$
\mathbf{A}^{m \times n} \cdot \mathbf{B}^{n \times s} = \mathbf{C}^{m \times s},
$$

that is, the product of an $m \times n$ matrix by an $n \times s$ matrix is an $m \times s$ matrix.

---

* In Thurstone [477, p. 10], these conditions are inadvertently ascribed to a *positive definite* matrix instead of a *positive semidefinite* matrix. Only if all the principal minors of a matrix are greater than zero (none equal to zero) is the matrix said to be positive definite.

Multiplication of matrices is not commutative in general, that is,

(3.7) $$\mathbf{AB} \neq \mathbf{BA}.$$

Thus, in the example above the product $\mathbf{C} = \mathbf{AB}$ certainly is different from the product

$$\mathbf{D} = \mathbf{BA} = \begin{bmatrix} b_{11}a_{11} + b_{12}a_{21} & b_{11}a_{12} + b_{12}a_{22} & b_{11}a_{13} + b_{12}a_{23} \\ b_{21}a_{11} + b_{22}a_{21} & b_{21}a_{12} + b_{22}a_{22} & b_{21}a_{13} + b_{22}a_{23} \\ b_{31}a_{11} + b_{32}a_{21} & b_{31}a_{12} + b_{32}a_{22} & b_{31}a_{13} + b_{32}a_{23} \end{bmatrix}.$$

Hence it is important to specify in what order matrices are multiplied. In the product $\mathbf{AB}$ the matrix $\mathbf{B}$ is said to be *premultiplied* by the matrix $\mathbf{A}$, or $\mathbf{A}$ is *postmultiplied* by $\mathbf{B}$.

18. Alternative rules for matrix multiplication.—In the course of numerical computations it is sometimes more expeditious to multiply two matrices by some other rule than the conventional row-by-column. Following is a listing of all the permutations for given matrices $\mathbf{A}$ and $\mathbf{B}$:

(3.8)
$$\begin{cases} \mathbf{AB} & \text{means row-by-column multiplication of } \mathbf{A} \text{ and } \mathbf{B}; \\ \mathbf{AB'} & \text{means row-by-row multiplication of } \mathbf{A} \text{ and } \mathbf{B}; \\ \mathbf{A'B} & \text{means column-by-column multiplication of } \mathbf{A} \text{ and } \mathbf{B}; \\ \mathbf{A'B'} & \text{means column-by-row multiplication of } \mathbf{A} \text{ and } \mathbf{B}. \end{cases}$$

19. Inner product of two vectors.—The "inner product" or "dot product" of two vectors is defined to be the sum of the products of pairs of corresponding numbers in the two vectors. Thus, if the two vectors are $\mathbf{a} = (a_1\ a_2\ a_3)$ and $\mathbf{b} = (b_1\ b_2\ b_3)$, their inner product is given by

(3.9) $$\mathbf{a} \cdot \mathbf{b'} = a_1 b_1 + a_2 b_2 + a_3 b_3.$$

20. Scalars.—In order to distinguish the ordinary quantities of algebra (i.e., real and complex numbers) from matrices, the former are called *scalars* and will here be designated in italics. The product of a matrix $\mathbf{A}$ by a scalar k ($k\mathbf{A}$ or $\mathbf{A}k$) is defined to be the matrix each of whose elements is k times the corresponding element of $\mathbf{A}$. All the laws of ordinary algebra hold for the multiplication of matrices by scalars.

21. Diagonal and scalar matrices.—A matrix in which the diagonal elements do not all vanish and all remaining elements are zero is called a *diagonal matrix*. A special instance of such a matrix is one in which all the elements of the diagonal are identical; it is then called a *scalar matrix*. If a scalar matrix

$$\mathbf{K} = \begin{bmatrix} k & 0 & \cdots & 0 \\ 0 & k & \cdots & 0 \\ \cdot & \cdot & \cdots & \cdot \\ \cdot & \cdot & \cdots & \cdot \\ 0 & 0 & \cdots & k \end{bmatrix}$$

is premultiplied or postmultiplied by any matrix $\mathbf{A}$ of the same order as $\mathbf{K}$, the following relationships become evident:

(3.10)
$$\mathbf{KA} = \mathbf{AK} = k\mathbf{A}.$$

In particular, the matrix

(3.11)
$$\mathbf{I} = \begin{bmatrix} 1 & 0 & \cdots & 0 \\ 0 & 1 & \cdots & 0 \\ \cdot & \cdot & \cdots & \cdot \\ \cdot & \cdot & \cdots & \cdot \\ 0 & 0 & \cdots & 1 \end{bmatrix}$$

is called the *identity matrix*, and it has the property that, if $\mathbf{A}$ is any matrix whatever,

(3.12)
$$\mathbf{IA} = \mathbf{AI} = \mathbf{A}.$$

It is evident that, in matrix algebra, all scalar matrices may be replaced by the corresponding scalars and, conversely, that all scalars may be considered as standing for the corresponding scalar matrices. The identity matrix $\mathbf{I}$ corresponds to unity in ordinary algebra, and hence in products of matrices the factor $\mathbf{I}$ may be suppressed.

22. Inverse matrix.—If a square matrix

$$\mathbf{A} = \begin{bmatrix} a_{11} & a_{12} & \cdots & a_{1n} \\ a_{21} & a_{22} & \cdots & a_{2n} \\ \cdot & \cdot & \cdots & \cdot \\ a_{n1} & a_{n2} & \cdots & a_{nn} \end{bmatrix}$$

is nonsingular, i.e., $|\mathbf{A}| \neq 0$, then there exists another matrix

(3.13)
$$\mathbf{A}^{-1} = 1/|\mathbf{A}| \begin{bmatrix} A_{11} & A_{21} & \cdots & A_{n1} \\ A_{12} & A_{22} & \cdots & A_{n2} \\ \cdot & \cdot & \cdots & \cdot \\ A_{1n} & A_{2n} & \cdots & A_{nn} \end{bmatrix} = \begin{bmatrix} a^{11} & a^{21} & \cdots & a^{n1} \\ a^{12} & a^{22} & \cdots & a^{n2} \\ \cdot & \cdot & \cdots & \cdot \\ a^{1n} & a^{2n} & \cdots & a^{nn} \end{bmatrix}$$

in which A_{kj} denote the cofactors of the elements of $\mathbf{A}$, and the matrix of these cofactors (with $1/|\mathbf{A}|$ factored out) is called the *adjoint* of matrix $\mathbf{A}$. The matrix $\mathbf{A}^{-1}$, with elements denoted by a^{jk}, is called the *inverse* of $\mathbf{A}$ and is itself a nonsingular matrix which has the property

(3.14)
$$\mathbf{AA}^{-1} = \mathbf{A}^{-1}\mathbf{A} = \mathbf{I}.$$

It should be noted that the rows and columns of cofactors in the adjoint matrix are interchanged, i.e., the element A_{kj} in the jth row and k^{th} column of the adjoint of $\mathbf{A}$ is the cofactor of the element a_{kj} in the kth row and j^{th} column of $\mathbf{A}$.

23. Theorems on transpose and inverse of products of matrices.—The transpose of a product of matrices is equal to the product of their transposes taken in reverse order. Thus,

$$(3.15) \qquad (\mathbf{ABC})' = \mathbf{C}'\mathbf{B}'\mathbf{A}'.$$

The inverse of a product of matrices is the product of their inverses taken in reverse order. For example,

$$(3.16) \qquad (\mathbf{ABC})^{-1} = \mathbf{C}^{-1}\mathbf{B}^{-1}\mathbf{A}^{-1}.$$

3.3. *Solution of Systems of Linear Equations: Method of Substitution*

In general, a system of n linear equations in n unknowns can be solved by means of determinants [385, p. 129]. While the determinantal method may have some undisputed theoretical advantages, a more economical procedure is desired, especially when dealing with a large number of variables. The systems of equations which appear in factor analysis have symmetric matrices of coefficients and so lend themselves to special methods of solution. Gauss's method of substitution* produces a routine scheme for the solution of such a set of equations, including a complete check on the arithmetical work.

The method of substitution will be outlined in general terms and illustrated with a simple problem involving least-squares prediction. For simplicity, suppose a dependent variable z_4 is to be predicted from three independent variables by means of the regression equation:

$$(3.17) \qquad z_4 = \beta_1 z_1 + \beta_2 z_2 + \beta_3 z_3,$$

where the β's are to be determined. The normal equations in this case are:

$$(3.18) \qquad \begin{aligned} r_{11}\beta_1 + r_{12}\beta_2 + r_{13}\beta_3 &= r_{14}, \\ r_{21}\beta_1 + r_{22}\beta_2 + r_{23}\beta_3 &= r_{24}, \\ r_{31}\beta_1 + r_{32}\beta_2 + r_{33}\beta_3 &= r_{34}, \end{aligned}$$

where, of course, $r_{jj} = 1$ and the conditions for symmetry $r_{jk} = r_{kj}$ are satisfied for $j, k = 1, 2, 3$. The system of equation (3.18) is to be solved for the three unknown β's in terms of the known correlations.

In broad outline, the method involves the solution of the first of equations (3.18) for β_1 in terms of β_2 and β_3. This solution is then substituted in the last two of equations (3.18). From the first of the resulting equations, β_2 is solved in terms of β_3 and substituted into the second equation. Thus, an explicit expression for β_3 is obtained; and then working backwards, values of β_2 and β_1 are found. The complete algebraic

---

* This method is referred to as the "Doolittle Solution" in many textbooks on statistics. Convenient forms for the solution of a set of normal equations, arising in the problem of curve-fitting, were devised by M. H. Doolittle and presented in T. W. Wright and J. F. Hayford [534, pp. 101–24].

expressions involved in this method of substitution are shown by Harman [196, pp. 60–62].

The substitutions can be accomplished routinely as indicated in Table 3.1 for the following numerical example:

$$1.000\beta_1 + .693\beta_2 + .216\beta_3 = .571,$$

(3.19) $$.693\beta_1 + 1.000\beta_2 + .295\beta_3 = .691,$$

$$.216\beta_1 + .295\beta_2 + 1.000\beta_3 = .456.$$

Table 3.1

Illustration of the Method of Substitution

Line	Independent Variables			Dependent Variable	Total	Instructions
	z_1	z_2	z_3	z_4		
				Forward Solution		
1	1.	.693	.216	.571	2.480	From first eq. (3.19)
2	−1.	−.693	−.216	−.571	−2.480	Line 1 divided by negative of lead element
3	—	1.	.295	.691	1.986	From second eq. (3.19)
4	—	−.480	−.150	−.396	−1.026	−.693 times line 1
5	—	.520	.145	.295	.960	Sum of lines 3 and 4
6	· —	−1.	−.279	−.567	−1.846	Line 5 divided by negative of lead element
7	—	—	1.	.456	1.456	From third eq. (3.19)
8	—	—	−.047	−.123	−.170	−.216 times line 1
9	—	—	−.040	−.082	−.122	−.279 times line 5
10	—	—	.913	.251	1.164	Sum of lines 7, 8, 9
11	—	—	−1.	−.275	−1.275	Line 10 divided by negative of lead element
				Back Solution		
12	—	—	β_3	.275	—	From line 11, negative of entry in z_4 column
13	—	—	β_2	.490	—	From line 6: .567 − .279(.275)
14	—	—	β_1	.172	—	From line 2: .571 − .693(.490) − .216(.275)

The coefficients of the unknowns and the constant terms are recorded in lines 1, 3, and 7, with the elements below the diagonal omitted. By dividing throughout by the negative of the lead element (1 in the example), the effect is to express β_1 in terms of β_2 and β_3, i.e.,

(3.20) $$\beta_1 = .571 - .693\beta_2 - .216\beta_3,$$

where the constant term must be reversed in sign because it was already on the right-hand side of the equation. The actual value of β_1 is not determined until the last step, in line 14. By proceeding with the instructions from line 3 to line 6, the substitutions

38

are accomplished to express β_2 in terms of β_3, namely,

(3.21) $$\beta_2 = .567 - .279\beta_3,$$

where, again, the derived value of the constant term must be reversed in sign. Finally, the substitutions leading to the explicit value

(3.22) $$\beta_3 = .275$$

are made in lines 7 to 11. The back solution yields β_3 immediately from line 11; β_2 by substituting the computed value of β_3 into the expression (3.21) for β_2 as given in line 6; and β_1 by substituting the values of β_2 and β_3 into (3.20) as shown schematically in line 2.

If sums are obtained for each row, and the operations listed under "Instructions" are applied to the "Total" column, a check on the arithmetical work can be obtained at each step of the process. However, certain adjustments must be made for the elimination of columns of figures in successive blocks. For example, in checking the total in line 4, the operation of multiplying the total in line 1 by $-.693$ must be adjusted for the elimination of 1.000 from the first column, to get

$$-.693(2.480 - 1.000) = -1.026,$$

which checks precisely with the sum. Similarly, a check of the total in line 8 is given by

$$-.216(2.480 - 1.000 - .693) = -.170,$$

and a check of the total in line 9 is given by

$$-.279(.960 - .520) = -.123,$$

where the last value differs from the sum of the entries in line 9 by only one unit in the last decimal place.

3.4. *Solution of Systems of Linear Equations: Square Root Method*

An alternative to the method of the preceding section will be developed now. The advantages of the square root method include greater compactness, requiring less recording, and permitting greater ease in finding the entries to be used. Not only is the square root method more expedient for solving a symmetric set of equations, but it is especially useful in obtaining the inverse matrix in solving problems in statistics.

The square root method will be described in general terms and illustrated with the same numerical example employed in the last section. In Table 3.2 computing procedures are presented for the solution of a general system of equations (3.18), and illustrated with the numerical data of (3.19). The step-by-step procedure, immediately following, is readily extended to any number of variables.

Step 1. Enter the intercorrelations among the independent variables and their correlations with the dependent variable on the first three lines of the worksheet.

Table 3.2

The Square Root Method

Line	Independent Variables			Dependent Variable	Total	Check
	z_1	z_2	z_3	z_4		
	Schematic					
1	r_{11}	r_{12}	r_{13}	r_{14}	t_1	r'_{14}
2	*	r_{22}	r_{23}	r_{24}	t_2	r'_{24}
3	*	*	r_{33}	r_{34}	t_3	r'_{34}
4	s_{11}	s_{12}	s_{13}	s_{14}	s_{1t}	s'_{1t}
5		$s_{22.1}$	$s_{23.1}$	$s_{24.1}$	$s_{2t.1}$	$s'_{2t.1}$
6			$s_{33.12}$	$s_{34.12}$	$s_{3t.12}$	$s'_{3t.12}$
7	β_1	β_2	β_3		$R^2_{4.123}$	$R_{4.123}$
	Illustration					
1	1.000	.693	.216	.571	2.480	.571
2	*	1.000	.295	.691	2.679	.691
3	*	*	1.000	.456	1.967	.456
4	1.000	.693	.216	.571	2.480	2.480
5		.721	.202	.410	1.332	1.333
6			.955	.262	1.217	1.217
7	.171	.492	.274		.563	.750

* Terms below the diagonal of a symmetric matrix are deleted for simplicity. Terms below the diagonal of the "square root" matrix are actually zero, and are simply omitted.

Step 2. Obtain the sums by rows, i.e.,

$$(3.23) \qquad t_j = \sum_{k=1}^{4} r_{jk}. \qquad (j = 1, 2, 3)$$

Note: entries in "Check" column for lines 1, 2, 3 are described in Step 10.

Step 3. The actual square root process is begun by using r_{11} as a pivot to get the first element in line 4 simply by

$$(3.24_1) \qquad s_{11} = \sqrt{r_{11}},$$

and the remaining elements by the formula:

$$(3.24_2) \qquad s_{1k} = r_{1k}/s_{11}. \qquad (k > 1)$$

Note: Since $r_{11} = 1$, the elements of line 4 are equal, respectively, to the elements of line 1.

Step 4. The calculation in the "Total" column of line 4 is carried out as for any other column, yielding s_{1t}. This value should agree, except for rounding errors, with the sum s'_{1t} ("Check" column) of all elements computed in Step 3.

Step 5. The formulas for the elements of line 5 are:

(3.25)
$$s_{22\cdot1} = \sqrt{r_{22} - s_{12}^2},$$
$$s_{2k\cdot1} = (r_{2k} - s_{1k}s_{12})/s_{22\cdot1}. \qquad (k > 2)$$

Step 6. Check line 5 by comparing the calculated value, $s_{2t\cdot1}$, with the row sum, $s'_{2t\cdot1}$.

Step 7. The formulas for the elements of line 6 are:

(3.26)
$$s_{33\cdot(2)} = \sqrt{r_{33} - s_{13}^2 - s_{23\cdot1}^2},$$
$$s_{3k\cdot(2)} = (r_{3k} - s_{1k}s_{13} - s_{2k\cdot1}s_{23\cdot1})/s_{33\cdot(2)}, \qquad (k > 3)$$

where the notation $s_{3k\cdot(2)}$ is used instead of the specific $s_{3k\cdot12}$ to suggest an easy generalization when the number of variables already eliminated is more than 2.

Step 8. Apply row sum check to line 6.

Step 9. The values of the regression coefficients are obtained by application of the following formulas (back solution):

(3.27)
$$\beta_3 = s_{34\cdot12}/s_{33\cdot12},$$
$$\beta_2 = (s_{24\cdot1} - s_{23\cdot1}\beta_3)/s_{22\cdot1},$$
$$\beta_1 = (s_{14} - s_{13}\beta_3 - s_{12}\beta_2)/s_{11}.$$

Step 10. A check on the entire computations can be made by substituting the regression coefficients into the normal equations (3.18). The results are designated by $r'_{14}, r'_{24}, r'_{34}$ and should agree (except for rounding errors) with the original correlations of independent with dependent variables.

Step 11. The multiple correlation coefficient can be computed by use of the usual formula involving the β's and r's, viz.,

(3.28)
$$R^2_{4\cdot123} = \beta_1 r_{14} + \beta_2 r_{24} + \beta_3 r_{34}.$$

From the formal solution of the three-variable problem it can be verified that

(3.29)
$$
\begin{bmatrix} r_{11} & r_{12} & r_{13} \\ r_{21} & r_{22} & r_{23} \\ r_{31} & r_{32} & r_{33} \end{bmatrix} =
\begin{bmatrix} s_{11} & 0 & 0 \\ s_{12} & s_{22\cdot1} & 0 \\ s_{13} & s_{23\cdot1} & s_{33\cdot12} \end{bmatrix}
\begin{bmatrix} s_{11} & s_{12} & s_{13} \\ 0 & s_{22\cdot1} & s_{23\cdot1} \\ 0 & 0 & s_{33\cdot12} \end{bmatrix}
$$

More generally, the square root method can be formulated in matrix notation, as follows:

(3.30)
$$\mathbf{R} = \mathbf{S'S},$$

whence the term "square root of a matrix" is seen to correspond to the ordinary square root of an algebraic expression. The identity of equation (3.30) with the fundamental theorem of factor analysis, equation (2.50), clearly indicates why factor analysts independently discovered the square root method, although it was referred to by various names (see **6.3**). In other words, the square root method applied to a matrix **R** yields a matrix **S** such that premultiplication by its transpose (i.e., column-by-column multiplication of **S** by itself) reproduces the matrix **R**. It is convenient, at times, to refer to the "square root operation," by which is meant $(\mathbf{S}')^{-1}$, since $(\mathbf{S}')^{-1}$ operating (premultiplying) on **R** produces **S**. Then the square root operation can be applied to other matrices than the basic one from which it is derived.

At times it is more convenient to arrange the work in adjacent vertical sections rather than in horizontal blocks. This is especially true if there are a large number of variables to which the square root operation is to be applied.

While the square root method may be applied to any symmetric matrix, some difficulties will be encountered if the matrix is not positive definite; then certain of the diagonal elements may turn out to be zero or negative, and the process may degenerate or lead to imaginary numbers. When working with a correlation matrix (with unities in the diagonal), the square root method will proceed without any complications. However, when the diagonal values are replaced by communalities (less than or at most equal to one), then special considerations must be made to obtain the "real" portions of the solution (see **6.3**).

3.5. *Calculation of the Inverse of a Matrix*

There are many situations in factor analysis where the inverse of a matrix is either required explicitly, or, if it were readily available, could lead to simplification in the work. One example is in regard to the estimation of communality, which is treated in chapter 5. A lower bound to the communality is the squared multiple correlation of a variable with the remaining variables, and the calculation of these multiple correlations is expedited by use of the inverse of the correlation matrix. Another example involves the calculation of a factor pattern from a factor structure for an oblique solution (see chaps. 11, 13, 15), in which the inverse of the matrix of factor correlations simplifies the task. The inverse of the matrix of factor correlations is also employed in the short method of estimating oblique factors (see **16.7**). All of these examples point to the usefulness of an efficient means for determining the inverse of a given matrix. The solution to this problem can be accomplished by the methods of this section.

While the inverse of a matrix is defined in **3.2**, paragraph **22**, such a mathematical statement does not provide a practical means for its calculation with numerical data. The methods for solving systems of linear equations described in the last two sections can be employed in getting the inverse of a matrix. The procedure can be demonstrated with the simple problem of deriving the inverse of the following matrix of correlations among three variables:

$$\mathbf{R} = \begin{bmatrix} 1 & r_{12} & r_{13} \\ r_{21} & 1 & r_{23} \\ r_{31} & r_{32} & 1 \end{bmatrix}.$$

Table 3.3

Calculation of the Inverse of a Matrix: Square Root Method

Instructions	Schematic		Numerical Example												
Original matrices	**R**	**I**	1.00	.72	.75	.49	.42	.28	1	0	0	0	0	0
			*	1.00	.78	.42	.36	.24		1	0	0	0	0
			*	*	1.00	.35	.30	.20			1	0	0	0
			*	*	*	1.00	.42	.28				1	0	0
			*	*	*	*	1.00	.24					1	0
			*	*	*	*	*	1.00						1
Square root operation $(\mathbf{S}')^{-1}$	**S**	$(\mathbf{S}')^{-1}$	1.00	.72	.75	.49	.42	.28	1.00	0	0	0	0	0
			*	.69	.35	.10	.08	.06	−1.04	1.45	0	0	0	0
			*	*	.56	−.09	−.08	−.06	−.69	−.91	1.79	0	0	0
			*	*	*	.86	.23	.15	−.52	−.26	.19	1.16	0	0
			*	*	*	*	.87	.09	−.31	−.15	.11	−.31	1.15	0
			*	*	*	*	*	.94	−.16	−.09	.07	−.16	−.11	1.06
Column-by-column multiplication by $(\mathbf{S}')^{-1}$, i.e., premultiplication by $\mathbf{S}^{-1}$	(Result is **I**, except for rounding errors— may be left blank)	$\mathbf{R}^{-1}$	2.95	*	*	*	*	*	−.68	−1.38	−.48	−.34	−.17	
			*	3.02	*	*	*	*	−1.68	−.24	−.16	−.10		
			*	*	3.26	*	*	*	.18	.12	.08			
			*	*	*	1.47	*	*	−.34	−.17				
			*	*	*	*	1.33	*	−.12					
			*	*	*	*	*	1.13						

* See footnote to Table 3.2.

43

The property (3.14), that the product of a matrix by its inverse is an identity matrix, may be put in the form:

$$(3.31) \quad \begin{bmatrix} 1 & r_{12} & r_{13} \\ r_{21} & 1 & r_{23} \\ r_{31} & r_{32} & 1 \end{bmatrix} \begin{bmatrix} e_{11} & e_{12} & e_{13} \\ e_{21} & e_{22} & e_{23} \\ e_{31} & e_{32} & e_{33} \end{bmatrix} = \begin{bmatrix} 1 & 0 & 0 \\ 0 & 1 & 0 \\ 0 & 0 & 1 \end{bmatrix}$$

where the elements of the inverse matrix $\mathbf{R}^{-1}$ are denoted by e's. The problem is to determine the elements of the inverse matrix from the known correlations.

Upon carrying out the matrix multiplication indicated in the left-hand member of (3.31), and setting each resulting element equal to the corresponding element of the identity matrix on the right, the following equations are obtained:

$$(3.32_1) \quad \begin{cases} 1 \cdot e_{11} + r_{12}e_{21} + r_{13}e_{31} = 1, \\ r_{21}e_{11} + 1 \cdot e_{21} + r_{23}e_{31} = 0, \\ r_{31}e_{11} + r_{32}e_{21} + 1 \cdot e_{31} = 0; \end{cases}$$

$$(3.32_2) \quad \begin{cases} 1 \cdot e_{12} + r_{12}e_{22} + r_{13}e_{32} = 0, \\ r_{21}e_{12} + 1 \cdot e_{22} + r_{23}e_{32} = 1, \\ r_{31}e_{12} + r_{32}e_{22} + 1 \cdot e_{32} = 0; \end{cases}$$

$$(3.32_3) \quad \begin{cases} 1 \cdot e_{13} + r_{12}e_{23} + r_{13}e_{33} = 0, \\ r_{21}e_{13} + 1 \cdot e_{23} + r_{23}e_{33} = 0, \\ r_{31}e_{13} + r_{32}e_{23} + 1 \cdot e_{33} = 1. \end{cases}$$

It will be noted that each set of three equations involves the same matrix of coefficients, the correlation matrix $\mathbf{R}$. Hence, the work can be so organized that the solution for all the e's can be made simultaneously by either of the methods described in **3.3** or **3.4**.

When the inverse of a small matrix is required it can be obtained by the method of **3.3**; however, when a larger matrix is involved, the square root method will be found more efficient. To illustrate the procedure, a matrix of correlations of six hypothetical variables will be inverted. This is accomplished in Table 3.3, where general instructions are given and the work is outlined in schematic form as well as the actual calculation for the numerical example. The square root operation is applied both to the correlation matrix $\mathbf{R}$ and to the identity matrix, yielding $\mathbf{S}$ and $(\mathbf{S}')^{-1}$, respectively. Then, when the latter is premultiplied by $\mathbf{S}^{-1}$ the result is the inverse of the original matrix $\mathbf{R}$. The proof of the last result follows simply by taking the inverses of both sides of equation (3.30):

$$(3.33) \quad \mathbf{R}^{-1} = \mathbf{S}^{-1}(\mathbf{S}')^{-1}.$$

4

Geometric Concepts Essential to Factor Analysis

4.1. *Introduction*

The understanding of factor analysis methods is enhanced by the use of geometry to supplement and extend the algebraic and matrix ideas. The geometric foundation developed in this chapter furnishes a basis for subsequent analysis and comparison of methods. Since the number of variables subjected to a factor analysis usually is quite numerous, and since the dimension of the geometric space will be found to be intimately related to this number, the geometry of concern will be "higher dimensional".

After a very brief exposition of the nature of higher dimensional geometry, a coordinate system is introduced, so that the succeeding development can be made analytically. Then, in **4.4**, the notion of linear dependence is developed, which paves the way for one of the fundamental theorems of factor analysis. Before the application of these geometric ideas to the factor problem is made, certain necessary formulas for distance and angle are developed in **4.5** and **4.7** for rectangular coordinates and, in **4.8** for general coordinates. The formulas in terms of general coordinates are included so that a geometric interpretation of oblique forms of factorial solutions may be made. The theory of orthogonal transformations, presented in **4.6**, forms the basis upon which some actual analyses are obtained in later chapters.

In **4.9** a variable is interpreted as a point, or a vector, in higher dimensional space. The standard deviation of the variable then becomes a distance, and the correlation between two variables is the cosine of the angle between the two vectors representing the variables. The direct application of the geometric theorems to the fundamental problems of factor analysis is made in the final section. There it is shown that the dimension of the smallest space which contains the vectors representing a given set of variables is equal to the rank of the matrix of correlations with communalities in the diagonals.

45

4.2.   *Geometry of N Dimensions*

The concept of higher dimensions is arrived at by geometric and algebraic means. The notions of point, line, and plane may be generalized to higher dimensional objects, and extended geometric interpretations of algebraic relationships may be given. The deductions made in the higher dimensional spaces are based upon the analogous theory in three-dimensional space.

The basic axioms [437, chap. I] for Euclidean geometry may be assumed and such modifications made as are necessary to insure that the space has a sufficiently high dimensionality. The point, straight line, and plane are taken as undefined elements, and later corresponding elements of higher dimensional space may be defined in terms of these.

Starting with four given non-coplanar points, all the points, lines, and planes can be obtained which constitute a three-dimensional space. The space, or manifold, determined by these points is essentially ordinary space of three dimensions. All that is necessary is to postulate that there is at least one point *not* in the three-dimensional space to generate a four-space. The three-dimensional region does not now constitute the whole of space but merely a subspace of the space of four dimensions. The three-dimensional region is called a *hyperplane* lying in the four-space, analogous to a plane lying in a three-space. A hyperplane in a space of four dimensions is determined by four non-coplanar points, a point and a plane, or by two skew lines.

Some of the elementary geometric properties of the elements in a three- and four-dimensional projective* space may now be enumerated. In a three-dimensional space two planes intersect in a line; a line cuts a plane in a point; and any three planes have a point in common, while four planes do not in general have a point in common. In a four-dimensional space two hyperplanes intersect in a plane, three hyperplanes intersect in a line, and four in a point, while five do not in general have any point in common; a hyperplane cuts a plane in a line, and a line in a point; two planes have in general only one point in common, and a plane and a line in general have no point in common.

The notion of dimensionality may be viewed in another manner. A point in a line is said to have one degree of freedom (of motion); in a plane, two; and in ordinary space, three. The point being taken as element, a line is said to be of one dimension; a plane, two; and ordinary space, three. These spaces are called *linear spaces*, or *flat spaces*, i.e., a plane is a *two-flat* and ordinary space is a *three-flat*. An $(N - 1)$-flat in an N-space will be called a *hyperplane*. The linear spaces point, line, plane, three-flat, $\cdots$, hyperplane, N-flat are manifolds determined by one, two three, four, $\cdots$, N, $N + 1$ points,† respectively, and having zero, one, two, three, $\cdots$, $N - 1$, N dimensions.

---

* In assuming a projective space, the discussion is simplified by avoiding the special cases of parallel elements.

† It is understood that the set of p points, which determine a $(p - 1)$-flat, do not lie in a $(p - 2)$-flat.

4.3. *Cartesian Coordinate System*

The geometric ideas are found to be most useful and easily formulated when they are given analytic representation. A point P may thus be represented by the *vector* $(x_1, x_2, \cdots, x_N)$. Each x_i is a real number, and all N numbers may be called a *system* or *N-tuple*. By a "point" is meant simply one of the undefined elements of the space which is characterized by a given set of axioms, so that a set of points is really an arbitrary set of any whatever elements. On the other hand, the N-tuple $(x_1, x_2, \cdots, x_N)$ may be called an "arithmetic point." A correspondence between a set of "geometric points" and a set of "arithmetic points" is called a *coordinate system.** The numbers, $x_1, x_2, \cdots, x_N$, which constitute the representation of P, are called the coordinates of P. For purposes of factor analysis, the distinction between a "geometric" and the corresponding "arithmetic" point is not essential, and the word "point" will be used for either one. The notation $P:(x_i)$ will frequently be used to designate the point and its coordinates.

An N-dimensional Euclidean space is assumed, and in this space a non-homogeneous *Cartesian coordinate system* is set up. The points $O:(0, 0, \cdots, 0)$, and $E_1:(1, 0, \cdots, 0)$, $E_2:(0, 1, 0, \cdots, 0), \cdots, E_N:(0, \cdots, 0, 1)$ are called the origin and unit points, respectively. The N lines Ox_i ($i = 1, 2, \cdots, N$), each passing through the origin and one of the unit points, are the *coordinate axes*. The N hyperplanes† $\pi_i = Ox_1 x_2 \cdots)x_i(\cdots x_N$, each passing through O and containing $N - 1$ axes are the *coordinate hyperplanes*. A hyperplane π_i is said to be "opposite" to the axis Ox_i. The *coordinates* $(x_1, x_2, \cdots, x_N)$ of any point P are equal, respectively, to its distances from each coordinate hyperplane measured along a line parallel to the opposite axis; or, in other words, the distance cut off on each axis by a hyperplane parallel to the respective opposite coordinate hyperplane. For example, the coordinate x_1 is equal to the distance (denoted by x_1) cut off on the Ox_1 axis by a hyperplane parallel to the coordinate hyperplane π_1.

4.4. *Linear Dependence*

The N-tuple $(x_1, x_2, \cdots, x_N)$, which represents a point P, may be considered as a vector which joins the origin O to the point P. Such a vector is sometimes called a "radius vector." Two fundamental operations in vector algebra are multiplication by a number and addition of vectors. More precisely, if P is a point represented by the vector $(x_1, x_2, \cdots, x_N)$ and c is any number, then according to **3.2**, paragraph **20**, cP is the point

$$(cx_1, cx_2, \cdots, cx_N).$$

---

* The coordinate systems introduced in this volume always produce a one-to-one correspondence between the geometric and arithmetic points. This restriction may be removed, however. A correspondence may carry each point P into a set of arithmetic points, as, for example, in a *homogeneous coordinate system.*

† The inverted parentheses are used in the designation of any hyperplane to indicate the omitted coordinate axis.

Also, according to **3.2**, paragraph **16**, if $P_1 : (x_{11}, x_{12}, \cdots, x_{1N})$ and $P_2 : (x_{21}, x_{22}, \cdots, x_{2N})$ are two points,* then $P_1 + P_2$ is the point

$$(x_{11} + x_{21}, x_{12} + x_{22}, \cdots, x_{1N} + x_{2N}).$$

In general, any linear combination of m points, $P_1 : (x_{11}, x_{12}, \cdots, x_{1N}), \cdots, P_m : (x_{m1}, x_{m2}, \cdots, x_{mN})$, may be defined by combining the two previous operations, as follows:

$$t_1 P_1 + t_2 P_2 + \cdots + t_m P_m,$$

where the t's are any numbers. By taking varying values of the t's, different linear combinations of the original m points can be obtained. Any one of these new points may be denoted† $P(t)$ or $P(t_1, t_2, \cdots, t_m)$, with coordinates given by

$$(4.1) \qquad\qquad x_i = \sum_{q=1}^{m} t_q x_{qi} \qquad\qquad (i = 1, 2, \cdots, N),$$

and is said to be *linearly dependent* on the original points $P_1, P_2, \cdots, P_m$. Each coordinate x_i of a point $P(t)$ is expressed as a linear combination of the corresponding coordinates $x_{1i}, x_{2i}, \cdots, x_{mi}$ of the m points $P_1, P_2, \cdots, P_m$. Perhaps the linear dependence of any new points on the m original points can be visualized better from the following expanded matrix equivalent of (4.1):

$$(4.2) \qquad (x_1 \, x_2 \cdots x_N) = (t_1 \, t_2 \cdots t_m) \begin{bmatrix} x_{11} & x_{12} & \cdots & x_{1N} \\ x_{21} & x_{22} & \cdots & x_{2N} \\ \cdots & \cdots & \cdots & \cdots \\ x_{m1} & x_{m2} & \cdots & x_{mN} \end{bmatrix}.$$

To clarify the foregoing ideas, consider the special case of $N = 3$ and two points $P_1 : (x_{11}, x_{12}, x_{13})$ and $P_2 : (x_{21}, x_{22}, x_{23})$. All the points $P(t)$ which are linearly dependent on the points P_1 and P_2 are given by the following coordinates:

$$
\begin{aligned}
& \qquad\qquad x_1 = t_1 x_{11} + t_2 x_{21} \\
P(t_1, t_2) : \ & \ x_2 = t_1 x_{12} + t_2 x_{22} \\
& \qquad\qquad x_3 = t_1 x_{13} + t_2 x_{23}
\end{aligned}
$$

for any whatever values of t_1 and t_2. For particular values of t_1 and t_2, the first coordinate of $P(t)$ is a linear combination of the first coordinates of P_1 and P_2; the second coordinate is the same linear combination of the second ones; and the third co-

---

* The double subscript notation is used on the coordinates in order to distinguish the points. Thus x_{qi} designates the ith coordinate of the point P_q.

† The symbol $P(t)$, or $P(t_1, t_2, \cdots, t_m)$, is the conventional function notation which is to be read, "P is function of t (in this case, a set of t's), or P is a function of $t_1, t_2, \cdots, t_m$." On the other hand, $P : (x_i)$ is the notation for a point P with coordinates x_i.

ordinate is again the same linear combination of the third ones. For example, if the coordinates of P_1 are $(1, 3, 4)$ and those of P_2 are $(2, 1, 5)$ and $t_1 = 1$, $t_2 = 2$, then $P(t)$ is given by the coordinates $x_1 = 5$, $x_2 = 5$, $x_3 = 14$.

The preceding description of linear dependence can be made, alternatively, by giving a direct definition of *linear independence*. Thus, a set of points $P_1, \cdots, P_m$ is linearly independent if the N conditions

$$(4.3) \qquad\qquad \sum_{q=1}^{m} t_q x_{qi} = 0 \qquad\qquad (i = 1, 2, \cdots, N)$$

imply that $t_1 = t_2 = \cdots = t_m = 0$. This can readily be shown to be consistent with the definition (4.1). For, if one of the coefficients were different from zero, say $t_1 \neq 0$, then (4.3) could be written in the form

$$x_{1i} = -\frac{t_2}{t_1} x_{2i} - \frac{t_3}{t_1} x_{3i} - \cdots - \frac{t_m}{t_1} x_{mi};$$

and, according to (4.1), the point P_1 would be one of the points $P(t)$ which is linearly dependent on the points $P_2, P_3, \cdots, P_m$. Having a positive definition of independence, the definition of linear dependence is given by its negation, that is, a set of m points is linearly dependent if the conditions (4.3) hold for the coefficients not all zero.

When a set of points is given, it may be of interest to know how many of them are linearly independent. Let $P_1:(x_{11}, x_{12}, \cdots, x_{1N})$, $P_2:(x_{21}, x_{22}, \cdots, x_{2N}), \cdots, P_n:(x_{n1}, x_{n2}, \cdots, x_{nN})$ be any set of n points. Either all these points coincide with the origin or at least one of them, say P_1, is independent. Of the remaining points, either they will all depend upon P_1 or at least one of them, say P_2, will be independent of P_1. Proceeding in this way an independent set of points, say $P_1, P_2, \cdots, P_m$, will be obtained upon which all the points $P_1, P_2, \cdots, P_n$ will be linearly dependent. A criterion for determing m may be obtained by means of the matrix

$$\mathbf{X} = (x_{ji}) = \begin{bmatrix} x_{11} & x_{12} & x_{13} & \cdots & x_{1N} \\ x_{21} & x_{22} & x_{23} & \cdots & x_{2N} \\ x_{31} & x_{32} & x_{33} & \cdots & x_{3N} \\ \cdot & \cdot & \cdot & \cdots & \cdot \\ x_{n1} & x_{n2} & x_{n3} & \cdots & x_{nN} \end{bmatrix},$$

whose rows are the n points in N space. An important result for linear dependence of points, and which will be utilized later to determine the number of common factors necessary to describe a set of variables, may be stated as:

THEOREM 4.1. *If m is the rank of the matrix $\mathbf{X}$, the points $P_1, P_2, \cdots, P_n$ are all dependent upon m of them, which are themselves independent.*

The proof of this theorem may be split into two parts. First consider the case where $n \leq N$. By hypothesis the matrix $\mathbf{X}$ is of rank m, so that without loss of generality it may be assumed that the determinant

$$D = \begin{vmatrix} x_{11} & x_{12} & \cdots & x_{1m} \\ x_{21} & x_{22} & \cdots & x_{2m} \\ \cdot & \cdot & \cdots & \cdot \\ x_{m1} & x_{m2} & \cdots & x_{mm} \end{vmatrix}$$

is different from zero. If $m = n$ the set of equations

$$\sum_{k=1}^{n} x_{kj}t_k = 0 \qquad (j = 1, 2, \cdots, n)$$

have the unique solution $t_1 = t_2 = \cdots = t_n = 0$, since $D \neq 0$. Then, according to the definition (4.3), the points $P_1, P_2, \cdots, P_n$ are linearly independent. If $m < n$ the points $P_1, P_2, \cdots, P_m$ may be shown to be independent by the preceding argument. This establishes the last part of the theorem.

Now to show that all n points are dependent upon these, form a new matrix by annexing a row and column to the matrix of D as follows:

$$\Delta = \begin{bmatrix} x_{11} & x_{12} & \cdots & x_{1m} & x_{1i} \\ x_{21} & x_{22} & \cdots & x_{2m} & x_{2i} \\ \cdot & \cdot & \cdots & \cdot & \cdot \\ x_{m1} & x_{m2} & \cdots & x_{mm} & x_{mi} \\ x_{p1} & x_{p2} & \cdots & x_{pm} & x_{pi} \end{bmatrix},$$

where $p = m + 1, \cdots, n$ and i is arbitrary. The determinant of this matrix, when expanded according to the elements of the last column, becomes

(4.4) $$|\Delta| = x_{1i}D_{1i} + x_{2i}D_{2i} + \cdots + x_{mi}D_{mi} + x_{pi}D,$$

where $D_{1i}, D_{2i}, \cdots, D_{mi}$ are the cofactors of $x_{1i}, x_{2i}, \cdots, x_{mi}$, respectively, and D is the cofactor of the last element x_{pi}. This expression vanishes, for, if $i \leq m$, two columns then have equal elements; and, if $i > m$, it vanishes, since the rank of $\mathbf{X}$ is m and every $(m + 1)$-order minor vanishes. The solution for x_{pi} from the expression (4.4) set equal to zero is

(4.5) $$x_{pi} = \sum_{q=1}^{m} t_q x_{qi} \qquad (p = m + 1, \cdots, n),$$

where the constants

(4.6) $$t_q = -\frac{D_{qi}}{D}$$

do not depend on the elements $x_{1i}, x_{2i}, \cdots, x_{mi}, x_{pi}$. It follows from definition (4.1) that the points P_p, whose coordinates are given in (4.5), are linearly dependent on the points $P_1, P_2, \cdots, P_m$, which are themselves independent.

While the situation would not arise in ordinary application of factor analysis, to complete the proof of the theorem consider the remaining case when $n > N$. In this case the points $P_j: (x_{j1}, x_{j2}, \cdots, x_{jN}, 0, \cdots, 0)$ are in a space of n dimensions. Then the foregoing argument can be applied to obtain the relation (4.5), and thus the theorem is established for all values of n.

The meaning of Theorem 4.1 may be demonstrated with the very simple example of the three points:

$$\begin{bmatrix} 1 & 3 & 4 \\ 2 & 1 & 5 \\ 5 & 5 & 14 \end{bmatrix}.$$

This matrix is seen to be of rank two because the third-order determinant is zero while a second-order determinant can be found which is different from zero. According to the theorem, since the matrix is of rank two, the three points are dependent upon two of them, which are themselves independent—a fact that was known about these particular points from the way the third point was constructed as the sum of the first point and twice the second.

Subspaces of the N-space may now be given analytical representation. If $P_1, P_2, \cdots, P_k$ are k linearly independent points, the set of all points linearly dependent on them is called a *linear k-space* and is defined by the equations

(4.7) $$x_i = \sum_{j=1}^{k} t_j x_{ji} \qquad (i = 1, 2, \cdots, N),$$

where the t's are a set of k parameters, and for each set of values $(t_1, t_2, \cdots, t_k)$ there is a corresponding point of the linear k-space. Any one of the original k linearly independent points is, of course, given by definition (4.7); for example, P_2 is given by $t_2 = 1$ and $t_1 = t_3 = \cdots = t_k = 0$. The k points $P_1, P_2, \cdots, P_k$ are said to determine the linear k-space. A linear 1-space consists of all points whose coordinates are proportional to those of a given point $P_1: (x_{11}, x_{12}, \cdots, x_{1N})$, and may be called a line through the origin. Its equations are given by

(4.8) $$x_i = t_1 x_{1i} \qquad (i = 1, 2, \cdots, N).$$

In an N-space, these are a set of N *parametric equations* of a line through the origin, where t_1 is known as the parameter.

In a plane, a linear 1-space consists of all points proportional to a given point, say $P_1: (x_{11}, x_{12})$, and passing through the origin. Its parametric equations are:

(4.9)
$$x_1 = t_1 x_{11},$$
$$x_2 = t_1 x_{12}.$$

Of course, this pair of equations reduces to the more elementary expression of a straight line through the origin:

(4.9′) $$y = bx$$

51

where y is the ordinate x_2, x is the abscissa x_1, and b is the slope x_{12}/x_{11}, derived from the given point P_1.

The transitive law for linear dependence may now be indicated. All points linearly dependent on m points $P_1, \cdots, P_m$ in a linear k-space are contained in that k-space. The coordinates of the m points are given by equations of the form (4.7), and any point linearly dependent on $P_1, \cdots, P_m$ is then obviously dependent on $P_1, \cdots, P_k$.

Furthermore, if the points $P_1, \cdots, P_k$ determine a linear k-space, there is no other linear k-space containing these points. A linear k-space is thus determined by any set of k independent points contained in it, and a linear k-space does not contain a set of l independent points, where $l > k$. For, by definition (4.1), it is implied that any k points in a set of l independent points are themselves independent, and hence determine a linear k-space contained in the larger set. Theorem 4.1 may then be stated as follows:

THEOREM 4.2. *If m is the rank of the matrix* $\mathbf{X}$, *the points* $P_1, P_2, \cdots, P_n$ *are all contained in a linear m-space but not in a linear μ-space, where $\mu < m$.*

A geometric interpretation of linear dependence can now be given. The m vectors P_q: $(x_{q1}, x_{q2}, \cdots, x_{qN})$, $(q = 1, 2, \cdots, m)$, employed in the definition (4.1), determine an m-dimensional subspace of the original N-space, and if $OP_1, OP_2, \cdots, OP_m$ are taken as the coordinate axes, then $t_1, t_2, \cdots, t_m$ in (4.1) are the coordinates x_i of $P(t)$.

A set of m vectors is said to *span* an n-space if every vector in this space can be expressed as a linear combination of the m given vectors. An important consideration is the smallest number of vectors which will span the space, and this turns out to be equal to the dimension of the space provided these vectors are linearly independent. Thus, any system of m linearly independent vectors spans an entire m-space and forms a *basis* for that space. An example of a basis is the set of unit vectors along the coordinate axes. A basis for a space certainly is not unique. As a matter of fact, there are an infinite number of bases for a given space [see 123, pp. 37–38]. This, in essence, is the indeterminacy of the factor problem. The choice of a particular basis, sometimes referred to as the "rotation" problem of factor analysis, is the subject of part iii of this text.

A linear k-space, as defined by equations (4.7), always contains the origin, since the origin is linearly dependent on any set of points. The notion of subspaces of the N-dimensional space may be generalized to spaces which do not include the origin. For this purpose, a *translation* of coordinates,

(4.10) $$y_i = x_i + c_i,$$

is defined. Then any set of points which corresponds, under a translation, to a linear k-space may be called a *flat k-space*, or merely a *k-flat*. As noted in **4.2**, a 0-flat is a single point; a 1-flat is a straight line, a 2-flat is a plane; and an $(N - 1)$-flat is a hyperplane.

4.5. *Distance Formulas in Rectangular Coordinates*

When the coordinate axes are mutually orthogonal, i.e., at right angles to one another, the reference system set up in **4.3** is called a *rectangular Cartesian system*. Some elementary formulas in *rectangular* coordinates are presented in this section.

For any two vectors or points $P_1: (x_{11}, x_{12}, \cdots, x_{1N})$ and $P_2: (x_{21}, x_{22}, \cdots, x_{2N})$, their *scalar product* (or *inner* or *dot* product) as defined in **3.2**, paragraph **19** is given by:

$$(4.11) \qquad P_1 \cdot P_2 = \sum x_{1i} x_{2i},$$

where summation with respect to i is understood. The *norm* of P_1 is defined as the positive square root of the inner product of P_1 with itself, that is,

$$(4.12) \qquad N(P) = \sqrt{P_1 \cdot P_1} = \sqrt{\sum x_{1i}^2};$$

and the *distance* between P_1 and P_2 is defined by

$$(4.13) \qquad D(P_1 P_2) = N(P_1 - P_2) = \sqrt{\sum (x_{1i} - x_{2i})^2}.$$

It is readily seen that the norm of a point is the distance from the origin to the point, that is, $N(P) = D(OP)$. The distance function satisfies the following familiar conditions of elementary geometry:

$$(4.14) \qquad \begin{cases} D(P_1 P_1) = 0, \\ D(P_1 P_2) > 0 \text{ if } P_1 \neq P_2, \\ D(P_1 P_2) = D(P_2 P_1), \\ D(P_1 P_2) + D(P_2 P_3) \geq D(P_1 P_3). \end{cases}$$

The first three of these relations are obvious. The fourth, however, requires some proof. It may be noted that distances are invariant under translations. Thus if two points P_1, P_2 are translated into two points P'_1, P'_2, then $D(P_1 P_2) = D(P'_1 P'_2)$, which may be verified by applying (4.10). The fourth formula of (4.14) will therefore be unaltered if the points P_1, P_2, and P_3 are transformed by a translation which carries P_2 into the origin. Then, by (4.12) and (4.13), the inequality of (4.14) becomes

$$(4.15) \qquad \sqrt{\sum x_{1i}^2} + \sqrt{\sum x_{3i}^2} \geqq \sqrt{\sum (x_{1i} - x_{3i})^2},$$

which may be verified algebraically.

Now the equality occurs in (4.15) if, and only if,

$$x_{3i} = -t_1 x_{1i} \qquad\qquad (i = 1, 2, \cdots, N),$$

where t_1 is a positive constant. These equations are of the form (4.8) and so represent a straight line through the origin with the points P_1 and P_3 on opposite sides of the origin. Hence, equality occurs in the fourth relations of (4.14) if, and only if, the coordinates of P_1, P_2, and P_3 are related by equations of the form

$$(4.16) \qquad A(x_{1i} - x_{2i}) + B(x_{3i} - x_{2i}) = 0,$$

where A and B are constants of like sign and not both zero. If the condition (4.16) is satisfied, and if $P_1 \neq P_2$ and $P_2 \neq P_3$, then P_2 is said to lie *between* P_1 and P_3.

4.6. *Orthogonal Transformations*

Of special interest to factor analysis are some theorems of elementary geometry which have to do with transformations which leave distances invariant. Such transformations, in which any point $P_1 : (x_{1i})$ is carried into $Q_1 : (y_{1i})$ and $P_2 : (x_{2i})$ is carried into $Q_2 : (y_{2i})$, have the following property

$$(4.17) \qquad \sum (x_{1i} - x_{2i})^2 = \sum (y_{1i} - y_{2i})^2.$$

From the condition that a point P_2 is between two others, P_1 and P_3, if, and only if,

$$D(P_1P_2) + D(P_2P_3) = D(P_1P_3),$$

it follows that a transformation which leaves distances unaltered carries straight lines into straight lines. Now, by a fundamental theorem of geometry,* the transformation is linear, that is, of the form

$$(4.18) \qquad y_{ji} = \sum_{k=1}^{N} \alpha_{ik} x_{jk} + c_i \qquad (i = 1, 2, \cdots, N; j = 1, 2, 3, \cdots).$$

Upon substituting the values of y_{1i} and y_{2i} from (4.18), equation (4.17) becomes

$$(4.19) \qquad \sum_{i=1}^{N} (x_{1i} - x_{2i})^2 = \sum_{i=1}^{N} \left[\sum_{k=1}^{N} \alpha_{ik}(x_{1k} - x_{2k}) \right]^2.$$

It now remains to find the conditions which the α's must satisfy in order that (4.19) should hold, and then the most general transformation which preserves distance will be specified. The right-hand side of (4.19) can be written as follows:

$$(4.20) \qquad \sum_{i=1}^{N} \sum_{k=1}^{N} \sum_{l=1}^{N} \alpha_{ik} \alpha_{il}(x_{1k} - x_{2k})(x_{1l} - x_{2l}).$$

Hence, equation (4.19) is satisfied when

$$(4.21) \qquad \sum \alpha_{ik} \alpha_{il} = \delta_{kl},$$

where δ_{kl} is the Kronecker delta which is equal to unity if $k = l$ and equal to zero if $k \neq l$. Any linear homogeneous transformation,

$$(4.22) \qquad y_{ji} = \sum_{k=1}^{N} \alpha_{ik} x_{jk},$$

whose coefficients satisfy (4.21) is called *orthogonal*, and its matrix an *orthogonal matrix*. The following theorem has thus been established:

THEOREM 4.3. *The distance between any two points is an invariant under a general rigid motion, that is, an orthogonal transformation followed by a translation.*

The concept of an orthogonal transformation can be expressed most clearly in matrix notation. To this end, let the sets of initial coordinates and final coordinates

* The theorem states that *any nonsingular transformation of an N-space into itself is linear if it carries straight lines into straight lines.* For a proof of this theorem see Veblen and Whitehead [498, pp. 12–15].

in the N-space be represented by rows of the following matrices:

$$\mathbf{X} = \begin{bmatrix} x_{11} & x_{12} & \cdots & x_{1N} \\ x_{21} & x_{22} & \cdots & x_{2N} \\ \cdots & \cdots & \cdots & \cdots \\ \cdots & \cdots & \cdots & \cdots \\ \cdots & \cdots & \cdots & \cdots \end{bmatrix} \quad \text{and} \quad \mathbf{Y} = \begin{bmatrix} y_{11} & y_{12} & \cdots & y_{1N} \\ y_{21} & y_{22} & \cdots & y_{2N} \\ \cdots & \cdots & \cdots & \cdots \\ \cdots & \cdots & \cdots & \cdots \\ \cdots & \cdots & \cdots & \cdots \end{bmatrix}.$$

Then, if

$$\mathbf{T} = \begin{bmatrix} \alpha_{11} & \alpha_{12} & \cdots & \alpha_{1N} \\ \alpha_{21} & \alpha_{22} & \cdots & \alpha_{2N} \\ \cdots & \cdots & \cdots & \cdots \\ \alpha_{N1} & \alpha_{N2} & \cdots & \alpha_{NN} \end{bmatrix},$$

the transformation (4.22) becomes:

(4.23) $$\mathbf{Y} = \mathbf{XT'}$$

The transformation matrix $\mathbf{T}$ is said to be orthogonal if and only if

(4.24) $$\mathbf{T'T} = \mathbf{I}.$$

In other words, the conditions (4.21) that the coefficients α_{ik} must satisfy in order that the transformation (4.22) be orthogonal imply an identity matrix. It also follows that a matrix $\mathbf{T}$ is an orthogonal matrix if it satisfies the condition (4.24).

4.7. *Angular Separation between Two Lines*

Other geometric ideas that are useful in factor analysis center around the notion of the angle between two lines. The only characteristic of a point is its position, as given by its coordinates in a frame of reference. A line is ordinarily distinguished not by coordinates but by its inclinations to the respective coordinate axes. The angles which a line OP makes with the axes, i.e., $\theta_i = \angle POx_i$, are called the *direction angles* of the line, and their cosines are called *direction cosines*. If the norm $N(P)$, i.e., the distance $D(OP)$, is denoted by ρ, then the direction cosines are given by

(4.25) $$\lambda_i = \cos \theta_i = x_i/\rho \qquad\qquad (i = 1, 2, \cdots, N).$$

By (4.12),

$$\rho^2 = \sum x_i^2,$$

and substituting the value of x_i from (4.25), gives

(4.26) $$\sum \lambda_i^2 = \sum \cos^2 \theta_i = 1.$$

This property, that the sum of the squares of the direction cosines of a line in N-space is equal to unity, is a direct extension of the one in ordinary space.

The parametric equations of a line through the origin O and a fixed point $P_1 : (x_{1i})$ are given by (4.8). The coordinates of any point $P : (x_i)$ on a line through the origin with the direction cosines λ_i are given by (4.25). When ρ is taken as a parametric variable along the line, the N equations (4.25) can be regarded as the equations of the line, which may be written

$$\rho = \frac{x_i}{\lambda_i} \qquad\qquad (i = 1, 2, \cdots, N).$$

Upon equating the N expressions for ρ, the following $N - 1$ equations arise:

(4.27)
$$\frac{x_1}{\lambda_1} = \frac{x_2}{\lambda_2} = \cdots = \frac{x_N}{\lambda_N}.$$

If $P : (x_1, x_2, \cdots, x_N)$ is taken as a variable point on the line, (4.27) can be regarded as the equations of the line.

By means of a translation, of the form (4.10), the equations of a line AP through an arbitrarily fixed point $A : (a_1, a_2, \cdots, a_N)$ and with the direction cosines λ_i are transformed from (4.27) to

(4.28)
$$\frac{x_1 - a_1}{\lambda_1} = \frac{x_2 - a_2}{\lambda_2} = \cdots = \frac{x_N - a_N}{\lambda_N}.$$

Moreover, if

(4.29)
$$\lambda_i = bl_i \qquad\qquad (i = 1, 2, \cdots, N),$$

where b is a constant different from zero, the equations of the line AP may be written in the form

(4.30)
$$\frac{x_1 - a_1}{l_1} = \frac{x_2 - a_2}{l_2} = \cdots = \frac{x_N - a_N}{l_N},$$

where the l_i are not now equal to, but only proportional to, the direction cosines. The numbers l_i are called *direction numbers* of the line.

The actual direction cosines of a line can readily be obtained from the numbers proportional to them. For, squaring both sides of (4.29) and summing for i, this equation becomes

$$b^2 \sum_i l_i^2 = \sum_i \lambda_i^2 = 1,$$

where the last equality follows from (4.26). Then the constant of proportionality is

$$b = \frac{1}{\sqrt{\sum l_i^2}},$$

and the direction cosines are given by

(4.31)
$$\lambda_i = \frac{l_i}{\sqrt{\sum l_i^2}}.$$

Hence (4.30) may be taken as the general form of the $(N - 1)$ equations of a line in N-space.

The coordinates of any point $P : (x_1)$ on a line through $A : (a_i)$ with direction numbers l_i are

$$(4.32) \qquad\qquad x_i = a_i + tl_i \qquad\qquad (i = 1, 2, \cdots, N),$$

where t is the common value in (4.30). Equations (4.32) may be regarded as a system of parametric equations of a line through a fixed point. The distance $D(AP)$ along the line from the fixed point A to any position of the variable point P is

$$D(AP) = \sqrt{\sum (x_i - a_i)^2} = t\sqrt{\sum l_i^2},$$

so that,

$$(4.33) \qquad\qquad t = \frac{D(AP)}{\sqrt{\sum l_i^2}}.$$

It is thus evident that the parameter t in equations (4.32) is proportional to the distance from the fixed point to a variable point on the line and is equal to this distance when the equations of the line are given in terms of the direction cosines.

Now a formula for the cosine of the angle between two lines in N-space may be derived. When two lines meet in a point,* a plane can be drawn through the point

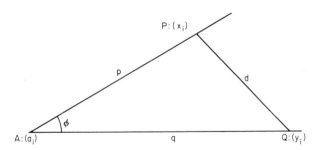

FIG. 4.1.—Angle between two lines

containing the two lines, and their inclination can be obtained from the trigonometric properties of a triangle in the plane. Let the two lines through $A : (a_i)$ be represented by the equations

$$(4.34)$$

$$\frac{x_1 - a_1}{\lambda_1} = \frac{x_2 - a_2}{\lambda_2} = \cdots = \frac{x_N - a_N}{\lambda_N},$$

$$\frac{y_1 - a_1}{\mu_1} = \frac{y_2 - a_2}{\mu_2} = \cdots = \frac{y_N - a_N}{\mu_N},$$

* If the lines do not meet in a point, the angle between the lines may be defined as the angle which one of the lines makes with a line parallel to the second, which intersects the first line.

where the x_i and y_i are the coordinates of the variable points on the lines, and the λ_i and μ_i are the direction cosines of the lines. On the first line take any point P at a distance p from A; on the second line take any point Q at a distance q from A; and connect the points P and Q with a line, which necessarily lies in the plane. The points and lines are plotted in the plane of the two given lines in Figure 4.1.

Let $\phi =$ angle PAQ and let $d = D(PQ)$, then the law of cosines applied to the triangle PAQ gives

(4.35) $$d^2 = p^2 + q^2 - 2pq \cos \phi.$$

The distance d is also given by formula (4.13), in which, according to (4.32), the coordinates of P are $x_i = a_i + p\lambda_i$ and those of Q are $y_i = a_i + q\mu_i$, so that

(4.36)
$$
\begin{aligned}
d^2 &= \sum (x_i - y_i)^2 = \sum (p\lambda_i - q\mu_i)^2, \\
&= p^2 \sum \lambda_i^2 + q^2 \sum \mu_i^2 - 2pq \sum \lambda_i \mu_i, \\
&= p^2 + q^2 - 2pq \sum \lambda_i \mu_i,
\end{aligned}
$$

since $\sum \lambda_i^2 = \sum \mu_i^2 = 1$ by (4.26). When the terms of (4.36) are identified with the corresponding ones of (4.35), the following result is obtained:

(4.37) $$\cos \phi = \sum \lambda_i \mu_i.$$

Thus the cosine of the angle of separation of two lines is given by the sum of the products of corresponding direction cosines of the lines, i.e., the scalar product of the vectors $(\lambda_1, \lambda_2, \cdots, \lambda_N)$ and $(\mu_1, \mu_2, \cdots, \mu_N)$.

By means of formula (4.37) another expression for the scalar product of two vectors or points may be written in place of (4.11). The coordinates of the two points $P_1 : (x_{1i})$ and $P_2 : (x_{2i})$ may be expressed as follows:

$$x_{1i} = \rho_1 \lambda_{1i}, \qquad x_{2i} = \rho_2 \lambda_{2i} \qquad\qquad (i = 1, 2, \cdots, N),$$

where ρ_1, ρ_2 are the respective distances from the origin to the points, and $\lambda_{1i}, \lambda_{2i}$ are the direction cosines of the lines OP_1 and OP_2. Then, substituting these values in (4.11), there arises

$$P_1 \cdot P_2 = \sum x_{1i} x_{2i} = \rho_1 \rho_2 \sum \lambda_{1i} \lambda_{2i},$$

which, according to (4.37), reduces to

(4.38) $$P_1 \cdot P_2 = \rho_1 \rho_2 \cos \phi_{12},$$

where ϕ_{12} is the angle $P_1 O P_2$. Formula (4.38) states that the scalar product of two vectors is the product of the lengths of the vectors by the cosine of their angular separation. This is very often taken as the definition of the scalar product.

4.8. *Distance and Angle in General Cartesian Coordinates*

In sections **4.5** and **4.7** formulas for distance and angle are presented in terms of rectangular coordinates. Now the restriction that the coordinate axes are mutually orthogonal will be removed, and more general formulas obtained. The formulas for distance and angle will then be in terms of general Cartesian coordinates and will simplify to the preceding ones when the angles between all pairs of reference axes are taken as 90°.

The general Cartesian coordinate system contains N reference axes Ox_i which may make any angles with one another. Then the angle between the x_i and x_k axes may be designated $\theta_{ik}(i, k = 1, 2, \cdots, N)$. As may be expected, the formulas for distance and angle in terms of general Cartesian coordinates will involve the inclinations of the reference axes.

Formulas for the distance function in general coordinates will first be given. In the plane the square of the length of the radius vector OP is readily found to be

$$\rho^2 = [D(OP)]^2 = x_1^2 + x_2^2 - 2x_1x_2 \cos(180° - \theta_{12}) = x_1^2 + x_2^2 + 2x_1x_2 \cos\theta_{12}.$$

This formula follows immediately on applying the law of cosines to the triangle POM, indicated in Figure 4.2. By induction, it can be shown that in N-space the

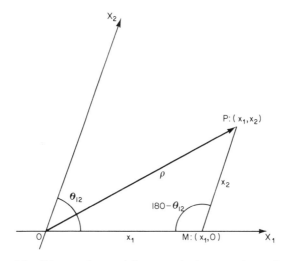

FIG. 4.2.—Distance from origin to a point in general coordinates

distance ρ from the origin O to an arbitrary point $P: (x_1, x_2, \cdots, x_N)$ is given by

(4.39)
$$\rho = \sqrt{\sum \sum x_i x_k \cos \theta_{ik}},$$

where $\sum \sum$ indicates summation for i and k from 1 to N. This convention for the double summation will be employed throughout this section. Similarly, the distance between any two points

$$P_1: (x_{11}, x_{12}, \cdots, x_{1N}) \quad \text{and} \quad P_2: (x_{21}, x_{22}, \cdots, x_{2N})$$

may be shown to be given by the following formula:

(4.40) $$D(P_1 P_2) = \sqrt{\sum \sum (x_{1i} - x_{2i})(x_{1k} - x_{2k}) \cos \theta_{ik}}.$$

The relations (4.39) and (4.40) reduce to the corresponding formulas (4.12) and (4.13) for distance in rectangular coordinates, inasmuch as $\cos \theta_{ik} = 0$ for every $i \neq k$.

There will now be given several properties of a line in terms of more general (not necessarily rectangular) coordinates. The direction of a line OP is determined by the ratios of the coordinates of an arbitrary point $P : (x_1, x_2, \cdots, x_N)$ on the line to the length $\rho = D(OP)$ from the origin to the point. These ratios, denoted by $\lambda_i = x_i / \rho$, are called the *direction ratios* of the line OP. Then if the coordinates of P are expressed in the form

(4.41) $$x_i = \rho \lambda_i \quad \text{or} \quad x_k = \rho \lambda_k,$$

and substituted in (4.39), there results

(4.42) $$\sum \sum \lambda_i \lambda_k \cos \theta_{ik} = 1.$$

The direction ratios become the direction cosines of a line when a general Cartesian coordinate system is specialized to a rectangular one. Then formula (4.42) reduces to (4.26).

An expression for the angle between two lines, in general coordinates, can now be deduced. For simplicity, let the two lines pass through the origin and be distinguished by the direction ratios $\lambda_i, \mu_i (i = 1, 2, \cdots, N)$, respectively. Select a point $P : (x_i)$ on the first line, and a point $Q : (y_i)$ on the second line, and let $p = D(OP)$, $q = D(OQ), d = D(PQ)$, and $\phi = $ angle POQ. Then

$$d^2 = p^2 + q^2 - 2pq \cos \phi.$$

But d is also given by (4.40), in which the coordinates of P are $x_i = p\lambda_i$ and those of Q are $y_i = q\mu_i$, so that after these values are substituted, the formula becomes

$$d^2 = p^2 + q^2 - 2pq \sum \sum \lambda_i \mu_k \cos \theta_{ik}.$$

By equating the two expressions for the square of the distance, the following formula for the angle between two lines is obtained:

(4.43) $$\cos \phi = \sum \sum \lambda_i \mu_k \cos \theta_{ik}.$$

This formula reduces to (4.37) when the axes make right angles with one another.

4.9. *Geometric Interpretation of Correlation*

In this and the following section there will be presented a number of applications of the preceding geometric ideas to the factor problem. The raw data are the values of n variables for each of N individuals. When the variables are in standard form, the matrix of such values:

$$\mathbf{Z} = (z_{ji}) = \begin{bmatrix} z_{11} & z_{12} & \cdots & z_{1N} \\ z_{21} & z_{22} & \cdots & z_{2N} \\ \cdots & \cdots & \cdots & \cdots \\ z_{n1} & z_{n2} & \cdots & z_{nN} \end{bmatrix} ,$$

may be interpreted as containing (by rows) the rectangular Cartesian coordinates of n points z_j ($j = 1, 2, \cdots, n$) in an N-space. Similar interpretation can be made of the elements in the matrix $\mathbf{X} = (x_{ji})$ of deviate values.

The length of the radius vector to a point x_j, according to formula (4.12), is

(4.44) $$\rho_j = \sqrt{\sum x_{ji}^2}.$$

According to definition (2.4), however, this expression simplifies as follows:

(4.45) $$\rho_j = \sqrt{N} s_j.$$

The standard deviation of a variable may thus be interpreted as being proportional to the distance from the origin to the point representing the variable, the constant of proportionality being $1/\sqrt{N}$.

By way of geometric representation of a set of values of two variables, x_j and x_k, it is customary to think of the x_{ji} and the x_{ki} as the coordinates of N points (x_{j1}, x_{k1}), $(x_{j2}, x_{k2}), \cdots, (x_{jN}, x_{kN})$ in the plane $x_j O x_k$. This plot of points is called a *scatter diagram*; and, by means of this representation, a better understanding of the relations involved in the definition (2.7) of a coefficient of correlation can be obtained. In general, for n variables this will be referred to as the *point representation*.

Even more important in some respects is a geometric representation not by N points in a plane (for two variables) but by two points in an N-space. The two variables are then represented by the vectors $x_j : (x_{j1}, x_{j2}, \cdots, x_{jN})$ and $x_k : (x_{k1}, x_{k2}, \cdots, x_{kN})$. Such a configuration for n variables will be called the *vector representation*.

The interpretation of the n rows of matrix $\mathbf{Z}$ as the coordinates of n points in an N-space is the vector representation of the variables. On the other hand, the same numbers in the matrix $\mathbf{Z}$ may be read in sets by columns to give N points in an n-space. In the latter case there will be a swarm of N points in the point representation of the n variables. While both concepts are employed in factor analysis, somewhat greater use is made of the notion of n vectors to represent the variables in a space corresponding to the N individuals.

If the direction cosines of these vectors are denoted by λ_{ji} and λ_{ki}, respectively, then by (4.25),

(4.46) $$\lambda_{ji} = \frac{x_{ji}}{\rho_j}, \qquad \lambda_{ki} = \frac{x_{ki}}{\rho_k} \qquad (i = 1, 2, \cdots, N),$$

where $\rho_j = D(Ox_j)$ and $\rho_k = D(Ox_k)$. Inserting these values in formula (4.37), it becomes

(4.47)
$$\cos \phi_{jk} = \sum \lambda_{ji}\lambda_{ki} = \frac{\sum x_{ji}x_{ki}}{\rho_j\rho_k},$$

where ϕ_{jk} is the angle of separation of the two lines. Then $\cos \phi_{jk}$ may be interpreted as the scalar product of the vectors x_j and x_k divided by the product of the lengths of these vectors. Upon substituting the values for ρ_j and ρ_k from (4.45), formula (4.47) reduces to:

(4.48)
$$\cos \phi_{jk} = \frac{\sum x_{ji}x_{ki}}{Ns_js_k} = r_{jk} \qquad (j, k = 1, 2, \cdots, n).$$

The coefficient of correlation between two variables (measured as deviates from their respective means) is the cosine of the angle between their vectors in N-space.

While the raw data of a study are the values of the variables, whether they are in arbitrary units or standardized, such data are usually reduced to correlation coefficients among the variables before a factor analysis is made. For this reason, it is important to put some of the preceding geometric notions in terms of the correlation matrix $\mathbf{R}$ instead of the matrix of standardized values $\mathbf{Z}$. In particular, it is desirable to have an interpretation of Theorem 4.2 in terms of the correlation matrix. To this end, the following is required first:

THEOREM 4.4. *The rank of the product of a matrix by its transpose is equal to the rank of the matrix.*

The proof follows immediately from another theorem [see 190, p. 138], which states that the rank of the product of any two matrices is less than or equal to the minimum of the rank of either one. Since the two matrices under consideration in Theorem 4.4 are transposes of one another, and have the same rank, the rank of the product is equal to this common rank.

The product of the matrix $\mathbf{Z}$ by its transpose $\mathbf{Z}'$ is equal to the correlation matrix $\mathbf{R}$ multiplied by the scalar N, viz.,

(4.49)
$$\mathbf{ZZ'} = N\mathbf{R},$$

which is readily seen by carrying out the matrix multiplication and substituting the definition of the variances and correlations for standardized variables. Since the theorem is concerned only with the ranks of the matrices, the non-zero factor N is irrelevant to it. The right-hand side of (4.49) might be represented by $\mathbf{R}^*$ to be absolutely rigorous, but for simplicity it will be written $\mathbf{R}$. With this understanding, the theorem may be restated as follows: If m is the rank of matrix $\mathbf{Z}$, then the rank of $\mathbf{R} = \mathbf{ZZ'}$ is equal to m. In other words, the rank of the correlation matrix is equal to the rank of the matrix of observed values.

A more powerful relationship between these two matrices (and also between the reproduced correlation matrix and the factor matrix) is the following:

THEOREM 4.5. *If $\mathbf{Z}$ is an n by N matrix of rank m, with real elements, then $\mathbf{ZZ'} = \mathbf{R}$ is a positive semidefinite real symmetric matrix (Gramian) of rank m.* [*]

[*] For proof see A. A. Albert [7, p. 65].

4.10. *Subspaces Employed in Factor Analysis*

The geometric notions introduced in this chapter make it possible to determine the minimum number of common factors necessary to describe a set of variables in the sense of equations (2.22). According to Theorem 4.2, the n points whose coordinates are given in the matrix $\mathbf{Z}$ are all contained in a linear m-space, where m is the rank of the matrix. In other words, the n vectors can be described in terms of m reference vectors. Furthermore, since the rank of the correlation matrix $\mathbf{R}$ is equal to the rank of the matrix of standardized values $\mathbf{Z}$ (according to Theorem 4.4), any property of the variables which is inferred only from the rank of the latter matrix may be stated in terms of the correlation matrix. It therefore follows from Theorem 4.2 that *the n variables can be expressed as linear functions of not less than m factors, where m is the rank of the correlation matrix.*

In case of the component analysis model (2.8), the correlation matrix contains ones in the diagonal and its rank usually is n. The variables would then be describable in terms of not less than n factors. If it is desired to describe the n variables in terms of fewer than n common factors, a pattern of the form (2.22) may be postulated. From such a pattern the correlations are reproduced, as before, but with communalities in place of ones in the diagonal. Then a factor pattern of the desired form can be obtained by employing a *reduced correlation matrix*, i.e., a correlation matrix with the ones replaced by communalities. The rank of this matrix is generally less than the order n. By the preceding argument, it is therefore apparent that the number of common factors in the pattern is equal to m, the rank of the reduced correlation matrix. This is the smallest number of factors that will account for the intercorrelations. Stated geometrically, the smallest space containing the n points is a flat m-space. Such a space will be referred to as the *common-factor space*. For purposes of reference the above ideas may be recapitulated in the following:

THEOREM 4.6. *If m is the rank of the reduced correlation matrix then the smallest number of linearly independent factors which will account for the correlations is m, or, the common-factor space is of m dimensions.*

It should be emphasized that while the dimension of the common-factor space can be determined by any of several methods (see part ii), such solutions do not provide unique positions of the factors. Any m linearly independent factors form a basis of the common-factor space, and, as noted before, the selection of a particular basis is considered in part iii.

In order to clarify the preceding ideas, the three important spaces will be reviewed. For any variable z_j the system $(z_{j1}, z_{j2}, \cdots, z_{jN})$ of N real numbers may be considered as the rectangular Cartesian coordinates of a point in an N-dimensional space. By means of this vector representation, the configuration of two variables is merely two dimensional, i.e., in a plane, although it has to be regarded as imbedded in an N-space. In general, the configuration of n vectors may be regarded as in an n-dimensional space which is imbedded in the original N-space. For purposes of factor analysis, this space may be reduced further, to the m-space which will contain the n vectors, as indicated in Theorem 4.6.

Before giving the final interpretation of the vectors representing the variables in the common-factor space, the geometric meaning of the linear expressions (2.9) which include unique as well as common factors will be indicated. The n vectors may then be considered in the total-factor space of the m common factors and n unique factors. The vector representation of any variable in this space is given by

$$z'_j : (a_{j1}, a_{j2}, \cdots, a_{jm}, 0, \cdots, 0, d_j, 0, \cdots, 0),$$

where the prime is employed to indicate the linear model (2.9) for the observed variable z_j. The first m coordinates are with respect to the common-factor axes, and the last n coordinates, consisting of only one value different from zero, are with respect to the unique-factor axes. For simplicity let it be assumed that the common factors are mutually orthogonal, and, as usual, the unique factors are orthogonal to all factors. Then the norm, or length, of such a vector, according to (4.12), is

$$(4.50) \qquad\qquad N(z'_j) = \sqrt{a_{j1}^2 + \cdots + a_{jm}^2 + d_j^2} = 1.$$

In other words, each of the vectors representing the variables in the total factor space is of unit length. The direction cosines of such a vector in this space are simply the coordinates of the end point. The cosine of the angle of inclination (ϕ'_{jk}) of two such vectors, z'_j and z'_k, then becomes

$$(4.51) \qquad\qquad \cos \phi'_{jk} = \sum_{p=1}^{m+n} \lambda'_{jp} \lambda'_{kp} = \sum_{p=1}^{m} a_{jp} a_{kp} = r'_{jk},$$

where λ'_{jp} and λ'_{kp} denote the sets of direction cosines of z'_j and z'_k, respectively. Equation (4.51) shows that the reproduced correlation for any two variables is the cosine of the angle between their vectors in the total-factor space. The reproduced correlation r'_{jk} will approximate the observed correlation r_{jk} to the extent that the mathematical models of the variables are adequate.

Now the final interpretation of the variables as vectors in the common-factor space can be made. The orthogonal projections of the n vectors from the total-factor space into the common-factor space of m dimensions are defined to be the vectors representing the variables in this subspace. Such a vector may be denoted by

$$z''_j : (a_{j1}, a_{j2}, \cdots, a_{jm}).$$

The coordinates of the end point of this vector are the same as the first m coordinates in the total-factor space. This property holds even if the common-factor axes are oblique, provided only that the unique-factor axes are orthogonal to the common-factor space. It will again be assumed for simplicity that the common factors are uncorrelated.

A projected vector in the m-space is usually of smaller magnitude than the corresponding vector in the total-factor space, being of the same length only if the variable has no unique variance. Likewise, the angles between pairs of vectors in the common-factor space are smaller and, consequently, their cosines larger. The length of a vector z_j'' in this space is given by

(4.52)
$$N(z_j'') = \sqrt{a_{j1}^2 + a_{j2}^2 + \cdots + a_{jm}^2} = h_j,$$

that is, the square root of the communality h_j^2 of the variable. The direction cosines of any two vectors z_j'' and z_k'' in the common-factor space are given by

(4.53)
$$\lambda_{jp}'' = a_{jp}/h_j, \qquad \lambda_{kp}'' = a_{kp}/h_k \qquad\qquad (p = 1, 2, \cdots, m).$$

Putting these values into (4.37), the cosine of the angle of inclination of these vectors becomes

(4.54)
$$\cos \phi_{jk}'' = \sum_{p=1}^{m} \lambda_{jp}'' \lambda_{kp}'' = \sum_{p=1}^{m} a_{jp} a_{kp} \Big/ h_j h_k.$$

It is obvious that this expression is generally larger than that given by (4.51), being equal to it only when $h_j h_k = 1$. Hence the angles between vectors in the common-factor space are smaller than the corresponding angles in the total-factor space.

The problem of interpreting a reproduced correlation r_{jk}' geometrically can be treated in the common-factor space. It is evident from (4.51) and (4.54) that

(4.55)
$$r_{jk}'' = \cos \phi_{jk}'' = r_{jk}'/h_j h_k.$$

The cosine of the angle of separation of two vectors representing variables in the common-factor space may be referred to as the correlation corrected for uniqueness. In other words, the expression (4.55) would be the value of the reproduced correlation between j and k if these variables were free from unique variance. Solving (4.55) explicitly for the reproduced correlation, there results

(4.56)
$$r_{jk}' = h_j h_k \cos \phi_{jk}'' = h_j h_k r_{jk}''.$$

Thus, by formula (4.38), the reproduced correlation between two variables is given by the scalar product of their vectors in the common-factor space. Of course, the observed correlation r_{jk} differs from the value given in (4.56), unless the residual is exactly zero.

Many concepts useful in factor analysis have been developed and given geometric interpretation in this chapter. In order to summarize these ideas, and to make them readily available for future reference, they are recapitulated in Table 4.1.

A simple illustration of the foregoing ideas is given for the case of only two factors. The common-factor space is of two dimensions, and the two (uncorrelated) factors F_1 and F_2 are represented in Figure 4.3 by unit vectors separated by a right angle. Each variable z_j of a set can be described in terms of the two common factors and a unique factor. The linear expressions for two such variables may be written as follows:

$$z_1' = a_{11}F_1 + a_{12}F_2 + d_1 U_1 + 0 \cdot U_2,$$

$$z_2' = a_{21}F_1 + a_{22}F_2 + 0 \cdot U_1 + d_2 U_2.$$

The geometric representation of these linear expressions for the original variables can be made in the total-factor space of four dimensions, defined by the two common

65

Table 4.1

Concepts Stemming from Vector Representation of Variables

(N = number of individuals; n = number of variables; m = number of common factors)

Concept	Sample Space			Total-Factor Space	Common-Factor Space
	Variables in Deviate Form	Variables in Standard Form	Variable Space		
Number of dimensions	N	N	n	$n + m$	m
Variables ($j = 1, 2, \cdots, n$)	x_j	z_j	$z'_j = a_{j1}F_1 +$ $\cdots + a_{jm}F_m$ $+ d_jU_j$	$z''_j = a_{j1}F_1 +$ $\cdots + a_{jm}F_m$
Coordinates ($i = 1, \cdots, N$; $p = 1, \cdots, m$)	x_{ji}	z_{ji}	a_{jp}, d_j	a_{jp}
Length of radius vector	$\rho_j = \sqrt{N}s_j$	$\rho_j = \sqrt{N}$	$\rho'_j = N(z'_j) = 1$	$\rho''_j = N(z''_j)$ $= h_j$
Direction cosines of vector corresponding to variable j	$\lambda_{ji} = \dfrac{x_{ji}}{\rho_j}$	$\lambda_{ji} = \dfrac{z_{ji}}{\sqrt{N}}$	$\lambda'_{jp} = a_{jp},$ $\lambda'_j = d_j$ $\lambda'_k = 0 \text{ for } k \neq j$ $(k = 1, \cdots, n)$	$\lambda''_{jp} = \dfrac{a_{jp}}{h_j}$
Angle between variables j and k	θ_{jk}	θ_{jk}	θ'_{jk}	θ''_{jk}
Cosine of angle	$\cos\theta_{jk}$ $= \sum_i \lambda_{ji}\lambda_{ki}$ $= \dfrac{\sum_i x_{ji}x_{ki}}{Ns_js_k}$ $= r_{jk}$	$\cos\theta_{jk}$ $= \sum_i \lambda_{ji}\lambda_{ki}$ $= \dfrac{\sum_i z_{ji}z_{ki}}{N}$ $= r_{jk}$	$\cos\theta'_{jk}$ $= \sum_{p=1}^{m+n} \lambda'_{jp}\lambda'_{kp}$ $= \sum_{p=1}^{m} a_{jp}a_{kp}$ $= r'_{jk}$	$\cos\theta''_{jk}$ $= \sum_{p=1}^{m} \lambda''_{jp}\lambda''_{kp}$ $= \dfrac{\sum_{p=1}^{m} a_{jp}a_{kp}}{h_jh_k}$ $= r''_{jk}$
Correlation between variables j and k	r_{jk}	r_{jk}	$r'_{jk} = \sum_{p=1}^{m} a_{jp}a_{kp}$	$r''_{jk} = h_jh_kr''_{jk}$

factors and the two unique factors. In this space the vectors representing z'_1 and z'_2 are of unit length, and their correlation is given by

$$r'_{12} = a_{11}a_{21} + a_{12}a_{22}.$$

Such essential information about the variables as the correlations can be obtained from the consideration of the common-factor space. The projections of the two

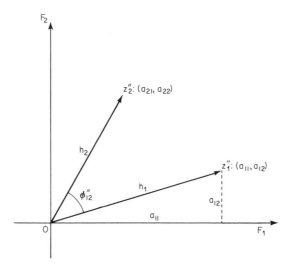

FIG. 4.3.—Common-factor space of two dimensions

vectors z'_1 and z'_2 into this space are indicated in Figure 4.3 by z''_1 and z''_2, respectively, and may be written analytically in the form

$$z''_1 = a_{11}F_1 + a_{12}F_2,$$

$$z''_2 = a_{21}F_1 + a_{22}F_2.$$

The lengths of these vectors are given by the square roots of their communalities, i.e.,

$$D(Oz''_1) = \sqrt{a_{11}^2 + a_{12}^2} = \sqrt{h_1^2},$$

$$D(Oz''_2) = \sqrt{a_{21}^2 + a_{22}^2} = \sqrt{h_2^2}.$$

The cosine of the angle (ϕ''_{12}) separating these vectors is given by

$$\cos \phi''_{12} = \frac{a_{11}}{h_1} \cdot \frac{a_{21}}{h_2} + \frac{a_{12}}{h_1} \cdot \frac{a_{22}}{h_2} = \frac{1}{h_1 h_2}(a_{11}a_{21} + a_{12}a_{22}),$$

or

$$r'_{12} = h_1 h_2 \cos \phi''_{12}.$$

This formula shows that the reproduced correlation of two variables is given by the product of the lengths of the two vectors by the cosine of their angle of separation in the common-factor space.

In the foregoing discussion it was necessary to employ distinct notation to clearly represent elements in the different spaces. Since it would be rather clumsy to retain primes and double primes in the remainder of this volume, they will be dropped when no confusion can arise as to the particular space involved.

67

5

The Problem of Communality

5.1. *Introduction*

In the preceding chapter it was shown that the dimension of the common-factor space is equal to the rank of the reduced correlation matrix. For a given set of observed correlations the rank of this matrix is effected by the particular values put in the principal diagonal, and it will also be recalled from **2.8** that the portions of the variances to be factored are determined by these diagonal elements. When unities are employed, i.e., assuming the component analysis model (2.8), the resulting descriptions of the n variables are in terms of n (rarely fewer) common factors. With the classical factor analysis model (2.9), the communalities are the basic quantities to be analyzed. Herein lies the trouble—there is no *a priori* knowledge of the values of the communalities. Either the rank of the correlation matrix or its diagonal values must be known, or approximated, in order to obtain a factor solution. According to Theorem 4.6, if the rank of the reduced correlation matrix is known (or can be assumed) to be m, then the common-factor space is of m-dimensions. Several procedures for getting factor solutions make suitable approximations of the number of common factors (with more or less refined statistical tests of the adequacy of the assumed m). Other procedures require some estimates of the communalities, i.e., the diagonal values of the correlation matrix rather than its rank. The latter approach is employed in the principal-factor method and the centroid method, treated in chapter 8, as preliminary multiple-factor solutions (which may subsequently be transformed to more desirable solutions by the methods of part iii). A problem that has been plaguing factor analysts since the beginning of the multiple factor approaches is the question of how to determine suitable approximations to "communality".

The general problem of communality is approached through the following considerations: (1) the conditions that the correlation coefficients must satisfy in order for their matrix to have a given rank; (2) the determination of communality under the assumption of the rank of the correlation matrix; (3) the theoretical solution for

68

communality; (4) the approximations to communality without prior knowledge of the rank; (5) a simple example in which a factor solution is obtained directly, once the communalities of the variables have been determined. The first of these items is covered in Sections **5.2** and **5.3**, while the determination of communality using assumed rank is developed and illustrated in **5.4**. The theoretical considerations are presented in **5.5**, and followed by practical methods in **5.6** and **5.7**, with examples of these methods in **5.8**. Finally, in **5.9**, a hypothetical example is employed to bring together the notions of communality and the factor model developed in the preceding chapters.

5.2. *Determination of the Common-Factor Space*

Theorem 4.6 states that the common-factor space is of m dimensions, where m is the rank of the reduced correlation matrix:

$$\mathbf{R} = \begin{bmatrix} h_1^2 & r_{12} & r_{13} & \cdots & r_{1n} \\ r_{21} & h_2^2 & r_{23} & \cdots & r_{2n} \\ r_{31} & r_{32} & h_3^2 & \cdots & r_{3n} \\ \cdots & \cdots & \cdots & \cdots & \cdots \\ r_{n1} & r_{n2} & r_{n3} & \cdots & h_n^2 \end{bmatrix}.$$

One of the major problems in factor analysis is to determine how much the rank of this matrix can be reduced from n by a suitable choice of the communalities for a given set of observed correlations. The number of linearly independent conditions that the unknown communalities h_j^2 must satisfy in order that the matrix $\mathbf{R}$ shall be of rank m can be determined by means of the following theorem (for proof see [101, p. 79]).

THEOREM 5.1. *The rank of the symmetric matrix* $\mathbf{R}$ *is* m *if an* m-*rowed principal minor* $\mathbf{R}_{mm}$ *is not zero and if zero is the value of every principal minor obtained by annexing to* $\mathbf{R}_{mm}$ *one row and the same column of* $\mathbf{R}$, *and also of every principal minor obtained by annexing two rows and the same two columns.*

The number of conditions imposed on the communalities can be found by formal application of the procedure set forth in this theorem. There are n rows in $\mathbf{R}$ and m in the nonvanishing principal minor $\mathbf{R}_{mm}$. This leaves $(n - m)$ rows which may be annexed, one at a time, to $\mathbf{R}_{mm}$, or $(n - m)$ determinants which must vanish. The $(n - m)$ rows may be added two at a time in $\binom{n - m}{2}$ ways to $\mathbf{R}_{mm}$, giving $(n - m)$ $(n - m - 1)/2$ additional determinants which must vanish. Hence the total number of independent conditions (i.e., the number of minors set equal to zero) that the communalities must satisfy in order that $\mathbf{R}$ be of rank m is*

(5.1) $v_m = (n - m) + (n - m)(n - m - 1)/2 = (n - m)(n - m + 1)/2.$

* The proof given here is incomplete in the sense that the v_m equations have not been shown to be linearly independent, i.e., that none of them follows from the others. Walter Lederman [334] arrives at the same number of conditions for the n unknown communalities, although by a different argument, and offers a proof of the linear independence of these equations.

In general, the v_m equations have solutions $h_1^2, h_2^2, \cdots, h_n^2$ only if the number of unknowns is greater than or equal to this number of conditions. If the number of unknowns is less than the number of equations, then the coefficients in the equations (the correlations) must satisfy certain relations in order that the number of independent conditions for the unknowns may be reduced to the number of unknowns, i.e., in order that the equations be consistent.

First, however, let it be assumed that the correlations are arbitrary values, in the sense that no constraints exist among them. Then the set of conditions can be satisfied only if they are no greater in number than the unknowns, viz.,

(5.2)
$$n \geq v_m.$$

The last inequality may be written in the following equivalent form:

(5.3)
$$\phi(m) = v_m - n = [m^2 - (2n + 1)m + n(n - 1)]/2 \leq 0.$$

Setting the quadratic $\phi(m)$ equal to zero and solving for m, the two roots are given by

(5.4)
$$m = [(2n + 1) \pm \sqrt{8n + 1}]/2.$$

It can readily be shown that the plot of the quadratic function $\phi(m)$, for any fixed value of n, is a parabola which opens up vertically. A typical member of this family of parabolas is shown in Figure 5.1 for the case of $n = 9$. While the complete mathematical function is depicted in this figure, only the left part of the curve up to the point where $m = n$ has any interpretive value for factor analysis. In general the curve crosses the m-axis at the two points whose abscissas are given in (5.4), and hence $\phi(m) \leq 0$ for values of m between these extremes. The rank of the correlation matrix, with unknown communalities and arbitrary correlations, may thus be reduced to the value m, which is given by

(5.5)
$$[(2n + 1) + \sqrt{8n + 1}]/2 \geq m \geq [(2n + 1) - \sqrt{8n + 1}]/2.$$

The smallest possible value for m is then the smallest integer greater than or equal to the value in the right-hand member of (5.5). In Table 5.1 there is listed the smallest rank that can be attained for a matrix of a given order, up to $n = 15$, when the correlations are assumed to be quite arbitrary.

Table 5.1

Minimum Rank under Assumption of Independent Correlations

n	2	3	4	5	6	7	8	9	10	11	12	13	14	15
m	1	1	2	3	3	4	5	6	6	7	8	9	10	10

Generally, the observed correlations from statistical variables cannot be considered as arbitrary or independent. The inequality in (5.2) may then be reversed, that is, the

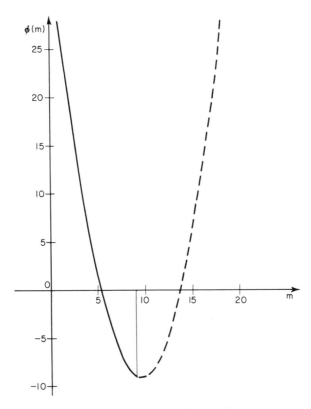

FIG. 5.1.—Function $\phi(m)$ for $n = 9$

number of unknowns may be less than the number of conditions which they must satisfy. The unknown communalities are then "overdetermined" in the sense that the larger number of equations may not be consistent. In order for a solution to exist, the coefficients in the equations must satisfy at least $\phi(m)$ relations. The differences $\phi(m) = (v_m - n)$, that is, the number of conditions that the correlations must satisfy so that a matrix of order n can be reduced to rank m, are given in Table 5.2.

The lower left-hand corner of the table has no entries because the rank cannot exceed the order of a matrix. A negative value represents a larger number of unknowns than conditions, so that there is an infinite number of solutions in such a case, the general solution involving $(n - v_m)$ arbitrary parameters. A zero value represents the case of as many unknowns as equations. For a given number of variables, n, a negative or zero entry indicates the rank m which the correlation matrix can attain without any restrictions on the correlations. In these cases the inequality (5.2) is satisfied, and the conditions on the communalities are met under the assumption that the correlations are independent variables. The value of m for the first negative or zero entry, reading down a column of Table 5.2, corresponds to the value of m, for the same n, in Table 5.1.

Table 5.2

Number of Linearly Independent Conditions on the Correlations: $\phi(m)$

m \ n	2	3	4	5	6	7	8	9	10	11	12	n
1	−1	0	2	5	9	14	20	27	35	44	54	$\binom{n-1}{2} - 1 = \dfrac{n(n-3)}{2}$
2	−2	−2	−1	1	4	8	13	19	26	34	43	$\binom{n-2}{2} - 2 = \dfrac{n(n-5)}{2} + 1$
3		−3	−3	−2	0	3	7	12	18	25	33	$\binom{n-3}{2} - 3 = \dfrac{n(n-7)}{2} + 3$
4			−4	−4	−3	−1	2	6	11	17	24	$\binom{n-4}{2} - 4 = \dfrac{n(n-9)}{2} + 6$
5				−5	−5	−4	−2	1	5	10	16	$\binom{n-5}{2} - 5 = \dfrac{n(n-11)}{2} + 10$
6					−6	−6	−5	−3	0	4	9	$\binom{n-6}{2} - 6 = \dfrac{n(n-13)}{2} + 15$
m												$\binom{n-m}{2} - m = \dfrac{n(n-2m-1)}{2} + \binom{m}{2}$

Of course, there would be little gained in parsimony of thought if the correlations in a study were indeed independent and required as many factors as indicated in Table 5.1. In a factor study the investigator usually selects the variables on some hypothesis of an underlying order, and the correlations cannot be expected to be independent. The relationships that exist among them lead to a rank of the correlation matrix lower than its order, if appropriate values are inserted in the principal diagonal. In the next section specific mathematical conditions are indicated which guarantee that the common-factor space is of one and two dimensions. In subsequent sections approximate methods are presented for the determination of higher dimensional common-factor spaces.

5.3. *Conditions for Reduced Rank of Correlation Matrix*

The number of independent relationships that must exist among the correlations in order that the rank shall be lower than the minimum in (5.5) is given by the positive values in Table 5.2. Thus for $n = 3$, no relationships are necessary to attain rank one; that is, three variables can always be described in terms of one common factor. Four variables, however, cannot be described by just one factor unless their intercorrelations satisfy two (independent) conditions. These well-known conditions, due to Spearman [440], are the vanishing of the *tetrads*, namely,

(5.6)
$$\begin{cases} r_{12}r_{34} - r_{14}r_{23} = 0, \\ r_{13}r_{24} - r_{14}r_{23} = 0. \end{cases}$$

It may be well to indicate how the conditions (5.6) are arrived at when $n = 4$ and $m = 1$, so that the method of generalization will be more evident. When there are just four variables, the reduced matrix of correlations is simply

$$\mathbf{R} = \begin{bmatrix} h_1^2 & r_{12} & r_{13} & r_{14} \\ r_{21} & h_2^2 & r_{23} & r_{24} \\ r_{31} & r_{32} & h_3^2 & r_{34} \\ r_{41} & r_{42} & r_{43} & h_4^2 \end{bmatrix}.$$

This matrix will be of rank one if all second-order minors vanish. By selecting appropriate minors—involving one row and column intersecting in the desired communality, and the other row and column different from each other—several linear equations result for the solution of each of the communalities. Thus, h_1^2 is given by any one of the following three equations:

$$\begin{vmatrix} h_1^2 & r_{13} \\ r_{21} & r_{23} \end{vmatrix} = 0, \qquad \begin{vmatrix} h_1^2 & r_{14} \\ r_{21} & r_{24} \end{vmatrix} = 0, \qquad \begin{vmatrix} h_1^2 & r_{14} \\ r_{31} & r_{34} \end{vmatrix} = 0,$$

or

(5.7)
$$h_1^2 = r_{12}r_{13}/r_{23} = r_{12}r_{14}/r_{24} = r_{13}r_{14}/r_{34}.$$

On eliminating h_1^2, the two equations (5.6) arise. The three separate solutions (5.7) for h_1^2 are consistent if the conditions (5.6) are satisfied.

Referring to Table 5.2 again, it is seen that five relationships must exist among the correlations of five variables if they are to be described in terms of only one common factor. From their correlation matrix, with unknown communalities in the principal diagonal, several linear equations for the solution of each of the communalities can be obtained by setting appropriate second-order minors equal to zero. The first communality, for example, is given by any one of the six equations:

$$\begin{vmatrix} h_1^2 & r_{13} \\ r_{21} & r_{23} \end{vmatrix} = 0, \qquad \begin{vmatrix} h_1^2 & r_{14} \\ r_{21} & r_{24} \end{vmatrix} = 0, \qquad \begin{vmatrix} h_1^2 & r_{15} \\ r_{21} & r_{25} \end{vmatrix} = 0,$$

$$\begin{vmatrix} h_1^2 & r_{14} \\ r_{31} & r_{34} \end{vmatrix} = 0, \qquad \begin{vmatrix} h_1^2 & r_{15} \\ r_{31} & r_{35} \end{vmatrix} = 0, \qquad \begin{vmatrix} h_1^2 & r_{15} \\ r_{41} & r_{45} \end{vmatrix} = 0,$$

or

(5.8) $h_1^2 = r_{12}r_{13}/r_{23} = r_{12}r_{14}/r_{24} = r_{12}r_{15}/r_{25} = r_{13}r_{14}/r_{34} = r_{13}r_{15}/r_{35} = r_{14}r_{15}/r_{45}.$

The five conditions that must be satisfied to assure a unique value of h_1^2 may be put in the equivalent form:

(5.9)
$$\begin{cases} r_{13}r_{24} - r_{14}r_{23} = 0, \\ r_{13}r_{25} - r_{15}r_{23} = 0, \\ r_{12}r_{34} - r_{14}r_{23} = 0, \\ r_{12}r_{35} - r_{15}r_{23} = 0, \\ r_{13}r_{45} - r_{14}r_{35} = 0. \end{cases}$$

Any other conditions must be linearly dependent on the above equations. Thus if instead of obtaining the solutions for h_1^2, those for h_2^2 were obtained, the resulting five conditions could then be shown to be dependent on the foregoing relations (see ex. 7).

In general, a set of n variables is contained in a one-dimensional common-factor space if $n(n - 3)/2$ relationships exist among their correlations, according to the last entry on the first line of Table 5.2. These conditions, whatever form they take, are equivalent to the following set:

(5.10)
$$\begin{cases} \dfrac{r_{12}r_{13}}{r_{23}} = \dfrac{r_{12}r_{14}}{r_{24}} = \cdots = \dfrac{r_{12}r_{1n}}{r_{2n}} = \dfrac{r_{13}r_{14}}{r_{34}} \\ \\ \qquad = \cdots = \dfrac{r_{13}r_{1n}}{r_{3n}} = \cdots = \dfrac{r_{1,n-1}r_{1n}}{r_{n-1,n}}. \end{cases}$$

For any variable z_e, a term of the form

(5.11)
$$t_{jk} = \frac{r_{ej}r_{ek}}{r_{jk}} \qquad \begin{pmatrix} e, j, k = 1, 2, \cdots, n \\ e \neq j \neq k \end{pmatrix}$$

is called a *triad*. When the matrix of correlations is of rank one then the communality of variable z_e is given by any one of the triads (5.11). It is readily seen that there are $\begin{pmatrix} n - 1 \\ 2 \end{pmatrix}$ triads in (5.10), or (subtracting one from this number), $n(n - 3)/2$ equations of condition for one general factor among n variables.

The number of conditions of the form (5.10) to determine whether a matrix is of rank one is considerably less than the number of tetrads. Every four variables give rise to three tetrads so that the total number of different tetrads for n variables is

(5.12)
$$3\binom{n}{4} = \frac{n(n-1)(n-2)(n-3)}{8}.$$

The difference between this number and the number of triad conditions is

(5.13)
$$\left[\frac{n(n-3)}{2}\right] \cdot \left[\frac{n(n-3)-2}{4}\right].$$

To indicate the magnitude of this number, suppose $n = 15$. The total number of tetrads is 4,095, while the number of triad conditions (5.10) is only 90. In other words, the labor of computing the conditions (5.10) is only about one-fortieth of that of computing the tetrads, for fifteen variables. For a large number of variables the economy of labor becomes more pronounced.

The necessary conditions for a matrix of correlations to attain rank two will next be considered. For five variables it is a well-known fact that one relationship must exist, namely, the following *pentad criterion*, first obtained by Kelley [305, p. 58]:

(5.14)
$$\begin{cases} r_{12}r_{23}r_{34}r_{45}r_{51} - r_{12}r_{23}r_{35}r_{41}r_{54} - r_{12}r_{24}r_{35}r_{43}r_{51} \\ \quad + r_{12}r_{24}r_{31}r_{45}r_{53} + r_{12}r_{25}r_{34}r_{41}r_{53} - r_{12}r_{25}r_{31}r_{43}r_{54} \\ \quad - r_{13}r_{24}r_{35}r_{41}r_{52} + r_{13}r_{25}r_{34}r_{42}r_{51} + r_{14}r_{23}r_{31}r_{45}r_{52} \\ \quad - r_{14}r_{25}r_{32}r_{43}r_{51} - r_{15}r_{23}r_{31}r_{42}r_{54} + r_{15}r_{24}r_{32}r_{41}r_{53} = 0. \end{cases}$$

This condition can be derived in a manner similar to the preceding. The correlation matrix for the five variables must have every third-order minor equal to zero if it is to be of rank two. By selecting appropriate minors, several linear equations for the solution of each of the communalities and hence the conditions for consistency can be obtained. Accordingly, for h_1^2 the following two determinants are employed:

$$\begin{vmatrix} h_1^2 & r_{13} & r_{15} \\ r_{21} & r_{23} & r_{25} \\ r_{41} & r_{43} & r_{45} \end{vmatrix} = 0, \qquad \begin{vmatrix} h_1^2 & r_{14} & r_{15} \\ r_{21} & r_{24} & r_{25} \\ r_{31} & r_{34} & r_{35} \end{vmatrix} = 0.$$

The two solutions for h_1^2 are:

$$h_1^2 = [r_{21}(r_{13}r_{45} - r_{15}r_{43}) - r_{41}(r_{13}r_{25} - r_{15}r_{23})]/(r_{23}r_{45} - r_{25}r_{43})$$
$$h_1^2 = [r_{21}(r_{14}r_{35} - r_{15}r_{34}) - r_{31}(r_{14}r_{25} - r_{15}r_{24})]/(r_{24}r_{35} - r_{25}r_{34}).$$

Equating these, the following single consistency condition results:

(5.15)
$$\begin{cases} [r_{24}r_{35} - r_{25}r_{34}][r_{21}(r_{13}r_{45} - r_{15}r_{43}) - r_{41}(r_{13}r_{25} - r_{15}r_{23})] \\ \quad - [r_{23}r_{45} - r_{25}r_{43}][r_{21}(r_{14}r_{35} - r_{15}r_{34}) - r_{31}(r_{14}r_{25} - r_{15}r_{24})] = 0. \end{cases}$$

If the correlations of five variables satisfy (5.15), or the equivalent condition (5.14), then five communalities can be determined to make the rank of the correlation matrix equal to two, i.e., the five variables can be described in terms of two common factors.

According to Table 5.2, the correlations among six variables must satisfy four independent conditions in order for their correlation matrix to attain rank two. It will be convenient to define the following:

(5.16)
$$|h_1^2\, r_{ab}\, r_{cd}| = \begin{vmatrix} h_1^2 & r_{1b} & r_{1d} \\ r_{a1} & r_{ab} & r_{ad} \\ r_{c1} & r_{cb} & r_{cd} \end{vmatrix},$$

that is, a representation of a determinant by the elements of the principal diagonal.

In order that a 6×6 matrix be of rank two, every third-order minor must vanish. Five such determinants (each involving the first row and column but otherwise unique rows and columns) are set equal to zero, as follows:

$$|h_1^2 \, r_{23} \, r_{45}| = |h_1^2 \, r_{23} \, r_{46}| = |h_1^2 \, r_{23} \, r_{56}| = |h_1^2 \, r_{24} \, r_{56}| = |h_1^2 \, r_{34} \, r_{56}| = 0.$$

The solutions for h_1^2 from these five equations follow:

(5.17)

$$
\begin{cases}
h_1^2 = \dfrac{r_{21}|r_{13} \, r_{45}| - r_{41}|r_{13} \, r_{25}|}{|r_{23} \, r_{45}|}, \\[2mm]
h_1^2 = \dfrac{r_{21}|r_{13} \, r_{46}| - r_{41}|r_{13} \, r_{26}|}{|r_{23} \, r_{46}|}, \\[2mm]
h_1^2 = \dfrac{r_{21}|r_{13} \, r_{56}| - r_{51}|r_{13} \, r_{26}|}{|r_{23} \, r_{56}|}, \\[2mm]
h_1^2 = \dfrac{r_{21}|r_{14} \, r_{56}| - r_{51}|r_{14} \, r_{26}|}{|r_{24} \, r_{56}|}, \\[2mm]
h_1^2 = \dfrac{r_{31}|r_{14} \, r_{56}| - r_{51}|r_{14} \, r_{36}|}{|r_{34} \, r_{56}|},
\end{cases}
$$

where

(5.18)
$$|r_{ab} \, r_{cd}| = \begin{vmatrix} r_{ab} & r_{ad} \\ r_{cb} & r_{cd} \end{vmatrix} = r_{ab} \, r_{cd} - r_{ad} \, r_{cb}.$$

Eliminating h_1^2 from the five equations (5.17), the four conditions which the correlations must satisfy are obtained. The equality of the right-hand members of equations (5.17) are the necessary conditions for six variables to be describable in terms of two common factors.

This process can be continued for any number of variables. The positive entries for $m = 2$ in Table 5.2 give the number of conditions that must exist among the correlations for a set of n variables to be describable in terms of only two common factors. In general, the correlations among n variables must satisfy $(n^2 - 5n + 2)/2$ conditions in order that their matrix shall be of rank two. These conditions may be obtained by eliminating any communality h_e^2 from $(n^2 - 5n + 4)/2$ equations of the form

(5.19)
$$h_e^2 = \frac{r_{ae}|r_{eb} \, r_{cd}| - r_{ce}|r_{eb} \, r_{ad}|}{|r_{ab} \, r_{cd}|} \qquad \begin{pmatrix} e, a, b, c, d = 1, 2, \cdots, n \\ e \neq a \neq b \neq c \neq d \end{pmatrix}.$$

It will be noted that many more conditions than the number indicated in Table 5.2 can be written for n variables by means of the foregoing procedure. Corresponding to any four indices in the denominator of (5.19) there is a third-order determinant of the form (5.16) which is to be set equal to zero for the calculation of a particular communality h_e^2. The total number of possible denominators, and hence, third-order determinants, for the calculation of the communalities would seem to be enormous. Fortunately, however, this number is considerably reduced owing to the symmetry of the correlation matrix and certain properties of second-order determinants.

Thus, of the 24 possible evaluations of a particular communality from the permutations of the four indices selected for the denominator in (5.19), only two determinations need be considered. The total number of third-order determinants which must vanish, for the rank of the $n \times n$ correlation matrix to be two, becomes:

$$(5.20) \qquad\qquad 2\binom{n-1}{4} = (n-1)!/12(n-5)!$$

The number of conditions which arise upon equating the evaluations of a communality from these determinants is in excess of that indicated in Table 5.2 for $n > 5$. Although all these values of a particular communality must necessarily be equal (statistically) if the rank is two, these conditions are not all independent. The use of the large set of conditions furnishes a check on the rank. In practice, however, it will be found sufficiently accurate to equate a smaller number of evaluations of communality for each variable of a set, as illustrated in the following section.

The procedure of this section can be generalized to obtain the necessary conditions for any correlation matrix $\mathbf{R}$ to be of rank m. In such case every $(m + 1)$-order minor must vanish. When m is greater than two the work of computing determinants of the fourth or higher order becomes so laborious that no explicit conditions corresponding to the tetrads or pentad criterion have been worked out. While it is of theoretical interest to note from Table 5.2 the number of conditions that must be satisfied by sets of variables for their correlation matrices to attain reduced rank, they cannot be put to practical use beyond an expected rank of two.

5.4. Determination of Communality from Approximate Rank

The problem of determining communalities classically has been put in the form: How much can the rank of the nth order correlation matrix be reduced by a suitable choice of diagonal values (communalities)? If m is the rank of the reduced correlation matrix then m is the smallest number of common factors necessary to account for the intercorrelations (Theorem 4.6); and if m can be reduced by the choice of communalities, then the number of required factors can be reduced and greater parsimony achieved.*

The concern in this section is with the calculation of communalities when some approximation to the rank of the reduced correlation matrix can be made. Such assumptions about the rank are also made in two methods of factor analysis (see chaps. 9 and 10); not, however, for purposes of computing communalities directly but rather as requirements of the particular methods, with the communalities coming out as a by-product. For the problem at hand, the reduced correlation matrix may

---

* As pointed out by Lederman [334], even when the rank of the correlation matrix is fixed the communalities may not be uniquely determined.

be expressed in the form

$$(5.21) \qquad\qquad \mathbf{R} = \mathbf{R}_o + \mathbf{H}$$

where $\mathbf{R}_o$ is the nth order correlation matrix but with diagonal elements all zero, and $\mathbf{H}$ is a diagonal matrix whose elements h_j^2 (the communalities) are to be determined. The algebraic problem to be solved is the determination of $\mathbf{H}$ such that $\mathbf{R}$ will have the minimum rank μ.

A more restrictive aspect of this problem, and the one of greatest interest to factor analysts, is the determination of "rank" when only off-diagonal elements of $\mathbf{R}$ are permitted in the minors. In other words, consider the "rank" to be m if the largest order of a non-vanishing minor of $\mathbf{R}_o$ is obtained by a selection of m of its rows and m *different* columns. This value m has been called the *ideal rank* by Albert [8], who obtained an algebraic solution for the communality problem for the case where $\mu = m$. In another paper [9], Albert proves that the solution produces unique communalities. Of course, in considering only minors with off-diagonal elements of $\mathbf{R}$, it follows that a fundamental condition underlying Albert's conclusions is that

$$(5.22) \qquad\qquad m < \frac{n}{2}.$$

Now, this exact mathematical condition will almost certainly never be met with empirical data. Thus, while Albert provides an exact algebraic solution for the communalities when the ideal rank is known and is less than $n/2$, it is a solution in theory only.

The idea of determining the communalities from the known rank of the correlation matrix can be exploited even when the rank is not known precisely. By approximating the rank of the matrix, the unknown communalities may be computed from the conditions imposed on the correlations to attain such rank, as indicated in the last section. A rough estimate of the rank of the correlation matrix is given by the number of distinct groups of variables. Of course, this is not a mathematically defined concept, but in any empirical study the investigator will have some idea of the grouping of variables—either from the descriptive content of the variables or from a preliminary study of the correlations themselves. A simple statistic on the grouping of variables (the "coefficient of belonging") is presented in **7.4**. In any event, once the rank is approximated, the method of the preceding section may be applied to check whether the correlations satisfy the necessary conditions for the assumed rank. If the conditions are satisfied then the communalities are given by the explicit formulas (5.11) for rank one and (5.19) for rank two, while direct computing formulas for higher rank are not very practical.

The actual process of determining the communalities involves a number of evaluations for each variable under the assumed rank of the matrix. The consistency of such values serves as a check on the rank, and their average is taken as the particular communality. Similar determinations are made for each variable of the set, and the assumed rank must check for all such determinations of communality.

Of course, the correlations need not satisfy the conditions for a given rank exactly with actual data because allowance must be made for chance errors.* It is suggested that for rank one all possible triads be written in the calculation of a particular communality. If the variation among these values can reasonably be assigned to chance fluctuations, the mean value may be taken as the communality.

In the case of rank two, all possible expressions (5.19) for the determination of each communality could be considered. Before averaging, however, those based upon insignificant denominators would need to be rejected. The variables yielding insignificant tetrads for the denominator of (5.19) can be identified when the design of the variables is known, and there are but two groups. In such a case each group of variables will approximate rank one, and the tetrads involving three variables of such a group will be insignificant. Knowing the combinations of variables which produce insignificant denominators, it is not necessary to consider the expressions (5.19) which involve them. The denominators should include two variables of each group, considerably reducing the total number of expressions for each communality.

When the rank of a correlation matrix is assumed, and the determination of the communalities is attempted, it may happen that some of the values exceed unity. Of course, such values of the communalities are not permitted, and they indicate that the particular rank assumed is inexact. Before the hypothesis of the specified rank is discarded, however, a number of evaluations of communality should be attempted. If, in general, several consistent values for each communality can be obtained, they should be averaged for the best determination of the communality. The justification for this procedure lies in the fact that the observed correlations are themselves subject to error, and the values to be supplied in the diagonal of the correlation matrix to produce a specified rank can only be expected to satisfy this hypothesis approximately. The final check lies in the agreement of the reproduced correlations from the solution employing these communalities, with the observed correlations. If the final residuals are insignificant, then the choice of the communalities is satisfactory.

Strictly speaking, the considerations in this section apply only when the rank of the correlation matrix is known, and when sampling errors and rounding-off errors in computations are disregarded. In practice, the sampling errors to which the correlation coefficients are subject will cause the correlation matrix generally to have a rank equal to its order. However, it is not the exact mathematical solution of such a matrix that is of interest to a factor analyst. Rather, it is the problem of analyzing the experimentally determined correlation coefficients in such a manner as to make the resulting discrepancies (residuals) insignificant in the statistical sense. Formally, the problem is to find a reproduced correlation matrix $\mathbf{R}^\dagger$ of minimal rank whose elements differ insignificantly from those in the (observed) reduced correlation matrix $\mathbf{R}$. Operationally this begs the question because the determination of the statistical significance of residuals poses problems as great as those inherent in the determination of com-

---

* No sampling error formula is known for the general expression of a communality computed from a higher-order determinant set equal to zero. An approximation to the standard error of a triad was obtained by Holzinger and Harman [243, sec **6.5**].

munalities. Statistical tests for the significance of residuals have been provided by Lawley [320] and Rao [394] employing the method of maximum likelihood, and the procedure is given in chapter 10.

To illustrate the foregoing procedure, some empirical data from Mullen [375] are employed. A set of eight physical variables were selected which were made up of two distinct groups. As will be noted from their correlations in Table 5.3, the first four variables are measures of "lankiness" while the last four are measures of "stockiness". Rank two is assumed for the correlation matrix, and checked in the process of obtaining the communalities.

Table 5.3

Correlations Among Eight Physical Variables for 305 Girls

Variable	1	2	3	4	5	6	7	8
1. Height	—	—	—	—	—	—	—	—
2. Arm span	.846	—	—	—	—	—	—	—
3. Length of forearm	.805	.881	—	—	—	—	—	—
4. Length of lower leg	.859	.826	.801	—	—	—	—	—
5. Weight	.473	.376	.380	.436	—	—	—	—
6. Bitrochanteric diameter	.398	.326	.319	.329	.762	—	—	—
7. Chest girth	.301	.277	.237	.327	.730	.583	—	—
8. Chest width	.382	.415	.345	.365	.629	.577	.539	—

Assuming rank two, the communality of any variable z_e can be obtained by averaging a number of evaluations (5.19). The calculation of such expressions can be facilitated by systematically considering the four indices a, b, c, d which determine the denominator of (5.19). In calculating the communality for variable $e = 1$, for example, the indices ab are taken to be 23, 24, and 34 (from the first group of four variables) and the indices cd are taken to be 56, 57, 58, 67, 68, and 78 (from the second group of four variables). When these pairs of variables are considered in every combination, 18 separate denominators are determined and hence 18 separate values of h_1^2. While 18 additional values can be obtained by interchanging the variables in only one of the pairs ab or cd, that was not done since the original values were deemed to be sufficiently consistent. Thus, 18 evaluations of the communality for each of the eight variables are obtained, and the mean values are taken as their best estimates. The resulting communalities are given in Table 5.4.

No exact standard for judging the consistency of the separate values is available, but the following simple guide may be used. The calculated communality may be regarded as a variance, and the usual formula for the standard error of a variance applied to it, namely,

(5.23) $$\sigma_{\sigma^2} = \sigma^2 \sqrt{2/N}.$$

If the variations of a set of values for a communality from their mean can be shown to be insignificant by use of formula (5.23), they would also be insignificant by a more accurate test. The standard errors for the eight communalities, as given by the above formula, are presented in Table 5.4. The maximum variation from the mean of the 18 separate values for each variable does not exceed 1.5 times the standard error, demonstrating the consistency of these values and justifying the assumed rank and the determinations of the communalities.

Table 5.4

Communalities for Eight Physical Variables

Statistic	h_1^2	h_2^2	h_3^2	h_4^2	h_5^2	h_6^2	h_7^2	h_8^2
Communality	.842	.881	.817	.815	.872	.647	.584	.502
Standard error	.068	.071	.066	.066	.071	.052	.047	.041

The direct application of the foregoing method of computing communalities is practical when m is one or two. For a larger number of factors the direct procedure becomes too cumbersome with the use of a desk calculator. While it is conceivable that the direct methods, involving the calculation of determinants of high order, might be feasible on electronic computers, it appears to be more economical to employ special techniques of factor analysis that do not require estimates of communality in advance but produce communalities as by-products (see chaps. 9 and 10).

5.5.   Theoretical Solution for Communality

Before considering practical means of approximating the communalities, a presentation is made in this section of the theoretical solution to the problem without explicit use of the rank of **R**. Employing the fundamental factor model (2.9) and the notation introduced in **4.10**, any variable z_j can be represented in the total-factor space of m common factors and n unique factors as follows:

$$(5.24) \qquad z_j' = a_{j1}F_1 + a_{j2}F_2 + \cdots + a_{jm}F_m + d_jU_j,$$

and in the common-factor space this becomes:

$$(5.25) \qquad z_j'' = a_{j1}F_1 + a_{j2}F_2 + \cdots + a_{jm}F_m.$$

The correlation between a variable and its "common" part is

$$(5.26) \qquad r_{j'j''} = \frac{a_{j1}^2 + a_{j2}^2 + \cdots + a_{jm}^2}{N(z_j')N(z_j'')} = \frac{h_j^2}{1 \cdot h_j} = h_j,$$

where the lengths of the vectors in the total-factor space and in the common-factor space are given in Table 4.1. But the multiple correlation of variable z_j with the linear combination of the m factors (represented by z_j'') is defined as the simple correlation coefficient between them, namely,

$$(5.27) \qquad R_{z_j \cdot F_1 F_2 \cdots F_m} = r_{z_j z_j''}.$$

81

Then, since z'_j is the mathematical model of z_j, the expression (5.26) may be put in the form

(5.28)
$$h_j^2 = R_{z_j \cdot F_1 F_2 \cdots F_m}^2.$$

which states that the communality of a variable is equal to the squared multiple correlation of that variable with the common factors.

While this result has been known since 1936 [403, 107, 172], it was not until recently [289, 292, 484] that a suggestion was made to adapt it for use in approximating the communalities. Since the z''_j as well as the F_p span the common-factor space, it follows from (5.25) and (5.28) that

(5.29)
$$h_j^2 = R_{z_j \cdot z''_1 z''_2 \cdots z''_n}^2.$$

Kaiser [289, p. 5] argues that if the n vectors z''_j are to lie in the common-factor space of m dimensions, then some of them will be redundant for computing the squared multiple correlation in (5.29). Since it is not necessary to include z''_j in the regression equation for h_j^2, this equation becomes

(5.30)
$$h_j^2 = R_{z_j \cdot z''_1 z''_2 \cdots)z''_j(\cdots z''_n}^2.$$

This states that the communality of a given variable is given by the squared multiple correlation of that variable on the $n - 1$ *common parts* of the remaining variables. The obvious difficulty of this apparent solution is that, in effect, the communalities of the $n - 1$ remaining variables must be known in order to compute the squared multiple correlation, i.e., the desired communality. In an attempt to obtain an approximation to the n communalities, Kaiser proposed an iterative procedure for use with an electronic computer. Unfortunately, the process converges only for restricted matrices and he has concluded that the method has "... no practical use because of its inability to solve the communality problem for empirical matrices" [292, p. 10].

There is hope that the iterative approximations to the theoretical solution may yet prove practical. Guttman [182] proposes a generalization and improvement of the preliminary procedure suggested by Kaiser [289]. This method is designed to solve for the diagonal matrix **H** with proper communalities* without requiring *a priori* approximations to the rank of **R** nor the extraction of common factors. The final solution is obtained by an iterative process in which trial values $\mathbf{H}_t$ eventually converge (for conditions, see [182, pp. 5–7]) to the desired matrix of communalities **H**.

It is convenient to designate the successive expressions for the reduced correlation matrix by $\mathbf{R}_t$, so that equation (5.21) becomes

(5.31)
$$\mathbf{R}_t = \mathbf{R}_o + \mathbf{H}_t \qquad (t = 1, 2, \cdots)$$

for any approximation $\mathbf{H}_t$ to the communalities. The iterative procedure involves the calculation of the inverse of $\mathbf{R}_t$ at each stage; and the diagonal matrix with the

---

* As noted in **3.2**, paragraph **15**, communality estimates are considered proper if they preserve the Gramian properties of the correlation matrix.

principal diagonal of $\mathbf{R}_t^{-1}$ is designated $\mathbf{D}_t$. Then, an entire class of iterative procedures is given [182, p. 2] by the following recurrence formula:

$$(5.32) \qquad\qquad \mathbf{H}_{t+1} = \mathbf{H}_t - \epsilon\mathbf{D}_t^{-1}, \qquad\qquad (t = 1, 2, \cdots)$$

where ϵ is some positive number. The iterative procedures implied by (5.32) differ from one another according to the choice of ϵ and the initial approximation $\mathbf{H}_1$.

The specific iterative process which Kaiser [289] employed is (5.32) with $\epsilon = 1$ and $\mathbf{H}_1 = \mathbf{I}$. As noted above, this process generally does not converge for empirical data. Guttman [182] makes several recommendations, the principal one being to take $\epsilon = \frac{1}{2}$ and $\mathbf{H}_1$ as the diagonal matrix of squared multiple correlations of each variable with the $n - 1$ remaining variables (further use of this concept is made in **5.7**). While this work seems promising, the real proof of the usefulness of these procedures must await the test of time.

From the preceding discussion it becomes apparent that there is no easy road to a solution of the communality problem. In the following sections, several practical avenues are suggested.

5.6. *Arbitrary Approximations to Communality*

Literally dozens of methods for estimating communalities have been proposed, but none of them has been shown to be superior to any of the others on the basis of closer approximation to the "true" values. As a matter of fact none of the methods has been demonstrated to lead to minimal rank of the correlation matrix. The choice among the various methods of approximation is generally made on the basis of available computational facilities and the disposition of the investigator to employ that method which intuitively seems best to approach the concept of communality. As a saving grace, there is much evidence in the literature that for all but very small sets of variables, the resulting factorial solutions are little affected by the particular choice of "communalities" in the principal diagonal of the correlation matrix.

Of the many arbitrary estimates of communality, the simplest is the *highest correlation* of a given variable z_j from among its correlations with all the other variables of the given set. This simple procedure has been used by Thurstone and his followers in a large number of studies involving the centroid solution (see **8.9**). They found this simple method of estimating communalities useful for large correlation matrices, but would not recommend it for small numbers of variables.

Another method for approximating the communality of a variable z_j is to employ a *triad*, i.e.,

$$(5.33) \qquad\qquad h_j^2 = r_{jk}r_{jl}/r_{kl},$$

where k and l are the two variables which correlate highest with the given variable. It can readily be seen that this formula would have the effect of moderating an extremely high, exceptional correlation. Still another estimate is given by the *average* of all the correlations of a given variable with each of the remaining ones, viz.,

$$(5.34) \qquad\qquad h_j^2 = \sum_{k=1}^{n} r_{jk}/(n - 1) \qquad\qquad (k \neq j).$$

A more satisfactory procedure for estimating communality follows from **5.4**. The *approximate rank* of the correlation matrix is assumed, making use of the groupings of variables, in order to get suitable estimates of the communality. This method involves the calculation for each communality of the average of expressions like (5.11) for $m = 1$ and (5.19) for $m = 2$, where m is the assumed rank of the correlation matrix. For small sets of variables it is expected that there will be only a few factors (see **5.2**). It may then be sufficiently accurate to *assume rank one or two* and employ the method of **5.4** for calculating approximations to the communalities. In practice, when the rank exceeds two, this method is not feasible because of the complexity of the formulas and the computational labor.

One simplification of this technique is accomplished by sectioning the correlation matrix into sub-groups of p variables, each approximately of rank one. The *unit-rank estimates* of the communalities may then be calculated by means of the formula:

$$(5.35) \qquad h_j^2 = \frac{1}{v} \sum_{k<l=1}^{p} r_{jk} r_{jl} / r_{kl}, \qquad (k, l \neq j),$$

where $v = \binom{p-1}{2}$ is the total number of different triads that can be arranged for the given variable z_j out of the subset of p variables which comprise the section of the correlation matrix of unit rank. This procedure seems much more satisfactory than estimating the communality by a single triad as in (5.33).

5.7. *Complete Approximations to Communality*

It may be convenient to distinguish the foregoing arbitrary estimates of communality, which generally involve only a few correlations, from estimates which are based upon the entire correlation matrix. The latter will be designated as "complete approximations" to communality. One such method might be the direct computation (best determination rather than estimate) of communalities by the method of **5.4**. This method involves an approximation to the rank, say m, and then taking as h_j^2 the average of all evaluations, from the $(m + 1)$-order determinants set equal to zero. Such a procedure is not feasible for $m > 2$, but perhaps some day the rapid selection of minors and the solution of such determinants will be programmed for high-speed electronic computers. Albert's algebraic solution referred to in **5.4** and the methods discussed in **5.5** are theoretical rather than practical instances of complete approximations to communality.

Perhaps the simplest procedure that would fall under the heading of "complete approximation" to communality involves, in essence, the calculation of the *first centroid factor* (see **8.9**). As a start, the highest correlation for each variable is inserted in the principal diagonal of the correlation matrix. Then the estimate of each communality is the ratio of the square of the column sum to the total sum of all the correlations in the matrix, i.e.,

$$(5.36) \qquad h_j^2 = \left(\sum_{k=1}^{n} r_{jk} \right)^2 \Big/ \sum_{k=1}^{n} \sum_{l=1}^{n} r_{kl},$$

where the self correlation is the highest correlation of the given variable with all other variables. While this formula does employ all correlations in the matrix, it will, nonetheless, tend to give an underestimate of the communality since it results from the employment of only one centroid factor.

A method similar to the preceding, but using the average instead of the highest correlation, leads to the following formula:

$$(5.37) \qquad h_j^2 = [n/(n-1)]\left[\left(\sum_{k=1}^{n} r_{jk}\right)^2 \middle/ \sum_{k=1}^{n}\sum_{l=1}^{n} r_{kl}\right], \qquad (k \neq j \text{ and } k \neq l).$$

in which the diagonal values are actually ignored. This formula employs the square of the coefficient of the *first averoid factor* [243, p. 193]. Just as in the case of formula (5.36), so also will formula (5.37) tend to give underestimates of the communalities.

Communality estimates may be calculated by use of the component analysis model (2.8), and then a conventional factor analysis solution in terms of the model (2.9) may be obtained. While this may sound involved, it is actually quite practical with electronic computers. Thus, a correlation matrix (with ones in the diagonal) of order n is analyzed into n principal components and the associated n eigenvalues (see chap. 8). It is then assumed that the dimension of the common-factor space is equal to the number of principal components for which the eigenvalues are greater than one [296, pp. 144–46]. The variance contributed (by this reduced number of principal components) to each variable is taken as the estimate of its communality.

In consideration of the indefiniteness of the communalities—the evasiveness of a fine hypothetical concept—it becomes very attractive to employ some objective measures even though they allegedly are not "communalities." It has been argued, and substantiated by empirical evidence, that it matters little what values are placed in the principal diagonal of the correlation matrix when the number of variables is large (say, $n > 20$). In such a case the actual arithmetic impact of these few diagonal values in relation to the many numbers off the diagonal is so small that the factorial results are not affected very much. Of course, this is a specious argument which would not stand up under a rigorous statistical test were one available. Nonetheless, the desire to employ well-defined, objective measures for the diagonal entries has led to some interesting procedures.

One method for estimating communality which has the semblance of being objective involves *iteration by refactoring*. This procedure would be limited to small matrices if the work were to be done on a desk calculator, but certainly would be suitable for any matrix if a high-speed electronic computer were available. The operation is initiated with unities or zeros or any other values in the principal diagonal and deciding *a priori* on the number of factors. Typically, such a procedure would involve: (a) the calculation of a principal-factor solution (see chap. 8), which is most readily adaptable to an electronic computer; (b) the determination of the sum of squares of factor coefficients (for the predetermined number of factors) as new estimates of communality; (c) the calculation of another principal-factor solution; and (d) repeating this process as many times as necessary until the recomputed diagonal values do not change from the preceding set.

Wrigley [538] employed such iteration-by-refactoring methods in an excellent empirical study, comparing some fifteen different methods of initial estimation of communality. For five methods of estimation, 100 iterations were made involving very extensive calculations. Although there is no formal proof of the convergence of the iterative process, this study would seem to indicate that it does. Convergence was found to be generally more rapid for low estimates than for high, with unities being especially poor as a starting point for finding the communalities. Wrigley concludes [538, p. 26] that for work with a desk calculator the most effective method is a modification of the arbitrary estimates of the highest correlation (for variables with high correlations the estimates are a little higher than the highest correlations, and for variables with low correlations the estimates are a little lower than the highest correlations). For work with an electronic computer, the squared multiple correlation of each variable with the remaining ones was found to be the best starting point.

The *squared multiple correlation* (*SMC*) of each variable with the remaining $n - 1$ observed variables has much to recommend it as an approximation to communality, quite aside from the foregoing convergence property. Wrigley [535] suggests that the *SMC*'s be called the "observed communalities" since they, and not the theoretical minimal-rank communalities, measure predictable common variance among the observed correlations. These values are certainly objective and they can be determined uniquely, without iteration, by use of the square root method (see **3.4**) for a small set of variables or by means of an electronic computer for a large set. To obtain the *SMC*'s for all the variables in a set, it is expeditious to calculate the inverse $\mathbf{R}^{-1}$ of the correlation matrix $\mathbf{R}$ (with unities in the diagonal), and then the *SMC* for variable z_j is given by

$$(5.38) \qquad SMC_j = R^2_{j \cdot 12 \cdots)j(\cdots n} = 1 - \frac{1}{r^{jj}},$$

where r^{jj} is the diagonal element in $\mathbf{R}^{-1}$ corresponding to variable z_j. These values are frequently calculated as an incidental step in the computer program for a principal-factor solution (see **8.7**).

The *SMC* has another very important property—it is the lower bound for the communality, i.e.,

$$(5.39) \qquad R^2_{j(n-1)} \leqq h^2_j,$$

where $(n - 1)$ stands for the set of variables excluding z_j. This property was first given by Roff [403], and explicitly proven by Dwyer [107]. Largely because of this property, Guttman [181] recommends the *SMC* as the "best possible" estimate of communality. The characteristics that make the *SMC*'s the "best possible" estimates include: (1) actual *equality* in (5.39) for many correlation matrices for which minimum rank m is attained; and (2) the tendency of the *SMC*'s to approach the communalities if the ratio of m to n tends to zero as n approaches infinity.

The insertion of *SMC*'s in the principal diagonal produces a reduced correlation matrix which is not Gramian, in general. While the *SMC*'s are not proper estimates of communality in this sense, they may be employed as lower bounds of the communalities with this recognition of the theoretical impropriety. The Gramian properties of the matrix can be restored by adjusting the off-diagonal values, as proposed by Guttman [176] in his image theory.

Since some approximation is made to the communalities in conventional factor analysis, there would seem to be an advantage in knowing the direction of the error from the true values. The SMC's are known to be less than (or at most equal to) the communalities. This logical consideration, together with the preceding properties, strongly recommend the SMC's as the most desirable approximations to communalities when suitable computing facilities are available. Fortunately, the impact of poor estimates is less relevant for large matrices, so that one may resort to arbitrary approximations if he does not have access to an electronic computer. On the other hand, the work of computing the SMC's is not so great for small matrices, where the approximations become much more important.

An implication of the use of SMC's is that the distinction between common and unique variance as indicated by the factor model (2.9) is a function of the particular variables under consideration rather than any hypothetical domain or universe of variables. Any SMC measures variance common to the particular variable and the remaining $n - 1$ variables selected for study, while the communality measures variance common to the variable and the factors resulting from the set of n variables. It should be recognized that in either event, the distinction between common and specific variance is relative to the particular set of variables. Wrigley challenges the value of communality as the most effective means of reducing the number of factors, and concludes [535, p. 96]: "The principal claim of communalities rests on the fact that they give a better fit than any other diagonal values to the correlations actually observed. The psychological advantages, however, appear to rest with the squared multiple correlations, which measure the proportion of common variance in any particular test selection." It is interesting to note that communalities with the property just mentioned by Wrigley are those determined by the minres solution (see chap. 9).

When factors are extracted one at a time, the diagonal values in each residual correlation matrix may be retained as computed or estimated anew. In general, when one of the "arbitrary approximations" to communality are employed, the values in the principal diagonal of each residual matrix should be re-estimated by the method used originally. For example, when the highest correlation for each variable is taken as its communality, the highest value in each column would again be used for the diagonal entry (in place of the value actually computed) in the matrix of residual correlations with the first factor removed.

On the other hand, when "complete approximations" to communality are employed, the diagonal values are not altered in the succeeding residual matrices. Instead, the factorization is carried to the point where all the diagonal values vanish, except for rounding and sampling errors.

In the past it was quite common to extract one factor at a time and to compute the residual matrix at each stage (e.g., centroid method discussed in **8.9**). Nowadays, with the use of electronic computers, all factors are extracted at one time. Hence it is very important when a method requires estimates of communality (rather than an estimate of the number of common factors), that "complete approximations" be employed.

5.8. *Examples of Approximations to Communality*

In order to illustrate the approximation methods of the last two sections, six hypothetical variables are employed and their correlations are given in Table 5.5. Because this is a "textbook example," with no sampling or rounding errors in the data, it is possible to obtain an exact algebraic solution for the communalities from a knowledge of the rank of the correlation matrix. Even a casual observation of the correlations in Table 5.5 indicates a clustering of the first three variables,* while the remaining ones correlate no more amongst themselves than with the first three variables. It is then reasonable to assume a rank of 2 for the correlation matrix, and to test this hypothesis by the method of **5.3**.

Table 5.5

Correlations Among Six Hypothetical Variables

Variable	1	2	3	4	5	6
1						
2	.72					
3	.75	.78				
4	.49	.42	.35			
5	.42	.36	.30	.42		
6	.28	.24	.20	.28	.24	

According to Table 5.2 there are four necessary conditions that the correlations must satisfy in order that the six variables be describable in terms of two common factors. These conditions are arrived at by equating the right-hand members of (5.17). The first three of these expressions are identically equal to .74, while the last two are indeterminate.† The necessary conditions among the correlations are satisfied mathematically, and the true rank of the reduced correlation matrix is two. The communality of each of the six variables is obtained by means of equation (5.19), with the several different evaluations for each variable being identical in this hypo-thetical example. These results are labelled "Actual" in Table 5.6. Following these actual communalities, the different approximations of the two preceding sections are presented in the successive columns of this table. It is only for heuristic reasons

* The "coefficient of belonging" is 221, according to **7.4**.
† This is due to the fact that the tetrads formed from variables 4, 5, 6 and any one of 1, 2, or 3 vanish. As a consequence the minors in the numerators of these expressions also vanish. It is thus apparent that four such variables are describable in terms of only one common factor.

that the several approximations to the communalities are summarized in a single table, rather than to imply any advantage of a particular estimate over another.

Table 5.6

Communality Estimates for Six Hypothetical Variables

Variable	Actual	Highest r	Triad (5.33)	Average (5.34)	Unit-Rank (5.35)	Centroid (5.36)	Averoid (5.37)	SMC (5.38)
1	.74	.75	.69	.53	.69	.73	.68	.66
2	.72	.78	.75	.50	.75	.68	.61	.66
3	.89	.78	.81	.48	.81	.62	.54	.69
4	.49	.49	.39*	.39	.49	.38	.37	.32
5	.36	.42	.36	.35	.36	.29	.29	.25
6	.16	.28	.16	.25	.16	.14	.14	.12

* Average of the two possible values : .29 and .49

The procedure for obtaining the numerical values for each method will be indicated. Of course, the method of *highest correlation* is self evident. For the *triad* method, formula (5.33) is employed, and for the first variable this becomes :

$$h_1^2 = r_{13}r_{12}/r_{23} = (.75)(.72)/.78 = .69,$$

because variables 2 and 3 correlate highest with it. A little ambiguity arises in applying this method to variable 4. The highest correlation is $r_{41} = .49$, but there is a tie for the second highest, viz., $r_{42} = .42$ and $r_{45} = .42$. Either of the following two determinations are appropriate :

$$h_4^2 = r_{41}r_{42}/r_{12} = (.49)(.42)/.72 = .29,$$

or

$$h_4^2 = r_{41}r_{45}/r_{15} = (.49)(.42)/.42 = .49,$$

and the average of these values is recorded in Table 5.6.

Approximations to the communalities by the *average* of all correlations of a given variable with the others are obtained by formula (5.34). While it would appear from this hypothetical example that the average correlation tends to give too low an estimate of communality, at least in one instance (variable 6) it is considerably higher than the actual value.

It was suggested in **5.6** that the communalities could be approximated from an assumed rank for the correlation matrix derived from the more-or-less natural groupings of variables. The simplest instance is to consider the rank to be equal to the number of groups, and the section of the correlation matrix corresponding to each group is assumed to be of rank one. The six hypothetical variables fall into two groups : $G_1 = 1, 2, 3$ and $G_2 = 4, 5, 6$, and the total matrix is assumed to be of rank 2. In this case, each *unit-rank* subgroup contains $p = 3$ variables and the number of different triads for each variable is simply $v = 1$. Formula (5.35) then simplifies to a

89

single term for the calculation of any of the communalities. For h_1^2 the expression is identical to that employed in the single triad method because the two highest correlations with variable 1 occur for the other two variables in the group G_1. On the other hand, (5.35) for variable 4 becomes:

$$h_4^2 = r_{45} r_{46}/r_{56} = (.42)(.28)/.24 = .49,$$

which involves different correlations than in either of the two calculations by the single triad method, yet yields the same result as for one of them.

The actual communalities and four instances of arbitrary approximations have been presented to this point. Three complete approximation methods will now be illustrated. For the first variable of the example, the *centroid* formula (5.36) yields:

$$h_1^2 = \left(\sum_{k=1}^{6} r_{1k} \right)^2 \bigg/ \sum_{k=1}^{6} \sum_{l=1}^{6} r_{kl} = (3.41)^2/16.00 = .73,$$

The *averoid* formula (5.37) produces:

$$h_1^2 = \frac{6}{5} \left(\sum_{k=2}^{6} r_{1k} \right)^2 \bigg/ \sum_{k=2}^{6} \sum_{l=2}^{6} r_{kl} = \frac{6}{5}(2.66)^2/12.50 = .68.$$

The general principle noted above, that the centroid and averoid formulas tend to give under-estimates of communalities, is borne out by the values for the six hypothetical variables as compared with their "actual" communalities.

Finally, the communality is estimated by the *squared multiple correlation* (SMC) of each variable with the remaining five variables. The actual process of inverting a matrix by use of the square root method is illustrated in Table 3.3 using the current example. The SMC's are computed according to formula (5.38) from the diagonal values of the inverse matrix, and the results appear in the last column of Table 5.6. The property of the SMC as a lower bound to the communality is clearly evident by comparison with the "actual" values.

The reader is cautioned not to make unwarranted generalizations about the relative merits of the various methods for estimating communality. The only purpose for exhibiting the different approximations side by side in Table 5.6 is to illustrate the procedures described in the earlier sections. It should be remembered that the data are small in number, artificial, and devoid of sampling errors. While the procedures for computing the several values in Table 5.6 may be instructive, the actual choice of method for approximating communality should be based on the considerations set forth above rather than the apparent superiority of any of the numerical values over the others.

5.9. Direct Factor Solution

From the general theory of factor analysis developed so far, it is possible to obtain a factor solution directly, without recourse to the formal procedures treated in the remainder of this text. For a small number of variables a very simple factor model might be appropriate. Then, from a knowledge of the correlations and approximations to the communalities, a complete factor pattern may be determined. In a practical situation, with any sizable number of variables, rather involved mathematical and computational methods are required to get a factor solution.

A direct factor solution for the hypothetical example of the last section will be obtained. As noted above, the correlations in Table 5.5 indicate a strong clustering of the first three variables but not so for the remaining three. A plausible model* is presented in Table 5.7, where uncorrelated factors are assumed for convenience.

Table 5.7

Factor Pattern Plan*

Variable	F_0	F_1
1	a_{10}	a_{11}
2	a_{20}	a_{21}
3	a_{30}	a_{31}
4	a_{40}	
5	a_{50}	
6	a_{60}	

* A factor pattern will usually be presented in such a tabular form with the coefficients of the respective factors appearing in the columns headed by the factors.

From the correlations in Table 5.5 and the communalities determined in the last section ("Actual" in Table 5.6), all the coefficients in the factor pattern can be obtained. Since the last three variables involve only one common factor, each of their communalities is merely the square of the coefficient of this factor, i.e.,

$$h_j^2 = a_{jo}^2 \qquad (j = 4, 5, 6).$$

Solving for these factor coefficients yields:

$$a_{40} = \sqrt{.49} = .7, \qquad a_{50} = \sqrt{.36} = .6, \qquad a_{60} = \sqrt{.16} = .4.$$

Next, the coefficients of F_o for the first three variables can be obtained from the following formula for the reproduced correlations:

$$r'_{jk} = a_{jo}a_{ko} \qquad (j = 1, 2, 3; \quad k = 4, 5, 6),$$

which is a simplification of (2.27) for the special factor model of Table 5.7. In this formula the a_{ko} are known and if the observed correlations are employed in place of the reproduced correlations, the unknown a_{jo} can be determined. While there are three possible determinations for each j, and an average might ordinarily be taken,

* The pattern plan is plausible because the correlations among the variables 1, 2, 3 are higher than those among 4, 5, 6. Such a plan is consistent with the hypothesis that an extra factor should be postulated for a group of variables with higher intercorrelations.

the three values are identical in the present case. These coefficients follow:

$$a_{10} = .7, \qquad a_{20} = .6, \qquad a_{30} = .5.$$

Finally, the coefficients of F_1 can be obtained from the following expression for the communality:

$$h_1^2 = a_{jo}^2 + a_{j1}^2 \qquad\qquad (j = 1, 2, 3),$$

or, explicitly:

$$a_{j1} = \sqrt{h_j^2 - a_{jo}^2} \qquad\qquad (j = 1, 2, 3),$$

where the communality and the coefficient of F_o are now known for the first three variables. The resulting coefficients are:

$$a_{11} = \sqrt{.74 - .49} = .5, \qquad a_{21} = \sqrt{.72 - .36} = .6, \qquad a_{31} = \sqrt{.89 - .25} = .8.$$

The complete factor solution is summarized in Table 5.8.

Table 5.8

Factor Pattern for Six Hypothetical Variables

Variable	F_0	F_1
1	.7	.5
2	.6	.6
3	.5	.8
4	.7	
5	.6	
6	.4	

While it was tacitly assumed that the residuals were precisely zero, some discrepancies between original and reproduced correlations would be expected with empirical data. The extent of agreement between these values is the measure of adequacy of a factor solution, the particular form of the solution being somewhat arbitrary. Thus, in the present example the particular factor model of Table 5.7 was postulated, but some other model might fit the data equally well.* Some standards for making a choice among the possible factor solutions are considered in the next chapter.

---

* See, for example, ex. 9, chap. 8.

6

Properties of Different Types of Factor Solutions

6.1. *Introduction*

Before leaving the foundations of factor analysis, a preview of what lies ahead will be presented in this chapter. Some simple, but fundamental, criteria are set forth explicitly; and in the subsequent enumeration of the popular factor models, the extent of adherence to these criteria is indicated in each case. This chapter serves to summarize the most popular types of factor solutions. It gives a brief overview of their properties and the distinguishing characteristics among them, but only schematic solutions are presented; formulas for the computation of the factor coefficients are not given in this chapter. The methods employed in obtaining numerical solutions are developed and illustrated in detail in parts ii and iii.

As noted several times before, there is a basic indeterminacy in factor analysis —an infinitude of factorizations of a correlation matrix may account for the observed data equally well. The realization of this fact posed a perplexing problem to factor analysts during the rapid growth of the subject in the 1930's and 1940's: How can a factor solution be determined which will be acceptable to other workers? While the principal-factor solution (chap. 8) is unique in the mathematical sense, at least to psychologists it is not acceptable as the final form. The search for a "psychologically meaningful" solution, which could be obtained by rotation from some arbitrary factorization of the correlation matrix, led Thurstone to formulate the concept of "simple structure" [468, chap. VI; 477, chap. XIV], which is discussed in **6.2** under criterion **10**.

Before enumerating some of the principles which have been proposed to objectify the particular choice of factors, a brief review of the problem will be made in geometric terms. As pointed out in chapter 4, the observations on a set of variables can be regarded as determining a number of vectors (corresponding to the variables) in a space equal to the number of subjects. By methods of factor analysis these vectors can generally be contained in a space of smaller dimension than the number of variables. The coordinate axes of this reduced space are the common factors, and the

93

original variables can be expressed linearly in terms of these factors. The determination of this common-factor space is in no way dependent on the particular coordinate frame of reference employed. This arbitrariness is represented geometrically by the infinite number of rotations possible from one set of coordinate axes to another.

For ease of mathematical description, and sometimes to facilitate psychological interpretation, it is common practice to change the frame of reference. In making such a transformation of coordinates it must be remembered that the geometric configuration, e.g., straight line or swarm of points, is left unaltered. The mathematical expressions or formulas describing the geometric configuration may change under transformation, but the configuration itself is invariant.

The *mathematician* usually is concerned with the geometric configuration only, using the frame of reference as a tool, and will prefer one reference system to another if it yields a simpler (and more elegant) expression for his configuration. For example, the elaborate formula consisting of six terms:

$$(6.1) \qquad AX^2 + BY^2 + CXY + DX + EY + F = 0$$

represents a geometric configuration (an ellipse) in one (arbitrary) frame of reference, while the expression

$$(6.2) \qquad \frac{x^2}{a^2} + \frac{y^2}{b^2} = 1$$

represents *precisely* the same configuration in another (arbitrary) reference frame selected so as to make the equation as simple as possible.

Unlike the mathematician, the *psychologist* frequently concerns himself with the interpretation of the frame of reference, using the configuration of points merely as the vehicle to get to the particular reference axes. Thus, in factor analysis the geometric configuration is a swarm of points, each one representing a test and the density of the points being a function of the correlations among the tests. A frame of reference may be selected for psychological interpretation on the basis of the particular configuration of points but the emphasis in the resulting psychological theory is on the coordinate axes, not the configuration alone.

The criteria listed in **6.2** provide the basis for the selection of the coordinate axes. Depending on how these standards are applied, and whether the empirical data satisfy the conditions, one or another of the solutions enumerated in **6.3** and **6.4** may be obtained. These are referred to as direct solutions since they are obtained by direct calculation from the correlation matrix. In contrast, the multiple-factor solutions introduced in **6.5** are always derived solutions, resulting from a transformation of one of the direct solutions of **6.3** or **6.4**. The computational methods for the direct solutions comprise part ii, and for the derived solutions part iii, of this text. Finally, in **6.6** a summary is presented of the assumptions, properties, and characteristics of the different types of factor solutions.

6.2.   *Criteria for Choice of Factor Solutions*

There are certain assumptions that can be made, and restrictions imposed, that make it possible to describe a given matrix of correlations uniquely in terms of a factorial reference system. However, such a solution is unique only in the sense of the particular criteria; and, selecting other criteria will generally lead to another unique solution. "Unique" is used here merely to denote the fact that any two workers accepting the same criteria and following the same procedures will arrive at an identical result for a given set of data. Some standards, or guides, which assist in defining and delineating the different types of solutions are presented in the following paragraphs.

1. Factor model.—A linear model for the variables is assumed. While the principal components, or component analysis, model (2.8) is of some interest, the bulk of the text is concerned with the classical factor analysis model (2.9) or (2.35) in matrix notation.

2. Principle of parsimony.—Following the principle common to all scientific theory, a law or model should be simpler than the data upon which it is based. Thus, the *number of common factors* should be less than the number of variables; and, in the linear description of each variable, the *complexity* should be low.

3. Contributions of factors.—A distinction among different factor solutions may be made on the basis of the contribution (2.13) of each factor to the variances of the variables. One standard may require *decreasing contributions*, i.e., each successive factor contributing a decreasing amount to the total communality. Another standard may require approximately *level contributions* of all factors.

4. Grouping of variables.—In many methods of factor analysis, a notion of the clustering or grouping of the variables is implied. Sometimes the groups are only roughly approximated, as suggested in **5.4** for the purpose of estimating the rank of the correlation matrix. At other times more precise methods are employed for careful assignment of the variables to one group or another. Examples of the latter are the "coefficient of belonging" (see **7.4**), and the method of "cluster analysis" developed by Tryon [483].

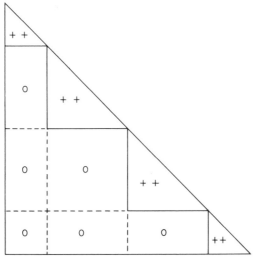

Fig. 6.1.—Intercorrelations exhibiting distinct groups of variables

If the variables of a study are re-numbered so that those that group together are in sequence then the table of intercorrelations may be represented schematically as in Figures 6.1 or 6.2. The plus signs represent correlations, the double plusses indicate even higher correlations among the variables constituting a group, and the zeros mean no correlation. In Figure 6.1 an hypothetical situation is depicted in which there are four well-pronounced groups of variables with no relationships between them. It is extremely unlikely that an empirical matrix of correlations would ever approach this simple form. On the other hand, it is to be expected that a set of relevant variables would be correlated throughout with higher correlations within groups, as indicated in Figure 6.2.

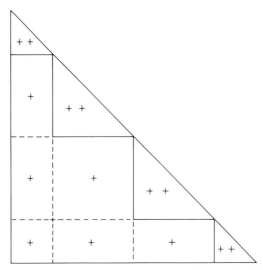

FIG. 6.2.—Intercorrelations showing grouping of variables with relationships between groups

5. Frame of reference.—A choice must be made between an *orthogonal* and an *oblique* reference system, i.e., whether the variables will be described in terms of *uncorrelated* or *correlated* common factors. The observed correlations are fitted equally well by solutions involving factors of either type. Generally it is more convenient to start with an orthogonal solution even if the preferred solution is oblique, arriving at the latter by transformation from the former.

6. Point representation: ellipsoidal fit.—In **4.9** two alternative modes of representing variables geometrically are indicated. It will be recalled that in the point representation there is one point for each of the N individuals, referred to a system of n reference axes—one for each variable. The points which are plotted in this n-space are contained in a common-factor space of only m dimensions (from Theorems 4.4 and 4.6). The loci of the swarm of points of uniform frequency density are, more or less, concentric, similar, and similarly situated m-dimensional ellipsoids, being exactly so for a normally distributed population [547, chap. XII]. It then seems natural to take the principal axes of these ellipsoids as the reference axes, and hence this standard is called *ellipsoidal fit*.

7. Vector representation: linear fit.—In chapter 4 it was shown that the variables may be regarded as vectors in an N-space, and that the correlation between any two is given by the cosine of their angular separation or by the scalar product of their vectors projected into the common-factor space. A group of variables having high intercorrelations is encompassed by a "cone" with a relatively small generating angle. If a *vector* or *reference axis* of the common-factor space is chosen in the midst of this cone, all variables in the group will correlate high with it. The degree of *linear fit* is measured by the extent to which the vectors representing the variables approach the reference axis. By selecting a number of such reference axes, each one passing through a cone of vectors, an oblique solution will generally be obtained.

8. Vector representation: planar fit.—The preceding type of geometric fit also satisfies planar fit in the sense that the vectors lying close to the reference axes will also lie close to the planes of pairs of these axes. In general, the degree of *planar fit* is measured by the proximity of the vectors representing the variables in the common-factor space to such reference planes. Variables which satisfy planar fit need not satisfy linear fit, i.e., their vectors may lie in the plane between the two reference axes without clustering near each one. Thus, greater freedom exists in the choice of the factor axes when reference planes are selected rather than specific reference axes close to clusters of vectors. If a solution can be found in which all vectors lie in one or another of the reference planes, then each variable will involve only two common factors in its linear description.

9. Vector representation: hyperplanar fit.—The two preceding criteria employed either one-spaces or two-spaces to approximate subsets of vectors representing the variables. A natural extension of these ideas is to larger and larger linear spaces— just short of the total space which obviously would offer no simplification. By *hyperplanar fit* in a common-factor space of m dimensions is meant that each vector representing a variable lies in an $(m - 1)$, or smaller, space. When a set of variables satisfies this standard, the complexity of any one of them is less than the total number of common factors. This does not appear as a very stringent criterion, because it is satisfied if each variable is merely of complexity $(m - 1)$ for m common factors. However, the strength of this standard lies in the fact that the hyperplane is the largest permissible space containing each variable. In other words, it is presumed that there will usually be smaller reference spaces which contain certain subgroups of variables. In particular, a vector which lies on a reference axis is contained in that one-space, and the variable it represents has a complexity of one. Similarly, if a vector lies in a reference plane, the variable is of complexity two. It is evident that standards **7** and **8** may be considered as special cases of hyperplanar fit. For, if a set of variables satisfies the criterion of linear fit, or planar fit, it certainly conforms to hyperplanar fit. The converse, of course, is not true generally.

10. Simple structure principles.—The criteria under consideration here are specifically intended for the multiple-factor solutions. Such solutions have been vaguely defined in the past, following some intuitive concepts of "simple structure" proposed by Thurstone. He was among the first to strive for an *objective* definition of this concept and an accompanying objective procedure for a simple structure solution. Since 1935 many individuals have made specific proposals for analytical or semi-analytical procedures for the attainment of simple structure or approximations to it. However, real strides in this direction were not realized until twenty years later. The accomplishments in analytical methods are described in chapters 14 and 15.

Thurstone's original three conditions for simple structure, were as follows [468, p. 156]:

1. Each row of the factor structure should have at least one zero.
2. Each column should have at least m zeros (m being the total number of common factors).
3. For every pair of columns there should be at least m variables whose entries vanish in one column but not in the other.

By way of definition, Thurstone states [477, p. 328]: "If a reference frame can be found such that each test vector is contained in one or more of the ... coordinate hyperplanes, then the combined frame and configuration is called a *simple structure*." This statement requires only the first condition, namely, that each row of the factor matrix should have at least one zero. The psychological basis for this definition might best be summarized in Thurstone's words [477, p. 58]: "Just as we take it for granted that the individual differences in visual acuity are not involved in pitch discrimination, so we assume that in intellectual tasks some mental or cortical functions are not involved in every task. This is the principle of 'simple structure' or 'simple configuration' in the underlying order for any given set of attributes."

The other two conditions for simple structure were proposed as insurance that the reference hyperplanes be distinct and overdetermined by the data. Thurstone has since extended the original three conditions to five criteria for the determination of the reference vectors for a simple structure. His criteria [477, p. 335], in the language of the present text, are as follows:

1. Each row of the factor matrix should have at least one zero.
2. If there are m common factors, each column of the factor matrix should have at least m zeros.
3. For every pair of columns of the factor matrix there should be several variables whose entries vanish in one column but not in the other.
4. For every pair of columns of the factor matrix, a large proportion of the variables should have vanishing entries in both columns when there are four or more factors.
5. For every pair of columns of the factor matrix there should be only a small number of variables with non-vanishing entries in both columns.

In the foregoing it was tacitly assumed that the factors are uncorrelated, otherwise the term "factor matrix" would be completely ambiguous. The factor pattern and factor structure coincide in an orthogonal solution, so there can be no misunderstanding of the meaning of the "factor matrix" in that event. When the factors are oblique, however, the pattern is distinct from the structure and any reference to the "factor matrix" is vague and can be misleading. This distinction will be developed further in chapter 13. The foregoing principles may lead to either an orthogonal or an oblique multiple-factor solution. The detailed distinctions are brought out in chapters 12–15.

In general, the rotation of axes in order to arrive at simple structure may be viewed as an attempt to reduce the complexity of the variables. The ultimate objective would be a uni-factor solution, in which each variable would be of complexity one. As noted before, an orthogonal uni-factor solution is practically impossible with empirical data, and not very likely even when the factors are permitted to be oblique. Nonetheless, this is the ultimate objective, and it is toward that end that the simple structure principles are proposed for the multiple-factor solution.

If the multiple-factor solution satisfies the five criteria listed above, then the graphical plot in the plane of each pair of factors will exhibit the following: (1) many points near the two final factor axes; (2) a large number of points near the origin; and (3) only a small number of points removed from the origin and between the two axes. When the 2-dimensional diagrams for all combinations of factors satisfy these three characteristics, Thurstone calls the structure "compelling," and concludes [477, p. 335]: "In the last analysis it is the appearance of the diagrams that determines, more than any other criterion, which of the hyperplanes of the simple structure are convincing and whether the whole configuration is to be accepted as stable and ready for interpretation." Such diagrams provide the basis for the graphical rotation methods of chapters 12 and 13. Various attempts to put the simple structure principles into objective terms are described in chapters 14 and 15, where analytical procedures are given for the multiple-factor solution.

6.3. *Solutions Requiring Estimates of Communalities*

While any matrix of correlations can be factor analyzed so that there is a reasonably close fit to the observed data, such solution may not yield the most desirable frame of reference. Sometimes the solutions answer the needs of the particular investigation; at other times, they serve as preliminary solutions to be transformed to more meaningful solutions of the type discussed in **6.5**. The solutions enumerated in this and the following section can all be obtained by direct calculation from the correlation matrix. The distinction between the solutions in this section and those in **6.4** corresponds to the a priori choice of communalities or the number of common factors—a requirement of the factor model (2.9) as noted in chapter 5. Three methods are considered in this section. Because of the general availability of electronic computers, the *principal-factor* solution is most popular today. The *centroid* solution hit its peak in the 1930's and 40's, and except for specialized situations is little used now. *Triangular diagonalization* is not at all a competing method for a preliminary solution, but it is of interest for its mathematical simplicity and is used in the course of obtaining another form of solution (see **6.4**, par. **3**).

1. Principal-factor solution.—The criterion of ellipsoidal fit, as described in **6.2**, paragraph **6**, determines the reference system of the *principal-factor* solution. The initial proposal to use the principal axes of the higher-dimensional ellipsoids goes back to Karl Pearson [386] before the subject of factor analysis was even born. More relevant to the present discussion is the work of Hotelling [259], who developed the procedures for *component analysis* of the correlation matrix based upon the model (2.8). The principal-factor solution follows essentially the same procedures, but operates on the *reduced* correlation matrix (i.e., with estimates of communalities in the diagonal) employing the model (2.9). An important distinction between principal components and principal factors is that the components are immediately expressible in terms of the observed variables while factor measurements can only be arrived at indirectly (see chapter 16). The general appearance and properties of a principal-factor solution will be indicated here, but its mathematical derivation and computing procedures are presented in chapter 8.

When the factors are represented by the principal axes of the ellipsoids, each successive one contributes a decreasing amount to the total communality. In other words, the first principal factor accounts for the maximum possible variance; the second factor accounts for a maximum in the residual space with the first factor removed; the third factor, a maximum in the residual space excluding the first two factors; and so on until the last common factor accounts for whatever communality remains. Assuming that m common factors account for the communality, a principal-factor pattern may be exhibited as follows:

$$(6.3) \quad \begin{cases} z_1 = a_{11}F_1 + a_{12}F_2 + a_{13}F_3 + \cdots + a_{1m}F_m, \\ z_2 = a_{21}F_1 + a_{22}F_2 + a_{23}F_3 + \cdots + a_{2m}F_m, \\ z_3 = a_{31}F_1 + a_{32}F_2 + a_{33}F_3 + \cdots + a_{3m}F_m, \\ \quad \cdot \quad \cdot \quad \cdot \quad \cdot \quad \cdot \quad \cdot \quad \cdot \quad \cdot \quad \cdots \quad \cdot \quad \cdot \\ z_n = a_{n1}F_1 + a_{n2}F_2 + a_{n3}F_3 + \cdots + a_{nm}F_m, \end{cases}$$

from which the unique factors have been omitted. In such a pattern the complexity of each variable is equal to the total number of common factors. The first factor is an ordinary general factor whose coefficients a_{j1} ($j = 1, 2, \cdots, n$) are all positive when the solution is based upon a table of positive correlations. On the other hand, approximately half the coefficients of each of the remaining factors are negative, that is, $F_2, F_3, \cdots, F_m$ are *bipolar factors*.* A bipolar factor is not essentially different from any other but is merely one for which several of the variables have significant negative projections. Such variables may be regarded as measuring the negative aspect of the usual type of factor. Thus, if a number of variables identified with "fear" are represented by positive projections, variables with negative projections might be interpreted as measuring "courage." It would appear simpler, however, to regard the factor merely as "fear," and the opposing set of variables as measures of "negative fear." Of course, the signs of all the coefficients of the factor may be changed without altering the adequacy of the solution. Such reversal in the foregoing example would

---

* This term was introduced by Cyril Burt [55]. In the present text, however, the term is used in a more general sense.

lead to the interpretation of the factor as "courage," and the subgroup of variables with negative coefficients would be regarded as measuring "negative courage." In the illustrations of the text a single name for a bipolar factor is employed. This is consistent with representing any factor by a single continuum.

Obviously a pattern of type (6.3) can reproduce a general table of correlations like that exhibited in Figure 6.2. The solution is thus perfectly satisfactory from a statistical point of view. Although a principal-factor pattern may be more complex than other preferred types, it may sometimes furnish a more convenient representation of a particular set of variables. Since the principal-factor pattern is not restricted to positive coefficients, it can reproduce negative as well as positive correlations. This type of solution may then be applied to any matrix of correlations.

2. Centroid solution.—This has been one of the most popular solutions in factor analysis, and was often misunderstood and misrepresented. The centroid method of analysis is intended to approximate the results that are obtained with the principal-factor method, but with considerable savings in labor. It also attempts to account for as much as possible of the total variance with each successive factor. However, the centroid solution is not unique for a given set of variables nor does it have the other interesting mathematical properties of the principal-factor solution. The appropriate perspective for the centroid method was set by Thurstone [477, p. 178]: "The centroid method of factoring and the centroid solution for the location of the reference axes are to be regarded as a computational compromise, in that they have been found to involve much less labor than the principal-axes solution." Of course, the capability now exists (see **8.6**) for obtaining a principal-factor solution in a matter of minutes. When electronic computers are not available, the centroid method will be found very effective for the calculation of a preliminary solution.

The general appearance of a centroid solution is indicated by (6.3), just as in the case of the principal-factor solution. For a matrix of positive correlations, the solution contains one general factor and the remaining are bipolar. A centroid solution can also be obtained for a matrix containing negative correlations, but the method becomes somewhat more involved. A complete development of the centroid method is presented in **8.9**.

3. Triangular decomposition.—As noted in **3.4**, the square root method may be used to reduce any symmetric matrix to a triangular matrix such that the product by its transpose is equal to the original matrix. This property corresponds to (2.50), the fundamental theorem of factor analysis. In other words, the *triangular decomposition* of a matrix constitutes a factor solution.

As a formal mathematical procedure for the solution of a set of simultaneous linear equations or the reduction of a matrix, the square root method must have been discovered over and over again, and may go back to the time of Gauss. Perhaps the earliest application to the solution of normal equations in least squares theory was made by Commandant A. L. Cholesky of the French Navy around 1915, and published after his death by Commandant Benoit [35] in 1924. It was rediscovered by Banachiewicz [24] in 1938 and presented as an efficient means for solving a system of linear equations and as a means for calculating determinants and their inverses.

The square root method was introduced in the American statistical literature in 1944 by Dwyer [109] who emphasized its use in correlation and regression, and who showed the relationship of this method to other methods of linear computation [111].

Concurrent with this development of the square root method as a means of solving formal mathematical and statistical problems, essentially the same technique was being devised for factor analysis. The method was applied specifically to a correlation matrix by McMahon [360] prior to 1923. Then during the rapid development of factor analysis theory in the 1930's, it was independently developed as the *diagonal method* by Thurstone [468, p. 78] and as the *solid staircase method* by Holzinger [234, No. 5]. A description of the square root method and its applications to factor analysis was presented by Harman [198] in 1954. An outline of computing procedures is given in **3.4**.

The n variables are described in terms of n (or possibly fewer) new uncorrelated factors, in the following form:

(6.4)
$$\begin{cases} z_1 = a_{11}F_1, \\ z_2 = a_{21}F_1 + a_{22}F_2, \\ z_3 = a_{31}F_1 + a_{32}F_2 + a_{33}F_3, \\ \quad . \quad . \quad . \quad . \quad . \quad . \quad . \quad . \quad . \\ z_n = a_{n1}F_1 + a_{n2}F_2 + a_{n3}F_3 + \cdots + a_{nn}F_n. \end{cases}$$

It is evident that a great many variations of this particular form of solution are possible, since any one of the variables may be selected to involve only one factor. For the full correlation matrix (with ones in the diagonal), the triangular decomposition (6.4) would involve all n factors. If the diagonal of the correlation matrix were replaced by communalities, then the reduced correlation matrix would no longer be positive definite and the square root process would lead to imaginary numbers if attempts were made to carry it to n factors.

In practice, interest would lie in only a few factors, especially if they were the most important in some sense. Such a procedure, with an accompanying computer program, has been developed by Albert Madansky [353]. The variables are rearranged in such an order that a minimum amount is subtracted from each pivot element, and thus provide the largest possible number for which the square root is taken and which is the denominator for the calculation of all other elements, e.g., (3.25), (3.26). The result is a triangular decomposition S in which the successive diagonal elements are the maximum possible. The most important factors then come out in sequence. This follows from the following argument: First, the value of the determinant of **R** is obtained from (3.30), namely,

(6.5)
$$|\mathbf{R}| = |\mathbf{S}| \cdot |\mathbf{S}'|.$$

Since the determinant of S is merely the product of its diagonal elements (and similarly for S'), it follows that the product of the squares of all the diagonal elements of S is equal to the determinant of R. Now, if each of the factors had equal weight, each would contribute an amount equal to the nth root of $|R|$. Hence, the value of the nth root may be used as a cut-off point for judging the importance of factors, cutting off at the number of factors for which the square of the diagonal exceeds the nth root. In the foregoing discussion, it was tacitly assumed that R was the full correlation matrix. However, even when communalities are put in the diagonal of the correlation matrix, the procedure for rearranging the order of the variables still assures the determination (of the reduced number) of factors in order of importance.

6.4. *Solutions Requiring Estimate of Number of Common Factors*

As noted at the beginning of **6.3**, all the solutions in that section and the present one are obtained by direct calculation from the correlation matrix. Such solutions may serve in their own rights, or they may be transformed to other desirable forms (see **6.5**). It will be recalled that the solutions enumerated in the last section required some estimates of communalities, while a corresponding requirement for the solutions of the current section is an estimate of the number of common factors. The first two methods are applicable to any matrix of correlations and may be viewed as alternatives to the principal-factor procedure. The third type of solution is rather specialized but may have some useful applications. The remaining three solutions, while properly falling within the scope of this section, are presented primarily for historical reasons.

1. Maximum-likelihood solution.—The reference system for the maximum-likelihood solution is not determined from the criteria in **6.2**, except for the choice of the classical factor analysis model (2.9). Instead, this solution is based on fundamental statistical considerations. It considers explicitly the differences between the correlations among the observed variables and the hypothetical values in the universe from which they were sampled. The first concerted efforts to provide a sound statistical basis for factor analysis were made by Lawley [320, 321] when he suggested the use of the "method of maximum likelihood," due to Fisher [128, 129], in order to estimate the universe values of the factor loadings from given empirical data. The maximum-likelihood method requires an hypothesis regarding the number of common factors and then, according to such hypothesis, there is derived a factor solution with accompanying communalities. Associated with the method is a test of significance to determine the adequacy of the hypothesis regarding the number of common factors.

While the mathematical development goes back to the early 1940's, the method did not become practical until quite recently. Even with the electronic computers of the 1950's and early 1960's, it took considerable time to solve the rather complex equations involved in the maximum-likelihood method. Furthermore, convergence of the process cannot always be assured, although there is strong indication that it will do so for most practical needs. In recent years, much work has gone into the development of more efficient algorithms, and together with advances in computer technology, there is good indication that the maximum-likelihood method may offer real competition to the principal-factor solution for the preliminary factorization of a correlation matrix.

A maximum-likelihood solution has the same general appearance (6.3) as a principal-factor solution; but it does not have the latter's property of accounting for a maximum amount of variance for a specified number of factors. Also, while a principal-factor solution is unique for a given body of data, a maximum-likelihood solution only determines the common-factor space uniquely. In other words, one maximum-likelihood solution differs from another by a rotation. To remove this inherent indeterminacy, the computing algorithm must provide some side condition which fixes the particular solution.

2. Minres solution.—A method of factor analysis which minimizes residuals (hence, the name "minres") was developed recently [207]. Specifically, this method estimates factor loadings in such a way as to make the sum of squares of off-diagonal residuals of the correlation matrix a minimum. In so doing, it literally follows the second objective enumerated in **2.3**, i.e., to "best" reproduce the observed correlations. This is in contrast to the principal-factor method which extracts the maximum variance. Again, however, a minres solution has the same general appearance (6.3) as a principal-factor solution. The minres solution is dependent upon an estimate of the number of common factors; the communalities, consistent with this hypothesis, are obtained as by-products of the method. These properties are common to the minres and maximum-likelihood solutions.

When one considers that the primary objective of the minres solution is identical with the objective of the classical factor analysis approach in general, the question immediately arises why the method was not developed before. The simple answer is that it could not have been accomplished without the power of the modern-day computer. Now that the minres solution is a practical procedure it may be preferable to either the principal-factor or the maximum-likelihood solution.

3. Multiple-group solution.—Unlike the two preceding methods which serve primarily as preliminary solutions for subsequent "rotation" to the multiple-factor solution, the multiple-group solution usually would be retained as the final form. What it has in common with all the other methods of this section is the requirement that the number of factors be estimated in advance; but it requires estimates of communalities as well. The basic concept in the multiple-group solution is that of grouping of variables. Either arbitrary or selected groups of variables provide the basis for the common factors (equal to the number of groups) to be extracted.

The common factors extracted in a single operation can be expected to be oblique to one another. Then the complete analysis should include the factor pattern, the factor structure, and the matrix of correlations among the factors. If it is desired to rotate the results to some other solution, the problem is simplified if an orthogonal frame of reference is obtained first. The orthogonal factor pattern and the transformation matrix from the oblique to the orthogonal solution, as well as the oblique factor pattern can all be obtained very efficiently by applying the square root method to the matrix of factor correlations and the oblique factor structure.

4. Simple factor models.—Another class of solutions is dependent on a prior decision regarding the number of factors and therefore deserves mention in this section. They are not alternatives for the preceding methods, but are of interest primarily from an historical viewpoint. Their common attribute is the quest for simplicity—in a sense they represent the ultimate in parsimonious description—but unfortunately their attainment can only be expected in very specialized circumstances.

The first, a *uni-factor* solution, certainly must be considered an ideal form hardly to be expected to fit any empirical data. Such a solution satisfies the standard of linear fit, and hence minimum complexity. For the vectors representing the variables to lie exactly on the reference axes, so that each variable would measure but a single factor, implies a matrix of correlations with properties as shown in Figure 6.1. While it is highly unlikely that empirical data would yield an *orthogonal* uni-factor solution, such an *oblique* solution might be approximated.

In the early days of factor analysis, very simple factor models were proposed in defense of certain theories in psychology. Thus, when Charles Spearman [438, 440] developed the psychological theory that all intellectual activity consisted of a "general" function and a "specific" function for each element, it conformed to the uni-factor model, albeit in a very limited sense. For in this case *all* the variables of a set are describable in terms of a single common factor, constituting the simplest instance of a uni-factor solution which could arise from a group of variables with correlations depicted by a single triangle in Figure 6.1 and which satisfy the conditions (5.10) for one general factor. Spearman's "Two-factor Theory" was named from the two kinds of factors—general and specific. In recent years, it has been the practice to use the adjectival descriptors of different factor solutions to denote the number (and sometimes the type) of common factors only, it being understood that the factor model (2.9) of common and unique factors apply to all. In this sense, Spearman's *two-factor* solution is a uni-factor or "single-factor" solution, but the old name is retained for historical reasons.

An attempt to meet the inadequacies of the preceding two-factor theory was made by Holzinger [234] in his proposal of the "Bi-factor Theory". The inadequacies became apparent in the 1930's when the complex psychological test batteries came into being. In developing a broader theory to cope with the greater demand, Holzinger nevertheless was guided by Spearman's earlier work. While he claimed no more for his bi-factor theory than an extension of the two-factor theory, it is in fact an alternative multiple-factor theory as well.

The essence of the *bi-factor* solution is that it includes a general factor in addition to uncorrelated group factors and unique factors. In this way the limitation of the two-factor solution is overcome, i.e., while an orthogonal uni-factor solution can only reproduce a matrix of correlations of the form in Figure 6.1, a bi-factor solution can fit a more general set of correlations as indicated in Figure 6.2. This modification of the uni-factor pattern is tantamount to substituting planar for linear geometric fit. When the vectors of a group of variables lie in a reference plane, each variable measures just two factors. If, furthermore, the vectors lie only in the reference planes formed by a general-factor (F_0) axis and one group-factor axis (none in the planes of

105

two group factors), the configuration can be described as a *pencil of planes* through the F_0 axis.*

6.5.   *Multiple-Factor Solutions*

In contrast to the solutions of the last two sections, which are calculated directly from a correlation matrix, the solutions considered in the present section can only be derived from some preliminary solution. *Multiple-factor* solution is a generic term, originated by Thurstone in the 1930's, and is used primarily to distinguish a general type of solution involving m common factors without a prior hypothesis regarding the grouping of variables to constitute group factors.

The essential features of a multiple-factor solution include "overlapping" group factors and avoidance of a general factor. By "overlapping" is meant that the several group factors do not involve distinct subsets of variables, i.e., several group factors appear in the description of a variable. Overlapping thus implies complexity of two or more for the variables in a multiple-factor pattern, and hence the prefix "multiple" is employed. Through the overlap of group factors, a table of correlations as in Figure 6.2 can be fit by such a solution.

A multiple-factor solution satisfies the criterion of hyperplanar fit.† In analytical terms this means that the complexities of the variables should not exceed $m - 1$, where m is the number of common factors. While this is the maximum complexity, it is desirable to obtain a solution in which the description of each variable can be made as simple as possible. Also, in spite of the necessary overlapping of factors, it is desirable to have as many zero coefficients in the columns as possible. More specific criteria for a multiple-factor solution are the "simple structure principles" of **6.2**, paragraph **10**.

Any matrix of correlations which can be factored into some preliminary solution could presumably be transformed into a multiple-factor solution, either orthogonal or oblique. Such a solution usually will have many zero coefficients. However, the particular configuration of zeros and overlap of group factors is not required for a multiple-factor solution, in general. As noted before, graphical methods (as indicated in chaps. 12 and 13) have been used in the past and more objective methods (see chaps. 14 and 15) are now available for the determination of multiple-factor solutions satisfying the simple structure principles.

Before leaving the enumeration of the different types of factor solutions, one more should be mentioned. Several statistical techniques are available for fitting a *prescribed factor pattern* [see 286, 287, 416]. The object of these procedures is to obtain a multiple-factor type of solution by postulating in a preliminary solution where the

---

* In ordinary space geometry a pencil of planes refers to the totality of planes through a line, i.e., all the planes linearly dependent on two distinct planes through the line. In the present setting, however, a pencil of planes in a space of $(m + 1)$ dimensions will refer to all the planes through a line which are mutually orthogonal. It is clearly seen that there are m such planes in the pencil through the F_0 axis.

† With special reference to psychology, Thurstone has called the factors determined by hyperplanar fit "primary factors," and the corresponding psychological attributes, "primary abilities."

106

positions of the zeros and large loadings should be in the desired factor pattern, rather than the transformation of the preliminary solution according to certain criteria of simple structure. It should be noted that a bi-factor solution also satisfies a prescribed factor pattern, but its special simplicity and mode of computation sets it apart from the more general treatment. However, a bi-factor solution can be determined as a special case of the general methods for fitting a prescribed factor pattern.

6.6. *Summary of Factor Solutions*

More than ten distinct types of factor solutions have been described in this chapter, but they are not equally "preferred" by workers in the field. Some are presented primarily because of their historical significance, some because they meet particular needs, and some because of their general applicability. The first requirement of a factor analysis is for the solution to adequately explain the interrelationships among many variables. Thus, there should be good statistical fit of the reproduced correlations to the observed correlations. Secondly, after statistical fit is satisfied, it may be desirable to simplify the factorial results and make them more meaningful in a particular subject-matter field.

With the general availability of computers, a typical approach of many investigators is to obtain a principal-factor solution for an observed correlation matrix, and then transforming it to the varimax multiple-factor solution (see chap. 14). One should not overlook other possibilities, however. The increased capabilities of computers make the maximum-likelihood solution more practical than in the past, and it may be preferred to the principal-factor method. Similarly, the new minres solution may turn out to yield the most desirable initial factorization of a correlation matrix. The multiple-group method may provide a useful final solution or it may also serve as a preliminary factorization for subsequent transformation to the multiple-factor form. For the (transformed) multiple-factor solution there is the choice between orthogonal and oblique factors, and then several alternative methods (see chaps. 14 and 15).

A summary of the different solutions is presented in Table 6.1; the assumptions, properties, and characteristics of each type are outlined briefly, and the important distinctions are brought out. It may also serve as a convenient reference source after the detailed development and computing procedures have been studied in the ensuing chapters.

The choice of one form of solution rather than another may take into consideration particular hypotheses or theories of a content area, as well as the standards presented in this chapter. Thus, if in the field of biology, a general growth factor were postulated then a factor analysis of a set of body measurements in the bi-factor form would be appropriate. On the other hand, if a general factor were denied by a theory in a certain field, then the multiple-factor form would be appropriate. Examples of well known psychological theories of human abilities are Spearman's Two-factor Theory, Holzinger's Bi-factor Theory, and Thurstone's Primary Factor Theory. The factor analysis techniques which were developed in support of such theories turned out to have greater applicability than the specific purposes for which they were originally conceived.

Table 6.1

Summary of Different Types of Factor Solutions

Type of Solution	Chapters where Developed	Factor Model	Principle of Parsimony		Prior Estimates of		Group-ing of Variables	Contribution of Factors	Geometric Fit	Distinguishing Characteristics
			Common Factors	Complexity of Variables	Commu-nality	Number of Factors				
Principal components	8	(2.8)	n	n	No	No	No	Decreasing	Ellipsoidal	All general factors (bipolar)
Principal-factor	8	(2.9)	m	m	Yes	No	No	Decreasing	Ellipsoidal	
Centroid	8	(2.9)	m	m	Yes	No	No	Decreasing	Ellipsoidal	
Triangular decomposition*	†	(2.9)	m	1 to m	Yes	No	No	Decreasing	Not appl.	Each successive factor involves one fewer variable
Maximum-likelihood	10	(2.9)	m	m	No	Yes	No	Decreasing	Not appl.	All general factors (bipolar)
Minres	9	(2.9)	m	m	No	Yes	No	Decreasing	Not appl.	
Multiple-group	11	(2.9)	m	1 (approx.)	Yes	Yes	Yes	Level	Linear	Group factors only (oblique solution)
Uni-factor	†	(2.9)	m	1	No	Yes	Yes	Level	Linear	Distinct group factors (only oblique feasible)
Two-factor	7	(2.9)	1	1	No	Yes	Yes	One large	Linear	One general factor
Bi-factor	7	(2.9)	$m + 1$	2	No	Yes	Yes	One large; others level	Planar	One general and m group factors
Multiple-factor	12, 13 14, 15	(2.9)	m	1 to $(m - 1)$	Depends on pre-liminary solution		No	Level	Hyper-planar	Overlapping group factors (ortho-gonal or oblique)

* The entries in the table are for the case of a reduced correlation matrix, i.e., with communalities in the diagonal. The triangular decomposition of the full correlation matrix would, of course, involve n factors.

† These are discussed in the present chapter without further development.

It should be remembered that when a particular theory is found to be compatible with experimental evidence, it does not follow that nature does in fact behave precisely as stated. No doubt, an alternative theory may be postulated which is also compatible with the data. The mathematical expressions (e.g., the factor patterns) of these theories may be different because of adherence to different criteria. Nonetheless, if both are consistent with the empirical evidence they are equally adequate on statistical grounds, and any preference must be made on other considerations. Certainly, it is wrong to argue that a particular factor solution is incorrect because it appears different than another. Factor analysis, as a statistical technique, yields solutions which are convertible from one to another, and a preference of form must depend upon appropriate content criteria. As in all empirical sciences, several equally satisfactory laws may be usefully employed, although they may be quite different formally.

PART II

DIRECT SOLUTIONS

7
Simple Factor Models

7.1. *Introduction*

In part i of this text, the foundation and formal groundwork was laid for factor analysis. The direct methods of analysis (in contradistinction to transformation methods) are developed in chapters 7 through 11. Certain techniques which were very useful in the early development of factor analysis are presented in this chapter, followed by more modern and powerful techniques for analyzing any correlation matrix in subsequent chapters. Because of its well-deserved pride of place in factor analysis, Spearman's two-factor solution is treated first.

From the present day perspective it seems only natural that the first approach to factor analysis should have involved the simplest possible model. That is in fact what happened, in 1904, when Spearman formulated a single common factor theory of intellective ability. According to his famous theorem (see sec. **5.3**), when the tetrads vanish every variable can be described in terms of a general factor *g* and a specific (now called, unique) factor *s*. The notion of a general factor was carried beyond its actual value as a single common factor which accounted for all the intercorrelations of a particular matrix to a psychological theory that *g* entered into *all* abilities. Actually, Spearman had cautioned [440, p. 76] that such a universal law "...must acquire a much vaster corroborative basis before we can accept it even as a general principle and apart from its inevitable corrections and limitations."

The two-factor solution is developed in **7.2**, and followed in **7.3** by an interesting situation where all the conditions for a single common factor are met but the resulting solution is inappropriate nonetheless. In section **7.4** an index is developed for judging the degree of cohesiveness of variables.

As is all too evident, the two-factor solution is very limited in its application since it implies a correlation matrix of unit rank. Aside from the controversial psychological theory involving a single general factor "*g*", the method of analysis was inadequate for the correlation matrices resulting from the complex psychological test batteries.

113

Holzinger, who had been one of the chief proponents of Spearman's "two-factor theory", developed the "bi-factor theory" to cover the more complex situations. His bi-factor "theory" of psychological behavior provides for the splitting of Spearman's single general factor into a general and several group factors, so that all variables can be described in terms of a general factor, a group factor, and a unique factor. The analysis of a correlation matrix leading to a bi-factor solution is presented in **7.5**, and illustrated with a 24-variable example in **7.6**.

7.2.   *Two-Factor Solution*

According to Spearman's fundamental theorem, the necessary and sufficient conditions for a set of n variables to be describable in terms of just one general factor and n unique factors are the vanishing of all tetrads, namely:

$$(7.1) \qquad r_{jk}r_{lm} - r_{lk}r_{jm} = 0 \qquad (j, k, l, m = 1, 2, \cdots, n; \quad j \neq k \neq l \neq m).$$

The number of such conditions increases very rapidly with the size of n, as indicated by (5.12). Actually, not all of these conditions are independent, and as shown in **5.3**, there are $n(n-3)/2$ equations of condition for one general factor among n variables. In the early days of factor analysis sound statistical tests were made before the factor model was accepted. In other words, all tetrad differences were computed from a table of correlations and the median of such a frequency distribution would be compared with its probable error. Formulas for the sampling errors of tetrad differences were developed by Spearman and Holzinger [444].

The two-factor pattern may be written as follows:

$$(7.2) \qquad z_j = a_{j0}F_0 + d_jU_j \qquad (j = 1, 2, \cdots, n),$$

where F_0 is the general factor and the U_j are the n unique factors, and again, as in the case of (2.9), the prime on z_j has been dropped for simplicity. When the correlations r_{jk} satisfy the tetrad conditions, or the equivalent conditions (5.10), the pattern (7.2) may be assumed and the coefficients a_{j0} and d_j have to be determined. Formulas will be developed for the computation of the a_{j0} under the assumption that the residuals vanish, i.e.,

$$(7.3) \qquad \bar{r}_{jk} = r_{jk} - r'_{jk}.$$

The correlations reproduced from the pattern (7.2) are given by

$$(7.4) \qquad r'_{jk} = a_{j0}a_{k0},$$

and, under the assumption that the residuals vanish, the observed correlations may be written

$$(7.5) \qquad r_{jk} = r'_{jk} = a_{j0}a_{k0}.$$

In the remainder of this section the reproduced correlations will be replaced by observed correlations. Upon multiplying equation (7.5) by the square of the

114

general-factor coefficient for any variable z_e, this equation becomes

(7.6) $$a_{e0}^2 r_{jk} = a_{e0}^2 a_{j0} a_{k0} = (a_{e0} a_{j0})(a_{e0} a_{k0}) = r_{ej} r_{ek},$$

and, summing over the correlations, there results

(7.7) $$a_{e0}^2 \sum_{j<k=1}^{n} r_{jk} = \sum_{j<k=1}^{n} r_{ej} r_{ek} \qquad (e \text{ is fixed, } j, k \neq e).$$

The symbol $\sum_{j<k=1}^{n} r_{jk}$ stands for the sum of all the correlations r_{jk}, where j and k each range over the variables $1, 2, \cdots, n$ but subject to the restriction that j is always less than k. In a symmetric matrix of correlations, this sum is merely the total of all the entries above (or below) the principal diagonal.

Since there is only one common factor, the coefficient of this factor for any variable is merely the square root of the communality of the variable. Hence formula (7.7) may be written explicitly for the square of the coefficient, or the communality, of any variable z_e, as follows:

(7.8) $$a_{e0}^2 = h_e^2 = \frac{\sum (r_{ej} r_{ek}; j, k = 1, 2, \cdots, n, \ j, k \neq e, j < k)}{\sum (r_{jk}; j, k = 1, 2, \cdots, n, \ j, k \neq e, j < k)}.$$

It will be observed that the diagonal elements of the correlation matrix do not enter into formula (7.8). In fact, the formula yields values of the communalities, which theoretically are the diagonal elements preserving the unit rank of the matrix. When the conditions (5.10) are satisfied by the observed correlations a single factor is postulated. The computed diagonal elements must also satisfy these conditions in order that the rank of the reduced correlation matrix be unity.

Formula (7.8) is actually much simpler than it appears. The denominator contains the sum of all correlations excluding the given variable e, while the numerator contains the sum of paired products of correlations of the given variable with each of the other variables. For example, the square of the general factor coefficient for the first variable in a set of five is given by:

(7.9) $$a_{10}^2 = \frac{r_{12} r_{13} + r_{12} r_{14} + r_{12} r_{15} + r_{13} r_{14} + r_{13} r_{15} + r_{14} r_{15}}{r_{23} + r_{24} + r_{25} + r_{34} + r_{35} + r_{45}}.$$

While formula (7.8) is simple enough, it can be expressed in a more convenient form for computational purposes, namely:

(7.10) $$a_{e0}^2 = \frac{\left(\sum_{j=1}^{n} r_{ej} \right)^2 - \sum_{j=1}^{n} r_{ej}^2}{2 \left(\sum_{j<k=1}^{n} r_{jk} - \sum_{j=1}^{n} r_{ej} \right)} \qquad (e \text{ is fixed, } j \neq e).$$

The adaptability of this formula to machine calculation will be clear from the following restatements of the terms in the formula. If $\mathbf{R}_0$ is the matrix of correlations with the elements in the principal diagonal omitted, then

$$\sum_{j=1}^{n} r_{ej} \text{ is the sum of the correlations in column } e \text{ of } \mathbf{R}_0,$$

$$\sum_{j=1}^{n} r_{ej}^2 \text{ is the sum of squares of the correlations in column } e \text{ of } \mathbf{R}_0,$$

$$\sum_{j<k=1}^{n} r_{jk} \text{ is the sum of all the correlations below the diagonal of } \mathbf{R}_0.$$

After the communalities have been obtained, the unique variances can be determined. As pointed out in **2.4**, the uniqueness for variable e is given by

$$d_e^2 = 1 - h_e^2.$$

If, in addition, the reliability coefficients of the variables are known, the uniqueness may be split into error variance and specificity by means of the last two of formulas (2.20).

An illustrative example will clarify the method of analysis described in this section. The correlations among five variables is presented in Table 7.1. Spearman [440] used

Table 7.1

Correlations among Five Tests, and Calculation of General Factor Coefficients

Test	1	2	3	4	5
1. Mathematical judgment					
2. Controlled association	.485				
3. Literary interpretation	.400	.397			
4. Selective judgment	.397	.397	.335		
5. Spelling	.295	.247	.275	.195	
Sum: $\sum r_{ej}$	1.577	1.526	1.407	1.324	1.012
Sum of squares: $\sum r_{ej}^2$	.6399	.6115	.5055	.4655	.2617
Denominator of (7.10)	3.692	3.794	4.032	4.198	4.822
a_{e0}^2	.5003	.4526	.3656	.3067	.1581
a_{e0}	.707	.673	.604	.554	.398

this example to demonstrate the applicability of his "two-factor theory". He computed all the tetrads and found their median to be .013. The probable error of a tetrad difference for a sample of the given size was found to be .011; and from this agreement, Spearman concluded that the observed data were adequately fit by the simple theory. Using the computing formula (7.10), the necessary sums for each variable are recorded in the lower part of Table 7.1, with the general-factor coefficients in the last line of the table.

7.3. *The Heywood Case*

In the preceding section, the theory and computational methods were described for the solution of a set of variables in terms of a single common factor. As indicated above, the fundamental conditions for such a solution are the vanishing of all tetrads, i.e., all second-order minors (not involving a diagonal element) of the correlation matrix must be zero. It is possible for such conditions to be met (ideal rank, in the sense of **5.4**, being unity), while one of the diagonal elements must be greater than unity in order for the reduced correlation matrix to be of rank one. This apparently startling situation is referred to as the "Heywood" case [229].

The classical example to illustrate the Heywood case consists of the correlations in Table 7.2. It can be verified readily that all the tetrads vanish, but upon applying

Table 7.2

Hypothetical Example Illustrating the Heywood Case

Var.	Correlations					Heywood Solution		Permissible Solution					
	1	2	3	4	5	a_{j0}	h_j^2	a_{j0}	a_{j1}	a_{j2}	a_{j3}	a_{j4}	h_j^2
1						1.05	1.10	.89	.3349	.2170	.1578	.1210	.99
2	.945					.90	.81	.90	.43				.99
3	.840	.720				.80	.64	.80		.59			.99
4	.735	.630	.560			.70	.49	.70			.71		.99
5	.630	.540	.480	.420		.60	.36	.60				.7937	.99

formula (7.10) the solution in the middle portion of Table 7.2 results. This solution reproduces the correlations perfectly, but it lacks one basic requirement to be a legitimate solution—the communalities must be positive numbers between 0 and 1. Because one of the communalities is greater than one, this solution is a Heywood case.

While the ideal rank of the correlation matrix of Table 7.2 is one, the actual rank of the matrix with acceptable numbers in the diagonal certainly exceeds one. If more than one common factor is permitted, an infinitude of solutions is possible in which no communality is greater than one. An example of a solution in terms of five common factors is given in the right-hand portion of Table 7.2. In this case each communality is just under one.

In case the ideal rank is greater than one, but lower than the rank of the reduced correlation matrix unless one of the diagonal values exceeds unity, the resulting solution is referred to as the generalized Heywood case. In all such instances, when a communality greater than one appears, there is pretty clear evidence that the rank of the correlation matrix must be higher than that which produced the Heywood case. Guttman [177] proves that there are many cases where the rank of all diagonal-free submatrices of the correlation matrix is small, but the minimum rank which preserves the Gramian properties is nevertheless very large compared with the number of variables. He concludes that merely studying the minors outside the main diagonal is not sufficient for determining communalities or the minimum possible rank.

7.4. *Grouping of Variables*

In the bi-factor method, and some of the subsequent methods of analysis (e.g., chap. 11), a prime consideration is the grouping of variables into subsets. Often, the study will be so designed that three, four, or more variables are of a kind which might measure the same factor. Such a hypothetical design of the variables is tested by the factor analysis, which provides the evidence for retaining or rejecting the original grouping of variables.

When factor analysis is employed as a tool in developing theories of behavior in a particular content field, then hypothetical grouping of variables is usually based upon previous research in which some of the factors have already been identified. The design can then be extended to include other groups of variables used to identify additional factors. In some cases it may be desirable to take a portion of a previous design and add new variables to obtain more refined measures of the factors already identified. The success of such a factor analysis depends in large measure on the skill with which the variables have been selected for the groups.

On the other hand, when factor analysis is used simply as a statistical tool in the simplification and interpretation of a correlation matrix, and grouping of variables is required, then some objective means of getting such groupings from the matrix itself would seem to be indicated. Such a procedure is readily available under the assumption that the variables of a group identifying a factor have higher intercorrelations than with the other variables of the total set. Such an index is designated as the "B-coefficient" or "coefficient of belonging" [243, p. 24], and is defined as 100 *times the ratio of the average of the intercorrelations among the variables of a group to their average correlation with all remaining variables.*

To distinguish between variables of different groups, the standard set-theory notations can be adapted to the present needs. The primary definitions follow:

(7.11)

(a) $e \in G_p$ means e is a variable in the group G_p.

(b) $(z_j; j \in G_p, p = 1, 2, \cdots, m)$ denotes the *system* of elements z_j for all values of j in groups G_p, where the range of p is indicated. The elements of the system are first designated, followed by a semicolon, and all the properties on the elements are to the right of the semicolon.

(c) $\sum (z_{ji}; i = 1, 2, \cdots, N)$ means the sum of all the elements in the system $(z_{ji}; i = 1, 2, \cdots, N)$. The index j is fixed, the summation extending over i. This sum is equivalent to the more conventional form $\sum_{i=1}^{N} z_{ji}$.

It will be found that these definitions aid in clarity and ultimate simplicity in describing much of the following theory.

Employing this notation, the B-coefficient may be expressed as follows:

(7.12)
$$B(j) = 100(S/n_S)/(T/n_T), \qquad (j \in G_p, \quad p = 1, 2, \cdots, m)$$

where the variables z_j are said to comprise a group G_p, the sum of intercorrelations among the variables of the group is given by

(7.13)
$$S = \sum (r_{jk}; \quad j, k \in G_p, \quad j < k)$$

and the sum of the variables in the group with all remaining variables is given by

(7.14)
$$T = \sum (r_{jk}; \quad j \in G_p, \quad k \text{ not in } G_p),$$

while n_S and n_T are the numbers of correlations in the sums S and T, respectively.

The B-coefficients are used to sort the variables on the basis of their intercorrelations. The grouping is begun by selecting the two variables which have the highest correlation. To these is added the variable for which the sum of the correlations with the preceding is highest. This process is continued, always adding a variable which correlates highest with those already in the argument of B, until a sharp drop appears in the value of B. When this occurs, the last variable added is withdrawn from the group. Another variable may be inserted in its place, but, if the drop in B is still large, it should be withdrawn. Thus a group of variables that belong together is determined. Then, excluding the variables that have already been assigned to such a group, the two others which have the highest remaining correlation are selected to start another group. To these variables are added others, exclusive of those that have already been assigned to groups, until a significant drop appears in B, at which stage another group is formed. It is desirable to start each new group with a B-coefficient as large as possible so as to have clearly defined groups. For this purpose it may be necessary to obtain the B-coefficients for more than one pair of variables without completing the groups. The pair yielding the highest B value may then be used to introduce the next group. This process is continued until all variables have been assigned to groups or else do not fit into any group.

If, in the course of determining a group of variables that belong together, the numbers of variables entering into the argument of B is designated by v then

(7.15)
$$n_S = \binom{v}{2} = v(v-1)/2$$

$$n_T = v(n-v)$$

and the basic definition (7.12) of B may be put in the form:

(7.16)
$$B(j) = 200(n-v)S/(v-1)T.$$

While this formula is used in calculating B-coefficients, several auxiliary formulas facilitate the computations. First, another expression for T in place of (7.14) will be

119

found convenient, namely:

(7.17) $$T = \sum (r_{je}; \quad j \in G_p, \quad e = 1, 2, \cdots, n, \quad j \neq e) - 2S.$$

Since the sums of the correlations of each variable with all others are usually obtained at the start of any analysis, these sums for the variables in the particular group less twice their intercorrelations yield the sum T.

Another aid in the computation of the B-coefficients is the sum of the correlations of the last variable added to the group with the preceding ones. Letting l denote the last variable added to the group, the proposed sum may be written

(7.18) $$L = \sum (r_{jl}; \quad j \in G_p, \quad j \neq l).$$

If a subscript v is appended to the sums L, S, and T to designate their values for v variables in the argument of B, then successive values of S and T may be obtained by means of the recurrence formulas:

(7.19) $$S_v = S_{v-1} + L_v$$

and

(7.20) $$T_v = T_{v-1} + \sum (r_{el}; \quad e = 1, 2, \cdots, n, \quad e \neq l) - 2L_v.$$

Actual computations of B-coefficients are shown later in this chapter, but a word of interpretation is in order here. A value of $B = 100$ means that the average of the intercorrelations of the selected subset is exactly the same as the average correlation of these variables with all the remaining ones. Such variables would not be regarded as "belonging together" any more than they belong with the other variables of the total set. As an arbitrary standard for "belonging together", a group of variables may be required to have a minimum B-coefficient of 130. Actually, there is no sampling error formula for judging the significance of the difference between two successive values of B. Knowledge of the nature of the variables may be of some assistance in deciding whether a drop in B is "significantly" large.

Since the B-coefficient is the ratio of two averages, its properties may be studied by means of them. The average of the intercorrelations of the variables in the group (the numerator of B) tends to decrease as the number of variables in B increases, since the variables are added on the basis of highest correlation with those already in the argument of B. Similarly, the average of the correlations of the variables in the group with all remaining variables (the denominator of B) tends to decrease with an increase in v. The decrease in the numerator is relatively greater, however, than that in the denominator.

To the numerator, which usually consists of a small number of correlations, are added a few additional correlations which are lower in value than the others and thus steadily decrease its value. On the other hand, from the large number of correlations in the denominator a small number of the larger values is taken away. The value of the denominator is decreased, but not so noticeably as that of the numerator. Thus the B-coefficient decreases, in general, as more variables are added to its argument.

120

An exception to this may occur with the addition of a variable to the subset which has relatively high correlations with the preceding variables but a low sum of correlations with the remaining variables. In this case the decrease in the numerator is relatively smaller than that in the denominator, and B increases. Similar reasoning accounts for the fact that a variable can be rejected from a group because of a large drop in the value of B and then appear in the group later, after several others have been added to the subset.

As the number of variables in the argument of B increases, the decreases in the above averages become less and these averages tend toward stability. A consequence of this is that an actual difference between two successive B values has a greater relative significance as the number of variables v increases.

7.5. *Bi-Factor Solution*

A bi-factor solution for n variables, in its simplest form, consists of n linear equations involving one general factor and m group factors (ignoring the unique factors). If the variables are rearranged according to the groups in which they fall, every variable will be expressed in terms of the general factor F_0, and, in addition, the variables in the first group will involve F_1; those in the second group, F_2; and so on to the variables in the last group which will involve F_m. In such a simple model, each of the group factors overlaps with the general factor but not with any of the other group factors. From such a model, the reproduced correlation between any two variables $j \in G_p$ and $k \in G_q$ is given by:

$$(7.21) \quad \begin{cases} r'_{jk} = \sum (z_{ji}z_{ki}; \quad i = 1, 2, \cdots, N)/N, \\ \quad = \sum ([a_{j0}F_{0i} + a_{jp}F_{pi}][a_{k0}F_{0i} + a_{kq}F_{qi}]; \quad i = 1, 2, \cdots, N)/N, \\ \quad = a_{j0}a_{k0} + a_{j0}a_{kq}r_{F_0F_q} + a_{jp}a_{k0}r_{F_pF_0} + a_{jp}a_{kq}r_{F_pF_q}, \\ \quad = a_{j0}a_{k0} + a_{jp}a_{kq}r_{F_pF_q}, \end{cases}$$

where the last equality follows from the fact that the general factor is uncorrelated with the group factors. If the two variables are in different groups, then

$$(7.22) \qquad\qquad r'_{jk} = a_{j0}a_{k0} \qquad\qquad (j \in G_p, \quad k \in G_q, \quad p \neq q),$$

but, if they are in the same group, their reproduced correlation becomes

$$(7.23) \qquad\qquad r'_{jk} = a_{j0}a_{k0} + a_{jp}a_{kp} \qquad\qquad (j, k \in G_p).$$

The bi-factor solution is obtained by first computing the general factor coefficients and then the coefficients of each of the group factors. Sometimes this is followed by some adjustments to the simple model, as may be suggested by a study of the residuals.

1. General-factor coefficients.—By appropriate choice of variables, a subset can be found such that the conditions for a single common factor are satisfied; and hence the procedure of **7.2** may be applied to get the general-factor coefficients. As a first step the variables are placed into groups, toward which end B-coefficients may be

121

useful. Then, it will be noted that a subset of variables consisting of one each from different groups satisfies the form of the two-factor pattern—there is only a general factor among the variables of such a subset, and a unique factor for each variable.

To indicate how a subset of variables is selected which involves only one common factor, consider three distinct groups G_p, G_q, and G_r, and take one variable from each of them. Such a triplet may be designated (e, j, k), where $e \in G_r$, $j \in G_p$, and $k \in G_q$ and $r \neq p \neq q$. Any one of the many triplets, as the indices take specific values in the different groups, has the property of involving only one common factor. From this property, it follows that the reproduced correlation between any two of these variables is given by (7.22). Next, replace these correlations obtained from the factor pattern by observed correlations* and multiply this equation by a_{e0}^2 to get:

$$(7.24) \qquad a_{e0}^2 r_{jk} = (a_{e0} a_{j0})(a_{e0} a_{k0}) = r_{ej} r_{ek} \qquad (e \in G_r, \quad r \neq p \neq q).$$

From this expression a value of the general-factor coefficient for variable z_e can be computed based entirely upon the correlations involving only the particular variables z_j and z_k. To obtain a more reliable evaluation of any general-factor coefficient, sum both sides of (7.24) for all values† of j and k which, together with e preserve the property of involving only one common factor. Thus, for any $e \in G_r$ the square of its general-factor coefficient is given by:

$$(7.25) \qquad a_{e0}^2 = \frac{\sum (r_{ej} r_{ek}; \quad j \in G_p, \quad k \in G_q, \quad p < q = 1, 2, \cdots, m, \quad p, q \neq r)}{\sum (r_{jk}; \quad j \in G_p, \quad k \in G_q, \quad p < q = 1, 2, \cdots, m, \quad p, q \neq r)}$$

The formula is comparable to (7.8) for the case where all the variables involve only one common factor.

An important extension of formula (7.25) should be noted. If the pattern plan of a set of variables is of the bi-factor form, but includes a number of variables which measure only the general and no group factors, additional terms can be included in this formula. For any two such variables, together with any other variable e, will involve only one common factor. The summations in (7.25) should extend to all such variables j, k; the only restriction being $j < k$ so that no correlation should be used more than once.

2. Group-factor coefficients.—Before the group-factor coefficients can be computed it is necessary to obtain the residual correlations with the general factor removed. Such *general-factor residuals* are defined by

$$(7.26) \qquad \dot{r}_{jk} = r_{jk} - a_{j0} a_{k0} \qquad (j, k = 1, 2, \cdots, n).$$

These residual correlations tend to be of the form shown in Figure 6.1, with the values in the rectangles being approximately zero. The standard error of a residual correlation is indicated in Table A of the Appendix.

---

* The tacit assumption is that the residuals vanish.

† If j and k are merely restricted to be in different groups, and the variables range over all groups, each correlation would appear twice, since $r_{jk} = r_{kj}$. To avoid this, the indices j and k are permitted to range over all groups, namely, $j \in G_p$ and $k \in G_q$ for $p, q = 1, 2, \cdots, m$, but under the condition $p < q$.

In the residual-factor space, the n variables can be described by a uni-factor pattern, i.e., the bi-factor solution may be considered as a uni-factor one with a general factor superimposed. The residual correlations (7.26) for each group of variables, taken alone, should have a matrix of rank one and hence measure only one common factor. While the method of **7.2** can be used for calculating the group-factor coefficients, there will usually be a relatively small number of variables in each group, and it seems more advisable to use the method of triads of **5.3**. By this procedure the group-factor coefficient for any variable $e \in G_p$ is given by

$$(7.27) \qquad a_{ep}^2 = \frac{1}{v_p} \sum \left(\frac{\dot{r}_{ej} \dot{r}_{ek}}{\dot{r}_{jk}} \right); \quad j, k \in G_p, \quad j < k, \quad j, k \neq e \qquad (p = 1, 2, \cdots, m),$$

where

$$(7.28) \qquad v_p = \binom{n_p - 1}{2}$$

and n_p is the number of variables in the group G_p.

The complete determination of a bi-factor pattern is possible by means of formulas (7.25) and (7.27). After all the coefficients have been computed, the *final residuals* can be obtained. These are the residuals with all factors removed, namely:

$$\bar{r}_{jk} = r_{jk} - r'_{jk},$$
$$(7.29) \qquad\qquad = r_{jk} - a_{j0}a_{k0} - a_{jp}a_{kp},$$
$$= \dot{r}_{jk} - a_{jp}a_{kp}.$$

If the variables j and k do not belong to the same group, then $\bar{r}_{jk} = \dot{r}_{jk}$, i.e., the general-factor residuals *are* the final residuals and must not be significantly different from zero. On the other hand, the general-factor residuals for variables within a group must be significant to warrant the postulation of an additional factor among them. Approximate sampling errors of residuals are given in the Appendix.

3. Adjustments.—When it is found that certain residuals between variables of different groups are significant, it may be necessary to modify the simple bi-factor plan. The same is true if certain general-factor residuals within a group are practically zero. Since the bi-factor solution involves the formulation of a mathematical model (the pattern plan) and the calculation of numerical values for this model, it should be possible to establish some measure of "goodness of fit." Rough approximations to the sampling errors for factor coefficients and residuals (indicated in the Appendix) may serve as guides in verifying the appropriateness of a particular factor solution to the given data. Moreover, procedures are now available for fitting a prescribed factor pattern by statistical means [see 286, 287, 416]. The prescribed model could, of course, be a bi-factor plan. Before such procedures were available, the practice was to first obtain a simple or pure bi-factor pattern, and then in the course of the analysis certain modifications would be made. A new or revised pattern plan might be suggested from the B-coefficients for different subgroups of variables, from the crude tests of significance of residuals, or simply from inspection of the general-factor residuals.

7.6.   *Illustrative Example*

In order to illustrate the bi-factor solution, and also for subsequent factorial methods, an empirical set of data will be employed. The particular example consists of twenty-four psychological tests given to 145 seventh and eighth grade school children in a suburb of Chicago, and is largely an outgrowth of the Spearman-Holzinger Unitary Trait Study [234]. The initial data were gathered by Holzinger and Swineford [245], while applications of these data by Holzinger and Harman [243], Kaiser [293], Neuhaus and Wrigley [379] and others have made this example a classic in factor analysis literature.

The list of the twenty-four variables, their means, standard deviations, and reliability coefficients are given in Table 7.3. Their correlations are presented in Table 7.4. In the last row of the latter table is given the sum of the correlations for each variable with all the others. In obtaining such a sum for any variable, all 23 entries in its row and column must be added since only half of the symmetric matrix is recorded in the table.

Table 7.3

Basic Statistics for Twenty-Four Psychological Tests

Test X_j	Mean $\overline{X}_j$	Standard Deviation s_j	Reliability Coefficient r_{iJ}
1. Visual Perception	29.60	6.90	.756
2. Cubes	24.84	4.50	.568
3. Paper Form Board	15.65	3.07	.544
4. Flags	36.31	8.38	.922
5. General Information	44.92	11.75	.808
6. Paragraph Comprehension	9.95	3.36	.651
7. Sentence Completion	18.79	4.63	.754
8. Word Classification	28.18	5.34	.680
9. Word Meaning	17.24	7.89	.870
10. Addition	90.16	23.60	.952
11. Code	68.41	16.84	.712
12. Counting Dots	109.83	21.04	.937
13. Straight-Curved Capitals	191.81	37.03	.889
14. Word Recognition	176.14	10.72	.648
15. Number Recognition	89.45	7.57	.507
16. Figure Recognition	103.43	6.74	.600
17. Object-Number	7.15	4.57	.725
18. Number-Figure	9.44	4.49	.610
19. Figure-Word	15.24	3.58	.569
20. Deduction	30.38	19.76	.649
21. Numerical Puzzles	14.46	4.82	.784
22. Problem Reasoning	27.73	9.77	.787
23. Series Completion	18.82	9.35	.931
24. Arithmetic Problems	25.83	4.70	.836

Table 7.4

Intercorrelations of Twenty-Four Psychological Tests for 145 Children

Test: j	1	2	3	4	5	6	7	8	9	10	11	12	13	14	15	16	17	18	19	20	21	22	23	24
1	—																							
2	.318	—																						
3	.403	.317	—																					
4	.468	.230	.305	—																				
5	.321	.285	.247	.227	—																			
6	.335	.234	.268	.327	.622	—																		
7	.304	.157	.223	.335	.656	.722	—																	
8	.332	.157	.382	.391	.578	.527	.619	—																
9	.326	.195	.184	.325	.723	.714	.685	.532	—															
10	.116	.057	-.075	.099	.311	.203	.246	.285	.170	—														
11	.308	.150	.091	.110	.344	.353	.232	.300	.280	.484	—													
12	.314	.145	.140	.160	.215	.095	.181	.271	.113	.585	.428	—												
13	.489	.239	.321	.327	.344	.309	.345	.395	.280	.408	.535	.512	—											
14	.125	.103	.177	.066	.280	.292	.236	.252	.260	.172	.350	.131	.195	—										
15	.238	.131	.065	.127	.229	.251	.172	.175	.248	.154	.240	.173	.139	.370	—									
16	.414	.272	.263	.322	.187	.291	.180	.296	.242	.124	.314	.119	.281	.412	.325	—								
17	.176	.005	.177	.187	.208	.273	.228	.255	.274	.289	.362	.278	.194	.341	.345	.324	—							
18	.368	.255	.211	.251	.263	.167	.159	.250	.208	.317	.350	.349	.323	.201	.334	.344	.448	—						
19	.270	.112	.312	.137	.190	.251	.226	.274	.274	.190	.290	.110	.263	.206	.192	.258	.324	.358	—					
20	.365	.292	.297	.339	.398	.435	.451	.427	.446	.173	.202	.246	.241	.302	.272	.388	.262	.301	.167	—				
21	.369	.306	.165	.349	.318	.263	.314	.362	.266	.405	.399	.355	.425	.183	.232	.348	.173	.357	.331	.413	—			
22	.413	.232	.250	.380	.441	.386	.396	.357	.483	.160	.304	.193	.279	.243	.246	.283	.273	.317	.342	.463	.374	—		
23	.474	.348	.383	.335	.435	.431	.405	.501	.504	.262	.251	.350	.382	.242	.256	.360	.287	.272	.303	.509	.451	.503	—	
24	.282	.211	.203	.248	.420	.433	.437	.388	.424	.531	.412	.414	.358	.304	.165	.262	.326	.405	.374	.366	.448	.375	.434	—
$\sum_{e \neq j} r_{je}$	7.528	4.751	5.309	6.045	8.242	8.182	7.909	8.306	8.156	5.666	7.089	5.877	7.584	5.443	5.079	6.609	6.009	6.808	5.754	7.755	7.606	7.693	8.678	8.220

1. B-coefficients.—First, the grouping of variables as described in **7.4** will be illustrated. The analysis into groups is begun by selecting the two tests—5 and 9—which have the highest correlation, namely, $r_{59} = .723$. The value of $B(5, 9)$ is computed by means of formula (7.16) in Table 7.5. The tests j, comprising the argument of B, are for this case z_5 and z_9, and their correlation appears as the value of L and S, since there is only this one correlation in each of the sums. The value T may be obtained by (7.17) as follows:

$$T = \sum r_{5e} + \sum r_{9e} - 2r_{59} = 8.242 + 8.156 - 2(.723) = 14.952,$$

where the sums of the correlations are taken from Table 7.4. Then the value of the B-coefficient is

$$B(5, 9) = 200(24 - 2)(.723)/(2 - 1)(14.952) = 213.$$

The form of computation indicated by Table 7.5 will be found very convenient. In addition, the sum L defined in (7.18) and the recurrence formulas (7.19) and (7.20) greatly facilitate the calculation of successive B values.

To illustrate the use of these formulas, the value B (17, 18, 19, 15, 16) will be calculated, showing all details. Here, $v = 5$, and the last variable added, l, is 16. From definition (7.18), using conventional summation notation with j ranging over the four variables of the group other than the last one, there results:

$$L_5 = \sum_{j \neq 16} r_{j,16} = r_{17,16} + r_{18,16} + r_{19,16} + r_{15,16} = 1.251,$$

where the individual correlations are taken from Table 7.4. The sum S_5 may be obtained from the value S_4 by means of equation (7.19) as follows:

$$S_5 = S_4 + L_5 = 2.001 + 1.251 = 3.252.$$

It should be noted that there are two S_4 values but that one has been rejected as indicated by note (10). The next entry is merely

$$200(n - v) = 200(24 - 5) = 3,800.$$

The sum T_5 is given by formula (7.20) in terms of the preceding value T_4, which is in the row (17, 18, 19, 15) for $v = 4$, not in the row (17, 18, 19, 16). Its value is

$$T_5 = T_4 + \sum_{e \neq 16} r_{e,16} - 2L_5 = 19.648 + 6.609 - 2(1.251) = 23.755,$$

where the sum of the correlations of Test 16 with all other tests is taken from Table 7.4. Then

$$(v - 1)T = 4(23.755) = 95.020,$$

and

$$B(17, 18, 19, 15, 16) = 3800(3.252)/95.020 = 130.$$

Following the procedure outlined in **7.4**, all the variables are grouped by means of B-coefficients. The groups G_p ($p = 1, 2, 3, 4, 5$) as determined in Table 7.5, may be

126

defined by

$$G_1 = (1, 2, 3, 4),$$

$$G_2 = (5, 6, 7, 8, 9),$$

(7.30)

$$G_3 = (10, 11, 12, 13),$$

$$G_4 = (14, 15, 16, 17, 18, 19),$$

$$G_5 = (20, 21, 22, 23, 24).$$

The grouping by B-coefficients adheres to the original design of this set of tests because most of these tests had been used in factor experiments before and because the abilities they measured were quite well known. This may not be true in general. In a number of published studies the B-coefficients and the succeeding factor solutions failed to verify some postulated factors.*

2. Bi-factor solution.—A simple bi-factor plan of a general factor and five distinct group factors is implied by the grouping of variables (7.30), and is subsequently modified as indicated in the course of analysis. In calculating the bi-factor loadings, it is tacitly assumed that all entries in the correlation matrix are positive (small negative values are treated as zeros). The general-factor coefficients are computed by means of formula (7.25), making use of appropriate worksheets to facilitate the numerical work. The loadings on the general factor are in the first column of the body of Table 7.6, which includes the entire bi-factor solution.

The general-factor residuals are computed by (7.26) and are presented below the diagonal in Table 7.7. These residuals should be insignificant except for those within groups, if the grouping of variables is reasonable. In the first four groups, the intra-group residuals are consistently positive and larger than the intergroup values (with the one exception, $\dot{r}_{10,24} = .255$). However, within G_5 there are a number of negative residuals and very small positive ones, indicating that no additional factor is required for these variables. Hence, the bi-factor plan is modified by eliminating the group factor for G_5, and the general-factor residuals among these variables are taken as the final residuals.

Next, the coefficients of each of the group factors are computed by means of formula (7.27), employing the general-factor residuals (in italics) in Table 7.7. These calculations for the loadings on B_1, B_2, and B_3 are straightforward, and the results are shown in Table 7.6. When the triads in (7.27) were computed for any variable in G_4, however, it was found that they varied widely and hence the six variables could not be assumed to measure a single factor. In fact, mere inspection of the general-factor residuals points to a grouping of 14, 15, 16, and 17; another grouping of 17, 18, and 19; and acceptance of the general-factor residuals for 14, 15, and 16

---

* An example of this appeared in the factor solution obtained by Holzinger and Harman [241]. In preparing the test battery, Professor Thurstone had postulated that "verbal reasoning, numerical reasoning, and space reasoning would be separate factors and that these would be different from verbal abstraction and visual imagery" [470, p. 11]. Both solutions cut across these predetermined groupings that had guided the test construction and revealed some different factors.

127

Table 7.5

Calculation of *B*-Coefficients

j	*v*	*L*	*S*	200(*n* − *v*)	*T*	(*v* − 1)*T*	$B(j) = \dfrac{200(n-v)S}{(v-1)T}$	Notes
(5, 9)	2	.723	.723	4400	14.952	14.952	213	—
(5, 9, 7)	3	1.341	2.064	4200	20.179	40.358	215	—
(5, 9, 7, 6)	4	2.058	4.122	4000	24.245	72.735	227	—
(5, 9, 7, 6, 8)	5	2.256	6.378	3800	28.039	112.156	216	—
(5, 9, 7, 6, 8, 23)	6	2.276	8.654	3600	32.165	160.825	194	(1)
(10, 12)	2	.585	.585	4400	10.373	10.373	248	—
(10, 12, 13)	3	.920	1.505	4200	16.117	32.234	196	(2)
(10, 12, 11)	3	.912	1.497	4200	15.638	31.276	201	(3)
(10, 12, 11, 13)	4	1.455	2.952	4000	20.312	60.936	194	(4)
(10, 12, 11, 13, 24)	5	1.715	4.667	3800	25.102	100.408	177	(5)
(10, 12, 11, 13, 21)	5	1.584	4.536	3800	24.750	99.000	174	(6)
(20, 23)	2	.509	.509	4400	15.415	15.415	145	(7)
(1, 4)	2	.468	.468	4400	12.637	12.637	163	(8)
(1, 4, 3)	3	.708	1.176	4200	16.530	33.060	149	—
(1, 4, 3, 2)	4	.865	2.041	4000	19.551	58.653	139	—
(1, 4, 3, 2, 21)	5	1.189	3.230	3800	24.779	99.116	124	(9)
(17, 18)	2	.448	.448	4400	11.921	11.921	165	—
(17, 18, 19)	3	.682	1.130	4200	16.311	32.622	145	—
(17, 18, 19, 16)	4	.926	2.056	4000	21.068	63.204	130	(10)
(17, 18, 19, 15)	4	.871	2.001	4000	19.648	58.944	136	—
(17, 18, 19, 15, 16)	5	1.251	3.252	3800	23.755	95.020	130	—
(17, 18, 19, 15, 16, 14)	6	1.530	4.782	3600	26.138	130.690	132	—
(17, 18, 19, 15, 16, 14, 24)	7	1.836	6.618	3400	30.686	184.116	122	(11)
(17, 18, 19, 15, 16, 14, 22)	7	1.704	6.486	3400	30.423	182.538	121	(12)
(20, 23)	2	.509	.509	4400	15.415	15.415	145	—
(20, 23, 22)	3	.966	1.475	4200	21.176	42.352	146	—
(20, 23, 22, 21)	4	1.238	2.713	4000	26.306	78.918	138	—
(20, 23, 22, 21, 24)	5	1.623	4.336	3800	31.280	125.120	132	—
(20, 23, 22, 21, 24, 18)	6	1.652	5.988	3600	34.784	173.920	124	(13)
(20, 23, 22, 21, 24, 16)	6	1.641	5.977	3600	34.607	173.035	124	(13)

NOTES ON TABLE 7.5

(1) Test 23 is rejected because of 22 points' drop in *B* for *v* = 6.

(2) Test 13 is rejected because 52 points' drop in *B* seems to be too great even for *v* = 3.

(3) Test 11 is retained, although it causes a drop of 47 points in *B*, because it is of the same general nature as Tests 10 and 12.

(4) Test 13 is retained, although it was previously rejected from the group. After Test 11 was put in the group, Test 13 seemed to belong together with the others, causing a drop of only 7 points in the value of *B* for *v* = 4.

(5) Test 24 is rejected because of 17 points' drop in *B* for *v* = 5.

(6) Test 21 is rejected because of 20 points' drop in *B* for *v* = 5.

(7) Before continuing with the group which starts with Tests 20 and 23, another pair of tests will be tried to see if they yield a value of *B* greater than 145.

(8) Tests 1 and 4, although having a lower correlation than the pair 20 and 23, produce a higher value of the *B*-coefficient. Hence the next group is started with Tests 1 and 4. [*continued on p.* 129]

Table 7.6

Bi-Factor Pattern for Twenty-Four Psychological Tests

Test j	General Deduction B_0	Spatial Relations B_1	Verbal B_2	Perceptual Speed B_3	Recog- nition B_4	Associative Memory B_5	Doublet D_1	Unique U_j
1	.589	.484	—	—	—	—	—	.647
2	.357	.285	—	—	—	—	—	.889
3	.401	.479	—	—	—	—	—	.781
4	.463	.317	—	—	—	—	—	.828
5	.582	—	.574	—	—	—	—	.576
6	.575	—	.559	—	—	—	—	.597
7	.534	—	.708	—	—	—	—	.463
8	.624	—	.375	—	—	—	—	.686
9	.560	—	.628	—	—	—	—	.540
10	.388	—	—	.594	—	—	.377	.595
11	.521	—	—	.478	—	—	—	.707
12	.404	—	—	.642	—	—	—	.652
13	.576	—	—	.438	—	—	—	.690
14	.388	—	—	—	.545	—	—	.743
15	.351	—	—	—	.476	—	—	.806
16	.496	—	—	—	.353	—	—	.793
17	.422	—	—	—	.361	.493	—	.670
18	.515	—	—	—	—	.468	—	.718
19	.442	—	—	—	—	.278	—	.853
20	.644	—	—	—	—	—	—	.765
21	.645	—	—	—	—	—	—	.764
22	.644	—	—	—	—	—	—	.765
23	.734	—	—	—	—	—	—	.679
24	.712	—	—	—	—	—	.377	.592
Contribution of factor	6.874	0.645	1.678	1.185	0.779	0.539	0.284	—

with 18 and 19 as final residuals. These changes may be justified by the crude tests of significance of residuals and by the B-coefficients for the two subsets of variables, namely,

$$B(14, 15, 16, 17) = 202 \quad \text{and} \quad B(17, 18, 19) = 177,$$

where these calculations are based on the general-factor residuals among the six

Notes on Table 7.5 contd.

(9) Test 21 is rejected because of 15 points' drop in B for $v = 5$ and seemingly different nature of Test 21 from Tests 1, 2, 3, and 4.

(10) Test 16 is rejected because of 15 points' drop in B to see if some other test will cause a smaller drop. If some other test cannot be found which causes a smaller drop in B, then Test 16 will be retained in the group at this stage because a drop of 15 points for $v = 4$ does not seem to be definitely significant.

(11) Test 24 is rejected because of 10 points' drop in B for $v = 7$.

(12) Test 22 is rejected because of 11 points' drop in B for $v = 7$.

(13) Tests 18 and 16, although they had previously been allocated to another group, are put into the argument of B along with 20, 21, 22, 23, 24 to see if the latter group of tests must be extended to other tests in the battery. The drop in B in each case, along with the seemingly different nature of Tests 18 and 16, seems to warrant their rejection from this group.

Table 7.7

Residual Correlations*

k \\ j	1	2	3	4	5	6	7	8	9	10	11	12	13	14	15	16	17	18	19	20	21	22	23	24
G₁ 1	—	-.030	-.065	.042	—	—	—	—	—	—	—	—	—	—	—	—	—	—	—	—	—	—	—	—
2	*.108*	—	.037	-.025	—	—	—	—	—	—	—	—	—	—	—	—	—	—	—	—	—	—	—	—
3	*.167*	*.174*	—	-.033	—	—	—	—	—	—	—	—	—	—	—	—	—	—	—	—	—	—	—	—
4	*.195*	*.065*	*.119*	—	—	—	—	—	—	—	—	—	—	—	—	—	—	—	—	—	—	—	—	—
G₂ 5	-.022	.077	.014	-.042	—	-.034	-.061	.000	.037	—	—	—	—	—	—	—	—	—	—	—	—	—	—	—
6	-.004	.029	.037	.061	*.287*	—	.019	-.042	.041	—	—	—	—	—	—	—	—	—	—	—	—	—	—	—
7	-.011	-.034	.009	.088	*.345*	*.415*	—	.020	-.059	—	—	—	—	—	—	—	—	—	—	—	—	—	—	—
8	-.036	-.066	.132	.102	*.215*	*.168*	*.286*	—	-.053	—	—	—	—	—	—	—	—	—	—	—	—	—	—	—
9	-.004	-.005	-.041	.066	*.397*	*.392*	*.386*	*.183*	—	—	—	—	—	—	—	—	—	—	—	—	—	—	—	*.117*
G₃ 10	-.113	-.082	-.231	-.081	.085	-.020	-.046	.043	-.047	—	-.002	.047	-.075	—	—	—	—	—	—	—	—	—	—	—
11	.001	-.036	-.118	-.131	.041	.053	-.035	-.025	-.012	*.282*	—	-.089	.026	—	—	—	—	—	—	—	—	—	—	—
12	.076	.001	-.022	-.027	-.020	-.137	.037	.019	-.113	*.428*	*.218*	—	-.002	—	—	—	—	—	—	—	—	—	—	—
13	.150	.033	.090	.060	.009	-.022	.039	-.008	-.043	*.185*	*.235*	*.279*	—	—	—	—	—	—	—	—	—	—	—	—
G₄ 14	-.104	-.036	.021	.114	.054	.069	-.015	-.014	.043	.021	.148	-.026	-.028	—	.025	.028	.020	.000	.000	—	—	—	—	—
15	.031	.006	-.076	-.036	.025	.049	-.085	-.044	.051	.018	.057	.031	-.063	*.234*	—	-.017	.025	.000	.000	—	—	—	—	—
16	.122	.095	.064	.092	-.102	.006	.003	-.014	-.036	-.068	.056	-.081	-.005	*.220*	*.151*	—	-.012	.000	.000	—	—	—	—	—
17	-.073	-.146	.008	-.008	-.038	.030	-.116	-.008	.038	.125	.142	.108	-.049	*.177*	*.197*	*.115*	—	.000	.000	—	—	—	—	—
18	.065	.071	.004	.013	-.037	-.129	-.010	-.071	-.080	.117	.082	.141	.026	*.001*	*.153*	*.089*	*.231*	—	.000	—	—	—	—	—
19	.010	-.046	.135	-.068	-.067	-.003	-.010	-.002	-.026	.019	.060	-.069	.008	*.035*	*.037*	*.039*	*.137*	*.130*	—	—	—	—	—	—
G₅ 20	-.014	.062	.039	.041	.023	.065	.107	.025	.085	-.077	-.134	-.014	-.130	.052	.046	.069	-.010	-.031	-.118	—	-.002	.002	.000	.000
21	-.011	.076	-.094	.050	-.057	-.108	-.030	-.040	-.095	.155	.063	-.094	-.053	-.067	.006	.028	-.099	.025	.046	*.002*	—	.000	.000	.000
22	.034	.002	-.008	.082	.066	.016	.052	-.045	.122	-.090	-.032	-.067	-.092	-.007	.020	-.036	.001	-.015	.057	*.048*	*-.041*	—	.000	.000
23	.042	.086	.089	-.005	.008	.009	.013	.043	.093	-.023	-.131	.053	-.041	-.043	-.002	-.004	.023	-.106	.021	*.036*	*-.022*	*.030*	—	.000
24	-.137	-.043	-.083	-.082	.006	.024	.057	-.056	.025	.255	.041	.126	-.052	.028	-.085	-.091	.026	.038	.059	*-.093*	*-.011*	*-.084*	*-.089*	—

*The values in italics are not final; they are factored further; and the final residuals corresponding to them appear above the principal diagonal.

variables. The results of this modification lead to the factor coefficients of B_4 and B_5 in Table 7.6.

Finally, one further adjustment was made for the exceptionally large general-factor residual between variables 10 and 24. A *doublet* (factor through only two variables) is assumed for these variables. As noted in Table 5.2, it takes at least three variables to determine the factor weights for a single factor uniquely, and when there are only two variables their description of a common factor is quite arbitrary. In the example, approximately one standard error was subtracted from the residual before the variance was divided equally between the two variables. The resulting doublet factor coefficients for the variables are shown in Table 7.6.

To complete the linear description of each test in terms of factors there remains the determination of the unique factor coefficients. These are given by

$$d_j = \sqrt{1 - h_j^2},$$

as described in **2.4**. The sums of squares of coefficients of the common factors in Table 7.6 are computed and recorded as the communalities in Table 7.8. The complement of each of these numbers from unity is the uniqueness, which is also recorded in Table 7.8. Then, taking square roots yields the coefficients of the respective unique factors in Table 7.6.

While factorial methods yield the communality and uniqueness of each variable, the latter variance may be split into the specificity and error variance simply from the knowledge of the reliability of the variable. The reliability of each of the 24 psychological tests is recorded in Table 7.8, as well as the error variance and specificity which follow from formulas (2.20). In addition to this apportionment of the unit variance of each test, the index of completeness of factorization, as computed by (2.21), is given in the last column of Table 7.8.

It is of interest to judge how well a particular factor solution fits the empirical data. Generally, only crude procedures for "when to stop factoring" are employed (although more rigorous statistical tests are available for certain types of solutions as given in sec. **9.5** and **10.4**). Among the rules employed is the decision, in advance, to analyze up to 50% (or 75%) of the total variance of a battery of tests; or a suitable proportion of the total reliability, leaving room for some specific factors; or, that only factors which include at least 5% (or 2%) of the total variance can have any practical value, in the sense of being identifiable. Other approximate methods may involve some crude standards for the size and distribution of the final residuals.

In a bi-factor solution there is not as much choice of whether to continue factoring or not. The pattern plan predetermines, in a large sense, the proportion of the total variance that will be explained by the analysis. Cognizance of the kind of empirical rules that are used in such a solution as the principal-factor type may also be of benefit in judging the adequacy of a bi-factor solution. Thus, the common-factors of Table 7.6 account for just 50% of the total variance of the twenty-four tests, and on this basis the solution would not be deemed "over-factored". The doublet D_1 certainly is not identifiable; and B_1, B_4, and B_5 each account for less than 5% (but

131

Table 7.8

Apportionment of Test Variances

Test j	Communality h_j^2	Reliability r_{jj}	Uniqueness $d_j^2 = 1 - h_j^2$	Error Variance $e_j^2 = 1 - r_{jj}$	Specificity $b_j^2 = d_j^2 - e_j^2$	Index of Factorization $C_j = 100\dfrac{h_j^2}{r_{jj}}$
1	.581	.756	.419	.244	.175	76.9
2	.209	.568	.791	.432	.359	36.7
3	.390	.544	.610	.456	.154	71.7
4	.315	.922	.685	.078	.607	34.1
5	.668	.808	.332	.192	.140	82.7
6	.643	.651	.357	.349	.008	98.8
7	.786	.754	.214	.246	−.032	104.2
8	.530	.680	.470	.320	.150	77.9
9	.708	.870	.292	.130	.162	81.4
10	.503[a]	.952	.497	.048	.449	52.8
11	.500	.712	.500	.288	.212	70.2
12	.575	.937	.425	.063	.362	61.4
13	.524	.889	.476	.111	.365	58.9
14	.448	.648	.552	.352	.200	69.1
15	.350	.507	.650	.493	.157	69.0
16	.371	.600	.629	.400	.229	61.8
17	.551	.725	.449	.275	.174	76.0
18	.484	.610	.516	.390	.126	79.4
19	.273	.569	.727	.431	.296	47.9
20	.415	.649	.585	.351	.234	63.9
21	.416	.784	.584	.216	.368	53.1
22	.415	.787	.585	.213	.372	52.7
23	.539	.931	.461	.069	.392	57.9
24	.507[b]	.836	.493	.164	.329	60.6

[a] The communality with the doublet D_1 included is .641.
[b] The communality with the doublet D_1 included is .645.

more than 2%) of the total variance, so that their practical significance may be questioned.

The index C_j of completeness of factorization provides another guide to the adequacy of the solution. The analysis of psychological tests into common factors should not be carried to the point where real specific factors disappear. In the example there is only one value of C_j in excess of 100. It is ignored, as probably due to chance errors either in the factor weights or in the reliability coefficient. If, however, there were several such values for high reliability coefficients, there would be good reason to consider a modification of the factor solution.

In considering the statistical fit of the factor model in **2.6** the standard (2.30) was suggested for judging the agreement of the reproduced correlations with the observed ones. This requires the standard deviation of the final residuals to be less than the standard error of a zero correlation. The frequency distribution of the final residuals is presented in Table 7.9, where the standard deviation is shown to be .0655. Since this value is less than the standard error (.0830) of a zero correlation for a sample of 145 cases, the required condition is satisfied.

3. Factor names.—A few words about the naming of factors may be in order. It will be recalled that the fundamental purpose of factor analysis is to comprehend a large class of phenomena (the values of a set of variables) in terms of a small number of concepts (the factors); and, this description is taken to be a linear function of the factors. In a mathematical or physical theory it may be sufficient to know that twenty-four variables can be described linearly in terms of only six new hypothetical ones—that is usually quite an accomplishment, and it is of little concern as to what the six new variables are called. But in the biological and social sciences—psychology, for example—the practical identification of these new variables (the factors) makes it highly desirable to have them named.

Table 7.9

Frequency Distribution of Final Residuals

Value of Residual	Frequency	Value of Residual	Frequency
.150– .169	3	−.130––.111	8
.130– .149	5	−.150––.131	6
.110– .129	6	−.170––.151	—
.090– .109	8	−.190––.171	—
.070– .089	12	−.210––.191	—
.050– .069	25	−.230––.211	—
.030– .049	33	−.250––.231	1
.010– .029	30		
−.010– .009	39	Total	276
−.030––.011	29		
−.050––031	29	Mean	−.0004
−.070––.051	15		
−.090––.071	17	Standard deviation	.0655
−.110––.091	10		

The coefficients of a factor pattern indicate the correlations of the variables with the respective factors and furnish the basis for naming them. In the case of oblique factors, to be discussed in later chapters, the structure furnishes the correlations of the variables with the factors, and so it is similarly employed in naming the factors. The investigator is guided by the magnitude of the factor weights in the selection of appropriate names for the factors. The name selected is usually suggested by the nature of the variables having the largest correlations with the factor under consideration. This name should be consistent with the nature of the remaining variables which have low correlations with the factor.

The common factors in the example are named from the pattern given in Table 7.6 and the brief descriptions of the tests. The factor B_0 has positive weights throughout and correlates highest with such deductive tests as Series Completion (23), Woody-McCall Arithmetic (24), Problem Reasoning (22), and Word Classification (8). Hence B_0 might be called a "general deductive factor." This name is consistent with the nature of the remaining variables—those involving a lesser amount of deductive ability have correspondingly smaller factor weights.

The remaining common factors are named from the subgroups of tests which have significant correlations with them. The first group factor is named from the "spatial" subgroup (Tests 1–4), the second from the "verbal" subgroup of tests, and similarly for the remaining factors. The names of the six common factors are indicated in Table 7.6. In addition to the common factors, there is one unique factor for each of the twenty-four tests. If a name were desired for any unique factor, it would be obtained from the description of the particular test. The only unnamed factor is the doublet D_1 involved in Speed of Adding (10) and Woody-McCall Arithmetic (24). This doublet appears to measure "arithmetic speed," which might appear as a more significant factor if more tests of this type were introduced in a battery to experiment for this purpose.

For future work with this factor pattern the doublet will be dropped from consideration, since, as was remarked before, it takes at least three variables to define a factor. The six common factors may be referred to by means of symbols or the descriptive names, which are tentatively assigned for that purpose. The particular name by which a factor is designated, however, should not raise an issue for dispute. If another investigator chooses to call these factors by other names, he is free to do so. The naming of factors is not a problem of factor analysis, which is a branch of statistics, but some descriptive names may be highly desirable in a particular field for purposes of classification.

8
Principal-Factor and Related Solutions

8.1. *Introduction*

The principal-factor solution is probably the most widely used technique in factor analysis. It was not always that way; the method requires considerable calculations which were much too time-consuming before electronic computers were available. The foundation for "the method of principal axes" was laid at the turn of the century by Karl Pearson [386]. However, it was not until the 1930's that the principal-factor method as we now know it was developed by Hotelling [259] at the suggestion of Kelley. Subsequently, Kelley [305] developed an alternative procedure which twenty years later proved to be the most useful one for adaptation to high-speed electronic computers (although the later work was done independently). The first applications of electronic computers to this problem in factor analysis were made by Wrigley and Neuhaus [539, 540].

The methods of this chapter are addressed to the first of the two alternative objectives distinguished in **2.3**—to extract the maximum variance from the observed variables. A typical situation where this is useful is in the reduction of a large body of data to a more manageable set. Of greatest interest, of course, are the measurements that vary the most among the individuals. Therefore, if a small number of linear combinations of the original variables can be found which account for most of the variance then considerable parsimony is gained.

Actually, three methods are considered in this chapter. The fundamental method is "component analysis" which is introduced in **8.2**. Then, an adaptation of it—the principal-factor solution—is developed in sections **8.3–8.6** for both hand methods and computer operations. The procedures with a desk calculator are presented in detail in **8.5**, using the example of eight physical variables. Four different sets of data are used in **8.7** to illustrate various features of the principal-factor solution. A technique for fixing the coordinate system in a given factor space for *any solution* is developed in **8.8** and the relationship to the principal-factor method is noted.

Finally, an approximation to the principal-factor method—the centroid method—is described in **8.9**. This was very popular before computers made the principal-factor solution feasible.

8.2. *Component Analysis*

The method of principal components, or component analysis, is based upon the early work of Pearson [386] with the specific adaptations to factor analysis suggested by the work of Hotelling [259]. As noted in **6.2**, when the point representation of a set of variables is employed, the loci of uniform frequency density are essentially concentric, similar, and similarly situated ellipsoids. The axes of these ellipsoids correspond to the principal components. The method of component analysis, then, involves the rotation of coordinate axes to a new frame of reference in the total variable space—an orthogonal transformation wherein each of the n original variables is describable in terms of the n new principal components.

An important feature of the new components is that they account, in turn, for a maximum amount of variance of the variables. More specifically, the first principal component is that linear combination of the original variables which contributes a maximum to their total variance; the second principal component, uncorrelated with the first, contributes a maximum to the residual variance; and so on until the total variance is analyzed. The sum of the variances of all n principal components is equal to the sum of the variances of the original variables.

Since the method is so dependent on the total variance of the original variables, it is most suitable when all the variables are measured in the same units. Otherwise, by change of units or other linear transformations of the variables, the ellipsoids could be squeezed or stretched so that their axes (the principal components) would have no special meaning. Hence, it is customary to express the variables in standard form, i.e., to select the unit of measurement for each variable so that its sample variance is one. Then, the analysis is made on the correlation matrix, with the total variance equal to n. For such a matrix (symmetric, positive definite), all n principal components are real and positive.

The formal development of the method of component analysis will not be presented.* Instead, the development will be for the factor-analytic adaptation of the method. The important distinction is that the model (2.8) is employed in component analysis as contrasted to the model (2.9) for factor analysis. All the variance of the variables is analyzed in terms of the principal components, while the communality is analyzed in terms of the common factors. Hence, the distinction comes from the amount of variance analyzed—the numbers placed in the diagonal of the correlation matrix. Analysis of the correlation matrix, with ones in the diagonal, leads to principal *components*, while analysis of the correlation matrix with communalities leads to principal *factors*. It will be shown in chapter 16 that the principal components can

---

* For detailed discussion of the method of principal components, see the original work of Hotelling [259] and the more recent treatment by Anderson [11, chap. 11]; and for consideration of statistical inference in component analysis, see Anderson [12].

be expressed simply in terms of the observed variables, while approximation procedures are required for the measurement of factors.

Before the mathematical and computing procedures are presented, it may be of interest to see what the results of a component analysis look like. This is shown in Table 8.1 for the simple numerical example introduced in chapter 2. The main body of the table contains numbers which, when read by columns correspond to the principal components, and when read by rows correspond to the variables. Thus,

Table 8.1

Principal Components for Five Socio-Economic Variables[a]

Variable	P_1	P_2	P_3	P_4	P_5	Variance
1	.5810	.8064	.0276	−.0645	−.0852	1.0000
2	.7671	−.5448	.3193	.1118	−.0216	1.0002
3	.6724	.7260	.1149	−.0072	.0862	.9999
4	.9324	−.1043	−.3078	.1582	.0000	1.0000
5	.7911	−.5582	−.0647	−.2413	.0102	.9999
Variance	2.8733	1.7966	.2148	.1000	.0153	5.0000
Per cent	57.5	35.9	4.3	2.0	0.3	100.0

[a] Again, the only reason for showing the results to so many decimal places is to provide a means for checking numerical calculations.

the entries in the rows are the coefficients of the P's in the linear expressions (2.8) for the z's; they are also the correlations of the variables with the principal components. The direction of a principal component may be reflected, i.e., all entries in a column may be multiplied by −1 without affecting any of the results.

The sums of squares of entries in the rows are the variances of the variables. The variance of each principal component (sum of squares in each column) is shown in the next to last row. The principle of maximum contribution to variance of each successive component is clearly demonstrated. In this example, the first two principal components account for more than 93 per cent of the variance—leading to a reduction in the data that would satisfy the most discerning investigator.

8.3. *Principal-Factor Method*

While the method of principal components was devised for the model (2.8), Thomson [459] was the first to apply it to the classical factor analysis model—although, at the time, his application was only to the Spearman two-factor solution. More generally, by the "method of principal factors" is meant the application of the method of principal components to the reduced correlation matrix (i.e., with communalities in place of the ones in the principal diagonal). This is the method that is developed in detail in this and the following three sections.

From the classical factor-analysis model (2.9), the relevant portion for the determination of the common-factor coefficients may be written:

(8.1) $$z_j = a_{j1}F_1 + \cdots + a_{jp}F_p + \cdots + a_{jm}F_m, \qquad (j = 1, 2, \cdots, n)$$

137

where the unique factor has been omitted, and hence the precise representation should be z_j'' but the primes are dropped for simplicity. The sum of squares of factor coefficients gives the communality of a particular variable, while any term a_{jp}^2 indicates the contribution of the factor F_p to the communality of z_j. The first stage of the principal-factor method involves the selection of the first-factor coefficients a_{j1} so as to make the sum of the contributions of that factor to the total communality a maximum. This sum is given by

$$(8.2) \qquad V_1 = a_{11}^2 + a_{21}^2 + \cdots + a_{n1}^2,$$

and the coefficients a_{j1} must be chosen so as to make V_1 a maximum under the conditions

$$(8.3) \qquad r_{jk} = \sum_{p=1}^{m} a_{jp} a_{kp} \qquad (j, k = 1, 2, \cdots, n),$$

where $r_{jk} = r_{kj}$ and r_{jj} is the communality h_j^2 of variable z_j. The conditions (8.3) say that the observed correlations are to be replaced by the reproduced correlations, implying the assumption of zero residuals.

In order to maximize a function of n variables when the variables are connected by an arbitrary number of auxiliary equations, the method of Lagrange multipliers [16, pp. 152–57] is particularly well adapted. This method is employed to maximize V_1, which is a function of the n variables a_{j1} under the $\frac{1}{2}n(n+1)$ conditions (8.3) among all the coefficients a_{jp}. Let

$$(8.4) \qquad 2T = V_1 - \sum_{j,k=1}^{n} \mu_{jk} r_{jk} = V_1 - \sum_{j,k=1}^{n} \sum_{p=1}^{m} \mu_{jk} a_{jp} a_{kp},$$

where $\mu_{jk}(=\mu_{kj})$ are the Lagrange multipliers. Then set the partial derivative of this new function T with respect to any one of the n variables a_{j1} equal to zero, namely,

$$(8.5) \qquad \frac{\partial T}{\partial a_{j1}} = a_{j1} - \sum_{k=1}^{n} \mu_{jk} a_{k1} = 0,$$

and similarly put the partial derivative with respect to any of the other coefficients $a_{jp}(p \neq 1)$ equal to zero, that is,

$$(8.6) \qquad \frac{\partial T}{\partial a_{jp}} = -\sum_{k=1}^{n} \mu_{jk} a_{kp} = 0 \qquad (p \neq 1).$$

The two sets of equations (8.5) and (8.6) may be combined as follows:

$$(8.7) \qquad \frac{\partial T}{\partial a_{jp}} = \delta_{1p} a_{j1} - \sum_{k=1}^{n} \mu_{jk} a_{kp} = 0 \qquad (p = 1, 2, \cdots, m),$$

where the Kronecker $\delta_{1p} = 1$ if $p = 1$ and $\delta_{1p} = 0$ if $p \neq 1$.

Multiply (8.7) by a_{j1} and sum with respect to j, obtaining

$$(8.8) \qquad \delta_{1p} \sum_{j=1}^{n} a_{j1}^2 - \sum_{j=1}^{n} \sum_{k=1}^{n} \mu_{jk} a_{j1} a_{kp} = 0.$$

138

Now, the expression $\sum\limits_{j=1}^{n} \mu_{jk}a_{j1}$ is equal to a_{k1} according to (8.5), and, setting $\sum\limits_{j=1}^{n} a_{j1}^2 = \lambda_1$, equation (8.8) may be written as follows:

$$(8.9) \qquad \delta_{1p}\lambda_1 - \sum_{k=1}^{n} a_{k1}a_{kp} = 0.$$

Upon multiplying (8.9) by a_{jp} and summing for p, this equation becomes

$$(8.10) \qquad a_{j1}\lambda_1 - \sum_{k=1}^{n} a_{k1}\left(\sum_{p=1}^{m} a_{jp}a_{kp}\right) = 0,$$

or, upon applying the conditions (8.3),

$$(8.11) \qquad \sum_{k=1}^{n} r_{jk}a_{k1} - \lambda_1 a_{j1} = 0.$$

The n equations, one for each value of j, represented by the expression (8.11) may be written in full as follows:

$$(8.12) \quad \begin{cases} (h_1^2 - \lambda)a_{11} & + r_{12}a_{21} + & r_{13}a_{31} + \cdots + & r_{1n}a_{n1} = 0, \\ r_{21}a_{11} + (h_2^2 - \lambda)a_{21} + & r_{23}a_{31} + \cdots + & r_{2n}a_{n1} = 0, \\ r_{31}a_{11} + & r_{32}a_{21} + (h_3^2 - \lambda)a_{31} + \cdots + & r_{3n}a_{n1} = 0, \\ \cdot \quad \cdot \quad \cdot \quad \cdot \quad \cdot \quad \cdot & \cdots \quad \cdot \quad \cdot \quad \cdot \quad \cdot \\ r_{n1}a_{11} + & r_{n2}a_{21} + & r_{n3}a_{31} + \cdots + (h_n^2 - \lambda)a_{n1} = 0, \end{cases}$$

where the parameter of (8.11) is designated by λ without a subscript.

Thus, the maximization of (8.2) under the conditions (8.3) leads to the system of n equations (8.12) for the solution of the n unknowns a_{j1}. A necessary and sufficient condition for this system of n homogeneous equations to have a nontrivial solution is the vanishing of the determinant of coefficients of the a_{j1} [190, p. 174]. This condition may be written:

$$(8.13) \qquad \begin{vmatrix} (h_1^2 - \lambda) & r_{12} & r_{13} & \cdots & r_{1n} \\ r_{21} & (h_2^2 - \lambda) & r_{23} & \cdots & r_{2n} \\ r_{31} & r_{32} & (h_3^2 - \lambda) & \cdots & r_{3n} \\ \cdot & \cdot & \cdot & \cdots & \cdot \\ r_{n1} & r_{n2} & r_{n3} & \cdots & (h_n^2 - \lambda) \end{vmatrix} = 0.$$

If the determinant in (8.13) were expanded it would lead to an n-order polynomial in λ. In expanded form, or in determinantal form, an equation such as (8.13) is known as a *characteristic* equation. Extensive mathematical theory has been developed on the properties of characteristic equations [e.g., 376, 516]. For factor analysis, some of the important properties include the fact that all roots are real and that a q-fold multiple root substituted for λ in (8.13) reduces the rank of the determinant to $(n - q)$.

When a simple root of the characteristic equation is substituted for λ in (8.12) a set of homogeneous linear equations of rank $(n - 1)$ is obtained. This set of equations has a family of solutions, all of which are proportional to one particular solution. From the above analysis, it follows that the factor of proportionality is $\lambda_1 = \sum_{j=1}^{n} a_{j1}^2$. But this expression is precisely V_1, the quantity which is to be maximized. In other words, V_1 is equal to one of the roots of the characteristic equation (8.13), namely, the largest root λ_1.

The problem of finding the coefficients a_{j1} of the first factor F_1, which will account for as much of the total communality as possible, is then solved. The largest root λ_1 of (8.13) is substituted in (8.12), and any solution $\alpha_{11}, \alpha_{21}, \cdots, \alpha_{n1}$ is obtained. Then, to satisfy the relation (8.2), these values are divided by the square root of the sum of their squares and then multiplied by $\sqrt{\lambda_1}$. The resulting quantities are

$$(8.14) \qquad a_{j1} = \alpha_{j1}\sqrt{\lambda_1}/\sqrt{(\alpha_{11}^2 + \alpha_{21}^2 + \cdots + \alpha_{n1}^2)} \qquad (j = 1, 2, \cdots, n),$$

which are the desired coefficients of F_1 in the factor pattern (8.1).

In the mathematical literature the roots (λ's) of a characteristic equation (8.13) are referred to as "eigenvalues". The solution to the set of equations (8.12) corresponding to each eigenvalue leads to a vector (a set of α's) which is called an "eigenvector". The generalized mathematical problem is usually expressed in the form: Find a number λ and an n-dimensional vector $\mathbf{q} \neq \mathbf{O}$ such that

$$(8.15) \qquad \mathbf{Rq} = \lambda \mathbf{q}.$$

Any number λ_p satisfying this equation is called an *eigenvalue* of $\mathbf{R}$ and its associated vector $\mathbf{q}_p = \{\alpha_{1p}, \alpha_{2p}, \cdots, \alpha_{np}\}$ is called an *eigenvector* of $\mathbf{R}$. An eigenvector scaled according to (8.14) is designated $\mathbf{a}_p = \{a_{1p}, a_{2p} \cdots, a_{np}\}$.

The foregoing expression may be viewed another way. The term $\mathbf{Rq}$ represents a transformation of the vector $\mathbf{q}$, and (8.15) says that this transformed vector is proportional to the original one, with λ the proportionality factor. In general, of course, it is not to be expected that the transformed vector would be proportional to the original one. However, when that is the case then a quantity λ exists such that (8.15) is satisfied. Such a λ must be a root of the characteristic equation (8.13). For each root λ_p the system of equations (8.12) has a non-zero solution $\mathbf{q}_p = \{\alpha_{1p}, \alpha_{2p}, \cdots, \alpha_{np}\}$. Furthermore, the n roots $\lambda_1, \lambda_2, \cdots, \lambda_n$ lead to n vectors $\mathbf{q}_1, \mathbf{q}_2, \cdots, \mathbf{q}_n$ so that (8.15) may be written:

$$(8.16) \qquad \mathbf{R}(\mathbf{q}_1 \mathbf{q}_2 \cdots, \mathbf{q}_n) = (\lambda_1 \mathbf{q}_1, \lambda_2 \mathbf{q}_2, \cdots, \lambda_n \mathbf{q}_n),$$

or, upon constituting a matrix $\mathbf{Q}$ of the n vectors,

$$(8.17) \qquad \mathbf{RQ} = \mathbf{Q\Lambda},$$

where

$$\mathbf{\Lambda} = \mathrm{diag}(\lambda_1, \lambda_2, \cdots, \lambda_n).$$

When the analysis is in terms of principal components (with unities rather than communalities in the principal diagonal of $\mathbf{R}$), then the vectors in $\mathbf{Q}$ are linearly independent so that their determinant is different from zero and $\mathbf{Q}$ has an inverse. Then from (8.17) it follows that

$$(8.18) \qquad \mathbf{Q}^{-1}\mathbf{R}\mathbf{Q} = \Lambda,$$

which brings $\mathbf{R}$ into diagonal form in which the elements of Λ are the eigenvalues and the columns of $\mathbf{Q}$ are the eigenvectors. Furthermore, since the correlation matrix is symmetric, i.e., $\mathbf{R} = \mathbf{R}'$, transposing in the expression (8.18) yields:

$$(8.19) \qquad \mathbf{Q}'\mathbf{R}(\mathbf{Q}^{-1})' = \Lambda.$$

From this expression it follows that the rows of $(\mathbf{Q}^{-1})'$ are the eigenvectors $\mathbf{q}_1, \mathbf{q}_2, \cdots,$ $\mathbf{q}_n$ and that therefore $\mathbf{Q}$ is *orthogonal*, with the property:

$$(8.20) \qquad \mathbf{Q}\mathbf{Q}' = \mathbf{I} \quad \text{or} \quad \mathbf{Q}^{-1} = \mathbf{Q}'.$$

Then, for $\mathbf{R}$ symmetric, (8.18) becomes:

$$(8.21) \qquad \mathbf{Q}'\mathbf{R}\mathbf{Q} = \Lambda.$$

This expression—sometimes referred to as the Spectral Theorem [450, pp. 222–24] —says that the matrix $\mathbf{R}$ of any symmetric (quadratic) form may be diagonalized by means of an orthogonal transformation $\mathbf{Q}$ and that the resulting elements of Λ and $\mathbf{Q}$ are real with the n eigenvectors linearly independent.

When the analysis is in terms of principal factors (based upon estimates of communalities in $\mathbf{R}$), then only m (less than n) positive eigenvalues and associated real eigenvectors are obtained. When these eigenvectors are scaled according to (8.14) they are designated by $\mathbf{a}_1, \mathbf{a}_2, \cdots, \mathbf{a}_m$ instead of by $\mathbf{q}$'s, and the matrix of these m vectors by $\mathbf{A}$. (There are still n elements of each of these column vectors so that $\mathbf{A}$ is of dimension $n \times m$.) While $\mathbf{A}$ does not have an inverse, the corresponding "orthogonality" property is

$$(8.22) \qquad \mathbf{A}'\mathbf{A} = \Lambda_m = \text{diag}(\lambda_1, \lambda_2, \cdots, \lambda_m),$$

or, in expanded algebraic form:

$$(8.23) \qquad \begin{cases} \sum_{j=1}^{n} a_{jp}^2 = \lambda_p \\ \\ \sum_{j=1}^{n} a_{jp}a_{jq} = 0 \end{cases} \qquad (p, q = 1, 2, \cdots, m; \quad p \neq q).$$

It will be noted that (8.9) represents a special instance of the orthogonality property.

The digression in the last four paragraphs gave some of the highlights of the mathematical theory as it pertains to component analysis and to principal-factor analysis. Returning to the formal development, the coefficients a_{j1} of the first factor F_1 were determined in (8.14). Conceptually, it helps to think of the method in terms of one principal factor at a time, even though in practice they are all computed simultaneously. The next problem is to find a factor which will account for a maximum of the residual communality. In order to do this, it is necessary to obtain the first-factor residual correlations. Furthermore, in obtaining still other factors the residual correlations with two, three, $\cdots$, $(m - 1)$ factors removed are employed, and hence a suitable notation is required. A convenient notation for the residual correlation of r_{jk} with s factors removed is $_s r_{jk}$. Thus, when the first factor has been obtained, the first-factor residuals become

$$(8.24) \qquad _1 r_{jk} = r_{jk} - a_{j1} a_{k1} = a_{j2} a_{k2} + a_{j3} a_{k3} + \cdots + a_{jm} a_{km}.$$

More generally, the matrix of the first-factor residuals may be expressed by:

$$(8.25) \qquad \mathbf{R}_1 = \mathbf{R} - \mathbf{R}_1^\dagger$$

where

$$(8.26) \qquad \mathbf{R}_1^\dagger = \mathbf{a}_1 \mathbf{a}_1'$$

represents the $n \times n$ symmetric matrix of products of first-factor coefficients, i.e., the reproduced correlations from the first factor alone.

In determining the coefficients of the second factor F_2, it is necessary to maximize the quantity

$$(8.27) \qquad V_2 = a_{12}^2 + a_{22}^2 + \cdots a_{n2}^2,$$

which is the sum of the contributions of F_2 to the residual communality. This maximization is subject to the conditions (8.24), which are analogous to the restrictions (8.3) in the case of the first factor. The theory of characteristic equations provides the basis for determining the coefficients of the second and subsequent factors. It is not necessary to carry through an analysis for maximizing the contributions of F_2 to the residual communality. Instead, it will be shown that the required maximum eigenvalue of $\mathbf{R}_1$ is, in fact, the second largest eigenvalue of the original correlation matrix $\mathbf{R}$.

If $\mathbf{a}_p$ stand for the m eigenvectors of $\mathbf{R}$ (properly scaled), it can be determined whether they are also eigenvectors of $\mathbf{R}_1$. Postmultiplying the matrix $\mathbf{R}_1$ by any vector $\mathbf{a}_p$ yields

$$(8.28) \qquad \mathbf{R}_1 \mathbf{a}_p = (\mathbf{R} - \mathbf{a}_1 \mathbf{a}_1') \mathbf{a}_p$$

from the definition (8.25) of the residual matrix. Expanding this expression, and applying (8.15) produces:

$$(8.29) \qquad \mathbf{R}_1 \mathbf{a}_p = \mathbf{R} \mathbf{a}_p - \mathbf{a}_1 \mathbf{a}_1' \mathbf{a}_p = \lambda_p \mathbf{a}_p - \mathbf{a}_1 \mathbf{a}_1' \mathbf{a}_p.$$

Now consider the two cases: $p = 1$ and $p \neq 1$. (a) When $p = 1$, $\mathbf{a}_1' \mathbf{a}_1 = \lambda_1$ according to (8.9), so that the above expression reduces to

$$(8.30) \qquad \mathbf{R}_1 \mathbf{a}_1 = \mathbf{O}.$$

In other words, the eigenvector corresponding to the largest eigenvalue λ_1 of $\mathbf{R}$ is also an eigenvector of $\mathbf{R}_1$ but its associated eigenvalue in $\mathbf{R}_1$ is zero. (b) When $p \neq 1$,

$\mathbf{a}_1' \mathbf{a}_p = \mathbf{O}$ according to (8.9), and expression (8.29) becomes:

$$(8.31) \qquad\qquad \mathbf{R}_1 \mathbf{a}_p = \lambda_p \mathbf{a}_p - \mathbf{a}_1 \cdot \mathbf{O} = \lambda_p \mathbf{a}_p, \qquad\qquad (p \neq 1),$$

which says that, except for λ_1, the eigevenvalues of $\mathbf{R}_1$ are identical with those of $\mathbf{R}$ and their associated eigenvectors are also identical. The expressions (8.30) and (8.31) prove that the eigenvectors of $\mathbf{R}_1$ are identical with those of $\mathbf{R}$, and that they have corresponding eigenvalues except that corresponding to the eigenvector $\mathbf{a}_1$ in $\mathbf{R}_1$ is a zero eigenvalue in place of the λ_1 in $\mathbf{R}$.

From the foregoing it is clear that the λ_2 of $\mathbf{R}$ is the largest eigenvalue of $\mathbf{R}_1$. In other words, to obtain the coefficients of the second factor F_2 from the largest eigenvalue of the residual matrix $\mathbf{R}_1$ it suffices to extract the second largest eigenvalue of the original matrix $\mathbf{R}$. By the same type of argument, the successive eigenvalues and their associated eigenvectors are obtained directly from the original correlation matrix $\mathbf{R}$, until m factors have been extracted.

When unities are placed in the principal diagonal of $\mathbf{R}$ then usually $m = n$. If some numbers less than unities (estimates of communalities) are placed in the diagonal, and the positive semi-definite property of $\mathbf{R}$ is preserved, then m will usually be less than n, and all eigenvalues will be real and non negative. However, the reduced correlation matrix $\mathbf{R}$ (i.e., with communality estimates in the diagonal) will not be positive semi-definite in practice, and both positive and negative eigenvalues may be expected. Of course, the negative eigenvalues, and the associated imaginary eigenvectors, must be extraneous to a practical problem. Even to retain all the real eigenvectors would be an over-factorization because the sum of the positive eigenvalues is greater than the original sum of communalities (the negative eigenvalues will reduce that sum to the starting value). Since the total communality for the n variables is the trace of the reduced correlation matrix, the factorization process should be stopped when the sum of the eigenvalues is equal to this value. The investigator will usually be satisfied with an even smaller number of factors, as indicated in the examples below.

The theoretical development of this section provides the logical basis for the principal-factor solution, but it does not furnish an actual means of computation. The direct solution of a characteristic equation (8.13) and sets of linear homogeneous equations (8.12) would entail insuperable algebraic efforts. Practical means of obtaining principal-factor solutions are discussed in the following sections.

8.4. *Additional Theory*

A method of determining the principal axes is developed in this section, based upon two fundamental papers of Hotelling [259, 261]. This method involves an iterative scheme which yields a root of the characteristic equation and the coefficients of the associated factor simultaneously. The roots appear in descending order of magnitude upon successive applications of the method. For this reason the method is especially suitable in practical situations where only a few of the largest characteristic roots and the associated factor coefficients are required. Usually a small number of roots will account for the total (estimated) communality.

The iterative process is begun by selecting an arbitrary set of n numbers, and transforming them again and again by use of the observed correlations until they converge to the desired coefficients of the first principal factor. As noted in the last section, an operation $\mathbf{Rq}_1$ represents a transformation of the vector $\mathbf{q}_1 = \{\alpha_{11}, \alpha_{21}, \cdots, \alpha_{n1}\}$ into some new vector. Geometrically, this may be thought of as a rotation of a line through the origin (for which the α_{j1} are proportional to the direction cosines) to a new line for which numbers proportional to the direction cosines are in the column vector $(\mathbf{Rq}_1)$. In general, the new line will be distinct from the original one. However, when a line remains stationary under such a transformation, then the new vector must be proportional to the original vector as indicated in (8.15). This may be expressed by the matrix equation:

$$(8.32) \qquad\qquad (\mathbf{R} - \lambda\mathbf{I})\mathbf{q}_1 = \mathbf{O},$$

or, in expanded algebraic form:

$$(8.33) \qquad r_{j1}\alpha_{11} + r_{j2}\alpha_{21} + \cdots + (h_j^2 - \lambda)\alpha_{j1} + \cdots + r_{jn}\alpha_{n1} = 0,$$

remembering that the communality is used in place of the self correlation. As j takes the values 1 to n, it is readily seen that these equations are identical with (8.12). Thus, for any invariant line, the direction cosines are proportional to a solution of (8.12), where λ is a root of the characteristic equation (8.13). Hence it follows that *the invariant lines are the desired principal axes.* It is thus apparent that, if a set of numbers $\alpha_{11}, \alpha_{21}, \cdots. \alpha_{n1}$ can be found which lead to (8.32), the numbers $\mathbf{Rq}_1$ are proportional to the direction cosines of the principal axes. The coefficients of one of the principal factors can be obtained from the latter set of numbers. Furthermore, λ is the sum of the contributions of this factor to the communalities of the variables.

In practice, of course, it cannot be expected that the arbitrary numbers α_{j1} will be so selected as to be proportional to the direction cosines of one of the principal axes. The iterative process then involves the use of the derived numbers $\mathbf{Rq}_1$ as a new set of arbitrary numbers in place of α_{j1}, and the transformation of the new vector $\mathbf{Rq}_1$ becomes $\mathbf{R}(\mathbf{Rq}_1)$. Formal matrix manipulation of this transformation reduces it to:

$$(8.34) \qquad\qquad \mathbf{R}(\mathbf{Rq}_1) = \mathbf{R}(\lambda\mathbf{q}_1) = \lambda(\mathbf{Rq}_1) = \lambda^2\mathbf{q}_1$$

upon repeated application of (8.32) and factoring out the scalar λ according to **3.2**, paragraph **21**. This transformation effectively does the job of two iterations.

The property exhibited in (8.34) may be generalized to any power, say m, for any vector $\mathbf{q}$, as follows:

$$(8.35) \qquad\qquad \mathbf{R}^m\mathbf{q} = \lambda^m\mathbf{q}.$$

Then the improvement in the iteration process need not end with the employment of $\mathbf{R}^2$. After doubling the speed of convergence by squaring $\mathbf{R}$, it can be doubled again by squaring $\mathbf{R}^2$, i.e., by multiplying a set of trial values by $\mathbf{R}^4$, and thus the equivalent of four multiplications by $\mathbf{R}$ is obtained. Upon squaring again, a matrix $\mathbf{R}^8$ is obtained, and multiplication by it is equivalent to eight multiplications by $\mathbf{R}$, and so forth to any power of the correlation matrix. This squaring process is continued until the convergence is so rapid that additional matrix squaring is not worth while. A scheme for determining the number of times a matrix should be squared is developed in the next section, in connection with the actual computing procedures.

The iterative process is continued until the ratios among the quantities obtained at any stage converge to the corresponding ratios among the coefficients of F_1 to any specified degree of accuracy. The proof of the convergence of these ratios to those of the coefficients a_{j1} of the first principal factor is given by Hotelling [259, Sec. 4]. A convenient procedure is to divide each of the trial values by a fixed one of them, say the largest. Then the next value obtained, corresponding to this number, will be an approximation to the characteristic root λ_1.

The second and remaining principal factors may be determined by the same method, and the convergence can be accelerated by the use of a convenient power of the matrix of residual correlations. It is not necessary, however, to obtain this power of the residual matrix by repeated squarings, as was done in the case of the original matrix of correlations. Instead, the determination already made of the power of $\mathbf{R}$ and the following algebraic properties of matrices can be employed for this purpose.

In getting the square of the residual matrix algebraically from (8.25), namely:

$$(8.36) \qquad \mathbf{R}_1^2 = \mathbf{R}^2 - 2\mathbf{R}\mathbf{R}_1^\dagger + \mathbf{R}_1^{\dagger 2},$$

it is possible to express the last two terms by quantities already known, so that the actual squaring of $\mathbf{R}_1$ is obviated. Thus, from the definition (8.26):

$$\mathbf{R}_1^{\dagger 2} = (\mathbf{a}_1 \mathbf{a}_1')(\mathbf{a}_1 \mathbf{a}_1')$$
$$= \mathbf{a}_1 (\mathbf{a}_1' \mathbf{a}_1) \mathbf{a}_1'$$
$$= \mathbf{a}_1 \lambda_1 \mathbf{a}_1', \qquad \text{from (8.22),}$$
$$= \lambda_1 \mathbf{a}_1 \mathbf{a}_1', \qquad \text{since } \lambda_1 \text{ is a scalar,}$$

and applying definition (8.26) to the last expression produces:

$$(8.37) \qquad \mathbf{R}_1^{\dagger 2} = \lambda_1 \mathbf{R}_1^\dagger.$$

Also, from the expression (8.15) for the particular case of the first principal factor (with coefficients $\mathbf{a}_1$) of the correlation matrix $\mathbf{R}$, the following relationship

$$\mathbf{R}\mathbf{a}_1 = \lambda_1 \mathbf{a}_1$$

provides the basis for expressing $\mathbf{R}\mathbf{R}_1^\dagger$ in terms of known quantities. Postmultiplying by $\mathbf{a}_1'$ and applying definition (8.26) yields:

$$(8.38) \qquad \mathbf{R}\mathbf{R}_1^\dagger = \lambda_1 \mathbf{R}_1^\dagger.$$

Upon substituting the known quantities from (8.37) and (8.38) for the terms in (8.36),

145

the square of the residual matrix becomes:

(8.39)
$$\mathbf{R}_1^2 = \mathbf{R}^2 - \lambda_1 \mathbf{R}_1^\dagger.$$

In other words, actual squaring of the residual matrix is not necessary since the square of the correlation matrix and the matrix of products of first-factor coefficients are available.

In similar fashion, it can be shown that for any positive integer e,

(8.40)
$$\mathbf{R}_1^e = \mathbf{R}^e - \lambda_1^{e-1} \mathbf{R}_1^\dagger.$$

Thus the eth power of the residual matrix is expressed in terms of the eth power of the original correlation matrix, obviating actual multiplications of the residual matrix.

From the foregoing development the order of procedure of the iterative scheme may be summarized. Using $\mathbf{R}^e$ as the basis for selecting the set of trial values, this set rapidly yields the values of the first-factor coefficients* and the characteristic root λ_1. Furthermore, the value λ_1^e will be determined from the multiplication of the set of trial values by $\mathbf{R}^e$, and λ^{e-1} can be obtained by division. Then multiplying λ^{e-1} by each element of $\mathbf{R}_1^\dagger$ and subtracting from the corresponding element of $\mathbf{R}^e$, the eth power of the residual matrix is obtained. The second-factor coefficients are obtained from $\mathbf{R}_1$ and $\mathbf{R}_1^e$ in the same manner as the first-factor coefficients are determined from $\mathbf{R}$ and $\mathbf{R}^e$. It may not be necessary to employ the eth power of $\mathbf{R}_1$ in calculating the second-factor coefficients when rapid convergence is evident. Then some lower power of $\mathbf{R}_1$, or $\mathbf{R}_1$ itself, is employed. This is illustrated in the next section. To calculate the third-factor coefficients, the matrices $\mathbf{R}_2$ of second-factor residuals and $\mathbf{R}_2^e$ (or some lower power of $\mathbf{R}_2$) are employed. The latter matrix is obtained conveniently by an expression of the form (8.40) relating the second- to the first-factor residuals. Further factors are determined similarly until approximately all the communality is analyzed.

8.5.   *Computing Procedures With Desk Calculator*

A principal-factor pattern can be obtained for any matrix of correlations. Since the work entailed is very laborious for problems with many variables, procedures employed with high-speed electronic computers are indicated in **8.6**. For a limited number of variables, the method of **8.4** using desk calculators is feasible. The numerical calculations are exhibited in the following outline form, employing the example of eight physical variables of Section **5.4** for illustrative purposes.

1. Organization of data.—Because of the symmetry of the correlation matrix, it usually suffices to write only half the table. For the principal-factor method, however, where squaring of the correlation matrix is involved, it will be found more convenient to write the symmetric matrix in full. Thus, for the example, the correla-

---

* Burt [54] points out that to factor a matrix $\mathbf{R}^e$ is equivalent to obtaining a Spearman general factor. This arises from the fact that, with a sufficient number of self-multiplications, any symmetric matrix can be reduced as closely as desired to a matrix of rank one.

tions from Table 5.3 are repeated in the upper and lower parts of the reduced correlation matrix **R** in Table 8.2.

The first requirement in applying the principal-factor method (in accord with the basic factor model) is to determine some suitable estimates of communality. The communalities in Table 8.2 come from the original study of Mullen [375] involving 17 physical variables of which the present example is a subset. These values differ only slightly from those computed in Table 5.4 by assuming an approximate rank of two for the correlation matrix.

Table 8.2

Reduced Correlation Matrix: **R**

	1	2	3	4	5	6	7	8	S_j	$\alpha_{j1}^{(1)}$
1	.854	.846	.805	.859	.473	.398	.301	.382	4.918	1.000
2	.846	.897	.881	.826	.376	.326	.277	.415	4.844	.985
3	.805	.881	.833	.801	.380	.319	.237	.345	4.601	.936
4	.859	.826	·801	.783	.436	.329	.327	.365	4.726	.961
5	.473	.376	· .380	.436	.870	.762	.730	.629	4.656	.947
6	.398	.326	.319	.329	.762	.687	.583	.577	3.981	.809
7	.301	.277	.237	.327	.730	.583	.521	.539	3.515	.715
8	.382	.415	.345	.365	.629	.577	.539	.579	3.831	.779

2. Trial values for first-factor coefficients.—Obtain the sums S_j of the rows of **R**, and divide these by the largest sum to get the first set of trial values $\alpha_{j1}^{(1)}$. It should be noted that these numbers are not used immediately as trial values. Actually, the correlation matrix is first squared an appropriate number of times in order to hasten the convergence of the trial values to numbers directly proportional to the desired factor coefficients.

Square the matrix of correlations to get the result in Table 8.3. Of course, only the diagonal elements and the entries above (or below) the diagonal need be calculated because the square of a symmetric matrix is also symmetric. The complete matrix is written, however, for convenience of further squaring.

Table 8.3

Square of Correlation Matrix: $\mathbf{R}^2$

	1	2	3	4	5	6	7	8	$S_j^{(2)}$	$T_j^{(2)}$	$\alpha_{j1}^{(2)}$
1	3.450	3.450	3.301	3.325	2.577	2.185	1.903	2.179	22.370	22.370	1.0000
2	3.450	3.475	3.322	3.333	2.471	2.093	1.815	2.115	22.074	22.075	.9868
3	3.301	3.322	3.181	3.188	2.341	1.983	1.718	2.003	21.037	21.039	.9405
4	3.325	3.333	3.188	3.213	2.461	2.084	1.810	2.085	21.499	21.499	.9611
5	2.577	2.471	2.341	2.461	2.966	2.550	2.278	2.372	20.016	20.016	.8948
6	2.185	2.093	1.983	2.084	2.550	2.200	1.965	2.041	17.101	17.102	.7645
7	1.903	1.815	1.718	1.810	2.278	1.965	1.765	1.820	15.074	15.074	.6739
8	2.179	2.115	2.003	2.085	2.372	2.041	1.820	1.925	16.540	16.540	.7394

147

A check is available on the squaring process. Compute the product of **R** by the column of values S_j of Table 8.2. These values,

$$T_j^{(2)} = \sum_{k=1}^{8} r_{kj} S_k, \qquad (j = 1, 2, \cdots, 8),$$

should agree, except for errors of rounding, with the respective sums $S_j^{(2)}$ of the rows of $\mathbf{R}^2$.

Take as the next set of trial values the numbers $\alpha_{j1}^{(2)}$, which are the quotients of $T_j^{(2)}$ by the largest check sum $T_j^{(2)}$. Compare the trial values $\alpha_{j1}^{(2)}$ with the corresponding $\alpha_{j1}^{(1)}$ of the first set. When there is no appreciable variation between two successive sets of trial values, then the squaring process has been carried far enough. In the present case the values $\alpha_{j1}^{(2)}$ differ sufficiently from the corresponding $\alpha_{j1}^{(1)}$ so that further squaring is recommended. A reasonable standard is to obtain agreement between successive trial values to within five units in the last decimal place desired in the final results. Here it is planned to retain three decimal places for the factor coefficients, the same as in the original correlations. Hence the absolute values of discrepancies between trial values should be less than .005.

Square the matrix of correlations a sufficient number of times to make the successive sets of trial values approximately equal. In calculating the various powers of **R**, always determine the check column T_j first. Thus for the eth power of **R**, the column of values $T_j^{(e)}$ can be calculated from $\mathbf{R}^{e/2}$ and $S_j^{(e/2)}$ before the elements of $\mathbf{R}^e$ are obtained. Then the values of $\alpha_{j1}^{(e)}$ may be computed and if they agree with the values $\alpha_{j1}^{(e/2)}$, the calculation of the elements of $\mathbf{R}^e$ is obviated.

In the illustrative example, the values $T_j^{(4)}$ are obtained from $\mathbf{R}^2$ and $S_j^{(2)}$, and the $\alpha_{j1}^{(4)}$ are calculated. These values are not close enough to the corresponding $\alpha_{j1}^{(2)}$ and so the elements of $\mathbf{R}^4$ are computed in Table 8.4. Next, the values of $T_j^{(8)}$ are determined in Table 8.5. Since the maximum difference between $\alpha_{j1}^{(8)}$ and $\alpha_{j1}^{(4)}$ is only three thousandths, it is therefore not necessary to calculate the entries of $\mathbf{R}^8$.

Table 8.4

Fourth Power of Correlation Matrix: $\mathbf{R}^4$

	1	2	3	4	5	6	7	8	$S_j^{(4)}$	$T_j^{(4)}$	$\alpha_{j1}^{(4)}$
1	65.54	64.94	61.95	63.06	56.04	47.80	42.00	46.59	447.92	447.93	1.0000
2	64.94	64.38	61.41	62.49	55.27	47.13	41.41	45.98	443.01	443.02	.9890
3	61.95	61.41	58.59	59.61	52.67	44.91	39.45	43.82	422.41	422.43	.9431
4	63.06	62.49	59.61	60.67	53.86	45.93	40.36	44.78	430.76	430.76	.9617
5	56.04	55.27	52.67	53.86	50.40	43.06	37.97	41.61	390.88	390.90	.8727
6	47.80	47.13	44.91	45.93	43.06	36.80	32.45	35.55	333.63	333.64	.7448
7	42.00	41.41	39.45	40.36	37.97	32.45	28.62	31.33	293.59	293.60	.6555
8	46.59	45.98	43.82	44.78	41.61	35.55	31.33	34.39	324.05	324.05	.7234

3. First-factor coefficients.—The last set of trial values is used as the trial vector q_1 in (8.32) to make certain that the squaring process has indeed produced an invariant line, i.e., the derived numbers are immediately proportional to the α_{j1} according to (8.32). In Table 8.6 the first column of arbitrary numbers α_{j1} are the values $\alpha_{j1}^{(8)}$,

Table 8.5

Eighth Power of Correlation Matrix: $\mathbf{R}^8$

	1	2	3	4	5	6	7	8	$S_j^{(8)}$	$T_j^{(8)}$	$\alpha_{j1}^{(8)}$
1	—	—	—	—	—	—	—	—	—	176738	1.0000
2	—	—	—	—	—	—	—	—	—	174853	.9893
3	—	—	—	—	—	—	—	—	—	166733	.9434
4	—	—	—	—	—	—	—	—	—	169980	.9618
5	—	—	—	—	—	—	—	—	—	153733	.8698
6	—	—	—	—	—	—	—	—	—	131201	.7423
7	—	—	—	—	—	—	—	—	—	115430	.6531
8	—	—	—	—	—	—	—	—	—	127505	.7214

Table 8.6

Calculation of the F_1 Coefficients

Variable j	α_{j1}	$\mathbf{Rq}_1$	α_{j1}	$a_{j1} = \dfrac{\alpha_{j1}\sqrt{\lambda_1}}{\sqrt{\sum \alpha_{j1}^2}}$
1	1.0000	4.4556	1.0000	.858
2	.9893	4.4083	.9894	.849
3	.9434	4.2038	.9435	.810
4	.9618	4.2852	.9618	.825
5	.8698	3.8757	.8698	.747
6	.7423	3.3076	.7423	.637
7	.6531	2.9099	.6531	.561
8	.7214	3.2142	.7214	.619

$$\lambda_1 = 4.4556, \quad \sum_{j=1}^{8} \alpha_{j1}^2 = 6.0487$$

$$\sqrt{\lambda_1}/\sqrt{\sum \alpha_{j1}^2} = .85827$$

determined by the squaring process. These numbers are then multiplied by $\mathbf{R}$. After all the $\mathbf{Rq}_1$ values have been obtained, they are divided by the largest of them to get the new quantities α_{j1} (the same notation being used for simplicity). Since the maximum discrepancy between the old and the new values α_{j1} is only .0001, these numbers are accepted as stationary. The value of $\mathbf{Rq}_1$ corresponding to $\alpha_{11} = 1.0000$ is the first characteristic root λ_1. Then the coefficients of the first factor can be calculated by means of (8.14), as indicated in the last column of Table 8.6.

A check on the final determination of the a_{j1} is provided by

$$\sum_{j=1}^{n} a_{j1}^2 = \lambda_1.$$

In other words, the sum of the contributions of the first factor to the total

149

communality must be equal to the first characteristic root. The value of λ_1 from the analysis is 4.4556 and the sum of the squares of the coefficients is 4.455, so that the check is satisfied (within rounding errors).

4. First-factor residuals.—To assist in calculating the residuals with the first factor removed, a table of products of the first-factor coefficients may be prepared. Such a product matrix $\mathbf{R}_1^{\dagger}$ for the given data is presented in Table 8.7, where the symmetric elements above the diagonal have been omitted for simplicity.

Table 8.7

Product Matrix: $\mathbf{R}_1^{\dagger} = (a_{j1}a_{k1})$

	1	2	3	4	5	6	7	8	E_{j1}	$a_{j1}D_1$
1	.736	—	—	—	—	—	—	—	5.067	5.067
2	.728	.721	—	—	—	—	—	—	5.014	5.014
3	.695	.688	.656	—	—	—	—	—	4.783	4.784
4	.708	.700	.668	.681	—	—	—	—	4.873	4.872
5	.641	.634	.605	.616	.558	—	—	—	4.411	4.412
6	.547	.541	.516	.526	.476	.406	—	—	3.763	3.762
7	.481	.476	.454	.463	.419	.357	.315	—	3.312	3.313
8	.531	.526	.501	.511	.462	.394	.347	.383	3.655	3.656

To check the calculation of the elements of the product matrix $\mathbf{R}_1^{\dagger}$, obtain the sums of the rows (for the matrix with all elements included) and compare with the corresponding values of $a_{j1}D_1$ where

$$D_1 = \sum_{k=1}^{n} a_{k1}.$$

The sum of the first-factor coefficients for the given data is $D_1 = 5.906$. The sums E_{j1} and check sums $a_{j1}D_1$ are also recorded in Table 8.7.

Subtract the values in $\mathbf{R}_1^{\dagger}$ from the corresponding entries in $\mathbf{R}$ to get the matrix of first-factor residuals $\mathbf{R}_1$. This matrix is presented in Table 8.8, and is written in full to simplify later multiplications with it. The sums of the rows are given in a column alongside the matrix $\mathbf{R}_1$, and they should be equal to the differences between the

Table 8.8

Matrix of First-Factor Residuals: $\mathbf{R}_1$

	1	2	3	4	5	6	7	8	S_{j1}	$a_{j2}^{(1)}$
1	.118	.118	.110	.151	−.168	−.149	−.180	−.149	−.149	−.6082
2	.118	.176	.193	.126	−.258	−.215	−.199	−.111	−.170	−.6939
3	.110	.193	.177	.133	−.225	−.197	−.217	−.156	−.182	−.7429
4	.151	.126	.133	.102	−.180	−.197	−.136	−.146	−.147	−.6000
5	−.168	−.258	−.225	−.180	.312	.286	.311	.167	.245	1.0000
6	−.149	−.215	−.197	−.197	.286	.281	.226	.183	.218	.8898
7	−.180	−.199	−.217	−.136	.311	.226	.206	.192	.203	.8286
8	−.149	−.111	−.156	−.146	.167	.183	.192	.196	.176	.7184

corresponding sums in $\mathbf{R}$ and $\mathbf{R}_1^{\dagger}$, that is,

$$S_{j1} = S_j - E_{j1}.$$

5. Trial values for second-factor coefficients.—To obtain the best set of trial values for calculating the second factor coefficients, an appropriate power of $\mathbf{R}_1$ is employed. It is not necessary, however, to perform repeated squarings on $\mathbf{R}_1$, since formula (8.41) gives any power of the residual matrix in terms of that power of the original correlation matrix and the product matrix. Furthermore, since the actual entries of $\mathbf{R}_1^2$, or any higher power of $\mathbf{R}_1$, are not required for the determination of trial values if the sums of the rows are known, additional labor can be saved. The values $S_j^{(2)}$ and E_{j1} may be considered as elements of the matrices $\mathbf{R}^2$ and $\mathbf{R}_1^{\dagger}$, respectively. Then, according to (8.41),

$$S_{j1}^{(2)} = S_j^{(2)} - \lambda_1 E_{j1},$$

so that $S_{j1}^{(2)}$, the sum of the elements in row j of the matrix $\mathbf{R}_1^2$, can be obtained without calculating the individual entries in $\mathbf{R}_1^2$.

Construct Table 8.9, in which each block contains the derivation of the trial values from the power of $\mathbf{R}_1$ represented by the superscript on α_{j2}. In the first block the

Table 8.9

Determination of Trial Values for Calculating the F_2 Coefficients

Variable j	S_j	E_{j1}	S_{j1}	$\alpha_{j2}^{(1)}$	$S_j^{(2)}$	$\lambda_1 E_{j1}$	$S_{j1}^{(2)}$	$\alpha_{j2}^{(2)}$
1	4.918	5.067	−.149	−.608	22.37	22.58	−.21	−.57
2	4.844	5.014	−.170	−.694	22.07	22.34	−.27	−.73
3	4.601	4.783	−.182	−.743	21.04	21.31	−.27	−.73
4	4.726	4.873	−.147	−.600	21.50	21.71	−.21	−.57
5	4.656	4.411	.245	1.000	20.02	19.65	.37	1.00
6	3.981	3.763	.218	.890	17.10	16.77	.33	.89
7	3.515	3.312	.203	.829	15.07	14.76	.31	.84
8	3.831	3.655	.176	.718	16.54	16.29	.25	.68

values of S_j and E_{j1} are copied from Tables 8.2 and 8.7, and the sums S_{j1} are obtained by subtraction. Then the trial values $\alpha_{j2}^{(1)}$ are calculated by dividing the sums S_{j1} by the largest one (in absolute value), that is, by $S_{51} = 2.45$. Record the values of $S_j^{(2)}$ from Table 8.3 in the second block of Table 8.9, retaining only two decimal places since all the work is based upon three significant figures, and one additional figure is sufficient to assure the accuracy of the three figures. Compute the products $\lambda_1 E_{j1}$, with the value $\lambda_1 = 4.4556$ taken from Table 8.6. The sums $S_{j1}^{(2)}$ are obtained simply by subtraction, and the corresponding $\alpha_{j2}^{(2)}$ are then determined. These values are truly significant to only one decimal place, and in the one significant figure they agree with $\alpha_{j2}^{(1)}$. If the calculations in another block were attempted, the corresponding values

151

of $S_j^{(4)}$ and $\lambda_1^3 E_{j1}$ would be equal to three significant figures. For example, $S_1^{(4)} = 448$ and $\lambda_1^3 E_{11} = 448$. Hence the sums $S_{j1}^{(4)}$ (that is, $S_j^{(4)} - \lambda_1^3 E_{j1}$) are insignificant and $\alpha_{j2}^{(4)}$ cannot be obtained. It therefore follows that the best set of trial values for calculating a_{j2} is $\alpha_{j2}^{(2)}$.

The numbers $\alpha_{j2}^{(2)}$ are used as the first set of trial values α_{j2} by which to multiply the matrix $\mathbf{R}_1$ to obtain the first column of $\mathbf{R}_1 \mathbf{q}_2$ in Table 8.10. Then division of

Table 8.10

Calculation of the F_2 Coefficients

Variable j	α_{j2}	$\mathbf{R}_1\mathbf{q}_2$	α_{j2}	$\mathbf{R}_1\mathbf{q}_2$	α_{j2}	$\mathbf{R}_1\mathbf{q}_2$	α_{j2}	$a_{j2} = \dfrac{\alpha_{j2}\sqrt{\lambda_2}}{\sqrt{\sum \alpha_{j2}^2}}$
1	$-.57$	$-.865$	$-.580$	$-.8856$	$-.5851$	$-.8852$	$-.5851$	$-.328$
2	$-.73$	-1.100	$-.737$	-1.1152	$-.7368$	-1.1148	$-.7369$	$-.414$
3	$-.73$	-1.097	$-.735$	-1.1118	$-.7345$	-1.1112	$-.7345$	$-.412$
4	$-.57$	$-.902$	$-.605$	$-.9129$	$-.6031$	$-.9129$	$-.6034$	$-.339$
5	1.00	1.492	1.000	1.5136	1.0000	1.5129	1.0000	$.561$
6	$.89$	1.348	$.903$	1.3666	$.9029$	1.3660	$.9029$	$.507$
7	$.84$	1.300	$.871$	1.3144	$.8684$	1.3142	$.8687$	$.488$
8	$.68$	$.987$	$.662$	1.0005	$.6610$	1.0001	$.6610$	$.371$

$$\lambda_2 = 1.5129, \qquad \sum_{j=1}^{8} \alpha_{j2}^2 = 4.8027$$

$$\sqrt{\lambda_2} / \sqrt{\sum \alpha_{j2}^2} = .56126$$

these values by the largest one (1.492) yields the next set of trial values, which are also designated by α_{j2} for simplicity. Multiplication of $\mathbf{R}_1$ by these new values and division of the derived values by the largest one of them produces the next set of trial values. This process is continued until corresponding trial values in successive sets agree to three significant figures. Keep four figures if three significant figures are desired for the factor coefficients. Three iterations were sufficient, in the present example, for stability in the trial values α_{j2}.

6. Second-factor coefficients.—When trial values α_{j2} have been found that are stabilized, i.e., satisfy an equation like (8.32) but for the second factor, then the coefficients for such a factor can be computed. The value 1.5129 corresponding to $\alpha_{52} = 1.0000$ is the characteristic root λ_2, and the coefficients of the second factor are given by a formula like (8.14), as indicated in the last column of Table 8.10.

The calculation of the coefficients a_{j2} can be checked by means of the formula

$$\sum_{j=1}^{n} a_{j2}^2 = \lambda_2.$$

In the example, the sum of the squares of the eight coefficients is 1.511 and $\lambda_2 = 1.5129$, agreeing within errors of rounding.

7. Adequacy of solution.—To obtain additional factors, residuals would be calculated with all preceding factors removed and then trial values for the new factor coefficients would be determined, following the outline of paragraphs **4, 5,** and **6**.

For the given data no further factors are required. The second-factor residuals—obtained by subtracting the products $a_{j2}a_{k2}$ from the corresponding first-factor residuals $_1r_{jk}$ of Table 8.8—are recorded in Table 8.11. These residuals are obviously insignificant and so may be considered as final.

Table 8.11

Matrix of Second-Factor Residuals: $\mathbf{R}_2$

	1	2	3	4	5	6	7	8
1	.010	—	—	—	—	—	—	—
2	−.018	.005	—	—	—	—	—	—
3	−.025	.022	.007	—	—	—	—	—
4	.040	−.014	−.007	−.013	—	—	—	—
5	.016	−.026	.006	.010	−.003	—	—	—
6	.017	−.005	.012	−.025	.002	.024	—	—
7	−.020	.003	−.016	.029	.037	−.021	−.032	—
8	−.027	.043	−.003	−.020	−.041	−.005	.011	.058

Inasmuch as the problem of factor analysis is to account for the total communality variance, a more definite check on the adequacy of a solution is afforded by the extent to which the sum of the contributions of the factors agrees with the original total communality. In the present example, two common factors account for practically 100 per cent of the communality. The percentage contributions of the individual factors are presented in Table 8.12, where the complete principal-factor pattern is exhibited.

8. Interpretation of principal factors.—The coefficients of the first factor in Table 8.12 are all large and positive, indicating an important general factor of physical growth (*G*) among these variables. On the other hand, the second factor has loadings of opposite signs for the two subgroups of variables. From the nature of the variables, this bipolar factor might be called "Stockiness." If desired, of course, the signs of all the coefficients of this factor may be changed. Then this factor might be labeled "Lankiness."

Whatever name is selected for a bipolar factor, its opposite characteristic should be clearly recognizable. A more fundamental approach is to find a basic term which connotes the entire continuum. For example, a bipolar factor which is named "Heat" (or, "Cold") would have the opposite characteristic "Cold" (or, "Heat"). A name representing both of these characteristics is "Temperature." These two approaches may be indicated schematically as in Figure 8.1.

Inasmuch as "Stockiness" and "Lankiness" are not clearly distinguishable as opposites (according to *a* of Fig. 8.1), neither of these seems to be an appropriate

153

Table 8.12

Principal-Factor Pattern for Eight Physical Variables

Variable j	Pattern Coefficients[a]			Communality		
	G	BT	U_j	(1) Original	(2) Calculated	(1)−(2)
1. Height	.858	−.328	.395	.854	.844	.010
2. Arm span	.849	−.414	.328	.897	.892	.005
3. Length of forearm	.810	−.412	.417	.833	.826	.007
4. Length of lower leg	.825	−.339	.452	.783	.796	−.013
5. Weight	.747	.561	.357	.870	.873	−.003
6. Bitrochanteric diameter	.637	.507	.581	.687	.663	.024
7. Chest girth	.561	.488	.669	.521	.553	−.032
8. Chest width	.619	.371	.692	.579	.521	.058
Total	—	—	—	6.024	5.968	.054
Contribution of factor (V_p)	4.455	1.511	—	—	—	—
Per cent of total original communality	74.0	25.1	—	—	99.1	.9

[a] Since the reliability of any one of these physical variables is close to unity, the unique factor in each case may be considered as essentially the specific factor. The index of completeness of factorization (2.21) is then approximately 100 times the calculated communality of each variable.

name for the bipolar factor. In an attempt to get a name, of the type b, which transcends the specific descriptions of the variables, the term "Body Type" (BT) has been adopted. On this continuum, variables describing different body types have projections of opposite sign.

The diagram for these eight variables in the plane of the two principal factors is presented in Figure 8.2, the coordinates coming from Table 8.12. The two subgroups of variables lie in the first and fourth quadrants. Hence the projections of all the points form a single cluster on the positive end of the G axis. The projections on the BT

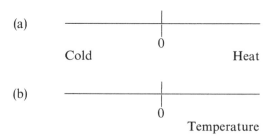

FIG. 8.1.—Example of alternative ways of naming a bipolar factor

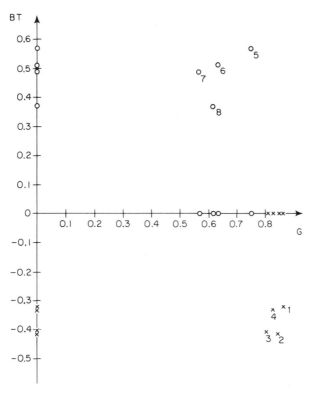

Fig. 8.2.—Eight physical variables plotted with respect to two principal-factor axes

axis, on the other hand, fall into two clusters which are widely separated. The projections on the respective axes give the geometric basis for the interpretation of the general and bipolar factors.

8.6. *Outline of Electronic Computer Program*

Factor analysis has been troubled with the practical difficulty of requiring an excessive amount of computational work. This is indicated, more or less, throughout the text but is especially evident in this chapter. On the other hand, the foregoing development of the principal-factor method points to a certain elegance and precision of mathematical form lacking in earlier methods. For this reason, alone, it is a highly desirable form of factorization of a correlation matrix, in spite of the fact that bipolar type factors may not be acceptable to psychologists. The procedure usually recommended by psychologists is to initiate the analysis of a correlation matrix by means of some arbitrary solution and then rotate it to some (psychologically) more meaningful solution (see part iii). Thurstone, the leader and chief proponent of this philosophy, has stated [477, p. 509]: "When the principal-axes solution becomes available with less computational labor, it will, no doubt, be preferred by all students of this subject, and they will start the rotational problem with the principal-factor matrix."

155

While the computation of principal-factor solution for an 8-variable problem is feasible by the method outlined in **8.5** (generally requiring less than ten hours of hand calculations), the situation is entirely different for a problem of the order of magnitude of the 24-variable example of **7.6**. The computational labor is simply prohibitive for the complete principal-factor analysis by hand methods. The time required for the calculation of the first-factor weights, alone, for the twenty-four variables is more than seventy hours [243, p. 175]. The determination of each additional factor is estimated to require upwards of forty hours. In 1941, Holzinger and Harman [243] recommended that the application of the direct principal-factor method to large sets of variables await the development of appropriate computing machinery.

The time has arrived in which the principal-factor method is feasible, even for very large matrices of correlations. What makes it possible is the rapid development and availability of high-speed digital electronic computers. While there are financial constraints to the procurement of such computing facilities, most universities and government and industrial research centers have such equipment and make it available, frequently without cost, to individuals engaged in research. The principal-factor method can now be considered in its own right as a preferred type of solution, or as an excellent reduction of the correlation matrix which provides a basis for rotation to some other form of solution.

While the computing procedure developed in **8.4** is appropriate for desk calculators, it is not the most expeditious method for programming a high-speed digital computer. There, it will be recalled, one eigenvalue and its associated eigenvector was calculated, and then the others were determined successively. With a computer it is more convenient to obtain all the eigenvalues and their associated eigenvectors simultaneously.

The factor analysis theory of **8.3** leads to a classical problem in mathematics— the determination of the eigenvalues and associated eigenvectors of the reduced correlation matrix **R**. The computation procedures on numerical methods for the solution of systems of linear equations, with the associated problems of matrix inversion and characteristic equations are then available to factor analysis. In the publication *Mathematical Methods for Digital Computers* [200] there is not only a chapter on factor analysis proper, but Part II on matrices and linear equations has a direct bearing on factor analysis. Modern day computing adaptations of the original work done by Jacobi [278] more than a century ago has been found very effective in programming the principal-factor solution on all present-day electronic computers. The earliest programs written were for the ORDVAC [539], the Johnniac [161], and the IBM 704 [418]. These programs have since been adapted to the latest computers throughout the world. Improvements in speed and accuracy of the convergence process have been the subject of many papers (see, for example, [427], [428], [516], [521]), and no doubt will continue for a long time to come. It is the intent of this section to provide the general spirit of the basic computing routine.

The essence of the modified Jacobi method involves the diagonalization of the matrix **R** by performing a sequence of orthogonal transformations on it, designed to reduce *one* off-diagonal element to zero at each stage. Each orthogonal transformation is of the form $\mathbf{B}_{jk}\mathbf{RB}'_{jk}$ where

$$(8.41) \qquad \mathbf{B}_{jk} = \begin{bmatrix} 1 & & & & & & & & \\ & \cdot & & & & & & & \\ & & \cdot & & & & & & \\ & & & \cdot & & & & & \\ & & & & 1 & & & & \\ & & & & \cos\theta_{jk} & & -\sin\theta_{jk} & & \\ & & & & & 1 & & & \\ & & & & & & \cdot & & \\ & & & & & & & 1 & \\ & & & & \sin\theta_{jk} & & \cos\theta_{jk} & & \\ & & & & & & & 1 & \\ & & & & & & & & \cdot \\ & & & & & & & & & \cdot \\ & & & & & & & & & & 1 \end{bmatrix},$$

with the four elements in the intersections of rows and columns j and k as indicated, all other diagonal elements unity, and all other elements zero. The angle of rotation θ_{jk} is chosen so as to transform the element r_{jk} into zero, and is defined by

$$(8.42) \qquad\qquad \tan 2\theta_{jk} = \frac{2r_{jk}}{h_j^2 - h_k^2}.$$

When an element is reduced to zero it does not, in general, remain at zero during subsequent transformations. However, the sum of squares of off-diagonal elements is decreased each time by an amount corresponding to $2r_{jk}^2$, and thus Jacobi's method guarantees the convergence of the off-diagonal elements of $\mathbf{R}$ to zeros (to a designated number of decimal places) with a sufficient number of iterations.

In the process of reducing the original matrix $\mathbf{R}$ to a diagonal matrix $\mathbf{D}$, the off-diagonal elements are considered systematically. Since the original correlations r_{jk} are altered by the transformations (8.41), it would seem more appropriate to designate a general off-diagonal element by d_{jk} and the intermediate derived matrices by $\mathbf{D}$'s with suitable subscripts indicated below. Thus, at any stage of a specific transformation directed at reducing one off-diagonal element d_{jk} to zero, the following notation will be employed:

$$(8.43) \qquad\qquad {}_v\mathbf{D} = \mathbf{B}_{jk(v-1)}\mathbf{D}\mathbf{B}'_{jk}$$

where the sequencing of the transformations is derived from:

$$(8.44) \qquad\qquad v = n(j-1) - \frac{j(j+1)}{2} + k$$

in which $j = 1, 2, \cdots, n - 1$ and $k = j + 1, j + 2, \cdots, n$, producing the $n(n - 1)/2$ possible pairs (j, k).

At any stage the product of the v individual transformations may be designated

$$(8.45) \qquad _v\mathbf{B} = \mathbf{B}_{jk} \cdots \mathbf{B}_{13}\mathbf{B}_{12},$$

where v is given by (8.44), and when *all* combinations of j and k have been tried, the product of these transformations in the ith iteration is designated:

$$(8.46) \qquad \mathbf{B}_i = \text{II}(\mathbf{B}_{jk}; \quad j < k = 1, 2, \cdots, n), \qquad (i = 1, 2, \cdots, \mu).$$

The diagonalizing effect of the ith iteration is given by:

$$(8.47) \qquad \mathbf{D}_i = \mathbf{B}_i\mathbf{D}_{i-1}\mathbf{B}'_i \qquad (i = 1, 2, \cdots, \mu).$$

If the product (in the indicated order) of the transformation matrices through the ith iteration is defined by:

$$(8.48) \qquad \mathbf{P}_i = \mathbf{B}_i\mathbf{B}_{i-1} \cdots \mathbf{B}_2\mathbf{B}_1,$$

then formula (8.47) can be expressed in terms of the original matrix $\mathbf{R}$ as follows:

$$(8.49) \qquad \mathbf{D}_i = \mathbf{P}_i\mathbf{R}\mathbf{P}'_i.$$

After a specified number of iterations μ, the solution to the problem will be in the form:

$$(8.50) \qquad \mathbf{D}_\mu = \mathbf{B}_\mu\mathbf{D}_{\mu-1}\mathbf{B}' = \mathbf{BRB}' = \mathbf{D} = (\delta_{pq}\lambda_p)$$

where

$$(8.51) \qquad \mathbf{B} = \mathbf{P}_\mu = \mathbf{B}_\mu\mathbf{B}_{\mu-1} \cdots \mathbf{B}_2\mathbf{B}_1.$$

The diagonal elements λ_p of $\mathbf{D}$ are the eigenvalues of $\mathbf{R}$, and the rows of the final transformation matrix $\mathbf{B}$ contain the corresponding eigenvectors

$$\boldsymbol{\alpha}'_p = (\alpha_{1p}, \alpha_{2p}, \cdots, \alpha_{np})$$

of $\mathbf{R}$. The row vector is shown as the transpose of the column vector previously defined in **8.3**. Since each individual transformation matrix is orthogonal (and hence the product of such matrices is orthogonal), the resulting final matrix $\mathbf{B}$ is orthogonal and therefore the eigenvectors are normalized. Then the coefficients of each factor F_p are obtained simply by multiplying the square root of the eigenvalue by its associated eigenvector, namely:

$$(8.52) \qquad \mathbf{a}_p = \boldsymbol{\alpha}_p\sqrt{\lambda_p}.$$

This formula corresponds to (8.14) in which the first arbitrary eigenvector had to be normalized as well as converted to factor weights.

In general, when the rank m of $\mathbf{R}$ is equal to its order n, there will be n real non negative eigenvalues, and coefficients for n common factors will ensue. If, however, the reduced correlation matrix $\mathbf{R}$ is positive semi-definite and of rank $m < n$ then there will be $n - m$ zero eigenvalues and there will be only m common factors with non zero coefficients. Of course, if the Gramian properties are not satisfied by the reduced correlation matrix, then some of the eigenvalues will be negative and the coefficients of the corresponding factors will be imaginary.

An outline of the foregoing procedures for programming a large-scale digital electronic computer is presented in the flowchart of Figure 8.3. The detailed description of each step in this flowchart is as follows:

1. The $n(n + 1)/2$ distinct elements of the reduced correlation matrix $\mathbf{R}$ are stored by rows, each row starting with its diagonal element. Also stored are the trace $T(\mathbf{R})$, the order of the matrix, n, and the maximum number of iterations, μ (it may be desired to stop the machine after a predetermined number of iterations regardless of the degree of convergence). The matrix $\mathbf{R}$ also is put in the working location $_v\mathbf{D}$ as the initial $_0\mathbf{D}$.

2. The identity matrix is put in the $_v\mathbf{B}$ locations as the initial $_0\mathbf{B}$. The counter j is set to 1 and k to 2.

3. The d_{jk} element of $_v\mathbf{D}$ (initially, r_{jk} of $\mathbf{R}$) is tested to see if it is zero to the specified (ϵ_1) degree of accuracy. If d_{jk} is zero to the degree ϵ_1 proceed to step 7, otherwise to step 4.

4. Compute $\mathbf{B}_{jk}$ as indicated in formula (8.41), using formula (8.42) and well-known trigonometric identities to get the values of the sine and cosine of the transformation angle (employing only algebraic functions of the argument).

5. Compute $_v\mathbf{D}$ according to formula (8.43), remembering that $_0\mathbf{D} = \mathbf{R}$.

6. Compute $_v\mathbf{B}$ according to formula (8.45), which is equivalent to $_v\mathbf{B} = \mathbf{B}_{jk(v-1)}\mathbf{B}$, and again, $_0\mathbf{B} = \mathbf{I}$.

7. If k has reached n then all columns have been considered for the particular choice of the row j and the test of step 9 is made. Otherwise proceed to step 8.

8. The index k is increased to continue with the next individual transformation in the particular iteration.

9. If j has not reached $n - 1$ proceed to step 10. When j has reached $n - 1$ then the ith iteration has been completed, i.e., the $\mathbf{B}_i$ of formula (8.46) is the last computed $_v\mathbf{B}$ when all combinations of j and k have been considered in this iteration, and the result of the iteration is $\mathbf{D}_i$. The test of step 11 is then made.

10. The index j is increased to $j + 1$ (with the associated k as $j + 2$) to continue with the next series of individual transformations, involving the elements of the new row, in the particular iteration i.

11. As a check on the preceding calculations, the trace of the resulting matrix $\mathbf{D}_i$ is determined to see that it does not vary from the original value, according to the property:

$$\sum_{j=1}^{n} h_j^2 = T(\mathbf{R}) = T(\mathbf{D}_i) = \sum_{j=1}^{n} \lambda_j.$$

If the test is satisfied go to step 13. Otherwise proceed to step 12.

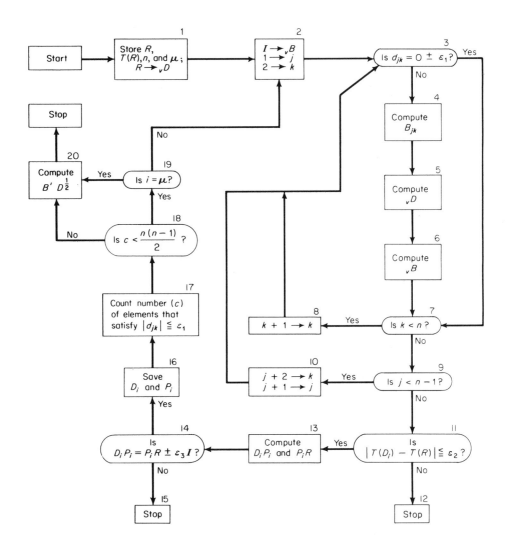

FIG. 8.3.—Flowchart for programming the principal-factor solution

160

12. This is a conditional stop. The magnitude of the allowable error ϵ_2 is to be determined by the user of the program. Instructions to the computer operator should include what to do in the event the stop occurs. The instructions may call for certain memory locations to be printed out; or if the user desires, it may even include a continuation of the process after a record is made of the stop.

13. Compute $\mathbf{D}_i\mathbf{P}_i$ and $\mathbf{P}_i\mathbf{R}$, employing the $\mathbf{P}_i$ of formula (8.48) for the product of all the transformation matrices through the ith iteration.

14. Another check is provided by postmultiplying both sides of formula (8.49) by $\mathbf{P}_1$, noting that $\mathbf{P}_i'\mathbf{P}_i = \mathbf{I}$ from the orthogonality property of $\mathbf{P}_i$. If each element of $\mathbf{D}_i\mathbf{P}_i$ agrees with the corresponding element of $\mathbf{P}_i\mathbf{R}$ within the specified (ϵ_3) degree of accuracy, proceed to step 16. Otherwise go to step 15.

15. This conditional stop is treated the same way as step 12.

16. The $\mathbf{D}_i$ and $\mathbf{P}_i$ are retained in temporary storage, being changed as a result of each successive complete iteration.

17. Count the number (c) of off-diagonal elements d_{jk} that are zero within the specified (ϵ_1) degree of accuracy.

18. If all off-diagonal elements are not zero to the degree ϵ_1, go to step 19. Otherwise the process has converged, so proceed to step 20.

19. If the number of iterations i has not reached the maximum number μ, go back to step 2 to initiate the next iteration. Otherwise go to step 20.

20. Since the eigenvectors appear in the rows of $\mathbf{B}$, and since the factor matrix $\mathbf{A}$ conventionally contains the coefficients of the respective factors in columns, the conversion (8.52) for all the common factors may be expressed by:

$$A = B'D^{1/2}.$$

8.7. Illustrative Examples

To demonstrate the feasibility of the principal-factor method, now that computers are generally available, several examples will be given.

1. Five socio-economic variables.—First, it should be pointed out that the principal-component solution of Table 8.1 was obtained on a relatively slow Philco 2000 in a matter of a few seconds. If, instead of ones in the diagonal, SMC's are used as estimates of communality* for the reduced correlation matrix the resulting eigenvalues become:

$$2.73429, \quad 1.71607, \quad .03955, \quad -.02452, \quad -.07261,$$

and the solution in terms of two factors is shown in Table 8.13. Of course, since the SMC's are lower bounds for the communalities (see **5.7**), the amount of variance accounted for by these two principal factors (4.450) is less than the 4.670 of the first two principal components. More important, of course, is the fact that the solution

---

* Most principal-factor computer programs provide an option for the values to go in the diagonal of the correlation matrix, with SMC's as one of the choices; and the desired values are computed as the initial step in the analysis.

in Table 8.13 is for a different model than that in Table 8.1. Even if only the first two principal components are retained, it doesn't make the latter solution equivalent to the former. The models (2.8) and (2.9) make for a fundamental difference in the way the components or the factors are measured (see chapter 16).

Table 8.13

Principal-Factor Solution for Five Socio-Economic Variables
(Communality estimates: SMC's)

Variable	Common Factors[a]		Communality		
	P_2	P_2	(1) Original	(2) Calculated	(1)−(2)
1. Total population	.62533	.76621	.96859	.97811	−.00952
2. Median school years	.71417	−.55535	.82227	.81845	.00382
3. Total employment	.71414	.67949	.96918	.97170	−.00252
4. Misc. profess. services	.87979	−.15879	.78572	.79924	−.01352
5. Median value house	.74107	−.57764	.84701	.88285	−.03584
Contribution of factor (V_p)	2.73429	1.71607	4.39277	4.45035	−.05758
Per cent of original communality	62.2	39.1	—	101.3	−1.3

[a] The P's in this table and in Table 8.1 are used as generic symbols for principal factors or components, the text making it clear which is implied.

Another recommendation for estimates of communality is that determined from all the principal components whose eigenvalues are greater than one. From Table 8.1 it can be seen that only the first two components have eigenvalues greater than one. The "communalities" of the five variables calculated from these components are:

$$.98783, \quad .88515, \quad .97930, \quad .88023, \quad .93746.$$

If these values are inserted in the diagonal of the correlation matrix, the resulting factorization yields the following eigenvalues:

$$2.79652, \quad 1.75496, \quad .10642, \quad .02094, \quad -.00888,$$

and a solution, again in terms of two factors, is obtained which accounts for slightly more of the variance than that shown in Table 8.13. Rather than exhibiting that solution, another solution was obtained by iteration—the preceding communalities were used initially, then replaced by the communalities obtained from the first two factors of the resulting solution, and the process repeated until the communalities agreed to three decimal places on successive trials. This was accomplished in 14 iterations, with resulting communalities:

$$1.00000, \quad .76687, \quad .95562, \quad .79837, \quad .97142.$$

The principal-factor solution, with these communalities, is shown in Table 8.14.

162

Table 8.14

Alternate Principal-Factor Solution for Five Socio-Economic Variables
(Communality estimates: iteration by refactoring)

Variable	Common Factors[a]		Communality
	P_1	P_2	
1. Total population	.622	.785	1.000
2. Median school years	.702	−.524	.767
3. Total employment	.701	.681	.956
4. Misc. profess. services	.882	−.145	.798
5. Median value house	.779	−.604	.971
Contribution of factor (V_p)	2.756	1.740	4.492
Per cent of communality	61.3	38.7	

[a] See footnote to Table 8.13.

While there is considerable similarity between the results in Tables 8.13 and 8.14, there are also some differences due to the different choices for the communalities. The differences are more apparent in this small problem than they would be if the number of variables were larger; the relative effect of the n diagonal values (out of the total of n^2 elements involved in the calculations) decreases with an increase in n. Before leaving this example, it should be pointed out that the process employed in getting the result of Table 8.14 served as a forerunner for the method of minimum residuals (minres) which is presented in chapter 9. The solution of Table 8.14 may be seen to be very close to the minres solution of Table 9.2.

2. Eight emotional traits.—Next, an example of eight variables is presented from a field of psychology for which Burt provided the correlations many years ago. He discussed the factorial analysis of emotional traits in another paper [55], pointing out the bipolar nature of the resulting factors, but did not actually obtain a principal-factor solution.

The correlations for these traits are given in Table 8.15, including communalities which were estimated from a solution essentially of the bi-factor form. A principal factor analysis disclosed the fact that two common factors adequately accounted for these communalities. The principal-factor pattern is given in Table 8.16.

The first factor may appropriately be called "General emotionality" (G), although the present sample of emotional traits is small. The second factor may be named from the traits with significant coefficients. As a rough estimate, the standard error of a factor coefficient may be taken from Table B of the Appendix. Thus, for $N = 172$ and an average correlation $r = .48$, the standard error is .064 and any coefficient as large as .20 could certainly be considered significant. The traits with significant coefficients are anger (.60), wonder (.32), and tenderness (−.51). Since wonder and anger are indicative of an egocentric personality, and tenderness is indicative of timidity, the factor characterizing these two opposing emotions may be called

Table 8.15

Intercorrelation of Eight Emotional Variables for
172 Normal Children Aged Nine to Twelve

Variable	1	2	3	4	5	6	7	8
1. Sociability	.94	—	—	—	—	—	—	—
2. Sorrow	.83	.94	—	—	—	—	—	—
3. Tenderness	.81	.87	.89	—	—	—	—	—
4. Joy	.80	.62	.63	.50	—	—	—	—
5. Wonder	.71	.59	.37	.49	.57	—	—	—
6. Disgust	.54	.58	.30	.30	.34	.28	—	—
7. Anger	.53	.44	.12	.28	.55	.38	.63	—
8. Fear	.24	.45	.33	.29	.19	.21	.10	.12

Table 8.16

Principal-Factor Pattern for Eight Emotional Traits

Variable	Common Factors		Communality		
	G	E	(1) Original	(2) Calculated	(1)−(2)
1. Sociability	.98	.06	.94	.96	−.02
2. Sorrow	.95	−.14	.94	.92	.02
3. Tenderness	.81	−.51	.89	.92	−.03
4. Joy	.72	−.10	.50	.53	−.03
5. Wonder	.68	.32	.57	.56	.01
6. Disgust	.53	.14	.28	.30	−.02
7. Anger	.52	.60	.63	.63	.00
8. Fear	.35	−.14	.12	.14	−.02
Total	—	—	4.87	4.96	−.09
Contribution of factor (V_p)	4.17	.79	—	—	—
Per cent of total original communality	85.6	16.2	—	101.8	−1.8

"Egocentricity" (E). If it is desired to change the signs of all the coefficients, then the factor may be called "Timidity." In Burt's discussion fear and sorrow are classed with tenderness, and in the present analysis each of these traits has a coefficient of −.14. These values have some statistical significance and help substantiate the interpretation of the second factor.

Before leaving this example, it should be pointed out that an attempt was made to analyze these data with SMC's as communalities, but real computing difficulties were encountered. The most convenient way of getting the squared multiple correlations, according to (5.38), involves the calculation of the inverse of the correlation matrix (of course, the full matrix with ones in the diagonal). While such a matrix must be Gramian (see **3.2**, par. **15**), the value of the determinant of the correlation matrix, produced by the computer, is only .00062. Obviously, the determinant is so close to zero that the inverse of the matrix doesn't exist. When an "inverse" was calculated by the computer (it couldn't tell that the determinant was insignificantly different from zero), most of the diagonal elements were negative, and the corresponding SMC's greater than one. Another way of putting it is to say that the rank of the full correlation matrix is less than eight, and therefore a case of multicollinearity must exist among the eight variables.

3. Eight political variables.—Another example has been selected from a set of political variables in order to illustrate the applicability of the principal-factor solution in an entirely different field. The data also furnish a solution in which all the factors, including the first, are of the bipolar form. A set of eight variables was selected from a larger group of seventeen political variables, analyzed by Gosnell and Schmidt [162]. The smaller set includes the variables which are among the best measures of the factors given in Gosnell's solution. A brief description of these variables, measured in 147 Chicago election areas, follows:

1. *Lewis:* Percentage of the total Democratic and Republican vote cast for Lewis
2. *Roosevelt:* Corresponding percentage for Roosevelt
3. *Party voting:* Percentage that the straight-party votes were of the total
4. *Median rental:* Median rental (in dollars)
5. *Homeownership:* Percentage of the total families that own their homes
6. *Unemployment:* Percentage unemployed in 1921 of the gainful workers ten years of age and over
7. *Mobility:* Percentage of total families that have lived less than one year at present address
8. *Education:* Percentage of population, eighteen years and older, which completed more than ten grades of school

The intercorrelations of these variables are given in Table 8.17, in which communalities are also recorded. These communalities were computed by the method of **5.4**.

The principal-factor pattern is presented in Table 8.18. It may be observed that several variables have large negative coefficients for the first factor, in contrast with the positive coefficients found in the preceding solutions. In the present example the first factor, being of the bipolar type, may be named from the nature of the variables in the subsets (1, 2, 3) and (4, 7, 8). The variables of the first subset may be regarded as measures of the "Traditional Democratic Vote" (*TDV*), which is taken as the name of the factor. The variables of the second subset characterize the sociological level of the election areas and seem to be opposite in nature to the "Traditional Democratic Vote." The high weight for variable 6 (Unemployment) is consistent with the foregoing interpretation inasmuch as high unemployment is associated with traditional vote.

In the case of the second factor, the largest weights appear for variables 5 (Homeownership) and 7 (Mobility), being +.65 and −.56, respectively. Inasmuch as both Homeownership and lack of Mobility are aspects of a single characteristic, the second

165

Table 8.17

Intercorrelations of Eight Political Variables for 147 Election Areas

Variable	1	2	3	4	5	6	7	8
1. Lewis	.52	—	—	—	—	—	—	—
2. Roosevelt	.84	1.00	—	—	—	—	—	—
3. Party Voting	.62	.84	.78	—	—	—	—	—
4. Median Rental	−.53	−.68	−.76	.82	—	—	—	—
5. Homeownership	.03	−.05	.08	−.25	.36	—	—	—
6. Unemployment	.57	.76	.81	−.80	.25	.80	—	—
7. Mobility	−.33	−.35	−.51	.62	−.72	−.58	.63	—
8. Education	−.63	−.73	−.81	.88	−.36	−.84	.68	.97

Table 8.18

Principal-Factor Solution for Eight Political Variables[a]

Variable j	Common Factors		Communality		
	TDV	HP	(1) Original	(2) Calculated	(1)−(2)
1. Lewis	.69	−.28	.52	.55	−.03
2. Roosevelt	.88	−.48	1.00	1.00	.00
3. Party Voting	.87	−.17	.78	.79	−.01
4. Median Rental	−.88	−.09	.82	.78	.04
5. Homeownership	.28	.65	.36	.50	−.14
6. Unemployment	.89	.01	.80	.79	.01
7. Mobility	−.66	−.56	.63	.75	−.12
8. Education	−.96	−.15	.97	.94	.03
Total	—	—	5.88	6.10	−.22
Contribution of factor (V_p)	5.01	1.10	—	—	—
Per cent of total original communality	85.2	18.8	—	103.7	−3.7

[a] A principal-factor solution with SMC's as estimates of the communalities produced two factors with contributions of 5.01 and 1.28.

factor may be termed "Home Permanency" (*HP*). The negative factor weights for the first three variables again appear to verify the naming of this factor. This bipolar factor is conveniently described by a single name because the opposing variables may be considered as measures on a single scale in opposite directions.

4. Twenty-four psychological tests.—The final illustration is of a fair-sized problem. A problem of this magnitude is commonplace today, but in 1940 it took more than 100 hours to calculate the first two factors by hand methods. Therefore, it was quite an accomplishment to get a complete factorization on the ORDVAC at Aberdeen Proving Grounds in about 40 minutes (in 1952) and on an IBM 704 in about 8 minutes (in 1958). By 1965 this time was cut to about 2 minutes on the IBM 7094, and since then the time has been slashed to less than one minute on such large-scale machines as IBM System/360, CDC 6600, or GE 625.

For the correlation matrix of Table 7.4, with unities in the diagonal, the resulting roots of the characteristic equation are given in Table 8.19. This example demon-

Table 8.19

Contributions (Eigenvalues) of 24 Principal Components for Twenty-Four Psychological Tests

Order	Eigenvalue	Order	Eigenvalue
1	8.135	13	.533
2	2.096	14	.509
3	1.693	15	.477
4	1.502	16	.390
5	1.025	17	.382
6	.943	18	.340
7	.901	19	.334
8	.816	20	.316
9	.790	21	.297
10	.707	22	.268
11	.639	23	.190
12	.543	24	.172

strates that property of characteristic equations which says that all roots are real; and for the case of a positive semi-definite matrix $\mathbf{R}$, that all roots are non negative. While all twenty-four eigenvectors were obtained, for economy of space only the first ten principal components are presented in Table 8.20. In addition to the factor weights, the contribution V_p (equivalent to the eigenvalue λ_p) of factor P_p is given at the bottom of each column, along with the percentage that this number represents out of the total variance of 24.

The general characteristics of any principal-factor solution are demonstrated by the data in Table 8.20. First of all, the contributions of the factors to the total variance of the variables (or total communality, when that is being analyzed) decrease with each succeeding factor. This immediately provides a rough statistical guide as to the maximum error that might be introduced by stopping the analysis too soon. If the last factor retained contributes 5% to the total variance, it is known that the next factor, or any succeeding one, will not contribute as much as 5%. Of course, this determination of the effect of each succeeding factor can be judged from the eigenvalues (which are obtained first in the computer) without the actual computation of the factor weights. Another characteristic to be noted is that the first factor has positive loadings for every variable, since (almost) all correlations are positive in the original matrix. For all succeeding factors the positive and negative coefficients

167

Table 8.20

First Ten Principal Components for Twenty-Four Psychological Tests

Test	P_1	P_2	P_3	P_4	P_5	P_6	P_7	P_8	P_9	P_{10}
1	.616	−.005	.428	−.204	−.009	.070	.199	.220	−.153	.156
2	.400	−.079	.400	−.202	.348	.089	−.506	−.024	−.263	−.256
3	.445	−.191	.476	−.106	−.375	.329	−.083	−.356	−.060	.021
4	.510	−.178	.335	−.216	−.010	−.192	.461	.142	.135	−.266
5	.695	−.321	−.335	−.053	.079	.078	−.123	.028	−.232	−.010
6	.690	−.418	−.265	.081	−.008	.124	.001	.129	−.054	−.129
7	.677	−.425	−.355	−.072	−.040	.011	.081	.009	.001	−.091
8	.694	−.243	−.144	−.116	−.141	.119	.158	−.172	.115	−.065
9	.694	−.451	−.291	.080	−.005	−.071	−.009	.117	−.124	.029
10	.474	.542	−.446	−.202	.079	−.085	−.013	−.080	.079	−.099
11	.576	.434	−.210	.034	.002	.301	−.043	.320	−.004	.062
12	.482	.549	−.127	−.340	.099	.039	.158	−.301	−.132	.159
13	.618	.279	.035	−.366	−.075	.364	.130	.175	−.040	.104
14	.448	.093	−.055	.555	.156	.383	−.084	−.126	.262	.056
15	.416	.142	.078	.526	.306	−.057	.126	.072	−.304	.208
16	.534	.091	.392	.327	.171	.172	.081	.128	.297	−.212
17	.488	.276	−.052	.469	−.255	−.107	.248	−.214	−.152	−.137
18	.544	.386	.198	.152	−.104	−.252	−.019	−.003	−.344	−.287
19	.475	.138	.122	.193	−.604	−.139	−.341	.192	.102	.104
20	.643	−.186	.132	.070	.285	−.191	.026	−.294	.176	.057
21	.622	.232	.100	−.202	.174	−.226	−.161	.176	.323	−.000
22	.640	−.146	.110	.056	−.023	−.331	−.045	.131	.022	.368
23	.712	−.105	.150	−.103	.064	−.111	−.081	−.248	.067	.300
24	.673	.196	−.233	−.062	−.097	−.170	−.228	−.119	.154	−.185
V_p	8.137	2.097	1.692	1.501	1.025	.943	.900	.817	.790	.707
$100V_p/24$	33.9	8.7	7.0	6.2	4.3	3.9	3.8	3.4	3.3	2.9

are about equal in number. Sometimes a principal-factor solution will serve adequately as the final analysis of a correlation matrix, while in other situations it will be desirable to transform such a solution to a different frame of reference.

Psychologists, more often, are concerned with the analysis of the total communality rather than the total variance of a given set of variables. Employing the squared multiple correlations (SMC's) as estimates of the communalities, the following twenty-four eigenvalues were obtained:

$$
\begin{array}{cccccc}
7.665 & .447 & .254 & .028 & -.104 & -.199 \\
1.672 & .407 & .175 & -.014 & -.127 & -.235 \\
1.208 & .319 & .109 & -.048 & -.140 & -.247 \\
.920 & .305 & .046 & -.066 & -.161 & -.269
\end{array}
$$

from which it will be seen that thirteen are positive while eleven are negative—a circumstance to be expected when estimates of communalities rather than unities are inserted in the main diagonal of a correlation matrix. Since multiplication by the square root of the eigenvalue is involved in getting the factor weights, eleven of the principal factors are imaginary. For practical interpretation this must mean that the number of relevant factors necessary to describe the total communality (as estimated) of the twenty-four tests certainly must be less than or equal to thirteen. If the analysis is made in terms of all thirteen real factors, the communality (13.555) resulting from this solution will exceed the starting communality (11.943). This follows from the mathematical property that the contributions of the eleven imaginary factors will be negative and will reduce the contributions of the thirteen real factors to the actual amount with which the analysis was started.

The first five eigenvalues account for just about the total starting communality, and it might be argued, therefore, that only these factors have any practical significance. This conclusion also agrees with the criterion of retaining a number of factors equal to the number of principal components whose eigenvalues are greater than one (see Table 8.19). It would certainly seem that five factors would provide an adequate model for the description of the interrelationships among the twenty-four tests. As a matter of fact, four factors do almost as good a job, and the greater simplicity might warrant the slight loss in variance. For purposes of reference, all five principal factors are presented in Table 8.21. While psychological interpretations might be made of this solution, the more common practice is to transform it to another frame of reference, eliminating the bipolar factors and causing the variables identifying the factors to be more pronounced (see chaps. 14, 15).

8.8. *Canonical Form*

In this section, a general procedure is suggested for designating a coordinate system in a given factor space with properties closely related to those of the principal-factor method. As is well known (see **2.7**), a factor solution for a correlation matrix usually produces a unique factor space but not a unique set of common-factor loadings (exception being the principal-factor solution). For this reason it is desirable to specify a "canonical" form. Of course, rotation to such form has nothing to do with the "rotation problem" to obtain a more meaningful solution, which is treated in part iii of this text. Rotation to canonical form is merely a means to bring an arbitrary solution to a well-defined form in a mathematical sense. Among other values, it may be useful in resolving the question of the meaning of equivalence of two solutions— they may look different, but if they are truly equivalent, then, when each is brought to canonical form, they will be identical.

The canonical form employed in this text (especially in chaps. 9 and 10) has the property that successive factors account for maximum possible variance in the common-factor space determined by the original solution. This should not be confused with the alternative objective set forth in **2.3** of determining a solution, i.e., the common-factor space, with the property of extracting the maximum variance from the observed variables which has been the primary subject of this chapter.

The canonical form is arrived at in the following manner. Let

$\mathbf{A}$ = arbitrary form of factor matrix $(n \times m)$,
$\mathbf{B}$ = canonical form of factor matrix $(n \times m)$,
$\mathbf{T}$ = orthogonal transformation matrix $(m \times m)$;

Table 8.21

Principal-Factor Solution for Twenty-Four Psychological Tests
(Communality estimates: SMC's)

Test	Common Factors					Communality	
	P_1	P_2	P_3	P_4	P_5	Original	Calculated
1	.595	−.039	.369	−.184	−.073	.511	.531
2	.374	.026	.270	−.147	.121	.300	.250
3	.433	.115	.396	−.112	−.276	.440	.446
4	.501	.108	.290	−.178	.044	.409	.380
5	.701	.312	−.273	−.050	.003	.673	.666
6	.683	.404	−.213	.067	−.102	.677	.690
7	.676	.412	−.284	−.082	−.046	.684	.716
8	.680	.206	−.088	−.115	−.118	.564	.540
9	.690	.446	−.212	.076	.036	.713	.727
10	.456	−.469	−.446	−.128	.105	.579	.654
11	.589	−.372	−.198	.076	−.185	.541	.565
12	.448	−.491	−.154	−.263	.044	.537	.537
13	.590	−.268	.018	−.300	−.255	.539	.575
14	.435	−.063	−.012	.418	−.057	.358	.371
15	.390	−.102	.055	.362	.101	.293	.307
16	.512	−.098	.325	.259	.006	.429	.444
17	.471	−.212	−.036	.388	−.087	.412	.426
18	.521	−.331	.118	.145	.028	.443	.417
19	.450	−.115	.110	.167	−.178	.367	.287
20	.623	.135	.142	.049	.252	.464	.492
21	.596	−.220	.076	−.140	.204	.473	.471
22	.600	.103	.138	.053	.142	.449	.413
23	.685	.063	.160	−.096	.154	.561	.532
24	.635	−.169	−.192	−.009	.079	.527	.475
V_p	7.665	1.672	1.208	.920	.447	11.943	11.912
$100V_p/11.943$	64.2	14.0	10.1	7.7	3.7	100.	99.7

then

$$(8.53) \qquad\qquad \mathbf{B} = \mathbf{AT}$$

will yield the desired form of the factor solution, and the immediate problem is to determine the matrix $\mathbf{T}$. Premultiplying (8.53) by the transpose of $\mathbf{B}$ produces

$$(8.54) \qquad\qquad \mathbf{B'B} = \mathbf{T'A'AT}.$$

Then, setting $\mathbf{\Lambda} = \mathbf{B'B}$ and pre- and postmultiplying by $\mathbf{T}$ and $\mathbf{T'}$, respectively, yields

$$(8.55) \qquad\qquad \mathbf{TAT'} = \mathbf{TT'A'ATT'},$$

which finally reduces to

$$(8.56) \qquad\qquad \mathbf{A'A} = \mathbf{TAT'},$$

170

since $\mathbf{TT}' = \mathbf{I}$ from the orthogonality property of the transformation matrix (see **4.6**). The expression (8.56) is a special instance of (8.21) for the diagonalization of any symmetric matrix $\mathbf{R}$. By pre- and postmultiplying (8.21) by $\mathbf{Q}$ and $\mathbf{Q}'$, respectively, it becomes

$$(8.57) \qquad\qquad \mathbf{R} = \mathbf{Q\Lambda Q}'.$$

The similarity to (8.56) is obvious. It follows that $\mathbf{\Lambda}$ is a diagonal matrix of eigenvalues and the orthogonal transformation $\mathbf{T}$ is the matrix of corresponding eigenvectors of the matrix $\mathbf{A}'\mathbf{A}$. Thus, it is only necessary to determine the eigenvectors of an $m \times m$ matrix to obtain the transformation matrix which carries the arbitrary pattern matrix $\mathbf{A}$ into the canonical form $\mathbf{B}$. The general principal-factor computer routines are applicable to this problem.

Of course, the matrix of residuals remains unchanged whether computed from $\mathbf{A}$ or $\mathbf{B}$ since, according to (2.50),

$$(8.58) \qquad\qquad \mathbf{R}^\dagger = \mathbf{BB}' = \mathbf{ATT}'\mathbf{A}' = \mathbf{AA}',$$

the last equality following from the orthogonality of the transformation matrix. For convenience, after the canonical form of the solution is obtained, it is again designated by $\mathbf{A}$, rather than $\mathbf{B}$.

8.9.   *Centroid Method*

This method of factoring a correlation matrix provided a computational compromise for the principal-factor method before computers were generally available. Now the centroid method is primarily of historical interest. The fundamental formula of the centroid method was first employed by Burt [51, p. 53] in 1917, but applied to the problem of determining a single general factor of the Spearman type. The complete centroid method was developed by Thurstone [467] in conjunction with the analysis of large batteries of psychological tests into several common factors.

1. Derivation of method.—The name of the method connotes its close relationship to the mechanical concept of a centroid, or center of gravity. For this reason, the centroid form of analysis can best be described in geometric terms. As noted in **4.10**, the variables may be considered as represented by a set of n vectors which are contained in a space of m dimensions, where m is the number of common factors; and the scalar product of any pair of vectors is the correlation between them, as given in (4.56). The variables may also be considered as represented by the m coordinates of the end points of these vectors with respect to m mutually orthogonal arbitrary reference axes. Since the configuration of the vectors representing the variables completely determines the correlations, the reference system may be rotated without any effect on them. The arbitrary coordinate system may then be rotated so that the centroid point of the set of n points, along with the origin, determines the first axis of reference. Thus it is possible to obtain the projection of each of the vectors, or the coordinate of each variable, on the first axis of reference through the centroid.

171

Starting with a factor pattern of the usual form (2.22), the correlations are reproduced by means of equation (2.27) when the common factors are uncorrelated. Then, making the assumption that the residuals vanish, the observed correlations may be written

$$(8.59) \qquad r_{jk} = r'_{jk} = a_{j1}a_{k1} + a_{j2}a_{k2} + \cdots + a_{jm}a_{km} \qquad (j, k = 1, 2, \cdots, n),$$

where m is the number of common factors. The numerical values of a_{jp} $(p = 1, 2, \cdots, m)$ are determined by the position of the orthogonal reference axes, since a_{jp} is the pth coordinate of variable z_j.* In the arbitrary orthogonal reference system, the m coordinates for each of the n points are as follows:

$$P_1 : (a_{11}, a_{12}, \cdots, a_{1p}, \cdots, a_{1m})$$

$$\cdot \quad \cdot \quad \cdot \quad \cdot \quad \cdot \quad \cdot \quad \cdot$$

$$P_k : (a_{k1}, a_{k2}, \cdots, a_{kp}, \cdots, a_{km})$$

$$\cdot \quad \cdot \quad \cdot \quad \cdot \quad \cdot \quad \cdot \quad \cdot$$

$$P_n : (a_{n1}, a_{n2}, \cdots, a_{np}, \cdots, a_{nm})$$

Any one of the m coordinates of the centroid is the average of the corresponding coordinates of these n points, hence

$$(8.60) \qquad \text{Centroid} : \left(\frac{1}{n} \sum_k a_{k1}, \cdots, \frac{1}{n} \sum_k a_{kp}, \cdots, \frac{1}{n} \sum_k a_{km} \right),$$

where the summation is from 1 to n on the indicated index when the limits are not given specifically.

Now let the frame of reference be so selected that the first axis F_1 passes through the centroid. Then the centroid will have coordinates all zero except the first, i.e.,

$$(8.61) \qquad \sum_k a_{k2} = \sum_k a_{k3} = \cdots = \sum_k a_{km} = 0.$$

The m values (8.60) then reduce to

$$\frac{1}{n} \sum_k a_{k1}, 0, 0, \cdots, 0,$$

there being $(m - 1)$ zeros. Since the centroid lies in the first axis, the first coordinate is also the distance of the centroid from the origin.

It is now possible to determine the coefficients of the first centroid factor, i.e., the coordinates a_{j1}, in terms of the observed correlations. Thus, summing for all variables k in a fixed column j of the correlation matrix, there results

$$\sum_k r_{jk} = a_{j1} \left(\sum_k a_{k1} \right) + a_{j2} \left(\sum_k a_{k2} \right) + \cdots + a_{jm} \left(\sum_k a_{km} \right),$$

---

* More precisely, this variable should be designated by z''_j since it is represented in the common-factor space. See **4.10**.

which, on applying (8.61), becomes

$$(8.62) \qquad \sum_k r_{jk} = a_{j1}\left(\sum_k a_{k1}\right).$$

Then the sum of all the entries in the correlation matrix is simply

$$(8.63) \qquad \sum_j \sum_k r_{jk} = \left(\sum_j a_{j1}\right)\left(\sum_k a_{k1}\right) = \left(\sum_k a_{k1}\right)^2.$$

Now, the square-root of the left side of (8.63) may be substituted for the term in parentheses in (8.62) to yield the following basic centroid formula:

$$(8.64) \qquad a_{j1} = \frac{\displaystyle\sum_k r_{jk}}{\sqrt{\displaystyle\sum_j \sum_k r_{jk}}} = \frac{S_j}{\sqrt{T}} \qquad (j = 1, 2, \cdots, n),$$

where S_j is the sum of all the correlations in column j of the correlation matrix, and T is the total of all the correlations in the matrix, including the diagonal terms in both of these sums. In the above formula, the positive root was selected arbitrarily. Of course, if the negative sign of the radical had been chosen, the coefficients of the factor would all be changed in sign, yielding an equally acceptable factor. Formula (8.64) gives the coefficient of the first centroid factor F_1 for each variable z_j, or the first coordinate for each point representing a variable.

The next step is to get the first-factor residuals, from which the second coordinates are found. Since the residual correlations with one, two, $\cdots$, $(m-1)$ factors removed are employed in successive stages of the centroid method, the notation introduced in **8.3** is employed again. The first-factor residuals again are given by

$$(8.24) \qquad {}_1r_{jk} = r_{jk} - a_{j1}a_{k1} = a_{j2}a_{k2} + a_{j3}a_{k3} + \cdots + a_{jm}a_{km}.$$

The residual correlations may be regarded as the scalar products of pairs of residual vectors in a space of $(m-1)$ dimensions—the dimension of the residual space being equal to the number of terms in the right-hand member of (8.24) or the rank of the matrix of residual correlations, according to Theorem 4.6.

In this residual space, the $(m-1)$ coordinates for each of the n points may be designated by:

$$ {}_1P_1 : (a_{12}, a_{13}, \cdots, a_{1p}, \cdots, a_{1m}) $$
$$ \cdots : \cdots, \cdots, \cdots, \cdots, \cdots, \cdots $$
$$ {}_1P_k : (a_{k2}, a_{k3}, \cdots, a_{kp}, \cdots, a_{km}) $$
$$ \cdots : \cdots, \cdots, \cdots, \cdots, \cdots, \cdots $$
$$ {}_1P_n : (a_{n2}, a_{n3}, \cdots, a_{np}, \cdots, a_{nm}). $$

The $(m-1)$ coordinates of the centroid of these n points are

$$(8.65) \qquad \left(\frac{1}{n}\sum_k a_{k2}, \cdots, \frac{1}{n}\sum_k a_{kp}, \cdots, \frac{1}{n}\sum_k a_{km}\right),$$

which all vanish according to (8.61). Thus the centroid is at the origin in this $(m - 1)$ space, and formula (8.64) cannot be used directly for calculating the values of the second-factor coefficients. It will be noted that in obtaining (8.64) the expression (8.62) was divided by $\sum_k a_{k1}$, or n times the distance of the centroid from the origin. It was tacitly assumed that the centroid was not at the origin, for otherwise this division would not have been possible.

The immediate problem, then, is to remove the centroid from the origin in the $(m - 1)$ space, so that the preceding method can again be applied. By means of rotations of certain of the vectors about the origin through 180°—also called *reflections in the origin*—the centroid can be removed from the origin. If the coordinates of a point P_j, representing a variable z_j, are

$$(a_{j1}, a_{j2}, \cdots, a_{jm}),$$

then the reflected point $-P_j$, with coordinates

$$(-a_{j1}, -a_{j2}, \cdots, -a_{jm}),$$

represents the variable $-z_j$. Such a variable corresponds to the original variable measured in the opposite direction.

Now it is evident from (8.59) that to reverse the signs of the coordinates of P_j has the effect of reversing the signs of all the correlations of variable z_j with the remaining ones. Thus the reflection of a variable in the origin is accomplished merely by changing the signs of the correlations of this variable in the correlation matrix. Of course, the same argument holds for the residual $(m - 1)$ space as for the original common-factor space of m dimensions. Hence the reflection of a variable in the residual space is accomplished by changing the signs of the residual correlations for that variable.

In an attempt to determine which variables to reflect, Thurstone [468, p. 96] suggests that "it is desirable to account for as much as possible of the residual variance by each successive factor." While a rigorous mathematical application of this principle would lead to the principal-factor solution, the centroid procedure is only intended to approximate it. To have the second factor account for as much as possible of the residual variance, the reference axis which represents this factor should pass through a cluster of residual vectors. If there is a clustering of such vectors (i.e., a group of variables having high positive residual correlations), which is balanced by a scattering of vectors on the opposite side of the origin, since the centroid is at the origin, then the second reference axis should be made to pass through this cluster. Thus it would seem that the vectors which scatter, opposite to a cluster, should be reflected so as to fall in with the group. The second centroid coordinates can then be computed as in the first case. In application, those variables which have the greatest number of negative correlations would be reflected first, bringing them into the hemisphere of the cluster. For practical problems, Thurstone [468, p. 97] suggests reversing "the signs of one trait at a time until the number of negative coefficients in the residual table is less than $n/2$", that is, less than $n/2$ negative signs for any one variable, not the entire table. One need not stop with this, however, for, if it is desired to further "maximize" the variance removed by each successive factor, the reflections of variables may be continued until the sum of the residual correlations for each variable is as large (positively) as possible.

For the remainder of the analytical work it will be convenient to use a symbol to designate whether a point, representing a variable, has been reflected in the origin. Let ϵ_j stand for the algebraic sign of P_j, that is, the point $\epsilon_j P_j$ is $+P_j$ or $-P_j$. If P_j has not been reflected, ϵ_j is plus, but, if P_j has been reflected, then ϵ_j is minus. Furthermore, ϵ_j may be considered as an algebraic operator defined as follows:

$$\epsilon_j = \begin{cases} +1 \text{ if } z_j \text{ has not been reflected,} \\ -1 \text{ if } z_j \text{ has been reflected.} \end{cases}$$

Then ϵ_j can be attached to the coordinates of P_j, and it can be treated as any other algebraic quantity. Thus, if the first-factor residual correlations after reflection of certain variables are designated by r_{1jk} (in distinction to $_1r_{jk}$ before reflection), then they may be written as follows:

$$(8.66) \qquad r_{1jk} = \epsilon_j \epsilon_k (a_{j2}a_{k2} + a_{j3}a_{k3} + \cdots + a_{jm}a_{km}).$$

This result follows immediately from (8.24), where each a_{jp} and a_{kp} was replaced by $\epsilon_j a_{jp}$ and $\epsilon_k a_{kp}$, respectively, and then ϵ_j and ϵ_k were factored out algebraically. If neither z_j nor z_k was reflected, or if both variables were reflected, then $r_{1jk} = {}_1r_{jk}$; but, if only one or the other of z_j and z_k was reflected, then $r_{1jk} = -{}_1r_{jk}$. In other words, $r_{1jk} = \epsilon_j \epsilon_k ({}_1r_{jk})$.

The $(m-1)$ coordinates of the centroid of the n points, originally given in (8.65), become after reflection of variables:

$$\frac{1}{n}\sum_k \epsilon_k a_{kp} \qquad\qquad (p = 2, 3, \cdots, m).$$

Now the system of reference can be rotated about the first axis F_1 so that the second axis F_2 passes through this centroid*. Let it be assumed that this has been done, there being no need to change the notation for the coordinates. Then the coordinates of the centroid are

$$\frac{1}{n}\sum_k \epsilon_k a_{k2}, 0, 0, \cdots, 0,$$

since the centroid lies on the F_2 axis. From the values for the last $(m-2)$ coordinates the following useful expressions may be written:

$$(8.67) \qquad \sum_k \epsilon_k a_{k3} = \sum_k \epsilon_k a_{k4} = \cdots = \sum_k \epsilon_k a_{km} = 0,$$

corresponding to (8.61) in the case of the first centroid.

---

* The residual $(m-1)$ space is orthogonal to the first axis of reference F_1. The second axis F_2, i.e., the first one in the $(m-1)$ subspace, may then be rotated to any position in the residual space, and it will be at right angles to F_1.

Now the projections of the vectors on the second centroid axis can be expressed in terms of the residual correlations. Thus, summing (8.66) for all variables k in a fixed column j of the residual correlation matrix (after reflection of variables) and applying (8.67), there results

$$\sum_k r_{1jk} = \epsilon_j a_{j2} \sum_k \epsilon_k a_{k2}.$$

Then, summing for all columns,

$$\sum_j \sum_k r_{1jk} = \sum_j \epsilon_j a_{j2} \sum_k \epsilon_k a_{k2} = \left(\sum_k \epsilon_k a_{k2} \right)^2.$$

It follows that

$$\epsilon_j a_{j2} = \frac{\sum\limits_k r_{1jk}}{\sqrt{\sum\limits_j \sum\limits_k r_{1jk}}} = \frac{S_{j1}}{\sqrt{T_1}}$$

or, multiplying both sides by ϵ_j,

$$(8.68) \qquad\qquad a_{j2} = \frac{\epsilon_j S_{j1}}{\sqrt{T_1}} \qquad\qquad (j = 1, 2, \cdots, n),$$

where S_{j1} is the sum of all the entries in column j of the matrix of first-factor residual correlations and T_1 is the total of all the correlations in this matrix, the signs of all the entries being those after reflection. The ϵ_j indicates that, if the variable z_j was reflected, then the algebraic sign must be changed, but, if the variable was not reflected, then ϵ_j is merely $+1$. In other words, $\epsilon_j S_{j1}$ is the sum of all residual correlations for the unreflected variable z_j with all other variables. Hence, by defining

$$(8.69) \qquad\qquad {}_1 S_j = \epsilon_j S_{j1},$$

formula (8.68) may be put in the form

$$(8.70) \qquad\qquad a_{j2} = \frac{{}_1 S_j}{\sqrt{T_1}} \qquad\qquad (j = 1, 2, \cdots, n).$$

In this formula the numerator refers to the sum of the residual correlations for the unreflected variable j, while in the denominator T_1 still stands for the sum of all residual correlations after the sign changes. Formula (8.70) gives the coefficients of the second centroid factor F_2 for each variable.

The remaining factor weights can be obtained in a similar manner. To follow the basic principle of accounting for as much as possible of the variances of the variables by each factor, the variables are reflected in the residual subspaces to bring them into clusters. When the sign changes have been made, the centroid of the system of points in the residual space lies somewhere in the cluster of variables, and the next reference axis is selected through this centroid. Each successive centroid axis is at right angles to every one of the preceding axes because the residual space is orthogonal to the space of the centroid axes already established. Upon extracting each centroid factor, the residual correlations are reduced in magnitude, and the rank of each residual matrix is reduced by one, theoretically. The foregoing development was made without any restrictions on the diagonal elements. The number of factors ultimately obtained is dependent upon these diagonal values, leading to the question of "when to stop factoring."

If the simplest of the arbitrary estimates of communality (see **5.6**)—the largest correlation in each column of the correlation matrix—is selected for the diagonal element, then in each subsequent residual matrix the calculated diagonal term is not retained but replaced by the largest residual correlation, regardless of sign, in each column. This procedure does not furnish a standard for determining the number of common factors.

If, instead of modifying the diagonal entries at each stage, the analysis is applied directly, keeping the diagonal terms as calculated, then the number of factors is determined when the original diagonal values have been completely resolved. Only the common factors will be obtained if the correlation matrix contains communalities in the principal diagonal and these values are completely analyzed. In practice, it is recommended that appropriate complete estimates of the communalities, discussed in **5.7**, be employed. When such estimates are used and the straightforward centroid analysis is applied, the resulting solution terminates in a definite number of common factors.

2. Computing procedures.—When a high-speed electronic computer is available, there is no need to accept a substitute for the principal-factor solution. Without such facilities, however, a reasonable compromise is the centroid method using a desk calculator. The calculation of a centroid solution is demonstrated below, using the first thirteen of the twenty-four psychological tests introduced in **7.6**. The correlations, taken from Table 7.4, are recorded below the diagonal in Table 8.22. The communality estimates in the diagonal were available from a bi-factor solution of the thirteen tests.

To get the first-factor coefficients by (8.64), the sums S_j of correlations by columns and the total T of all the correlations in the matrix $\mathbf{R}$ are required. The column sums are shown at the bottom of Table 8.22, and are obtained by adding all the numbers in a particular row out to the diagonal and then down the corresponding column. The total $T = 57.314$ is obtained simply as the sum of all the S_j. Then, dividing S_j by $\sqrt{T} = 7.5706$ produces the coefficients of the first centroid factor shown in the last line of Table 8.22. A check on the computation is available by making use of the sum of the factor coefficients, denoted by D_1, as follows:

$$(8.71) \qquad D_1 = \sum a_{j1} = \sum S_j/\sqrt{T} = T/\sqrt{T} = \sqrt{T}.$$

Since $D_1 = 7.571$ the computational accuracy is substantiated.

The procedure for getting the first-factor residuals in the centroid method is precisely the same as that outlined in **8.5**, paragraph **4** above. The product matrix $\mathbf{R}_1^{\dagger}$ for the data is given in Table 8.23.

Table 8.22

Calculation of the C_1 Coefficients from the Correlation Matrix **R**

Variable	1	2	3	4	5	6	7	8	9	10	11	12	13
1	.558	—	—	—	—	—	—	—	—	—	—	—	—
2	.318	.203	—	—	—	—	—	—	—	—	—	—	—
3	.403	.317	.362	—	—	—	—	—	—	—	—	—	—
4	.468	.230	.305	.314	—	—	—	—	—	—	—	—	—
5	.321	.285	.247	.227	.646	—	—	—	—	—	—	—	—
6	.335	.234	.268	.327	.622	.641	—	—	—	—	—	—	—
7	.304	.157	.223	.335	.656	.722	.750	—	—	—	—	—	—
8	.332	.157	.382	.391	.578	.527	.619	.571	—	—	—	—	—
9	.326	.195	.184	.325	.723	.714	.685	.532	.758	—	—	—	—
10	.116	.057	.075	.099	.311	.203	.246	.285	.170	.554	—	—	—
11	.308	.150	.091	.110	.344	.353	.232	.300	.280	.484	.449	—	—
12	.314	.145	.140	.160	.215	.095	.181	.271	.113	.585	.428	.531	—
13	.489	.239	.321	.327	.344	.309	.345	.395	.280	.408	.535	.512	.599
S_j	4.592	2.687	3.168	3.618	5.519	5.350	5.455	5.340	5.285	3.443	4.064	3.690	5.103
a_{j1}	.607	.355	.418	.478	.729	.707	.721	.705	.698	.455	.537	.487	.674

The elements of this matrix are checked by means of the following relationship between the sums of complete rows E_{j1} and D_1:

$$(8.72) \qquad E_{j1} = \sum_k a_{j1}a_{k1} = a_{j1} \sum_k a_{k1} = a_{j1}D_1 \qquad (j = 1, 2, \cdots, n).$$

This check is shown for each of the thirteen variables in Table 8.23.

Table 8.23

Product Matrix : $\mathbf{R}_1^\dagger = (a_{j1}a_{k1})$

Variable	1	2	3	4	5	6	7	8	9	10	11	12	13
1	.368	—	—	—	—	—	—	—	—	—	—	—	—
2	.215	.126	—	—	—	—	—	—	—	—	—	—	—
3	.254	.148	.175	—	—	—	—	—	—	—	—	—	—
4	.290	.170	.200	.228	—	—	—	—	—	—	—	—	—
5	.443	.259	.305	.348	.531	—	—	—	—	—	—	—	—
6	.429	.251	.296	.338	.515	.500	—	—	—	—	—	—	—
7	.438	.256	.301	.345	.526	.510	.520	—	—	—	—	—	—
8	.428	.250	.295	.337	.514	.498	.508	.497	—	—	—	—	—
9	.424	.248	.292	.334	.509	.493	.503	.492	.487	—	—	—	—
10	.276	.162	.190	.217	.332	.322	.328	.321	.318	.207	—	—	—
11	.326	.191	.224	.257	.391	.380	.387	.379	.375	.244	.288	—	—
12	.296	.173	.204	.233	.355	.344	.351	.343	.340	.222	.262	.237	—
13	.409	.239	.282	.322	.491	.477	.486	.475	.470	.307	.362	.328	.454
E_{j1}	4.596	2.688	3.166	3.619	5.519	5.353	5.459	5.337	5.285	3.446	4.066	3.688	5.102
$a_{j1}D_1$	4.596	2.688	3.165	3.619	5.519	5.353	5.459	5.338	5.285	3.445	4.066	3.687	5.103

The first-factor residuals are shown in Table 8.24. In this residual-factor space the centroid must be at the origin, and hence the column sums should be zero except for rounding errors. To remove the centroid from the origin in the residual-factor space, and to increase the contribution of the second factor to the residual variance, certain variables are reflected in the origin. The variables to be reflected are determined as in Table 8.25. In the column headed "Reflected Variable," a minus sign is placed opposite any variable which is to be reflected. The remaining columns are introduced successively as variables are reflected. The process is begun by counting the number of negative signs for each variable in the residual matrix of Table 8.24 and recording in the column headed "Before Reflection." It should be noted that, although only half the symmetric residual matrix is recorded, the number of negative signs to be considered for each variable is that of the total matrix. In other words, when counting the number of negative signs read across the row and down the column for a specified variable.

Select the variable with the largest number of negative signs to be reflected first. If several variables have the same maximum number of negative signs, any one of them may be arbitrarily selected for reflection. In the example, variables 10 and 11 each have 9 negative signs, and z_{10} is selected for reflection. Opposite variable 10 in the first column of Table 8.25 place a minus sign to indicate that this variable is to be reflected. An adjustment in the number of negative signs for each variable is made as if variable 10 were reflected in Table 8.24 (i.e., as if all the signs for variable 10 were changed); and these results are recorded in the column headed "10" to indicate that the count of negative signs for each variable is that after variable 10 is reflected.

Upon reflection of a given variable, every residual which was positive becomes negative and every negative residual becomes positive, except that the value in the diagonal of the residual matrix remains unchanged. Therefore, for the variable being reflected the adjusted number of negative signs is $(n - 1)$ *minus* the number of negative signs it had before reflection. In the example, $n - 1 = 12$ and the entry for variable 10 after reflection is $12 - 9 = 3$.

It is not necessary to change all the signs of the residuals for the variable being reflected in order to count the number of negative signs for the other variables after the reflection. Instead, consider the sign of each entry except the diagonal in the row and column of Table 8.24 for the variable being reflected, and proceed as follows.

(a) If the entry for a particular variable, which was not previously reflected, is positive, *increase* by one the number of negative signs for that variable and record the new value for that variable in the next column of Table 8.25. For example, the entry for variable 11 in column 10 of Table 8.24 is positive, and since z_{11} was not previously reflected, the number of negative signs for it is increased one, from 9 to 10, in Table 8.25 after variable 10 is reflected.

(b) If the entry for a particular variable, which was not previously reflected, is negative, *decrease* by one the number of negative signs for that variable and record the new value for that variable in the next column of Table 8.25. For example, the entry for variable 1 in row 10 of Table 8.24 is negative, and since z_1 has not been

179

Table 8.24

First-Factor Residuals: $_1 r_{jk}$

Variable	1	2	3	4	5	6	7	8	9	10	11	12	13
1	.190	—	—	—	—	—	—	—	—	—	—	—	—
2	.103	.077	—	—	—	—	—	—	—	—	—	—	—
3	.149	.169	.187	—	—	—	—	—	—	—	—	—	—
4	.178	.060	.105	.086	—	—	—	—	—	—	—	—	—
5	−.122	.026	−.058	−.121	.115	—	—	—	—	—	—	—	—
6	−.094	−.017	−.028	−.011	.107	.141	—	—	—	—	—	—	—
7	−.134	−.099	−.078	−.010	.130	.212	.230	—	—	—	—	—	—
8	−.096	−.093	.087	.054	.064	.029	.111	.074	—	—	—	—	—
9	−.098	−.053	−.108	−.009	.214	.221	.182	.040	.271	—	—	—	—
10	−.160	−.105	−.265	−.118	−.021	−.119	−.082	−.036	−.148	.347	—	—	—
11	−.018	−.041	−.133	−.147	−.047	−.027	−.155	−.079	−.095	.240	.161	—	—
12	.018	−.028	−.064	−.073	−.140	−.249	−.170	−.072	−.227	.363	.166	.294	—
13	.080	.000	.039	.005	−.147	−.168	−.141	−.080	−.190	.101	.173	.184	.145
$\sum_k {}_1 r_{jk}$	−.004	−.001	.002	−.001	.000	−.003	−.004	.003	.000	−.003	−.002	.002	.001

Table 8.24a

Sign changes[a]

Variable	−1	2	3	4	5	6	7	8	9	−10	−11	−12	−13
1		−	−	−						−	−		
2					−	−	−	−	−				−
3					−	−	−		−				
4					−	−	−		−				
5	−	−	−	−									
6	−	−	−	−									
7	−	−	−	−									
8	−	−		−									
9	−	−	−	−									
10	−	−	−	−	−	−	−	−	−				
11	−	−	−	−	−	−	−	−	−				
12	−	−	−	−	−	−	−	−	−				
13	−	−	−	−	−	−	−	−	−				

[a] Original signs below diagonal; signs after reflection of variables above diagonal.

Table 8.24b

Residuals after Reflection (r_{1jk}) and Calculation of C_2 Coefficients

Variable	−1	2	3	4	5	6	7	8	9	−10	−11	−12	−13
1	.190	−.103	−.149	−.178	.122	.094	.134	.096	.098	−.160	−.018	.018	.080
2	—	.077	.169	.060	.026	−.017	−.099	−.093	−.053	.105	.041	.028	−.000
3	—	—	.187	.105	−.058	−.028	−.078	.087	−.108	.265	.133	.064	−.039
4	—	—	—	.086	−.121	−.011	−.010	.054	−.009	.118	.147	.073	−.005
5	—	—	—	—	.115	.107	.130	.064	.214	.021	.047	.140	.147
6	—	—	—	—	—	.141	.212	.029	.221	.119	.027	.249	.168
7	—	—	—	—	—	—	.230	.111	.182	.082	.155	.170	.141
8	—	—	—	—	—	—	—	.074	.040	.036	.079	.072	.080
9	—	—	—	—	—	—	—	—	.271	.148	.095	.227	.190
10	—	—	—	—	—	—	—	—	—	.347	.240	.363	.101
11	—	—	—	—	—	—	—	—	—	—	.161	.166	.173
12	—	—	—	—	—	—	—	—	—	—	—	.294	.184
13	—	—	—	—	—	—	—	—	—	—	—	—	.145
S_{j1}	.224	.141	.550	.309	.954	1.311	1.360	.729	1.516	1.785	1.446	2.048	1.365
$\epsilon_j S_{j1}$	−.224	.141	.550	.309	.954	1.311	1.360	.729	1.516	−1.785	−1.446	−2.048	−1.365
a_{j2}	−.060	.038	.148	.083	.257	.354	.367	.197	.409	−.482	−.390	−.553	−.368

180

Table 8.25

Number of Minus Signs for First-Factor Residuals after Successive
Reflections of Variables

Variable	Reflected Variable	Before Reflection	After Reflection of Successive Variable				
			10	11	12	13	1
1	–	7	6	5	6	7	5
2		7	6	5	4	5	6
3		7	6	5	4	5	6
4		7	6	5	4	5	6
5		7	6	5	4	3	2
6		8	7	6	5	4	3
7		8	7	6	5	4	3
8		6	5	4	3	2	1
9		8	7	6	5	4	3
10	–	9	3	2	1	0	1
11	–	9	10	2	1	0	1
12	–	8	9	10	2	1	0
13	–	5	6	7	8	4	3
Total		96	84	68	52	44	40
Difference			12	16	16	8	4

reflected, the number of negative signs for it is decreased one, producing 6 negative values after variable 10 is reflected.

General rules for sign changes are formulated conveniently in Table 8.26.

After one variable has been reflected, proceed to the next column of Table 8.25 and again select the variable with the largest number of negative signs for reflection. This is variable 11, with 10 negative signs, and the next column is headed "11". Adjust the number of negative signs for each variable as if z_{11} were reflected in Table 8.24, following the procedure outlined above, and record the results in Table 8.25. The reflection of variables is continued until the number of negative residuals for each variable is less than half the total number. In the example $n = 13$ so that the reflections are carried to the point where there are six or fewer negative signs for each variable. This is accomplished after five variables have been reflected.

Several exceptional situations should be noted. If zero values should appear in any of the correlation or residual tables, they may be treated as positive numbers in making sign adjustments for the reflection of variables. The diagonal values of the residual tables are not considered in the count of negative signs, for, if a variable is reflected, its "self-correlation" remains unchanged. It may happen that a variable which had already been reflected may again appear as the variable with a maximum number of negative signs after several other variables have been reflected. In this case the variable is reflected again, changing the minus to plus in the first column of Table 8.25, and the number of minus signs is adjusted for each of the variables.

The variables having minus signs in the first column of Table 8.25 now may actually be reflected in Table 8.24. In order to make the procedure perfectly clear, the

Table 8.26

Rules for Sign-Change Adjustments

Previous Reflections	Entry in Row (or Column) of Reflected Variable Is Positive	Entry in Row (or Column) of Reflected Variable Is Negative
Not previously reflected (or reflected an even number of times)	Increase one	Decrease one
Previously reflected once (or any odd number of times)	Decrease one	Increase one

additional Tables 8.24a and 8.24b are provided.* First place a minus sign before the column number of each variable which is to be reflected, i.e., before variables 1, 10, 11, 12, and 13 in Table 8.24a. Then the signs of the original first-factor residuals $_1r_{jk}$ may be changed to obtain the proper algebraic signs of the residuals after reflection of variables, i.e.,

(8.73) $$r_{1jk} = \epsilon_j\epsilon_k(_1r_{jk}).$$

Since the epsilons are merely algebraic symbols for the plus or minus signs, if neither z_j nor z_k was reflected, or if both variables were reflected, then $r_{1jk} = {_1r_{jk}}$; but, if only one or the other of z_j and z_k was reflected, then $r_{1jk} = -{_1r_{jk}}$. First go through the upper half of Table 8.24 (recorded separately as 8.24a for instructional purposes only), one row at a time, and insert minus signs according to the above rules. A convenient procedure is to look at each entry of the first column, note the adjusted sign, and when this sign should be minus, record a minus sign in the corresponding cell of the first row of the upper half of the table. Check the total number of minus signs for the first variable with the number given for that variable in Table 8.25. Then proceed to the second column of the lower half of the table, note the sign changes, and record the minus signs in the second row of the upper half of the table. The count of six minus signs for variable 2, in the second column and second row of the upper half of Table 8.24a, agrees with that given in the last column of Table 8.25. Continue this process of sign changes for every variable in Table 8.24a. As an additional check, the total number of minus signs in the upper half of Table 8.24a must be equal to one-half of the total given in the last column of Table 8.25.

Now, merely copy the values (without any algebraic signs) from the columns of the lower half of Table 8.24 into the corresponding rows of the upper half of Table 8.24 (actually done in Table 8.24b for the example). The values so obtained are the residuals of the reflected variables.

* In practice, however, these additional tables may be obviated by incorporating them in Table 8.24. That procedure is indicated by Table 8.27, in which the second factor residuals are shown.

Table 8.27

Second-Factor Residuals and Calculation of C_3 Coefficients

Variable	-1	-2	-3	-4	5	6	7	8	9	10	11	12	-13	Check
1	.186	.105	.158	.183	.107	.073	.112	.084	.073	.189	.041	.015	.058	
2	.105	.076	.163	.057	-.016	.030	.113	.100	.069	.087	.026	.007	.014	$T_2 = 2\sum_{j\leq k} r_{2jk} - \sum r_{2jj}$
3	.158	.163	.165	.093	.096	.080	.132	-.058	.169	.194	.075	-.018	.093	
4	.183	.057	.093	.079	.142	.040	.040	-.038	.043	.078	.115	.027	.036	
5	-.107	.016	-.096	-.142	.049	.016	.036	.013	.109	.103	.053	.002	.052	
6	-.073	-.030	-.080	-.040	.016	.016	.082	-.041	.076	.052	.111	-.053	.038	$T_2 = 2(5.334) - .927$
7	-.112	-.113	-.132	-.040	.036	.082	.095	.039	.032	.095	-.012	.033	.006	
8	-.084	-.100	.058	.038	.013	-.041	.039	.035	-.041	.059	-.002	.037	.008	$= 9.741$
9	-.073	-.069	-.169	-.043	.109	.076	.032	-.041	.104	.049	.065	-.001	.039	
10	-.189	-.087	-.194	-.078	.103	.052	.095	.059	.049	.115	.052	.096	.076	
11	-.041	-.026	-.075	-.115	.053	.111	-.012	-.002	.065	.052	.009	-.050	-.029	
12	-.015	-.007	.018	-.027	.002	-.053	-.033	.037	-.001	.096	-.050	-.012	-.020	
13	.058	.014	.093	.036	-.052	-.038	-.006	-.008	-.039	-.076	.029	-.020	.010	
$\sum_k 2r_{jk}$	-.004	-.001	.002	.001	.000	-.002	-.003	.003	.000	-.003	-.002	.001	.001	$T_2 = 9.741$
$S_{j2} = \sum_k r_{2jk}$	1.384	.831	1.342	.895	.762	.520	.803	.195	.786	1.245	.454	.103	.421	$\sqrt{T_2} = 3.1211$
$\epsilon_j S_{j2}$	-1.384	-.831	-1.342	-.895	.762	.520	.803	.195	.786	1.245	.454	.103	-.421	$1/\sqrt{T_2} = .3204$
a_{j3}	-.443	-.266	-.429	-.287	.244	.167	.257	.062	.252	.399	.145	.033	-.135	$D_3 = -.001$

183

The second-factor coefficients are calculated by (8.68), using the residuals after reflection (in the upper half of Table 8.24). After the column sums are obtained, the algebraic signs are changed for those variables that have been reflected. The coefficients in the last line of Table 8.24b are for the observed variables, not the reflected ones. A check on the computation of the coefficients for all factors after the first is provided by the fact that the sum of the coefficients must be approximately zero for a centroid system to have been obtained. The second-factor coefficients add to precisely zero.

The second-factor residuals are computed and recorded in and below the diagonal of Table 8.27. To remove the centroid from the origin in the new residual space, sign changes are carried out as above, with the variables to be reflected determined in Table 8.28. After reflection the residuals are shown in the upper triangle of Table 8.27, and the third-factor coefficients are calculated from these values. Then the third-factor residuals are determined and given in Table 8.29. The foregoing procedure may be repeated until a sufficient number of factors are extracted to account for the total communality.

The centroid solution for the thirteen psychological tests is summarized in Table 8.30. It is evident from this table that the three factors completely account for the total starting communality.

Table 8.28

Number of Minus Signs for Second-Factor Residuals after Successive Reflections of Variables

Variable	Reflected Variable	Before Reflection	After Reflection of Successive Variables				
			1	2	4	13	3
1	−	8	4	3	2	1	0
2	−	7	8	4	3	2	1
3	−	6	7	8	9	10	2
4	−	7	8	9	3	2	1
5		4	3	4	3	2	1
6		7	6	5	4	3	2
7		6	5	4	3	2	1
8		6	5	4	5	4	5
9		7	6	5	4	3	2
10		5	4	3	2	1	0
11		7	6	5	4	5	4
12		7	6	5	4	3	4
13	−	7	8	9	10	2	1
Total		84	76	68	56	40	24
Difference			8	8	12	16	16

Table 8.29

Third-Factor Residuals (Final)

Variable	1	2	3	4	5	6	7	8	9	10	11	12	13
1	−.010	—											
2	−.013	.005	—										
3	−.032	.049	−.019	—									
4	.056	−.019	−.030	−.003	—								
5	.001	.081	.009	−.072	−.011	—							
6	.001	.014	−.008	.008	−.025	−.012	—						
7	.002	−.045	−.022	.034	−.027	.039	.029	—					
8	−.057	−.084	.085	.056	−.002	−.051	.023	.031	—				
9	.039	−.002	−.061	.029	.048	.034	−.033	−.057	.040	—			
10	−.012	.019	−.023	.037	.006	−.015	−.008	.034	−.052	−.044	—		
11	.023	.013	−.013	−.073	.018	.087	−.049	−.011	.028	−.006	−.012	—	
12	.000	.002	.032	−.018	−.006	−.059	.025	.035	−.009	.083	−.055	−.013	—
13	−.002	−.022	.035	−.003	−.019	−.015	.029	.000	−.005	−.022	.049	−.016	−.008
$\sum_k {}_3 r_{jk}$	−.004	−.002	.002	.002	.001	−.002	−.003	.002	−.001	−.003	−.001	.001	.001

Table 8.30

Centroid Solution for Thirteen Psychological Tests

Test	Common-Factor Coefficients			Communality		
				(1) Original	(2) Calculated	(1) − (2)
	C_1	C_2	C_3			
1	.607	−.060	−.443	.558	.568	−.010
2	.355	.038	−.266	.203	.198	.005
3	.418	.148	−.429	.362	.381	−.019
4	.478	.083	−.287	.314	.318	−.004
5	.729	.257	.244	.646	.657	−.011
6	.707	.354	.167	.641	.653	−.012
7	.721	.367	.257	.750	.721	.029
8	.705	.197	.062	.571	.540	.031
9	.698	.409	.252	.758	.718	.040
10	.455	−.482	.399	.554	.599	−.045
11	.537	−.390	.145	.449	.461	−.012
12	.487	−.553	.033	.531	.544	−.013
13	.674	−.368	−.135	.599	.608	−.009
Total	—	—	—	6.936	6.966	−.030
Contribution of factor (V_p)	4.620	1.392	.954	—	—	—
Per cent of total original communality	66.6	20.1	13.8	—	100.4	−0.4

9
Minres Solution

9.1. *Introduction*

As noted in chapter 6, a choice must be made of either communality estimates or the dimension of the common-factor space when using the classical factor analysis model (2.9). The methods treated in the preceding chapter involve the assumption of communalities, while the methods in this and the next chapter require the choice of the number of common factors.

The word "minres" is a contraction of "minimum residuals," and designates a long-sought method for factoring. Now that it is available, it might well replace the principal-factor and the maximum-likelihood methods for initial factorization of a correlation matrix. As noted in **2.3**, one objective of factor analysis is to "best" reproduce the observed correlations. This objective can be traced to Thurstone's statement: "The object of a factor problem is to account for the tests, or their inter-correlations, in terms of a small number of derived variables, the smallest possible number that is consistent with acceptable residual errors" [477, p. 61]. In this chapter, the factor analysis problem as posed by Thurstone is solved by maximally (in the least-squares sense) reproducing the off-diagonal elements of the correlation matrix, and, as a by-product, obtaining communalities consistent with this criterion. The contrast between this objective and that of extracting maximum variance (treated in chap. 8) should be clearly understood.

A brief history leading to the current method and the formal statement of the problem is given in **9.2**. This is followed by the actual development of the method in **9.3**. Special procedures to restrict the derived communalities from exceeding unity are developed in **9.4**. A discussion of statistical tests for the significance of the number of common factors follows in **9.5**. Then a brief outline of the computing procedures is indicated in **9.6**, and numerical illustrations of the minres solution are given in the final section.

9.2. *Formulation of the Minres Solution*

Conceptually, the idea of getting a factor solution by minimizing the residual correlations is an obviously direct approach. The first practical solution, however, was not developed until 1965 by Harman and Jones [207]. The idea certainly is not new—its accomplishment, however, was dependent on the high-speed computer. No doubt it must have crossed the minds of many workers in factor analysis over the years. The first theoretical treatment appeared in 1936, when Eckart and Young noted that "if the least-squares criterion of approximation [of one matrix by another of lower rank] be adopted, this problem has a general solution which is relatively simple in a theoretical sense, though the amount of numerical work involved in applications may be prohibitive" [114, p. 211]. This was followed in the next couple of years by additional theoretical work by Householder and Young [267] and Horst [250].

More recently, several papers have appeared that seem to bear some relationship to the problem. Whittle [519] specifically considers the residual sum of squares, but in relation to the principal-component solution. Howe seeks an alternative approach to Lawley's maximum-likelihood equations (see chap. 10) and finds that his method —maximizing the determinant of partial correlations—"is approximately equivalent to minimizing the sum of squares of the partial correlations" [268, p. 22]. Even more germane is the 1962 paper by Keller [304], which is a generalized mathematical treatment skirting the precise problem to which the minres solution is addressed.

It should be noted that none of the foregoing papers considers the minimization of off-diagonal residuals—the minimization of the total residual matrix (including diagonal terms) leads to the conventional principal-factor solution (see chap. 8). The exclusion of the diagonal elements, although appearing trivial, is of paramount importance. More specifically, as will be amplified below, the diagonal elements of the sample correlation matrix (the communalities) are not fixed but are parameters to be determined along with the factor loadings.

Probably the first attempt to obtain a practical factor solution by minimizing off-diagonal residuals was suggested by Thurstone in 1954 and carried out by Rolf Bargmann and also by Sten Henrysson [see 479, p. 61]. More recently, Comrey [85] independently developed a computing procedure for such a solution. However, these investigators do not tackle the complete problem of determining a factor solution with the property that the sum of squares of residuals between observed and reproduced correlations be a minimum. Instead they consider what might be termed a "stepwise" minimum residual method,* obtaining one factor and a residual matrix, which is then the starting point for the factor in the next step; this process is continued until a desired number of factors are extracted. In general, of course, such a solution is different from one obtained under the least-squares criterion for the entire set of factors. There has been one other attempt, by Boldt [44], which is more specifically

---

* It may be of interest to note similar "stepwise" approximations to standard statistical procedures, namely, the determination of the coefficients in multiple regression *successively* rather than *simultaneously* [143], and an approximation to a maximum-likelihood factor solution [23].

related to the method treated in this chapter. He poses the problem in essentially the same form and considers solutions by procedures similar to those tried by Harman and Jones [207, sec. 4].

The minres method assumes the classical factor analysis model (2.9), which is repeated in matrix form as follows:

$$(2.35^{bis}) \qquad\qquad \mathbf{z} = \mathbf{Af} + \mathbf{Du}.$$

Only the common-factor loadings in the matrix $\mathbf{A} = (a_{jp})$ are the parameters to be estimated. Once such a solution is obtained, the fundamental theorem of factor analysis gives (assuming uncorrelated factors, without loss of generality):

$$(2.50^{bis}) \qquad\qquad \mathbf{R}^\dagger = \mathbf{AA'},$$

where $\mathbf{R}^\dagger$ is a matrix of reproduced correlations with communalities in the principal diagonal. What is required, then, is to get a "best" fit to the observed correlation matrix $\mathbf{R}$ by the reproduced correlations $\mathbf{R}^\dagger$ employing model (2.35).

A least-squares fit can be obtained either by

$$(9.1) \qquad\qquad \text{fitting } \mathbf{R} \text{ by } (\mathbf{R}^\dagger + \mathbf{D}^2),$$

or by

$$(9.2) \qquad\qquad \text{fitting } (\mathbf{R} - \mathbf{I}) \text{ by } (\mathbf{R}^\dagger - \mathbf{H}),$$

where

$$(9.3) \qquad\qquad \mathbf{H} = \mathbf{I} - \mathbf{D}^2 = \text{diag}(\mathbf{AA'})$$

is the diagonal matrix of communalities determined from the solution $\mathbf{A}$. In the case of (9.1), the minimization of residuals of the total matrix leads to the principal-component solution (see **8.2**). In the case of (9.2), however, minimizing only the off-diagonal residuals leads to the minres solution. This condition may be expressed more precisely by:

$$(9.4) \qquad\qquad \min_{\mathbf{A}} \|[\mathbf{R} - \mathbf{I}] - [\mathbf{AA'} - \text{diag}(\mathbf{AA'})]\|,$$

in which it is emphasized that both $\mathbf{A}$ and $\mathbf{H}$ vary. The norm as expressed in (9.4) may be written out algebraically as follows:

$$(9.5) \qquad\qquad f(\mathbf{A}) = \sum_{k=j+1}^{n} \sum_{j=1}^{n-1} \left(r_{jk} - \sum_{p=1}^{m} a_{jp}a_{kp} \right)^2,$$

which is to be minimized.

It should be noted that this function involves the $n(n - 1)/2$ off-diagonal residual correlations which are dependent upon the elements in the factor matrix $\mathbf{A}$. The objective of minres is to minimize the function $f(\mathbf{A})$, for a specified m, by varying the values of the factor loadings. The diagonal matrix of communalities is obtained as a by-product of the method.

It is tacitly assumed, for the moment, that the communality produced for each variable is not greater than one. Actually, if only the condition (9.5) is imposed, an occasional minres solution would be obtained for which a communality would exceed unity. Of course, such a situation must be remedied if the factor analysis is to be acceptable. After developing the basic theory, the side conditions

$$(9.6) \qquad\qquad h_j^2 = \sum_{p=1}^{m} a_{jp}^2 \leq 1 \qquad\qquad (j = 1, 2, \cdots, n)$$

are introduced which restrict the communalities to numbers between zero and one for a minres solution.

9.3.   *Minres Method*

As noted at the beginning of this chapter, the calculation of a minres solution is so complex that it is feasible only with the aid of an electronic computer. Even then, it can get very costly in computer time unless an efficient algorithm is available. Several mathematical approaches were investigated, and tested empirically on many problems, before the recommended procedure was developed [207]. Among the methods explored and discarded was (1) the technique* of repeated calculations of a principal-factor matrix A and its associated communalities H leading to improvements in the objective function f; and (2) several variants of a class of mathematical techniques known as "gradient methods." The latter methods seek an optimal value (maximum or minimum) of a function, iteratively, by proceeding from a trial solution to the next approximation in the direction of maximal change in the function.

While the foregoing methods produced acceptable solutions, they were too time-consuming. Another mathematical method—the Gauss-Seidel process [518, sec. 130] —proved to be much more efficient. This technique is sometimes called a "method of successive displacements" because it is an iterative process in which small changes are made in the variables and the corresponding new variables replace the original ones. It can be applied effectively to the computation of a minres solution. From the basic theorem of factor analysis (2.50), it is evident that if changes or displacements are introduced in only one row of A, the reproduced correlations will be linear functions of these displacements, and the objective function f will be quadratic only.† More explicitly, for any row j in A an increment ϵ_p $(p = 1, 2, \cdots, m)$ is added to each element:

$$a_{j1} + \epsilon_1, \quad a_{j2} + \epsilon_2, \quad \cdots, \quad a_{jp} + \epsilon_p, \quad \cdots \quad {}_{jm} + \epsilon_m.$$

The new factor loadings may be written in the form:

$$(9.7) \qquad\qquad b_{jp} = a_{jp} + \epsilon_p \qquad\qquad (p = 1, 2, \cdots, m),$$

---

* This technique was employed in arriving at the solution of Table 8.14. The corresponding minres solution is given in Table 9.1.

† This reduces the computing time considerably below that required in the gradient methods, where fourth-degree polynomials have to be solved [see 207].

where the b's are used for clarity; but ultimately, when the final set of factor loadings are obtained they are again designated by a's for simplicity of notation.

Then the reproduced correlations of the fixed variable j with any other variable k is

(9.8)
$$r^{\dagger}_{jk} = \sum_{p=1}^{m} a_{kp}b_{jp},$$

and the sum of squares of residual correlations with this variable is given by

(9.9)
$$f_j = \sum_{\substack{k=1 \\ k \neq j}}^{n} \left(r_{jk} - \sum_{p=1}^{m} a_{kp}b_{jp} \right)^2 \qquad (j \text{ fixed}).$$

Upon separating out the original factor loading from the incremental change, according to (9.7), the last expression becomes:

(9.10)
$$f_j = \sum_{\substack{k=1 \\ k \neq j}}^{n} \left(r^{*}_{jk} - \sum_{p=1}^{m} a_{kp}\epsilon_p \right)^2, \qquad (j \text{ fixed}),$$

where r^{*}_{jk} are the original residual correlations of variables k with the fixed variable j (without the incremental changes in its factor loadings), that is,

(9.11)
$$r^{*}_{jk} = r_{jk} - \sum_{p=1}^{m} a_{kp}a_{jp} \qquad (k = 1, 2, \cdots, n; \quad k \neq j).$$

To determine the values of the ϵ's which minimize the objective function f, first take the partial derivatives of (9.10) with respect to each of these, say ϵ_q, as follows:

$$\frac{\partial f_j}{\partial \epsilon_q} = 2 \sum_{\substack{k=1 \\ k \neq j}}^{n} \left(r^{*}_{jk} - \sum_{p=1}^{m} a_{kp}\epsilon_p \right)(-a_{kq}) \qquad (q = 1, 2, \cdots, m).$$

Then set these expressions equal to zero, and obtain the following implicit equations for the ϵ's:

(9.12)
$$\sum_{p=1}^{m} \left(\sum_{\substack{k=1 \\ k \neq j}}^{n} a_{kp}a_{kq} \right) \epsilon_p = \sum_{\substack{k=1 \\ k \neq j}}^{n} r^{*}_{jk}a_{kq}, \qquad (q = 1, 2, \cdots, m).$$

This may be put in matrix form,

(9.13)
$$\epsilon_j \, \mathbf{A'}_{)j(} \, \mathbf{A}_{)j(} = \mathbf{r}^0_j \mathbf{A},$$

where $\epsilon_j = (\epsilon_1, \epsilon_2, \cdots, \epsilon_m)$ is the row vector of incremental changes of the factor loadings for variable j, $\mathbf{A}_{)j(}$ is the factor matrix with the elements in row j replaced by zeros, and $\mathbf{r}^0_j$ is the row vector of residual correlations of variable j with all other variables (and 0 for the self-residual). Then the solution for the displacements to the factor loadings (for a given variable) that will minimize the objective function, is:

(9.14)
$$\epsilon_j = \mathbf{r}^0_j \, \mathbf{A}(\mathbf{A'}_{)j(} \, \mathbf{A}_{)j(})^{-1}.$$

The foregoing process is carried out systematically for all variables, in turn. Thus successive approximations of rows of factor loadings are obtained which yield a minimum value for the function f to any desired degree of accuracy. However, there is no guarantee that the resulting matrix of factor loadings will not lead to communalities greater than one. This problem is taken up in the next section.

9.4.   *Additional Theory*

When a factor solution leads to the communality of some variable being greater than one, it is referred to as a "Heywood case" (see **7.3**). To constrain the minres method to proper solutions, Harman and Fukuda [205] developed a mathematical programming procedure in which the final matrix **A** is obtained by minimizing (9.5) subject to the conditions (9.6). This is introduced as a modification to the basic computing procedure of the last section only in those instances when a communality exceeds one.

Starting with the computing procedure of **9.3**, the impact on the objective function (9.5) of replacing the a_{jp} (for a fixed variable j) by b_{jp}, as defined in (9.7), is given by (9.9). This function, then, is to be minimized subject to

$$(9.15) \qquad \sum_{p=1}^{m} b_{jp}^2 \leq 1,$$

i.e., the new values of the factor loadings must satisfy the constraints (9.6) as well. At this stage of the process, the r_{jk} and the a_{kp} are known and only the b_{jp} may vary.

If the minimum of f_j, as defined in (9.9), is obtained at a point $(b_{j1}, b_{j2}, \cdots, b_{jm})$ which belongs to the region defined by (9.15) there is no problem, and no modification is required. If the point does not belong to the region, then the problem gets complicated primarily because of the *inequality* in the side condition. This inequality may be removed by means of the following:

THEOREM 9.1. *If the minimum of f_j is attained at a point outside of the region defined by* (9.15), *then a minimum of f_j under the constraint* (9.15) *will be attained at a boundary point of the region, so that the constraint may be replaced by*

$$(9.16) \qquad \sum_{p=1}^{m} b_{jp}^2 = 1.$$

The proof [205, pp. 565–68] consists of transforming the quadratic form (9.9)—involving the diagonalization of a symmetric matrix and transformations of the variables b_{jp}—to the simplified expression:

$$(9.17) \qquad f_j = \sum_{p=1}^{m} (x_p - \xi_p)^2 + K$$

and subject to the constraint

$$(9.18) \qquad \sum_{p=1}^{m} \frac{x_p^2}{\lambda_p^2} \leq 1.$$

In these derived expressions, the x_p are functions of the original b_{jp} and are the quantities to be determined; while the λ_p (eigenvalues of an $m \times m$ matrix), the ξ_p, and K are all constants determined from the known r_{jk} and a_{kp} and the intervening transformations. From the simplified form (9.17), it is evident that f_j is the sum of a constant (K) and a square of the distance between a fixed point $(\xi_1, \xi_2, \cdots, \xi_m)$ and a variable point $(x_1, x_2, \cdots, x_m)$ belonging to the region defined by (9.18). Then, minimization of f_j is equivalent to locating a point satisfying (9.18) which is at the minimum distance from the given point $(\xi_1, \xi_2, \cdots, \xi_m)$.

If the given point belongs to the region, i.e.,

$$(9.19) \qquad \frac{\xi_1^2}{\lambda_1^2} + \frac{\xi_2^2}{\lambda_2^2} + \cdots + \frac{\xi_m^2}{\lambda_m^2} \leqq 1,$$

then this point itself is the minimizing point, and the solution is

$$(9.20) \qquad x_p = \xi_p \qquad (p = 1, 2, \cdots, m).$$

On the other hand, if the given point is *outside* the region, i.e.,

$$(9.21) \qquad \frac{\xi_1^2}{\lambda_1^2} + \frac{\xi_2^2}{\lambda_2^2} + \cdots + \frac{\xi_m^2}{\lambda_m^2} > 1,$$

then a point $(x_1, x_2, \cdots, x_m)$ belonging to the region must lie on its boundary in order to be at a minimum distance from the given point. Furthermore, since the x_p/λ_p are obtained by an orthogonal transformation from the original variables, distance is preserved; therefore the point on the boundary of the region can be expressed in terms of the b_{jp} as in (9.16).

Having reduced the side condition to an equality, conventional mathematical methods are applicable to the problem of minimizing the function under the constraint, when the minimum of f_j is attained outside the region (9.15). The proof of Theorem 9.1 provides additional information which facilitates the solution of the problem. First, it shows that when the minimum of f_j is attained in the region (9.15) its value is given by K in (9.17) and the minimizing point is (9.20). More important, for the case of the minimum of f_j being attained outside this region, the foregoing development suggests a much more tractable approach than that originally posed by the problem of minimizing (9.9) under the constraint (9.16). The simplified problem, which follows from (9.17) and (9.18), is to minimize

$$(9.22) \qquad (x_1 - \xi_1)^2 + (x_2 - \xi_2)^2 + \cdots + (x_m - \xi_m)^2$$

under the constraint

$$(9.23) \qquad \frac{x_1^2}{\lambda_1^2} + \frac{x_2^2}{\lambda_2^2} + \cdots + \frac{x_m^2}{\lambda_m^2} = 1.$$

The method of Lagrange's multipliers (as employed in **8.3**) is especially suitable to this problem. This involves the creation of a new function—the function (9.22) minus

μ (the Lagrange multiplier) times the function in (9.23)—and setting its partial derivatives with respect to the m variables x_p equal to zero. This leads to the equations

$$x_1 - \xi_1 - \mu\frac{x_1}{\lambda_1^2} = 0$$

(9.24)

$$x_2 - \xi_2 - \mu\frac{x_2}{\lambda_2^2} = 0$$

$$\cdot \quad \cdot \quad \cdot \quad \cdot \quad \cdot \quad \cdot \quad \cdot$$

$$x_m - \xi_m - \mu\frac{x_m}{\lambda_m^2} = 0,$$

which, together with (9.23), constitute a set of $(m + 1)$ equations in $(m + 1)$ unknowns $x_1, x_2, \cdots, x_m, \mu$.

The parameter μ can be determined from any one of the equations (9.24), namely,

(9.25)

$$\mu = \frac{\lambda_p^2(x_p - \xi_p)}{x_p} \qquad (p = 1, 2, \cdots, m),$$

and may be eliminated by setting any one of the m determinations equal to any other. Thus, each of the subsequent determinations (9.25) may be expressed in terms of the first, i.e.,

$$\lambda_p^2\left(1 - \frac{\xi_p}{x_p}\right) = \lambda_1^2\left(1 - \frac{\xi_1}{x_1}\right),$$

and, solving explicitly for the remaining unknowns x_p in terms of x_1 produces:

(9.26)

$$x_p = \frac{\lambda_p^2\xi_p x_1}{(\lambda_p^2 - \lambda_1^2)x_1 + \lambda_1^2\xi_1} \qquad (p = 2, 3, \cdots, m).$$

Before proceeding to the general solution to the problem of minimizing (9.22) under the constraint (9.23), some special situations should be noted. If $\xi_p = 0$ for any p, then $x_p = 0$ must be a solution in order to minimize the distance, and the terms corresponding to this p may be deleted. Furthermore, it may be assumed that $\xi_p > 0$ for every p. If an ξ_p were negative for any p, it could be replaced by $|\xi_p|$ and the resulting solution x_p replaced by $-x_p$. Therefore it may be assumed that every x_p is positive.

Substitution of the values (9.26) into (9.23) gives rise to a polynomial equation in x_1 of degree $2m$. The direct solution of such an equation can become quite cumbersome, so a numerical method of successive approximations is employed. The basis for it rests on the following:

THEOREM 9.2. *For a given x_1 between 0 and* $\min(\xi_1, \lambda_1)$, *with x_p $(p = 2, 3, \cdots, m - 1)$ determined by (9.26) and x_m by (9.23), if*

(9.27)

$$\lambda_m^2\left(1 - \frac{\xi_m}{x_m}\right) \geq \lambda_1^2\left(1 - \frac{\xi_1}{x_1}\right),$$

then

(9.28)
$$x_1 \lessgtr x_1^*,$$

where x_1^* designates the solution for x_1.

The proof begins with the fact that x_p is an increasing function of x_1 (the ζ's being assumed positive). Then the two conclusions are reached by the following reasoning: If $x_1 < x_1^*$, then x_p is less than its solution x_p^*, and, consequently x_m is larger than its solution x_m^*. Therefore,

$$\lambda_1^2\left(1 - \frac{\zeta_1}{x_1}\right) < \lambda_1^2\left(1 - \frac{\zeta_1}{x_1^*}\right) = \lambda_m^2\left(1 - \frac{\zeta_m}{x_m^*}\right) < \lambda_m^2\left(1 - \frac{\zeta_m}{x_m}\right).$$

If $x_1 > x_1^*$, then a similar argument leads to

$$\lambda_1^2\left(1 - \frac{\zeta_1}{x_1}\right) > \lambda_m^2\left(1 - \frac{\zeta_m}{x_m}\right),$$

completing the proof.

Before leaving the theoretical development of the minres method, certain of its features deserve emphasis. While the principal-factor solution, in general, is not a minres solution, the converse is always true—a minres solution results from application of the principal-factor method with appropriate diagonal entries. A principal-factor solution for a correlation matrix with minres communalities cannot be different from the minres solution that produced those communalities; if it were, both the off-diagonal and the diagonal sums of squares of residuals would be increased—in the former case because the off-diagonal sum is minimized by minres and in the latter case because the diagonal sum is zero for minres. This means that the principal-factor (for the specified communalities) and minres solutions are equivalent. When put in canonical form (see **8.8**) they are identical. In schematic form,

(9.29)
$$(\mathbf{R} - \mathbf{I} + \mathbf{H}_{\min}) \xrightarrow{\text{PFA}} \mathbf{A}_{\min}$$

the theorem states that a principal-factor analysis of a correlation matrix with minres communalities produces a minres factor solution. A corollary property is that a principal-factor solution of a correlation matrix with m-factor minres communalities will have a sum of the m largest eigenvalues equal to the sum of the communalities, while the remaining $n - m$ eigenvalues will be positive and negative and add to zero.

Just as a minres solution reproduces itself through PFA, so does a maximum-likelihood solution (see chap. 10), viz.,

(9.30)
$$(\mathbf{R} - \mathbf{I} + \mathbf{H}_{ML}) \xrightarrow{\text{PFA}} \mathbf{A}_{ML}.$$

Of course, the principal-factor analysis of the correlation matrix with maximum-likelihood communalities is in canonical form, while the original maximum-likelihood solution (from which the communalities were taken) probably is not, and must first be put in that form in order to verify the equivalence. Now, the factor matrix obtained

195

by (9.30) is a least-squares fit to $(\mathbf{R} - \mathbf{I} + \mathbf{H}_{\mathrm{ML}})$ with perfect fit of the diagonal, and must therefore be a minres solution. The obvious implication of this is that minres —with its computational advantages—may be used in place of the highly desirable maximum-likelihood solution.

9.5.   *Test of Significance for the Number of Factors*

In most of this book the subject of factor analysis is treated essentially in a mathematical fashion accepting the observed data at their face value rather than samples from some universe values. While allusions are made to the "true" values, reproduced correlations are replaced by observed correlations, residuals are assumed to vanish, and the like, nonetheless there is no formal use of statistical estimation theory. It is not intended to disparage the other work, but merely to call attention to the difference between the crude approximate procedures and formal statistical tests.

It should be apparent that factor analysis deals with fallible data—the individual measurements and the correlations among the variables are subject to the vicissitudes of sampling. As a consequence, there is also sampling variation present in the results of a factor analysis. In particular, the judgment concerning the statistical significance of the number (m) of common factors should be based on their contribution to the reproduced correlations as related to the actual sampling variations of these correlations.

The problem of placing factor analysis on a sound statistical foundation has plagued its proponents from the very inception of the theory. In the early days, when the subject was relatively simple, considerable attention was paid to the statistical theory underlying its practical applications. Spearman set forth the conditions for his "Two Factor" theory in appropriate statistical terms, and some work was done on sampling errors of "tetrad difference" [e.g., 444]. In the rapid advance of factor analysis in the 1930's, the emphasis was placed on the extension of the method to encompass matrices of correlations which obviously did not form a hierarchy in Spearman's sense. The bulk of the work in this period was devoted to developing computing methods for analysis of a complex battery of psychological tests into multiple factors. In going from a single general factor to many common factors, the statistical questions were complicated manifold, but tended to be overlooked. Of course there were notable exceptions, such as the work of Hotelling [259].

In the early 1940's the first concerted efforts were made by Lawley [320, 321] to provide a statistical basis for the new methods of factor analysis. He suggested the use of the "method of maximum likelihood," due to Fisher [128, 129], as the basis for estimating the universe values of the factor loadings from the given empirical data; and for such "efficient" methods of estimation, he provided a statistical test of significance concerning the number of factors required to explain the observed correlation coefficients. These methods are presented in the next chapter.

Prior to the breakthrough in 1940 by Lawley [320] several less fruitful attempts were made to establish statistical tests for the factor analysis model (2.9). Coombs [86] considered the residual matrix, after any number of factors had been extracted, as containing both common and error variance; and he introduced the notion of "critical value" for that point at which an additional factor would contain error variance overshadowing the common-factor variance. This attempt to determine significant factors was designed specifically for the centroid method, and was dependent upon sign changes of variables and the number of negative entries in the residual matrices. Another attempt, tied to the bi-factor method of analysis, was made by Holzinger and Harman [243, pp. 122–32]. After some laborious manipulations, in the spirit of the earlier work on standard errors of tetrad differences, approximate formulas were derived for the standard error of a residual and for a factor coefficient. These results are shown in Tables A and B of the Appendix. Still another attempt to derive a significance test for the number of common factors was made by Hoel [231]. While he initially developed a test for a principal-component solution, he subsequently modified it for the centroid solution in terms of the factor model (2.9).

Hotelling [259] was the first to provide a rigorous statistical test for the number of significant factors in a principal-component solution. More recently, Bartlett [28] has made further valuable contributions to significance tests. For an analysis into principal components, he presents χ^2 approximations for testing the statistical significance of the unreduced correlation matrix and of the residual roots, i.e., after several of the largest roots have been determined. Bartlett also recommends an adjustment in the χ^2 statistic for the conventional factor analysis model.

Probably the most important theoretical work that can be applied to the minres solution was performed by Rippe [401]. Specifically, he developed a large sampling criterion for judging the completeness of factorization. The test is independent of the particular type of factor solution (in contrast to the test of **10.4** which implies maximum-likelihood estimates of the factor loadings). Its basic assumption is that the original variables have a multivariate normal distribution, from which it follows that the correlations have a Wishart distribution (see **10.3**) and the sample values are maximum-likelihood estimates of the population correlations. While Rippe's development [401, pp. 193–96] is explicitly in terms of the sample covariance matrix, the results are equally applicable to a factor analysis of the sample correlation matrix.

The statistic for testing the significance of m factors, in the notation of the present text, may be put in the form:

$$(9.31) \qquad U_m = (N - 1) \log_e \frac{|\mathbf{AA'} + \mathbf{D}^2|}{|\mathbf{R}|},$$

which is asymptotically distributed as χ^2 with degrees of freedom equal to

$$(9.32) \qquad v = \tfrac{1}{2}[(n - m)^2 + n - m].$$

The test procedure is to reject the hypothesis of m common factors if U_m exceeds the value of χ^2 for the desired significance level; otherwise it would be accepted. Of course, if the hypothesis is rejected an alternate hypothesis of some larger number of factors may be assumed to explain the observed correlations.

It should be noted that the derivation of (9.31) was based upon the sampling variation of the observed correlation matrix $\mathbf{R}$ (and consequently on the sampling variation of the factor matrix $\mathbf{A}$). The variability of the individual correlations is, of

197

course, dependent on the sample size N. Since a correlation matrix would be subject to extreme variation for small samples, it is standard practice to apply factor analysis only to large samples. Hence, the large-sample approximations made in the course of arriving at (9.31) are not really additional constraints on good experimental practice.

The distinction between statistical significance and "practical significance" should be borne in mind. Statistical significance should convey the thought of a technical test with an associated probability level. Inferences about certain numerical values obtained from an empirical study cannot be made in an absolute sense, but must be made in terms of some kind of degree of belief, i.e., in a probabilistic sense. Statistical tests of hypotheses are then described in terms of some arbitrary levels of significance, which are usually expressed as percentages with popular values being 5 and 1 per cent. Then, if the difference between the theoretical value of a statistic and its value derived from the observed data were significant at the 1 per cent level, one would conclude that the difference was "real," rejecting the null hypothesis of no difference. However, there may be practical considerations which vitiate such a conclusion. There may be real statistical additional information, but it may have no practical importance. Thus, in testing an hypothesis for the number of common factors required to explain the relationships in an observed correlation matrix (based upon a very large sample), the last one or two factors may prove to be highly significant in a statistical sense and still have no practical significance.

On the basis of actual experience, factor analysts have developed crude guides for "when to stop factoring," as indicated in **2.6**. In addition to such crude judgments about the residual matrix (which, incidentally, a number of workers have shown to be remarkably close to the more exact statistical tests), another practical approach has been found to be useful. The proportions of the total variance (or total communality) accounted for by each factor is considered. If, after 75 per cent (or 80 per cent or 90 per cent) of the total variance is accounted for, any additional factor accounts for less than 5 per cent (or 2 per cent) it would not be retained. Such arbitrary consideration is quite apart from the statistical significance of such an additional factor—it is dropped because the decision was made beforehand that any factor having such small impact on the total variance could hardly have any practical significance.

Through very extensive applications of electronic computers, Kaiser [296] has arrived at a practical basis for finding the number of common factors that are necessary, reliable, and meaningful for the explanation of the correlations among the variables. His recommendation—after considering statistical significance, algebraically necessary conditions, psychometric reliability, and psychological meaningfulness—is that the number of common factors should be equal to the number of eigenvalues greater than one of the correlation matrix (with unities in the diagonal). He has found this number to run from a sixth to about a third of the total number of variables (in the example of Table 8.19 this number is 5 out of 24 variables).

It has been found by a number of workers that empirical tests of significance used by factor analysts frequently lead to about the same results as the more proper statistical tests. The problem of identifiable versus significant factors is aptly summed up by Danford [93, p. 150]: "Perhaps the statistician's complaint about arbitrariness has become a 'smoke-screen,' but practicing statisticians will admit that tests of significance are in many circumstances superfluous to an experienced worker... [since] tests of significance may or may not indicate meaningful factors... even the 'exact' tests are arbitrary."

9.6. *Computing Procedures*

The foregoing theoretical development can be adapted to ready calculation on an electronic computer. An abbreviated flowchart for programming the minres solution is presented in Figure 9.1. A more detailed description of each step follows.

1. The complete correlation matrix $\mathbf{R}$ (with ones in the diagonal) is input by rows. Also stored are such parameters as the number of variables, n; the number of factors, m (or a range m_1 to m_2); the maximum number of iterations, t; and the convergence criterion, ϵ (not to be confused with the vector ϵ_j of incremental changes). It is convenient to have the input data printed (possibly for checking purposes).

2. The subroutine for the calculation of the eigenvalues and eigenvectors of a real symmetric matrix is used many times in the course of getting a minres solution. An example of such a subroutine is the flowchart of Figure 8.3 (also see references in **8.6**).

3. At this point the subroutine has calculated and stored the arbitrary factor matrix $\mathbf{A}_0$ with which the minres method is started, consisting of the first m principal components. Actually, the program computes a minres solution for each value of m from m_1 to m_2, but that detail is not shown in the abbreviated flowchart. The initial factor matrix $\mathbf{A}_0$ is printed, along with the communalities for the variables and the variance of each factor.

4. Calculate the incremental changes ϵ_j, which may be done according to (9.14) using step 5. The iteration process is started with the determination of increments for the first variable from the initial factor matrix $\mathbf{A}_0$ and the first row of observed correlations $\mathbf{r}_1^0$.

5. A subroutine for the solution of a system of linear equations.

6. At this point, a new factor matrix $\mathbf{A}_1$ has been determined in which the loadings in the first row have been replaced by the computed values (9.7). This constitutes iteration 1. For each iteration i, a new factor matrix $\mathbf{A}_i$ is determined (the subscript on the $\mathbf{A}$ represents the iteration number, not the pivot variable).

7. The communality h_j^2 (of the new row of $\mathbf{A}$) is tested to see if it is greater than one. If $h_j^2 > 1$ proceed to step 8, otherwise to step 15.

8. The objective function f_j of (9.9) is expressed as a quadratic form $\mathbf{b}'\mathbf{W}\mathbf{b}$ in the m unknowns, b_{jp} (j fixed, $p = 1, 2, \cdots, m$), plus a linear expression in these variables and a constant [205, sec. 2]. The symmetric matrix is determined at this stage.

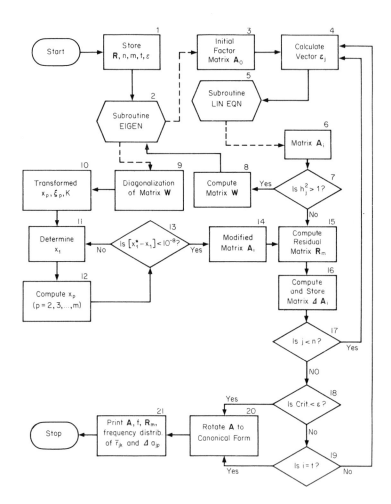

FIG. 9.1.—Flowchart for programming the minres solution

9. Diagonalization of the matrix $\mathbf{W}$ is accomplished by means of the subroutine of step 2. According to (8.21), any symmetric matrix may be diagonalized by means of an orthogonal transformation $\mathbf{Q}$, given by:

$$\mathbf{Q'WQ} = \mathbf{\Lambda},$$

where $\mathbf{\Lambda}$ is a diagonal matrix with elements $\lambda_1^2, \lambda_2^2, \cdots, \lambda_m^2$ which are the eigenvalues of $\mathbf{W}$, and the columns of $\mathbf{Q}$ are the eigenvectors of $\mathbf{W}$.

10. Additional transformations which lead to the derived unknowns x_p as functions of the original b_{jp}, and to the derived constants ξ_p and K as functions of the known r_{jk} and a_{kp}. The result of this step leads to equation (9.17) for the objective function, subject to the condition (9.18).

11. The process pivots on the first unknown x_1 and employs an iterative scheme implied by Theorem 9.2 for the determination of the remaining x's. The following initial value for x_1 seems convenient:

$$x_1^0 = \xi_1 \bigg/ \sqrt{\sum_{p=1}^{m} \left(\frac{\xi_p}{\lambda_p}\right)^2}.$$

12. Compute the remaining x_p ($p = 2, 3, \cdots, m - 1$) by use of (9.26) and x_m by use of (9.23).

13. The convergence of x_1 to x_1^*, according to Theorem 9.2, is tested. The loop, steps 11–13, constitutes the distance optimization routine, and the iteration process is continued until x_1 converges to its solution within 10^{-8}.

14. The modified matrix $\mathbf{A}_i$ is determined. This completes the modification loop, steps 8–14, to correct for $h_j^2 > 1$.

15. Compute residual matrix (with zeros in diagonal), according to (9.2), from the factor matrix $\mathbf{A}_i$ and the original correlation matrix $\mathbf{R}$. The designation $\mathbf{R}_m$ merely calls attention to the fact that the residual matrix is based upon m common factors, but the iteration number is omitted for the sake of simplicity.

16. Compute and store the matrix of changes in the factor loadings, from the preceding to the current iteration, for later use.

17. Test to see if each row of the factor matrix has been subjected to the Gauss-Siedel process. The loop from step 4 to step 17, for $j = 1, 2, \cdots, n$, constitutes a major iteration cycle. Thus, in the first major iteration cycle, the successive factor matrices $\mathbf{A}_1, \mathbf{A}_2, \cdots, \mathbf{A}_n$ are determined from the vectors $\epsilon_1, \epsilon_2, \cdots, \epsilon_n$ representing the incremental changes in the loadings for the n variables. Similarly, a set of n factor matrices are determined in each of the major iteration cycles.

18. At the conclusion of each major iteration cycle (i.e., after determining $\mathbf{A}_{cn}$, where $c = 1, 2, 3, \cdots$ is the number of the major iteration cycle), the following convergence criterion is applied:

$$\max_{j,p} |_{(i)}a_{jp} - _{(i-1)}a_{jp}| < \epsilon \qquad (j = 1, \cdots, n; \quad p = 1, \cdots, m),$$

201

where i is the iteration number. This test says that the maximum change in the factor loadings, as stored in step 16, must be less than ϵ. For most problems $\epsilon = .001$ is satisfactory.

19. If the factor loadings have not converged, a test is made to see whether the preset maximum number of iterations has been reached. As a precautionary measure, $t = 1,000$ is recommended (so the process will terminate with $i = cn$, which is the smallest multiple of n exceeding 1,000).

20. When the factor loadings have converged, or the maximum number of iterations reached, the last determined factor matrix is rotated to canonical form (see **8.8**). The subroutine of step 2 is again employed in this process.

21. The output of the program includes the minres factor matrix **A**; the final value of the objective function f; the matrix of final residuals; the frequency distributions of residuals and changes in factor loadings, along with their means and standard deviations; and the statistic U_m and the number of degrees of freedom v.

Although not shown in the flowchart, the computer program does determine U_m according to (9.31) and the associated number of degrees of freedom. The table lookup of χ^2 for comparison must be done manually.

9.7.   *Illustrative Examples*

A computer program following the procedures of **9.6** has been written [203] in FORTRAN and used on a Philco 2000 to get minres solutions for dozens of problems in the course of the experimental work, and subsequently adapted to such computers as **IBM 7044** and **CDC 3200**. It has been very satisfactory, not only in meeting the objective of minimizing the off-diagonal residuals but also in accomplishing this very efficiently. The time requirements for the calculation of minres solutions are indicated in Table 9.1. For a given problem, the time necessary to get a minres solution must be more than that required for a principal-factor analysis since the latter (at least the eigenvalue-eigenvector routine) is employed at several stages in the course of getting a minres solution. Nonetheless, the actual time requirements for the minres method are exceedingly short for small to modest-sized problems. With the new generation of fast computers the method should be practical even for very large problems.

Before considering the individual problems, a general note is in order. It should be apparent that the "best" fit of a model to empirical data, in the sense of the objective function f being a minimum, may not appear very convincing. If the model specifies two factors for a set of 50 variables, it is to be expected that the residuals may be of sizable magnitude, although the sum of squares of off-diagonal residuals has been minimized. All that can be said is that for the given hypothesis, the resulting minres solution best satisfies the least-squares criterion. As regards the actual significance of factors in the statistical sense, the procedure of **9.5** may be applied for large samples.

In any event, for a given hypothesis regarding the number of factors, it is desirable to obtain a stable factor solution. The objective, then, is to set a convergence criterion to guarantee the accuracy of the factor loadings. To be sure that the minres solution

Table 9.1

Computing Time for Minres Solutions

Problem Size		Time Estimates[a]	
		Philco 2000 (Model 210)	Computers of late 1960's
n	*m*		
5	2	3 sec	
8	2	5 sec	
8	3	18 sec	1–5 sec
9	2	5 sec	
9	3	12 sec	
24	4	39 sec	
24	5	3.0 min	5–30 sec
24	6	5.6 min	
36	12	8.0 min	40 sec
42	7	6.1 min	
42	8	6.2 min	30–60 sec
42	9	6.0 min	
42	10	12.5 min	
42	11	15.4 min	
42	12	26.3 min[b]	1–4 min
42	13	30.0 min[b]	
42	14	27.1 min	
42	15	31.8 min[b]	

[a] Based upon actual experience on the Philco computer and estimates of time on such large-scale machines as IBM System/360, CDC 6600, and GE 625.
[b] Did not converge to the standard of step 18 of the program flowchart, so that the time is for 1,008 iterations.

has stabilized, the maximum change from one iteration to the next of all factor loadings is required to be bounded by some pre-assigned small number, as specified in step 18 of the program flowchart.

1. Five socio-economic variables.—The first illustration is again for the simple numerical example introduced in chapter 2. From the previous experience with this problem, it seems reasonable to assume two common factors. Since the starting point for the minres calculations is an arbitrary factor matrix, the first two principal components are selected for that purpose (this is done automatically by the computer program, once the number of factors m is specified). The computer output gives the solution of Table 9.2, along with the final value of the objective function ($f = .00098$), the matrix of residuals and their frequency distribution, and the frequency distribution of changes in the factor loadings for the last iteration from the preceding one. While the latter data may be of interest in judging the adequacy of fit, and perhaps for the interpretation of results in a practical application, they are omitted here to conserve space. Also, tests for the statistical significance of the number of common factors are relegated to the problems and exercises for this chapter. It should be

203

Table 9.2

Minres Solution for Five Socio-Economic Variables
(Two common factors)

Variable j	F_1	F_2	h_j^2
1. Total population	.621	−.783	1.000
2. Median school years	.701	.522	.764
3. Total employment	.702	−.683	.958
4. Misc. profess. services	.881	.144	.797
5. Median value house	.781	.605	.976
Variance	2.756	1.739	4.495

evident from Table 9.2 that this problem involved a Heywood case. The first variable required the use of the modification loop (steps 8–14 of the program flowchart) in order to correct for $h_1^2 > 1$.

It is of interest to make certain comparisons of the minres and principal-factor results. Of course, the first two principal components account for more variance (4.670) than any other two factors, but the sum of squares of off-diagonal residuals produced from this initial matrix is not a minimum ($f = .01217$). For the minres solution of Table 9.2 the objective function was improved considerably. Also, while not designed to maximize variance, the two factors which provide "best" fit to the off-diagonal correlations do account for 90 per cent of the total variance in this simple problem.

2. Eight physical variables.—Next, the example of eight physical variables of **5.4** is used, with hypotheses of two and three common factors. The resulting minres solutions are presented in Table 9.3. From a quick glance at the two factor patterns, one would wonder whether there is sufficient justification for the more elaborate model—the fit of the two-factor solution is indicated by $f = .01205$, and of the three-factor solution by $f = .00452$. Also, the latter accounts for 77.1 per cent of the total variance, or slightly more than the 74.5 per cent accounted for by the former.

A closer look at the solution for $m = 2$ factors provides some additional information that may be useful for other applications of the minres method. If the model were to fit the data precisely, all residuals would vanish—but, of course, this is not to be expected of empirical data. The actual residuals range from −.027 to .044 with a mean of zero to more than four decimal places and a standard deviation of .021. From a practical point of view, the magnitude of the residuals may be considered too small to provide another meaningful factor. However, for adequate statistical explanation of the observed data on 305 cases a third factor may be required. The large sample test of **9.5** can provide an answer to such a question. The statistic (9.31) for this example becomes:

$$U_2 = 304 \log_e(.00125958)/(.00096740) = 79.8.$$

Table 9.3

Minres Solutions for Eight Physical Variables
(Two and three common factors)

Variable j	Hypothesis: $m = 2$			Hypothesis: $m = 3$			
	F_1	F_2	h_j^2	F_1	F_2	F_3	h_j^2
1. Height	.856	−.324	.838	.860	−.322	−.160	.868
2. Arm span	.848	−.412	.889	.867	−.432	.242	.998
3. Length of forearm	.808	−.409	.821	.803	−.396	.031	.803
4. Length of lower leg	.831	−.342	.808	.835	−.340	−.163	.839
5. Weight	.750	.571	.889	.751	.583	−.113	.915
6. Bitrochanteric diameter	.631	.492	.640	.626	.492	.019	.635
7. Chest girth	.569	.510	.583	.565	.508	.001	.577
8. Chest width	.607	.351	.492	.611	.362	.182	.537
Variance	4.449	1.510	5.959	4.480	1.533	.158	6.171

Here, again, a computer is necessary to obtain the determinants of the matrices of observed and reproduced correlations. The number of degrees of freedom is 21 according to (9.32). It will be found from Table D in the Appendix that for 21 degrees of freedom $\chi^2 = 46.8$ for $P = .001$. This says that the probability of getting a value of χ^2 in excess of 46.8 is only 1 in 1,000, and since the actual value $U_2 = 79.8$ is considerably greater, the hypothesis of $m = 2$ is rejected and it must be assumed that at least three common factors are required for adequate explanation of the observed data.

Next, the statistical test for $m = 3$ can be made. Of course, the determinant of the matrix of observed correlations remains unchanged. The determinant of the matrix of reproduced correlations from the solution with three factors is .00105459, slightly smaller than that for the solution with two factors. The statistic (9.31) then has the value $U_3 = 26.2$, with 15 degrees of freedom. The corresponding χ^2's are 37.7 for $P = .001$, 30.6 for $P = .01$, and 25.0 for $P = .05$. The hypothesis of three common factors would be rejected at the 5 per cent level but would be accepted at the 1 per cent level.

The solution with three common factors was used in an empirical investigation of the relationship between minres and maximum-likelihood solutions. As noted at the end of section **9.4**, a principal-factor analysis of a correlation matrix with maximum-likelihood communalities produces a maximum-likelihood solution which is equivalent to the original one from which the communalities were taken—yet this solution is a minres solution. According to the conditions for minres and for maximum-likelihood (see **10.3**), the two solutions should be identical only if the communalities are equal. How much the actual communalities for a set of n variables may differ and still produce practically equivalent results is a matter for empirical investigation (so long as it is understood that it is not mathematical equality that is sought). For the

205

current example the following solutions were obtained:
　　Maximum-likelihood (arbitrary initial matrix),
　　Principal-factor (ML communalities),
　　Minres (ML initial matrix), and
　　Maximum-likelihood (minres initial matrix).
After the maximum-likelihood solutions were put in canonical form, all four solutions were practically identical. Communalities and contributions of factors differed only in the third decimal place; and individual factor loadings, with only a few exceptions, agreed to within a few units in the third place. The equivalence of these solutions was found in spite of the fact that the 8 communalities range from .5 to 1.0 as can be seen in Table 9.3.

It should be noted, however, that the minres solution found to be equivalent to a maximum-likelihood solution was for a particular local maximum (solution 2 of Table 10.6), while another maximum-likelihood solution (number 1 of Table 10.6) differed from it. This problem—local versus global maximum or minimum—is unresolved for either the maximum-likelihood or the minres method. Even when a computing procedure converges there is no assurance that the optimal point (maximum or minimum) is for the entire surface in the multidimensional space or only for a local area. In practical usage, this question may be immaterial as long as a reasonably good solution is obtained.

3. Eight emotional variables.—Another eight-variable example is used for illustration—the eight emotional traits of **8.7**—primarily because of the difficulties encountered in trying to get a principal-factor solution based upon SMC's as communalities. Of course, no such difficulties arose in the minres method because no prior estimates of communalities are required. Instead, the hypothesis of two common factors was assumed (based on the prior experience with this problem), and the resulting minres solution is shown in Table 9.4.

Table 9.4

Minres Solution for Eight Emotional Traits
(Two common factors)

Variable j	F_1	F_2	h_j^2
1	.982	.065	.968
2	.935	−.111	.888
3	.833	−.550	.997
4	.720	−.091	.526
5	.676	.330	.566
6	.526	.164	.304
7	.515	.583	.605
8	.355	−.128	.142
Variance	4.176	.820	4.996

It is interesting to note that the minres solution is very similar to the principal-factor solution of Table 8.16. The most important differences occur for variable 3 (tenderness) for which the minres loadings are somewhat larger and the communality almost one-tenth bigger. The total communality (4.996) produced by the minres solution is larger than the estimated communality (4.87) on which the principal-factor analysis was performed. As regards interpretation of results, everything stated about the principal-factor solution in **8.7** applies equally well to the minres solution.

Because of the difficulties with this problem indicated in **8.7**, it was decided to make further explorations with the minres method. If the correlation matrix were indeed singular, what would happen if minres solutions were attempted for $m = 3, 4, \cdots, 8$? If multicollinearity exists among these eight variables, then solutions up to $m = 8$ should not be possible. That is, in fact, what happened. A brief summary of some of the pertinent findings is given in Table 9.5. It can readily be seen that all the correlations (given to two decimal places) are completely explained (mathematically) by the time $m = 6$. Any analysis from that point to $m = 8$ can only be a manipulation of "noise" in the computing system. Actually, the solution of Table 9.4 in terms of two factors still appears to be at the practical level. A solution for $m = 3$ might be considered if one really wanted to get a near perfect fit to the observed correlations.

Table 9.5

Characteristics of Minres Solutions for Eight Emotional Traits
(Two to six common factors)

Number of Factors m	Objective Function f	Number of Communalities equal to 1 (to 2 dec.)	Number of Iterations (max = 1000)	Time (on Philco 2000)
2	.07431	1	56	5.0 sec
3	.02605	2	88	18.7 sec
4	.01380	4	1,000	8.4 min
5	.00277	4	1,000	12.1 min
6	.00018	7	1,000	25.5 min

4. Twenty-four psychological tests.—The final illustrations involve a fair-sized problem. To demonstrate the practicability of the minres method, the twenty-four psychological tests (from Table 7.4) were analyzed in terms of 4, 5, and 6 factors. As indicated in Table 9.1, minres solutions were obtained for all three situations in about nine minutes on a relatively slow computer (in 1966) while the same task could be accomplished in less than one minute on existing truly fast computers.

To conserve space, the complete minres solution is shown only for the case of five common factors in Table 9.6. It should be recalled that a minres solution is in canonical

Table 9.6

Minres Solution for Twenty-four Psychological Tests
(Five common factors)

Test j	F_1	F_2	F_3	F_4	F_5	h_j^2
1	.597	.028	.341	.274	.020	.549
2	.372	−.033	.231	.208	−.036	.237
3	.420	−.111	.365	.127	.129	.355
4	.483	−.112	.228	.240	.006	.355
5	.686	−.308	−.277	.006	.002	.642
6	.685	−.404	−.181	−.102	−.017	.675
7	.676	−.420	−.294	.005	.084	.728
8	.673	−.200	−.096	.073	.076	.514
9	.695	−.452	−.204	−.120	.010	.743
10	.473	.511	−.498	.050	.038	.736
11	.555	.349	−.170	−.079	−.055	.468
12	.470	.493	−.203	.272	−.007	.580
13	.598	.254	−.025	.273	.111	.509
14	.426	.059	.025	−.329	−.302	.386
15	.392	.097	.105	−.258	−.314	339
16	.512	.090	.348	−.108	−.272	.477
17	.465	.207	.020	−.331	−.156	.393
18	.518	.318	.156	−.091	−.060	.405
19	.492	.182	.285	−.508	.621	1.000
20	.616	−.141	.119	.055	−.179	.449
21	.594	.208	.050	.139	.042	.419
22	.610	−.103	.125	−.020	.008	.398
23	.688	−.065	.128	.131	.003	.512
24	.651	.167	−.185	−.050	.087	.496
Variance	7.671	1.700	1.241	.985	.767	12.365

form with the factors appearing in the order of their contribution to the total variance
that is analyzed. Therefore, it is relatively easy to make direct comparisons with the
corresponding principal factors of Table 8.21. By looking at the variance accounted
for by each factor, it will be found that each of the minres factors accounts for more
than the corresponding principal factor—with only minor differences for the first
four factors and a very significant difference for the fifth. Upon looking more closely
it is found that variable 19 is primarily responsible for the additional variance of F_5.
As a matter of fact, in the principal-factor analysis a value of .367 was used as the
estimate of h_{19}^2 (and only .287 resulted from the solution), while the minres solution
produces the limiting value (1.00) for this communality. This was not the case for the
minres solution with four factors ($h_{19}^2 = .235$) but it remained at the limiting value
with six factors.

While the principal-factor method accounts for the maximum variance for a given
number of factors, it cannot account for more variance than originally put in the
correlation matrix (i.e., the estimates of the communalities). In the principal-factor

solution of Table 8.21, the squared multiple correlations were analyzed. These are known to be lower-bound estimates of the communalities. Therefore, it is not surprising that the minres solution accounts for almost 4 per cent more than the total communality calculated in the principal-factor solution. The by-product of the minres method—the communalities determined for the specified number of factors—certainly provides the best known approximation to the concept of communality.

In the discussion of this problem in **8.7** it was argued that five factors appeared to be the optimal number and that even four might suffice from a practical vantage point. That served as a guide in this chapter as well. Nonetheless, it is advisable to study the effect of the different number of factors. Without carrying this notion to an extreme, a comparison is made of certain statistics for the choices of four, five, and six factors. Table 9.7 presents such statistics. It should be obvious that as the complexity of the

Table 9.7

Frequency Distributions of Minres Residuals for Twenty-four Psychological Tests
(Four, five, and six common factors)

Class Interval	Frequency		
	$m = 4$	$m = 5$	$m = 6$
More than .0475	29	25	16
.0425– .0475	9	6	7
.0375– .0425	6	6	5
.0325– .0375	7	8	10
.0275– .0325	16	11	10
.0225– .0275	15	19	11
.0175– .0225	19	10	14
.0125– .0175	13	19	18
.0075– .0125	12	12	18
.0025– .0075	15	24	24
−.0025– .0025	9	11	25
−.0075—.0025	14	18	18
−.0125– −.0075	12	17	15
−.0175– −.0125	13	8	14
−.0225– −.0175	9	11	14
−.0275– −.0225	12	14	7
−.0325– −.0275	6	7	16
−.0375– −.0325	10	8	8
−.0425– −.0375	10	10	2
−.0475– −.0425	5	4	4
less than −.0475	35	28	20
Total	276	276	276
Mean	−.0000467	−.0000225	−.0000169
S.D.	.04089	.03708	.03186
$f(\mathbf{A})$	.45989	.37811	.27909

model is increased, the fit should be improved. This is evident from the actual frequency distributions and from the summary statistics (means, standard deviations, and the objective function). The extent to which the model fits the off-diagonal correlations may be judged not only by the decrease in the objective function as the model increases from four to five to six factors, but also by comparing these values with the corresponding ones for principal-component solutions. Thus, the improvement in the sum of squares of residuals for each hypothesis is given by:

$$m = 4: \quad f_{pc} - f_{min} = .46788$$

$$m = 5: \quad f_{pc} - f_{min} = .52775$$

$$m = 6: \quad f_{pc} - f_{min} = .55765.$$

Thus, while the objective function is smaller for a larger number of factors, whether computed for a principal-component or a minres solution, the difference between the two solutions becomes more pronounced as the number of factors in a model goes up.

Finally, the more precise statistical criterion of **9.5** is applied to test the hypothesis of five common factors. The values of the determinants, obtained on a computer, are as follows:

$$|\mathbf{AA'} + \mathbf{D}^2| = .0000507017$$

$$|\mathbf{R}| = .0000107920,$$

and for $N = 145$ cases, the statistic (9.31) becomes $U_5 = 222.8$. The number of degrees of freedom, according to (9.32) is $v = 190$. While Table D does not extend to such a large value of v the probability can be approximated from the normal distribution. This is accomplished by setting

$$z = \sqrt{2\chi^2} - \sqrt{2v - 1},$$

treating it as a normal deviate with unit variance, and reading the area under the normal curve from Table C in the Appendix. Then the probability for χ^2 corresponds to the area of a single tail of the normal curve beyond the particular deviate. If a χ^2 equal to U_5 is considered, the normal deviate becomes $z = 1.64$ and

$$P = .50 - .4495 = .05,$$

where the area from the mean to the deviate is taken from Table C. Hence the hypothesis of five common factors is accepted at the 5 per cent level of significance.

10

Maximum-Likelihood Solution

10.1. *Introduction*

It was mentioned in **9.5** that Lawley [320, 321] in the early 1940's made a fundamental contribution to factor analysis by providing a statistical basis for judging the
adequacy of the model (2.9), with a specified number of factors, to explain an empirical
correlation matrix. His statistical test for the number of common factors is dependent
upon a particular type of factor solution, namely, maximum-likelihood estimates of
the factor loadings. The amount of computation arising from this method restricted
its use to small problems in the 1940's and 1950's. While present-day computers make
the maximum-likelihood method feasible, the perplexing question of the actual
convergence of the process still remains.

Because this chapter is concerned with formal statistical theory, a brief summary
of some of the basic ideas in statistical estimation is presented in **10.2.** With this
foundation, the exposition of the maximum-likelihood methods in factor analysis
becomes more meaningful and clear. Such a development is given in **10.3**, including
the essential mathematics for estimating the factor coefficients. This is followed in
10.4 by an asymptotic χ^2 test of significance for the number of common factors.
Detailed computing procedures for estimating factor loadings by the maximum-
likelihood method and for testing an hypothesis regarding the number of factors are
outlined in **10.5** and illustrated with the example of eight physical variables. Further
discussion of numerical illustrations is given in **10.6**.

10.2. *Statistical Estimation*

Most of the development in this text has been essentially in terms of *mathematical*
solutions. While factor analysis methods were applied to sample correlation matrices,
the interpretation of results tacitly has been in terms of the population from which
the sample presumably was drawn. With the exception of the discussion in **9.5**, little
attention has been paid to the *statistical* problems of the uncertainty of conclusions

that might be derived from the empirical data. In this chapter, on the contrary, a conscious distinction is made between the intercorrelations of the observed variables and the hypothetical values in the universe from which they were sampled. Then, based on the observed data, estimates are obtained of the universe factor weights, under the assumption of the factor model (2.9), and the statistical significance of such hypotheses is determined.

To help clarify the ensuing methods of analysis, some of the fundamental concepts in statistical estimation are reviewed in this section. First of all, the process of estimation is concerned with making inferences about the values of unknown population parameters from the incomplete data of a sample. Suppose, for example, that the distribution function for a variable x is dependent upon two parameters, θ_1 and θ_2. This is usually represented by $f(x; \theta_1, \theta_2)$, and may be conceived as a distribution function of a single observation x. In contrast, the joint distribution of N (independent) observations $x_1, x_2, \cdots, x_N$ is given by the product of the individual functions, viz.,

$$\prod_{i=1}^{N} f(x_i; \theta_1, \theta_2).$$

When the foregoing is considered as a function of the θ's for fixed x's it is often called the "likelihood function" of the sample, and is denoted by L.

The typical estimation problem involves the determination of numerical values for θ_1 and θ_2 from a random sample of N observations. To estimate the parameters is then tantamount to finding functions of the observations—usually denoted by $\hat{\theta}_1(x_1, x_2, \cdots, x_N)$ and $\hat{\theta}_2(x_1, x_2, \cdots, x_N)$—such that the distribution of these functions in repeated samples will concentrate near the true values. Such functions of the sample values are called *estimators*.

Since there are many choices for an estimating function, the following criteria are frequently used in selecting among them:

1. An estimator $\hat{\theta}$ is said to be *consistent* if it converges (in a probabilistic sense) to the true parameter as the sample increases without limit, i.e.,

$$\lim_{N \to \infty} \hat{\theta} \to \theta$$

2. An estimator is said to be *efficient* if it has the smallest limiting variance. When an estimator is efficient it is also consistent.
3. An estimator is said to be *sufficient* if it utilizes all the information in the sample concerning the parameter.
4. If the expected value of the estimator is the true parameter, i.e.

$$E(\hat{\theta}) = \theta,$$

then the estimator is *unbiased*. While it is of some advantage to devise an unbiased estimate, it is not a very critical requirement.

The method of maximum likelihood is a well-established and popular statistical procedure for estimating the unknown population parameters because such estimators satisfy the first three of the above standards. Not all parameters have sufficient estimators but if one exists the maximum-likelihood estimator is such a sufficient estimator [369, p. 185]. However, a maximum-likelihood estimator will generally not be unbiased.* This method yields values of the estimators which maximize the likelihood function of a sample.

An application of the method of maximum likelihood to a well-known situation may be useful by way of introduction to the more complex problem treated in **10.3**. Consider the normal distribution for the single variable X:

$$(10.1) \qquad f(X;\mu,\sigma) = \frac{1}{\sqrt{2\pi}\sigma} e^{-(1/2\sigma^2)(X-\mu)^2}$$

which is dependent upon two parameters, the universe values of the mean and standard deviation. The likelihood function is defined by

$$(10.2) \qquad L = \prod_{i=1}^{N} f(X_i;\mu,\sigma),$$

and for the N independent observations takes the form:

$$(10.3) \qquad L = \frac{1}{(2\pi)^{N/2}\sigma^N} \exp - \left(\frac{1}{2\sigma^2}\right) \sum_{i=1}^{N} (X_i - \mu)^2.$$

To get the maximum-likelihood estimators of μ and σ it is necessary to maximize the likelihood function L. However, since likelihood functions are products, and many are expressed in terms of exponentials as in the example, it is customary to maximize the logarithm (to the base e) of the likelihood instead. This is done merely to simplify the mathematics because the maximum of the logarithm occurs at the same point as that of the likelihood itself. Proceeding in this manner, the logarithm of the likelihood (10.3) is

$$(10.4) \qquad \log L = -\frac{N}{2}\log 2\pi - N\log\sigma - \frac{1}{2\sigma^2}\sum_{i=1}^{N}(X_i - \mu)^2.$$

The maximum of this function of the two variables μ and σ can be obtained by setting its partial derivatives (with respect to each of the variables) equal to zero and solving for them. Thus,

$$(10.5) \qquad \frac{\partial(\log L)}{\partial\mu} = \frac{1}{\sigma^2}\sum_{i=1}^{N}(X_i - \mu) = \frac{1}{\sigma^2}\left(\sum_{i=1}^{N}X_i - N\mu\right),$$

$$\frac{\partial(\log L)}{\partial\sigma} = -\frac{N}{\sigma} + \frac{1}{\sigma^3}\sum_{i=1}^{N}(X_i - \mu)^2,$$

and upon equating these to zero, and solving for μ and σ^2, the following maximum-

* By getting the expected value of such an estimator, an unbiased statistic can be derived.

213

likelihood estimators are obtained:

$$\hat{\mu} = \frac{1}{N} \sum_{i=1}^{N} X_i = \overline{X}$$

(10.6)

$$\hat{\sigma}^2 = \frac{1}{N} \sum_{i=1}^{N} (X_i - \overline{X})^2.$$

These estimators of the universe μ and σ^2 correspond to the well-known first and second moments of the sample. It should be noted that while the estimator $\hat{\mu}$ is unbiased, the estimator $\hat{\sigma}^2$ is not. Actually, the expected value of this estimator is slightly less than the true parameter, viz.,

(10.7)
$$E(\hat{\sigma}^2) = \frac{N-1}{N} \sigma^2.$$

In other words, an unbiased estimate of σ^2 (but not the maximum-likelihood estimate) is

(10.8)
$$\tilde{\sigma}^2 = \frac{1}{N-1} \sum_{i=1}^{N} (X_i - \overline{X})^2.$$

10.3. *Maximum-Likelihood Estimates of Factor Loadings*

Instead of developing mathematical theory for the exact determination of the factor coefficients under such assumptions as those that led to the bi-factor, principal-factor, or minres solutions, the present approach is somewhat different. Under the assumption of a given number (m) of common factors, the method of maximum likelihood is applied to get estimators of the universe factor loadings from the sample of N observations on the n tests. Subsequent (see **10.4**) tests of significance can be applied to determine the adequacy of the hypothesis regarding the number of factors. Although the maximum-likelihood principle is relatively simple, the algebraic manipulations are not; therefore the detailed mathematical derivations will be omitted.

First, the model to be used will be stated, together with the assumptions as to distributions. Specifically, the expression (2.9) for a variable in standard form is adopted, more generally, to the case of any variable in its respective unit of measurement, as follows:

(10.9) $$x_j = a_{j1}F_1 + a_{j2}F_2 + \cdots + a_{jm}F_m + d_jU_j.$$

Without loss of generality, it may be assumed that the test scores have zero means. It is further assumed that all factors $F_1, F_2, \cdots, F_m, U_1, U_2, \cdots, U_n$ are independent, normally distributed variables with zero means and unit variances. A consequence of this assumption is that the x's have a multivariate normal distribution.

The question of orthogonal or oblique factors is of no consequence here. The statistical estimation problem is concerned explicitly with the prediction of factor loadings for orthogonal factors out of consideration of the mathematical difficulties that would otherwise ensue. Once the (maximum-likelihood) common-factor space

214

is determined, rotation to an oblique frame of reference may be made just as in the case of any other initial solution.

Before proceeding further, it is advisable to employ matrix notation in order to present a complex subject in a compact form. To this end, the necessary basic notation is summarized in Table 10.1.

Table 10.1

Notation for Matrices in Statistical Estimation of Factor Weights

Matrix			Order	Definition
Population	Estimator	Sample		
$\Sigma = (\sigma_{jk})$	$\hat{\Sigma}$	$S = (s_{jk})$	$n \times n$	Covariance matrix
$P = (\rho_{jk})$	$\hat{P}$	$R = (r_{jk})$	$n \times n$	Correlation matrix (unities in diagonal)
$A = (a_{jp})$	$\hat{A}$	—	$n \times m$	Matrix of common-factor coefficients
$D^2 = (d_j^2)$	$\hat{D}^2$	—	$n \times n$	Diagonal matrix of uniquenesses

The need for theory on the sampling distributions of statistics of many variables has led to a special branch of mathematical statistics—multivariate statistical analysis. To make the problem tractable in this complex subject, suitable conditions must be introduced. Thus, even the problem of determining the variance of a sample co-variance matrix is extremely difficult for samples from an arbitrary distribution. However, under the assumption that the sample comes from a multivariate normal distribution, the actual distribution function of the elements of the covariance matrix can be determined. This remarkable result was first derived by Wishart [526] in 1928, and may be expressed as follows:

$$(10.10) \qquad dF = K|\Sigma|^{-\frac{1}{2}(N-1)}|S|^{\frac{1}{2}(N-n-2)} \exp -\frac{N-1}{2} \sum_{j,k=1}^{n} \sigma^{jk} s_{jk} \prod_{j<k=1}^{n} ds_{jk},$$

where K is a constant involving only N and n, and in addition to the determinants of the population and sample covariance matrices, the notation σ^{jk} is employed for the elements of the inverse matrix Σ^{-1} according to 3.2, paragraph 22.

Considered as a function of the σ's, the expression (10.10), aside from the product of the differentials, is the likelihood function L of the sample. The remaining task is to find estimates $\hat{A}$ and $\hat{D}^2$ satisfying,

$$(10.11) \qquad \Sigma = AA' + D^2,$$

which maximize L. To this end the logarithm (to the base e) of the likelihood function for Wishart's distribution is first obtained:

$$(10.12) \qquad \log L = -\frac{N-1}{2}\left(\log|\Sigma| + \sum_{j,k=1}^{n} \sigma^{jk} s_{jk}\right) + \text{function independent of } \Sigma.$$

215

Corresponding to the maximization of L (or its logarithm) is the minimization of the expression,

$$(10.13) \qquad -\frac{2}{N-1} \log L = \log |\Sigma| + \sum_{j,k=1}^{n} \sigma^{jk} s_{jk} + \text{function independent of } \Sigma,$$

which may be more convenient to program.

The next steps consist of finding the partial derivatives of (10.13) with respect to each of the a_{jp} and d_j, $(nm + n$ variables in all), equating these to zero, and solving the resulting equations. Since this process involves extensive algebraic manipulations, only the results will be shown. It is convenient at this point, however, to note that Lawley [320] and others have shown that the estimation equations are independent of the scale of measurement of the x's in the sense that the estimated factor loadings for a particular variable are proportional to the standard deviation of that variable. Consequently, the estimation equations for the a's can be expressed in terms of the correlations rather than the covariances. The results, first obtained by Lawley [320, pp. 66–71], can be put compactly in the following matrix form:

$$(10.14) \qquad\qquad\qquad \mathbf{P} = \hat{\mathbf{A}}\hat{\mathbf{A}}' + \hat{\mathbf{D}}^2$$

$$(10.15) \qquad\qquad\qquad \hat{\mathbf{A}} = \hat{\mathbf{P}}\mathbf{R}^{-1}\hat{\mathbf{A}}$$

$$(10.16) \qquad\qquad\qquad \hat{\mathbf{D}}^2 = \mathbf{I} - \text{diag } \hat{\mathbf{A}}\hat{\mathbf{A}}'$$

$$(10.17) \qquad\qquad\qquad \hat{\mathbf{A}}'\mathbf{R}^{-1}\hat{\mathbf{A}} \text{ is diagonal}$$

where $\mathbf{P}$ (capital rho) is the population correlation matrix, $\hat{\mathbf{P}}$ is its estimator, and $\mathbf{R}$ is the corresponding matrix in the sample (of course, with unities in the diagonal). It should be noted that the a's in (10.11) are different from the q's in (10.14), since in the former case the specific units of the several variables are implied while in the latter case the variables are standardized. The same symbols are employed for the elements (and the matrices) in the two cases only for the sake of simplicity. Another point must be mentioned: the condition (10.17) is introduced solely to remove the inherent indeterminacy of $\mathbf{A}$ due to the arbitrariness of rotation. This condition is somewhat analogous to the orthogonality property (8.23) of the principal-factor solution; or, to the canonical form described in **8.8** and employed to fix the position of the minres solution in **9.6**. The latter condition can certainly be substituted for (10.17).

While equations (10.14) and (10.15), with the conditions (10.16) and (10.17), provide a basis for obtaining maximum-likelihood estimates of the factor loadings, they do entail considerable work, especially to get the inverse of the correlation matrix. The procedure may be simplified by making the assumption that the estimator $\hat{\mathbf{P}}$ is equal to the observed correlation matrix $\mathbf{R}$, so that (10.14) may be written:

$$(10.18) \qquad\qquad\qquad \mathbf{AA}' + \mathbf{D}^2 = \mathbf{R},$$

where, for simplicity, the caps have been removed from the estimates. Premultiplying both sides of (10.18) by $\mathbf{A'D}^{-2}$ yields*

(10.19)
$$(\mathbf{A'D}^{-2}\mathbf{A} + \mathbf{I})\mathbf{A'} = \mathbf{A'D}^{-2}\mathbf{R},$$

and defining

(10.20)
$$\mathbf{J} = \mathbf{A'D}^{-2}\mathbf{A}$$

can be put in the form

(10.21)
$$(\mathbf{I} + \mathbf{J})\mathbf{A'} = \mathbf{A'D}^{-2}\mathbf{R}.$$

Finally, this equation can be simplified to

(10.22)
$$\mathbf{JA'} = \mathbf{A\,D}^{-2}\mathbf{R} - \mathbf{A'},$$

which is amenable to an iterative method of solution. Equation (10.22) is employed along with (10.14) and (10.16), but the matrix $\mathbf{J}$ defined in (10.20) is required to be diagonal as an alternate condition to (10.17). The important effect of the simplified procedure is to replace the calculation of the inverse of a matrix of order n by one of order m—a tremendous saving since the number of common factors is usually much smaller than the number of variables.

The iterative method for solving (10.22) for the factor loadings, due to Lawley [321, p. 181], will now be described in the matrix notation of the present chapter, and illustrated with a numerical example in **10.5**. Since the factor loadings are computed one factor at a time, with succeeding factor weights being dependent on those already determined, it is convenient to designate the separate vectors of the factor-pattern matrix $\mathbf{A}$, viz.,

(10.23)
$$\mathbf{A} = (\mathbf{a}_1\,\mathbf{a}_2 \cdots \mathbf{a}_m),$$

where any one of the m column vectors is given by

(10.24)
$$\mathbf{a}_p = \{a_{1p}\,a_{2p} \cdots a_{np}\} \qquad (p = 1, 2, \cdots, m).$$

Corresponding to the trial values $\mathbf{a}_p$, the values derived from the iterative process are designated $\mathbf{b}_p$, with $\mathbf{B}$ for the complete pattern matrix and $\mathbf{E}^2$ for the new uniqueness matrix. The iteration equations, exemplified by the following for the case of three factors, are immediately generalizable to any number of factors:

$$\mathbf{b}_1 = (\mathbf{RD}^{-2}\mathbf{a}_1 - \mathbf{a}_1)/\sqrt{\mathbf{a}_1'\mathbf{D}^{-2}(\mathbf{RD}^{-2}\mathbf{a}_1 - \mathbf{a}_1)}$$

$$\mathbf{b}_2 = (\mathbf{RD}^{-2}\mathbf{a}_2 - \mathbf{a}_2 - \mathbf{b}_1\mathbf{b}_1'\mathbf{D}^{-2}\mathbf{a}_2)/\sqrt{\mathbf{a}_2'\mathbf{D}^{-2}(\mathbf{RD}^{-2}\mathbf{a}_2 - \mathbf{a}_2 - \mathbf{b}_1\mathbf{b}_1'\mathbf{D}^{-2}\mathbf{a}_2)}$$

(10.25) $\quad\mathbf{b}_3 = (\mathbf{RD}^{-2}\mathbf{a}_3 - \mathbf{a}_3 - \mathbf{b}_1\mathbf{b}_1'\mathbf{D}^{-2}\mathbf{a}_3 - \mathbf{b}_2\mathbf{b}_2'\mathbf{D}^{-2}\mathbf{a}_3)/$

$$\sqrt{\mathbf{a}_3'\mathbf{D}^{-2}(\mathbf{RD}^{-2}\mathbf{a}_3 - \mathbf{a}_3 - \mathbf{b}_1\mathbf{b}_1'\mathbf{D}^{-2}\mathbf{a}_3 - \mathbf{b}_2\mathbf{b}_2'\mathbf{D}^{-2}\mathbf{a}_3)}$$

$$\mathbf{E}^2 = \mathbf{I} - \text{diag } \mathbf{BB'}$$

* It is tacitly assumed that none of the uniquenesses vanishes.

To avoid further complications in notation, it is suggested that the **b**'s and **E** be replaced by **a**'s and **D** after each iteration before beginning the calculations anew. The computations by equations like (10.25) are repeated again and again until convergence is obtained to the desired degree of accuracy. The final matrix **A** contains the maximum-likelihood estimates of the factor loadings for the assumed number of common factors.

A variant of the preceding method was recently developed and a computer program made available [204]. While still based on the assumption (10.18), it does not merely discard the off-diagonal values of **J** (in substituting (10.20) for (10.17) as the side condition) but actually diagonalizes this matrix. The essential part of the program can be described as follows:

(10.26)

1. Start with an arbitrary factor matrix $\mathbf{A}_{\frac{1}{2}}$ (usually the first m principal components). The reason for the subscript $\frac{1}{2}$ will become clear in the ensuing steps.
2. $\mathbf{D}_i^2 = \text{diag}\,(\mathbf{I} - \mathbf{A}_{i-\frac{1}{2}}\mathbf{A}'_{i-\frac{1}{2}})$, where $i = 1, 2, 3, \cdots$ is the iteration number.
3. $\mathbf{J}_{i-\frac{1}{2}} = \mathbf{A}'_{i-\frac{1}{2}}\mathbf{D}_i^{-2}\mathbf{A}_{i-\frac{1}{2}}$, from definition (10.20).
4. $\mathbf{J}_i = \mathbf{Q}'_i\mathbf{J}_{i-\frac{1}{2}}\mathbf{Q}_i$, according to (8.21).
5. $\mathbf{A}_i = \mathbf{A}_{i-\frac{1}{2}}\mathbf{Q}_i$, rotation of $\mathbf{A}_{i-\frac{1}{2}}$ for which $\mathbf{J}_i$ is diagonal.
6. $\mathbf{A}_{i+\frac{1}{2}} = (\mathbf{RD}_i^{-2} - \mathbf{I})\mathbf{A}_i\mathbf{J}_i^{-1}$, from (10.22).
7. Test for convergence: $|\mathbf{A}_{i+\frac{1}{2}} - \mathbf{A}_{i-\frac{1}{2}}| < \epsilon$?

In the foregoing algorithm the subscripts with the $\frac{1}{2}$'s designate intermediate matrices that are employed in the course of a particular iteration, which is represented by a subscript without a $\frac{1}{2}$ in it. The point of departure is step 4 in which the matrix **J** is diagonalized. This is accomplished, in the ith iteration, by means of the Spectral Theorem (8.21) which states that for $\mathbf{Q}_i$ orthogonal (i.e., $\mathbf{Q}_i\mathbf{Q}'_i = \mathbf{I}$), the symmetric matrix $\mathbf{J}_{i-\frac{1}{2}}$ is diagonalized by the transformation matrix $\mathbf{Q}_i$ so that the new matrix $\mathbf{J}_i$ is the diagonal matrix of eigenvalues of $\mathbf{J}_{i-\frac{1}{2}}$; and the columns of $\mathbf{Q}_i$ are the (normalized) eigenvectors of $\mathbf{J}_{i-\frac{1}{2}}$. After the new matrix of factor loadings is obtained, the test for convergence is applied. The loop, steps 2–7, is repeated until the maximum change in the difference of factor loadings is below some specified level (usually $\epsilon = .001$).

Because the maximum-likelihood method has not been proved to converge (and, when it appears to converge it may be only to a relative maximum point), it is wise to apply an additional test. The likelihood function L must increase, of course, or, a negative fraction of it, as in (10.13), must decrease. The difference in this function of the likelihood from one iteration to the next is determined, and if it should fail to go down then there is evidence that the particular maximum point was missed, and the process has proceeded to another "mound." One could back off and try different values for the matrix **A** in the preceding iteration, or proceed with the new values (for which the likelihood function failed to behave properly) and continue to seek convergence to a new relative maximum. Incidentally, the test of behavior of the likelihood function should not be confused with the convergence test in step 7 of (10.26).

218

Another promising new algorithm, and a computer program, has been developed by Hemmerle [223]. In this paper, he indicates that in extracting 8 factors from a matrix of order 15 his method is almost five-fold more efficient than the original Lawley iteration scheme described above.

Probably the most important recent work on the maximum-likelihood solution is that of Joreskog [288]. He has devised a very efficient computational method that converges rapidly, regardless of the values with which the process is started. Furthermore, provision is made for the Heywood case. When the maximization of the likelihood function leads to one or more variables with uniquenesses essentially zero, an adjustment is made for such variables as follows: (1) the principal components of any such variables are obtained; (2) the remaining variables, with the effect of the recalcitrant variables partialed out, are analyzed by the maximum-likelihood method; (3) the two results are combined to give a complete maximum-likelihood solution for the total set of variables. Such a solution is discussed in **10.6**.

Before leaving the theoretical development of maximum-likelihood estimates of factor loadings, similar results obtained by another procedure should be noted. Rao [394] has developed a method—canonical factor analysis—primarily as an alternative to the principal factor method (chap. 8). Instead of asking that each factor account for as much as possible of the variation of the variables, he inquires for the factors which are maximally related to the variables. He solves this problem by a canonical correlation analysis of the hypothetical factors with the observed variables, employing the basic factor model (2.9). The results of this analysis are again maximum-likelihood estimates of factor loadings, but formally different from the earlier solution in this section. The canonical factor analysis method leads to an iterative procedure which Golub[160] has programmed for the Illiac. Even on such an electronic computer the process is slow. A numerical example solved by this procedure is given in **10.6**.

10.4. *Test of Significance for the Number of Factors*

The particular statistical test which is the subject of this section is for the determination of the number of significant common factors. Such a test is needed because implicit in the development of **10.3** is an assumption regarding this number. Fortunately, the problem of testing the hypothesis of a given number of factors has been solved for the case of maximum-likelihood estimates of the factor loadings based upon large samples. The solution rests on a theorem [see 369, p. 301] due to Wilks [523], which states that -2 times the logarithm of the likelihood ratio* is approximately distributed as χ^2 when N is large. This statistic, following Anderson and Rubin [14, p. 136], may be put in the form,

$$(10.27) \qquad U_m = -2 \log \lambda = N \log \frac{|\hat{\mathbf{P}}|}{|\mathbf{R}|},$$

---

* The likelihood ratio is defined [369, p. 298] as the quotient of: the maximum of the likelihood function in a specified subspace with respect to the parameters (e.g., the space of the m common factors, with dimension $nm - m[m - 1]/2$); to the maximum of the likelihood function in the total region with respect to the parameters (e.g., the total space of the n variables, with dimension $n[n - 1]/2$).

with base e for the logarithms. It should be noted that the likelihood ratio λ depends only on the sample observations—the sample correlation matrix and the estimate of the universe correlation matrix under the hypothesis H_0 of m factors. Since the likelihood ratio varies from 0 to 1, the expression in (10.27) increases as λ decreases, approaching infinity as λ approaches zero, and the critical region for U_m is the right-hand tail of the χ^2 distribution. The test procedure, then, is to reject the hypothesis H_0 of m factors if the value of U_m exceeds χ^2 for the desired significance level; otherwise it is accepted. If the hypothesis is rejected, an alternate hypothesis of some larger number of factors may be assumed to explain the observed correlations.

In applying the foregoing test, it is necessary to know the degrees of freedom associated with the χ^2 distribution. This number is the difference between the dimensionalities of the two regions (with respect to the parameters) involved in the likelihood ratio. For the hypothesis H_0 of m common factors, the number of degrees of freedom is given by

$$(10.28) \qquad\qquad v = \tfrac{1}{2}[(n - m)^2 - n - m].$$

For computing purposes, formula (10.27) can be simplified. By formally evaluating the ratio of the two determinants and making a series of approximations [see 320, p. 80], this expression can be reduced to

$$(10.29) \qquad\qquad U_m = N \sum_{j<k=1}^{n} \bar{r}_{jk}^2 / d_j^2 d_k^2,$$

where, as previously defined, the residuals are given by:

$$\bar{r}_{jk} = r_{jk} - r'_{jk},$$

and the reproduced correlations r'_{jk} are the elements of $\hat{\mathbf{P}}$.

For moderate-sized samples, Bartlett [28, pp. 82, 84] proposes the following multiplying coefficient as more accurate than the N in (10.27):

$$(10.30) \qquad\qquad N - n/3 - 2m/3 - 11/6.$$

Such a modification can also be employed in the computing formula (10.29). It should be remembered that the U_m statistic was developed for large-sample tests. While a slight correction for a moderate-size sample may be in order, the coefficient (10.30) cannot make the statistic any more appropriate when N is relatively small. The suggestion in this text is that the tests be employed only for large samples.

The foregoing test makes it possible to determine the statistical significance of the assumed number m of common factors at a given level of confidence. If m^* is the true number of common factors then it is to be expected that by selecting $m \geq m^*$ a good fit will be obtained, while for $m < m^*$ the fit will be poor. By this is meant that U_m for the former case will be small and for the latter case it will be large. A reasonable procedure is to select a confidence level, say 5%, and take as the estimate of the number of factors the smallest value of m which yields a nonsignificant U_m when compared with χ^2 at this level. Usually one would take sequential values of m, starting with a subjective judgment of the smallest number of factors required, making the test at each stage, and increasing m by one when U_m is significant, until a value of m is reached for which the corresponding U_m is nonsignificant. It should be noted that under the foregoing procedure the exact probability of concluding that $m > m^*$ is not known. However, this joint probability of rejecting the several hypotheses $m = 1, 2, \cdots, m^*$ is less than (or equal to) the probability of rejecting the single hypothesis $m = m^*$, at a given significance level.

The techniques described in this chapter are scientifically sound and powerful. They are also costly in regard to computing effort. Do they offer a more general guide for factor analysis? There is evidence that the test of significance for the number of common factors has applicability to situations where the maximum-likelihood method is not employed. Thus, if for any factorization the function U_m is computed and found to be insignificant when considered as a χ^2 then the particular factor solution may be assumed to contain the correct number of common factors and have an acceptable pattern of factor loadings. On the other hand, if it is found to be significant, no conclusion can be reached. It might still be true that a maximum-likelihood factorization with the same number of common factors would give an acceptable statistical fit. In other words, the test provides an upper limit for the number of common factors unless the factor loadings are estimated by an efficient method.

Before leaving this test, a comparison with the corresponding test in **9.5** is in order. There, it will be recalled, the statistic (9.31) was developed without specifying efficient estimates of the factor loadings (as in the present case of maximum-likelihood estimates). A consequence of this is that the number of degrees of freedom given by (9.32) is n greater than that given by (10.28). Hence the power* of the test in **9.5** is lower than in the present instance.

In addition to the mathematical contributions of Lawley and others, an empirical demonstration of the validity of the test has been provided by Henrysson [225]. Working with a table of random numbers from a normal population, he built 12 samples of 9 variables each containing 200 observations. After computing the variance-covariance matrix for each sample, he proceeded to estimate the factor loadings by the method of maximum likelihood under the assumption of $m = 1$ and to calculate U_1 by (10.29). For 27 degrees of freedom, the 12 values of U_1 ranged from 15.5 to 38.6 with associated χ^2 probabilities from .96 to .07. Assuming the values of P to be distributed rectangularly, the empirical results agree very well with the expected range of .85. Furthermore, upon combining the twelve samples, only one common factor was found to be significant for the explanation of the artificial data, as hypothesized.

10.5. *Computing Procedures*

While it is not expected that the maximum-likelihood method will be employed to estimate factor weights without very powerful computing facilities, nonetheless an outline of the procedure may be very useful. This can serve two purposes: (1) as

---

* By the power of a statistical test of an hypothesis is meant the probability that it rejects the alternative hypothesis when that alternative is false. The power is greatest when the probability of an error of the second kind (i.e., accepting a false hypothesis) is least.

a means of grasping the technique for a small number of variables and factors; and (2) as a basis for writing a computer program for handling larger problems, according to (10.25). In the following outline, the computing procedures are illustrated by means of the example of eight physical variables of **5.4**.

1. Organization of data.—The complete correlation matrix (with unities in the diagonal) constitutes the basic data. For the example, the correlations from Table 5.3 are repeated in the matrix **R** in Table 10.2.

Table 10.2

Correlation Matrix for Eight Physical Variables: **R**

	1	2	3	4	5	6	7	8
1	1.000	.846	.805	.859	.473	.398	.301	.382
2	.846	1.000	.881	.826	.376	.326	.277	.415
3	.805	.881	1.000	.801	.380	.319	.237	.345
4	.859	.826	.801	1.000	.436	.329	.327	.365
5	.473	.376	.380	.436	1.000	.762	.730	.629
6	.398	.326	.319	.329	.762	1.000	.583	.577
7	.301	.277	.237	.327	.730	.583	1.000	.539
8	.382	.415	.345	.365	.629	.577	.539	1.000

2. Hypothesis regarding number of common factors (m).—An assumption regarding the number of common factors must be made at the outset. This hypothesis is made on the basis of all available information, including any previous studies involving the given variables. The eight physical variables have been analyzed by many different methods and different investigators, but always with the same conclusion of two common factors. Hence, the immediate thought was to assume $m = 2$. Maximum-likelihood estimates were obtained under this assumption but a test of this hypothesis showed that at least three factors are statistically significant (see exs. 10 and 11). Therefore three common factors are assumed in the following calculations (and, as will be noted below, even this number is not sufficient). With $m = 3$ all ramifications of the computing procedures are exemplified, making the extension to a larger number of factors easy.

3. Initial set of trial values.—The iterative procedure, which ultimately leads to the maximum-likelihood estimates, is begun with some arbitrary first approximations to the factor loadings. While almost any set of numbers may do, the closer the approximation to the actual weights the faster will the process converge. Usually, some arbitrary factor analysis of the data, employing any of the methods described in earlier chapters, will do for the initial set of trial values.* As indicated above, an actual maximum-likelihood solution under assumption of $m = 2$ had been computed (in which the initial set of trial values came from a principal-factor solution). Hence, for the present needs, the trial values for the first two factors are taken to be the previously

---

* An initial minres solution has been found to hasten the convergence process.

222

Table 10.3

Maximum-Likelihood Estimates of Three Factors for Eight Physical Variables

Line	Instruction	Variable (j)							
		1	2	3	4	5	6	7	8
1	a_{j1}	.894	.896	.866	.871	.656	.554	.490	.551
2	a_{j2}	−.182	−.301	−.291	−.209	.663	.577	.587	.403
3	a_{j3}	−.070	.078	.011	−.101	−.148	−.051	−.292	.592
4	$d_j^2 = 1 - L_1^2 - L_2^2 - L_3^2$	.1627	.1005	.1652	.1875	.1082	.3576	.3301	.1835
5	L_1/L_4	5.495	8.915	5.242	4.645	6.083	1.549	1.484	3.003
6	L_2/L_4	−1.119	−2.995	−1.762	−1.115	6.128	1.614	1.778	2.196
7	L_3/L_4	−.430	.776	.067	−.539	−1.368	−.143	−.885	3.226
8	RL_5	26.326	26.461	25.426	25.662	20.183	17.060	15.316	17.813
9	$L_8 - L_1$	25.432	25.565	24.560	24.791	19.527	16.506	14.826	17.262
10	$a_{j1} = L_9/\sqrt{L_5 \cdot L_9}$	.883	.888	.853	.861	.678	.573	.515	.599
11	RL_6	−1.114	−2.181	−2.172	−1.375	7.226	6.238	6.426	5.255
12	$L_{11} - L_2$	−0.932	−1.880	−1.881	−1.166	6.563	5.661	5.839	4.852
13	$L_{12} - (L_6 \cdot L_{10})L_{10}$	−1.992	−2.946	−2.905	−2.199	5.749	4.973	5.221	4.133
14	$a_{j2} = L_{13}/\sqrt{L_6 \cdot L_{13}}$	−.223	−.330	−.325	−.246	.644	.557	.585	.463
15	RL_7	.079	.559	.310	.031	−.215	.086	−.303	1.790
16	$L_{15} - L_3$	.149	.481	.299	.132	−.067	.137	−.011	1.198
17	$L_{16} - (L_7 \cdot L_{10})L_{10}$	−.177	.153	−.016	−.186	−.318	−.075	−.201	.977
18	$L_{17} - (L_7 \cdot L_{14})L_{14}$	−.185	.142	−.027	−.194	−.296	−.056	−.181	.993
19	$a_{j3} = L_{18}/\sqrt{L_7 \cdot L_{18}}$	−.092	.070	−.013	−.096	−.147	−.028	−.090	.492
20	$d_j^2 = 1 - L_{10}^2 - L_{14}^2 - L_{19}^2$	.1621	.0977	.1666	.1889	.1040	.3606	.3844	.1848
.									
.		(Three iterations omitted in order to conserve space)							
.									
69	L_{58}/L_{68}	5.503	9.338	4.994	4.446	8.099	1.635	1.274	3.068
70	L_{62}/L_{68}	−1.604	−3.906	−2.111	−1.459	7.171	1.464	1.307	2.155
71	L_{67}/L_{68}	−.642	.875	−.077	−.481	−1.661	−.077	−.084	2.461
72	RL_{69}	27.279	27.270	26.172	26.492	22.155	18.610	16.674	19.115
73	$L_{72} - L_{58}$	26.404	26.395	25.332	25.642	21.448	18.016	16.142	18.503
74	$a_{j1} = L_{73}/\sqrt{L_{69} \cdot L_{73}}$	.874	.874	.838	.849	.710	.596	.534	.612
75	RL_{70}	−2.670	−3.898	−3.767	−2.932	6.931	5.869	6.015	4.720
76	$L_{75} - L_{62}$	−2.415	−3.532	−3.412	−2.653	6.305	5.337	5.469	4.290
77	$L_{76} - (L_{70} \cdot L_{74})L_{74}$	−2.553	−3.670	−3.544	−2.787	6.193	5.243	5.385	4.193
78	$a_{j2} = L_{77}/\sqrt{L_{70} \cdot L_{77}}$	−.258	−.370	−.358	−.281	.625	.529	.544	.423

Table 10.3 (continued)

Line	Instruction	Variable (j)							
		1	2	3	4	5	6	7	8
79	RL_{71}	−.278	.215	−.035	−.250	−.447	−.125	−.141	1.242
80	$L_{79} - L_{67}$	−.176	1.133	−.022	−.158	−.302	−.097	−.106	.751
81	$L_{80} - (L_{71} \cdot L_{74})L_{74}$	−.147	.162	.006	−.130	−.279	−.077	−.088	.771
82	$L_{81} - L_{71} \cdot L_{78})L_{78}$	−.167	.133	−.022	−.152	−.230	−.035	−.045	.804
83	$a_{j3} = L_{82}/\sqrt{L_{71} \cdot L_{82}}$	−.102	.081	−.013	−.093	−.141	−.021	−.028	.493
84	$d_j^2 = 1 - L_{74}^2 - L_{78}^2 - L_{83}^2$	.1592	.0927	.1694	.1916	.0854	.3645	.4181	.2035

computed maximum-likelihood weights. For the third factor, the trial values come from the third eigenvector of a principal-factor solution that was readily available. These initial factor loadings appear in the first three rows of Table 10.3 (they are written in rows rather than columns simply for convenience of printing). The uniquenesses are computed from these values and appear in line 4. The entries in the first four lines of Table 10.3 constitute the initial set of trial values.

4. Factor weights divided by uniquenesses.—The calculations implied in the iteration equations (10.25) are organized systematically in this and the following four steps, without always translating the matrix algebra explicitly into equivalent arithmetic operations. It will be noted that in getting the second approximation for each vector of factor loadings, the original vector ($\mathbf{a}_1$, $\mathbf{a}_2$, or $\mathbf{a}_3$) is multiplied by the inverse ($\mathbf{D}^{-2}$) of the diagonal matrix of uniquenesses. This is equivalent to dividing the factor loadings of a variable by its uniqueness. These results appear in lines 5, 6, 7 of Table 10.3.

5. Determination of next trial values of first-factor weights.—The first of equations (10.25) is reduced to convenient form for arithmetic computation in lines 8, 9, 10, with the first term becoming

$$\mathbf{RD}^{-2}\mathbf{a}_1 = \mathbf{R}L_5,$$

which is recorded as L_8. It should be perfectly clear when expressions that are really column vectors are recorded in rows for ease of printing, and transposes are not indicated to avoid pedantry.

The numerators for the second approximation to the first-factor weights are simply obtained in L_9. The denominators are more involved. Considering L_5 and L_9 as vectors, the expression under the radical is the dot product of these vectors as defined in **3.2** paragraph **19**. The square-root of this dot product is a constant by which each entry in line 9 is divided to get the next approximation b_{j1} according to (10.25). Actually, these factor loadings are again written as a_{j1} to simplify the notation.

6. Determination of next trial values of second-factor weights.—The next approximations to the second-factor loadings are provided by the second of equations

(10.25). The rather imposing matrix manipulations are reduced to straightforward calculations in lines 11–14 of Table 10.3. The work is quite similar to that of paragraph **5** except for the additional step which corrects for the previously revised values of the first-factor weights. This correction is the term

$$\mathbf{b}_1 \mathbf{b}_1' \mathbf{D}^{-2} \mathbf{a}_2$$

from (10.25). Translated into terms of Table 10.3, this becomes

$$L_{10} L_{10}' L_6 \quad \text{or} \quad L_6' L_{10} L_{10}' \text{(transposed)},$$

wherein careful attention is paid to the designation of the elements as column vectors (without primes) or row vectors (with primes). Written more simply, the correction appears in line 13. The remaining calculations leading to b_{j2} (but written a_{j2}) are essentially the same as in the case of the first factor.

7. Determination of next trial values of third-factor weights.—The third-factor loadings are calculated in lines 15–19 of Table 10.3 on the basis of the third of the iteration equations (10.25). Again, while the matrix algebra appears very imposing, the actual calculations follow the same pattern as in the case of the first and second factors. There is now a correction for the effect of the new first-factor weights (in L_{17}) and also a correction for the new second-factor weights (in L_{18}). If there were more than three common factors there would be additional such correction terms for each of the previously computed factors.

8. Determination of next trial values of uniquenesses.—After the new approximations to the maximum-likelihood estimates of the three sets of factor loadings have been determined in lines 10, 14, and 19, the new values of the uniqueness are calculated in line 20.

9. Convergence of factor weights.—The calculations involved in paragraphs **4–8** are repeated until the factor loadings in successive iterations do not change (to a designated number of decimal places). In the illustrative example, successive values of all corresponding factor loadings agreed to within .007 after 5 iterations. This is not sufficiently accurate, and is accepted here only for illustrative purposes. Such final factor loadings appear in lines 74, 78, 83, with the associated uniquenesses in line 84 of Table 10.3.

10. Residual matrix.—To assist in calculating the residuals, the reproduced correlations (r_{jk}') are first determined according to (2.50) since the factors are orthogonal. These appear in the upper half of Table 10.4. Then, subtracting these values from the corresponding observed correlations of Table 10.2, the residual correlations $(\bar{r}_{jk})$ are obtained and recorded in the lower half of Table 10.4.

11. Statistical test of hypothesis regarding number of factors.—The hypothesis of $m = 3$ for the illustrative example can now be tested. To assist in calculating the statistic as given by (10.29), the intermediate elements are computed in Table 10.5. The sum of the 28 elements below the diagonal is .15098, and upon multiplying this by the number of cases $N = 305$ the resulting statistic is $U_3 = 46.0$. The degrees of freedom, as given by (10.28), is $v = 7$. By referring to Table D in the Appendix it will be found that for 7 degrees of freedom a value of $\chi^2 = 18.5$ produces a probability

Table 10.4

Reproduced Correlations and Residuals[a]

Variable	1	2	3	4	5	6	7	8
1		.851	.826	.824	.474	.387	.329	.375
2	−.005		.864	.838	.378	.323	.263	.418
3	−.021	.017		.813	.373	.310	.253	.355
4	.035	−.012	−.012		.440	.359	.303	.355
5	−.001	−.002	.007	−.004		.757	.723	.629
6	.011	.003	.009	−.030	.005		.607	.578
7	−.028	.014	−.016	.024	.007	−.024		.543
8	.007	−.003	−.010	.010	.000	−.001	−.004	

[a] Reproduced correlations appear in the upper triangle and the residuals in the lower triangle.

Table 10.5

Elements for Calculation of χ^2 Test[a]

Variable	1	2	3	4	5	6	7	8
1	6.2854	.00002	.00044	.00122	.00000	.00012	.00078	.00005
2	.00136	10.7875	.00029	.00014	.00000	.00001	.00020	.00001
3	.01633	.01847	5.9032	.00014	.00005	.00008	.00026	.00010
4	.04000	.00788	.00431	5.2192	.00002	.00090	.00058	.00010
5	.00000	.00000	.00346	.00122	11.7096	.00002	.00005	.00000
6	.00207	.00030	.00130	.01289	.00064	2.7435	.00058	.00000
7	.01173	.00516	.00367	.00724	.00140	.00381	2.3918	.00002
8	.00154	.00053	.00290	.00256	.00000	.00000	.00024	4.9140

[a] The elements in this table consist of the following: (1) Above diagonal: $\bar{r}_{jk}^2$, squares of the residual correlations; (2) In diagonal: $1/d_j^2$, reciprocals of uniqueness; (3) Below diagonal: $\bar{r}_{jk}^2/d_j^2 d_k^2$, elements which are summed to get the function (10.29).

$P = .01$. Therefore, if the hypothesis of only three common factors is correct, the probability of getting a value of $\chi^2 > 18.5$ is only 1 in 100. Since the actual value 46.0 is considerably in excess of 18.5, the hypothesis is rejected and it must be assumed that more than three common factors are required for adequate explanation of the observed data. This is the conclusion on purely statistical grounds, but it is doubtful if a factor analyst or applied statistician would look for any more (practical) relationships among the variables from the third-factor residuals in the lower half of Table 10.4.

10.6. *Numerical Illustrations*

It should be quite evident from the work in the preceding section that the maximum-likelihood method for estimating factor weights requires tremendous computations. While this method implied insuperable computing difficulties in the past—causing it to lay dormant for almost two decades—the modern electronic computers make the method feasible. Still, there have been few numerical examples reported in the literature.

Additional problems will be considered in this section, but first a few more comments about the example of the eight physical variables. It came as a surprise to find that two factors inadequately reproduced their intercorrelations after the many crude guides pointed to precisely two clearly distinguishable clusters. What was even more surprising, then, was the large U_m for the hypothesis $m = 3$, indicating that a fourth factor really should be sought. At this point it was only natural to question the numerical calculations, and finding them to be accurate, to question the theoretical basis. One area of doubt was the approximations in going from formula (10.27) to the simpler computing formula (10.29). To this end, the determinants of the observed correlations and of the reproduced correlations (with two and with three factors) were calculated. These values were then employed in formula (10.27) to get $U_2 = 69.9$ and $U_3 = 51.0$ for the two-factor and three-factor cases, respectively. The corresponding values by use of formula (10.29) are 80.2 and 46.0. Of course the numbers differ a little, but the same conclusions would be drawn from the results of either formula —rejecting the hypothesis of two factors in the first case, and of three factors in the second case. This analysis lends credence to the use of the simpler formula.

In the course of experimenting with different maximum-likelihood procedures, the example of eight physical variables was used extensively. Such computer programs included two provided by Dr. Donald F. Morrison (when he was associated with the National Institutes of Health); a procedure* of Bargman [23] which is based on the model developed by Howe [268]; and the program outlined in (10.26). The two most interesting results are presented in Table 10.6. The first of these solutions was obtained by means of a program made available by the National Institutes of Health, starting with the first three principal components and converging to a maximum difference of .0005 in factor loadings of successive iterations. Solution 2 was obtained by means of a program [204] based upon (10.26), with the minres solution of Table 9.3 (for $m = 3$) as the initial approximations to the factor loadings. Convergence in the factor weights to within .005 was reached in about one minute on a Philco 2000 computer. It will be noted that these two solutions, although in canonical form, differ from each other. Furthermore, they are different from the crude results in Table 10.3. The disparate nature of the two solutions can be seen immediately from the wide discrepancies in factor loadings and communality for variable 8. No matter how similar the other numbers might appear, the complete solutions could not be the same in the light of the different fit to one of the variables. Diverse maximum-likelihood solutions for the same data arise, in part, because of the different standards for convergence— only 5 iterations when calculated by hand versus hundreds of iterations in one experimental run on a computer—but also because a different relative maximum may

* Actually a step-wise process in which each factor in turn is estimated by maximum-likelihood, but the result for a set of several factors is not the same as a maximum-likelihood solution for the specified number of factors.

Table 10.6

Two Maximum-Likelihood Solutions for Eight Physical Variables
(Three common factors)

Variable j	Solution 1				Solution 2			
	F_1	F_2	F_3	h_j^2	F_1	F_2	F_3	h_j^2
1	.845	.340	.065	.834	.862	.320	.164	.873
2	.841	.434	−.084	.902	.867	.432	−.243	.998
3	.806	.428	.006	.833	.808	.388	−.051	.807
4	.819	.360	.047	.802	.833	.343	.180	.843
5	.764	−.560	.272	.971	.748	−.584	.090	.910
6	.629	−.452	.106	.610	.625	−.499	.007	.640
7	.568	−.471	.116	.558	.569	−.515	−.020	.589
8	.678	−.461	−.542	.966	.603	−.344	−.164	.509
V_p	4.503	1.569	.405	6.477	4.481	1.532	.156	6.169

be sought, depending on the starting point in the iteration process and other aspects of the algorithm.

It is of interest to note the statistical inference that might be drawn from each of the solutions. The solution in Table 10.3, based on only 5 iterations on a desk calculator, is understandably crude, and the statistical test in **10.5**, step 11, led to the conclusion that three common factors were not sufficient to explain the observed data. For solution 1 of Table 10.6, the statistic (10.27) becomes

$$U_3 = 305 \log_e(.00113253)/(.00096740) = 48.1,$$

and since this is even larger than the value of 46.0 obtained in the preceding case, the same conclusion is reached. Solution 2, however, leads to a somewhat different inference. For that solution, the determinant of reproduced correlations is reduced to .00104685 and the associated statistic $U_3 = 24.1$. While this value is greater than $\chi^2 = 18.5$ with a probability $P = .01$ for $v = 7$ degrees of freedom, it does not exceed $\chi^2 = 24.3$ for $P = .001$. Therefore, solution 2 may be accepted at the 0.1 per cent level of significance.

The new maximum-likelihood procedure developed by Joreskog [288] was applied to the problem of eight physical variables. Four different sets of initial values for the uniquenesses were attempted (including those from the two different solutions of Table 10.6), and identical final results were obtained in each instance. No matter what starting values, the program determined that the uniqueness for variable 2 would have to be zero to attain a maximum. The effect of that variable was partialed out, and two maximum-likelihood factors were obtained from the matrix of partial correlations among the remaining seven variables. The latter solution is then combined with the principal component through variable 2 to yield the maximum-likelihood solution for the eight variables in terms of three factors. Since the result

228

is not in canonical form, the individual factor weights are not compared with those in Table 10.6. However, it is of interest to note that the communalities:

$$.873, 1.000, .806, ,844, .910, .641, .589, .509,$$

are almost identical with those of solution 2. Also, the test of goodness of fit of the new solution leads to the same conclusion as in the case of solution 2. It would appear from Joreskog's work that solution 2 is the true maximum-likelihood solution while the procedure that led to solution 1 had not really converged.

This example illustrates the general principle that one tends to underestimate the number of factors that are statistically significant. For twenty years, two factors had been considered adequate, but statistically two factors do *not* adequately account for the observed correlations based on a random sample of 305 girls. However, the third factor (whose total contribution to the variance ranges from 2 per cent to 5 per cent for the different solutions) has little "practical significance," and certainly a fourth factor would have no practical value.

The next illustration is for the 5 socio-economic variables introduced in **2.2**. In making a choice of hypothesis regarding the number of common factors, one, two, or three, all appear somewhat reasonable, but the selection of $m = 2$ is more in keeping with the previous work. Two different computer programs were employed on a Philco 2000, and with three different covergence standards (maximum change in factor loadings required to be less than .0005, .00001, and .000005) all the results were almost identical to three decimal places. In Table 10.7 the solution is shown in the arbitrary form produced by the basic maximum-likelihood program, and also after it has been put in the canonical form of **8.8**.

The striking similarity between this solution and the minres solution of Table 9.2 may be noted. Also, for this example, the maximum-likelihood solution is almost identical with the principal-factor solution of Table 8.13. The total communality

Table 10.7

Maximum-Likelihood Solution for Five Socio-Economic Variables (Two common factors)

Variable j	Arbitrary Form		Canonical Form		Communality
	F_1	F_2	F_1	F_2	h_j^2
1	.999	−.008	.621	.783	.998
2	.019	.899	.711	−.550	.809
3	.974	.109	.697	.689	.961
4	.446	.785	.891	−.147	.815
5	.030	.960	.766	−.580	.923
V_p	2.147	2.360	2.759	1.748	4.507

produced by the maximum-likelihood solution represents 90 per cent of the total variance of the five variables. This is a very exceptional situation that should not ordinarily be expected. Of course, even this high proportion must be less than the amount accounted for by the first two principal components (see Table 8.1). While the contributions of the factors and the total communality is of importance in both the minres and maximum-likelihood solutions, it must be remembered that these methods have other primary objectives than maximizing variance, which is the case only in the principal-factor methods.

A fair sized problem in terms of maximum-likelihood factors is shown in Table 10.8. This is the problem of thirteen psychological tests for which several solutions in terms of three factors have been obtained previously. The calculations for Table 10.8

Table 10.8

Maximum-Likelihood Solution for Thirteen Psychological Tests
(Five common factors)

Test j	Pattern Coefficients					Uniqueness d_j^2	Communality h_j^2
	F_1	F_2	F_3	F_4	F_5		
1	.492	.171	.512	−.058	.056	.460	.540
2	.305	.042	.292	−.228	−.049	.766	.234
3	.347	−.024	.544	−.034	−.150	.559	.441
4	.425	.010	.392	.198	−.020	.626	.374
5	.817	−.122	−.140	−.251	−.171	.206	.794
6	.795	−.241	−.029	.068	.233	.250	.750
7	.812	−.217	−.082	.239	−.032	.229	.771
8	.716	−.008	.085	.149	−.186	.423	.577
9	.799	−.283	−.089	−.083	.053	.264	.736
10	.419	.622	−.359	.086	−.055	.298	.702
11	.488	.474	−.057	−.173	.311	.407	.593
12	.367	.663	.015	.063	−.132	.404	.596
13	.550	.476	.266	.003	.075	.395	.605
V	4.597	1.510	1.042	.291	.273	—	7.713

were made on the Illiac, employing a canonical factor analysis program. As noted in **10.3** such an analysis leads to maximum-likelihood estimates of factor loadings. Tests for the number of common factors show five factors significant at the 5% level and three factors significant at the 1% level. The latter agrees with the subjective judgments made earlier regarding the number of factors for practical consideration.

A large-scale application of the maximum-likelihood method was made by Lord [342] in 1956, in a study of speed factors in tests and academic grades. Using Whirl-wind I, an early electronic computer, he analyzed 33 variables into 10 maximum-likelihood factors. Lord originally hypothesized at least 9 common factors, but he could not arrive at such a solution directly because imaginary numbers were produced for the factor loadings. He found that the method broke down unless extremely close initial approximations to the actual solution were available whenever m was large. Hence, he carried out the computations in stages: starting with $m = 4$ and somewhat arbitrary trial values, he obtained maximum-likelihood estimates of the factor loadings; then he took the hypothesis of $m = 5$, using the previously determined weights for the first four factors and guesses based upon the residuals for the fifth; proceeding in this manner he was able to obtain ten factors without encountering further difficulty. Tests for the number of common factors produced a significant χ^2, with a probability well below the 1% level, in each instance from $m = 4$ through $m = 9$. However, the χ^2 dropped sufficiently so that ten factors were found to be significant at the 7% level.

The final example to be considered consists of the twenty-four psychological tests whose correlations are given in Table 7.4. Rather than attempting to get a maximum-likelihood solution directly from the correlation matrix, with initial trial values of

Table 10.9

Maximum-Likelihood Solution for Twenty-four Psychological Tests (Four common factors)

Test j	F_1	F_2	F_3	F_4	h_j^2
1	.601	.019	.388	.221	.561
2	.372	−.025	.252	.132	.220
3	.413	−.117	.388	.144	.356
4	.487	−.100	.254	.192	.349
5	.691	−.304	−.279	.035	.648
6	.690	−.409	−.200	−.076	.689
7	.677	−.409	−.292	.084	.718
8	.674	−.189	−.099	.122	.515
9	.697	−.454	−.212	−.080	.743
10	.476	.534	−.486	.092	.757
11	.558	.332	−.142	−.090	.450
12	.472	.508	−.139	.256	.566
13	.602	.244	.028	.295	.510
14	.423	.058	.015	−.415	.354
15	.394	.089	.097	−.362	.304
16	.510	.095	.347	−.249	.451
17	.466	.197	−.004	−.381	.402
18	.515	.312	.152	−.147	.407
19	.443	.089	.109	−.150	.238
20	.614	−.118	.126	−.038	.408
21	.589	.227	.057	.123	.417
22	.608	−.107	.127	−.038	.399
23	.687	−.044	.138	.098	.503
24	.651	.177	−.212	−.017	.501
Variance	7.643	1.681	1.229	.911	11.464

principal components, it was decided to start with a minres solution. Assuming $m = 5$ and starting with the solution of Table 9.6, a maximum-likelihood solution was reached in just ten iterations and less than five minutes on a Philco 2000. However, this solution contained a Heywood case, the communality of variable 19 being greater than one. Since a simple procedure is not available which will force the maximum-likelihood communalities within the permissible range, it was decided to start over, using a minres solution with $m = 4$ for the initial matrix (note the experience with this problem in **9.7**). Again, a maximum-likelihood solution was reached in ten iterations and in less than five minutes. This solution, in canonical form, is shown in Table 10.9. The maximum-likelihood solution is almost identical with the minres solution: the communalities agree to within a unit in the second decimal place (only for test 11 is the difference .020); the differences in the contributions of factors are .003, .009, .011, and .005, respectively; and the 96 individual factor loadings, with only a few exceptions, differ mostly in the third decimal place.

11
Multiple-Group Solution

11.1. *Introduction*

In the preceding three chapters, methods were presented for the direct determination of a factor solution for a given correlation matrix. A common attribute of those solutions was the orthogonality of the factors. In the present chapter another direct method for factoring a correlation matrix is developed, but the resulting factors usually are oblique to one another. The method of this chapter is essentially in the spirit of the simple factor models of chapter 7. The resulting solution may serve either as a final form or as a stepping stone for transformation to the multiple-factor solution (see part iii).

The basic concepts involved in the multiple-group analysis are presented in **11.2**. This is followed by the theoretical development of the oblique solution in **11.3** and the orthogonal solution in **11.4**. While the formulas developed in these sections are certainly necessary to the understanding of the method, they do not provide a ready means for proceeding with the analysis. A schematic arrangement of the work, with an outline of the steps in the computation, is given in **11.5**. Finally, in Section **11.6** the complete numerical work is performed on an example of nine psychological variables involving three common factors.

11.2. *Concepts and Notation*

The concept of group factors in factor analysis should not be confused with the group-factor method for reducing a correlation matrix to a factor matrix which satisfies the fundamental theorem (2.46). During the rapid development of factor analysis in the 1930's, several workers dealt with group factors. Notable among these were Cyril Burt, who considered the "group factor method"; R. C. Tyron, who proposed "cluster analysis"; and K. J. Holzinger, who developed the "bi-factor" method of analysis. While these methods certainly involve the group factor concept, they are not specifically in the spirit of factoring a matrix in terms of multiple factors concurrently.

Horst [250] in 1937 anticipated the multiple-group method of factor analysis, but he did not carry the theoretical work to the stage of practical application. Similarly, in 1944 Guttman [173] presented the theory without computational procedures. It was not too surprising that Holzinger [237], in the same year, and Thurstone [474], a year later, presented simple computing procedures for "group factor analysis," without recognizing the similarity to the earlier theoretical developments. The several independently developed "multiple group methods" for factor analysis are compared and synthesized by Harman [198].

The basic distinction of the multiple-group method is the ability to extract a number of common factors in one operation. In order to maximally capitalize on the power of this method, it is necessary to select a number of linearly independent groups, which number approximates the rank of the reduced correlation matrix. This property has a function similar to the grouping of variables in the bi-factor method.

Except in rare circumstances, the common factors extracted in a single operation are oblique to one another. Therefore another basic concept is that of the matrix of correlations among the factors. Also, since the factors are correlated, the immediate results of a group-factor must lead to two matrices—a factor pattern and a factor structure—the first of these gives the coefficients of the factors in the linear descriptions of the variables, while the second gives the correlations of the variables with the factors.

These results of the group-factor analysis can be used to obtain a matrix of reproduced correlations; and hence the residual matrix can be determined. If the residual matrix is not sufficiently close to the null matrix then the multiple-group method can be applied, again, to the residual matrix.

After it is determined that the multiple-group solution adequately reproduces the observed correlations, some investigators may consider such a solution as a preliminary step to the "rotational" problem. In seeking "simple structure" (see **6.2**) by transformation of axes, the problem is simplified if an orthogonal frame of reference is first obtained. Hence, two additional concepts are introduced—an orthogonal factor matrix and the transformation matrix from the oblique to this orthogonal solution.

The foregoing concepts, which arise in the multiple-group method of factoring, are listed in Table 11.1. Also summarized in this table are the symbols associated with these concepts.

One of the principal differences that appears in the several developments of multiple-group methods of factor analysis really is concerned with the formulation of scientific hypotheses rather than with the *method* of analysis. Guttman and Holzinger suggest that the multiple-group methods be used in conjunction with some *a priori* psychological theory. Guttman emphasizes the fact that the computational procedures of multiple-group methods can be applied in any event, but most psychological meaning can be gained only through the testing by the data of preconceived hypotheses. These hypotheses are reflected in the specific manner of grouping the variables and in the resulting common factors (usually oblique).

On the other hand, Thurstone emphasizes that the multiple-group method of factoring is quite independent of the manner of grouping the variables, and in an

Table 11.1

Concepts and Notation

Concept	Notation	
Original correlations (reduced correlation matrix)	$\mathbf{R}$	
Grouping of variables	G_p	$(p = 1, 2, \cdots, m)$
Sums of correlations of variables with Groups	w_{jp}	$(j = 1, 2, \cdots, n)$
Sums of correlations among Groups	W_{pq}	$(p, q = 1, 2, \cdots, m)$
Oblique factor structure	$\mathbf{S} = (s_{jp})$	
Correlations among factors	$\boldsymbol{\Phi} = (r_{T_p T_q})$	
Oblique factor pattern	$\mathbf{P} = (b_{jp})$	
Reproduced correlations	$\mathbf{R}^{\dagger}$	
Residual matrix (m factors)	$\mathbf{R}_m$	
Transformation matrix (to orthogonal factor pattern)	$\mathbf{T}^{-1}$	
Orthogonal factor matrix	$\mathbf{A} = (a_{jp})$	

example, deliberately sets up groups in an arbitrary fashion, with little reference to the correlations. This thought is evident when Thurstone calls attention to the "unnecessary" restrictions that Holzinger placed upon the matrix of correlations in order to use his "simple method of factor analysis." These restrictions *are* unnecessary when the object is simply to get a reduction of the correlation matrix to a factor matrix by the expedient multiple-group method; they are *not* unnecessary when the object is to test some specified hypothesis by use of a multiple-group solution.

Thus, while Holzinger considers the multiple-group method suitable only if the correlation matrix is amenable to sectioning into portions of approximate unit rank, and Guttman prefers to group the variable so as to avoid or reduce the problem of rotation of axes, Thurstone conceives of the multiple-group method primarily as another (efficient) technique for initial factoring to provide an orthogonal factor matrix "which is the starting-point for the rotational problem" [477, p. 171].

There is no doubt about the effectiveness of the multiple-group methods in problems involving hand computations. Instead of extracting one factor at a time, and computing a residual matrix after each, the basic theorem underlying the multiple-group method implies that only one residual matrix need be computed after extracting several factors at one time. If a number of linearly independent groups is selected equal to the dimension of the common factor space then only one residual matrix will be necessary; otherwise, if the first estimate of the number of clusters is too small, the process has to be repeated again. If too many clusters should be selected then the case of multi-collinearity will be evident in the matrix of correlations among the group factors (and the inverse will not exist).

If the total number of common factors is not extracted in a single operation, then the multiple-group method can be applied again to the residual matrix obtained after the first operation; and this can be repeated as many times as necessary to bring the residuals down to negligible values. In the successive application of the multiple-group method, the common factors extracted at each stage are oblique to

235

one another, but the factors obtained in any single stage are orthogonal to all factors extracted in other stages. The implication of this is that if an *a priori* hypothesis involves an oblique structure then all the common factors must be extracted in one operation, or else subsequent rotation might be necessitated.

11.3. *The Oblique Solution*

As pointed out in the preceding section the end result of the multiple-group method of analysis may be an oblique factor solution, or if desired, an orthogonal solution which may be employed for subsequent rotation. In this section the procedures leading to the oblique solution are outlined. Further discussion of the geometric basis and other concepts associated with an oblique solution appears in chapter 13. However, in that chapter the oblique solution is obtained by transformation from some pre-computed orthogonal solution rather than from the correlation matrix directly as in this section.

The essence of the multiple-group method consists of representing the factors by reference axes passing through the centroids of the respective groups of variables. Since the clusters of variables would not ordinarily be at right angles to one another, the common factors obtained in a single operation of the multiple-group method are oblique also. The multiple-group method assumes a reduced correlation matrix as the starting point, with communalities in the principal diagonal estimated by one of the methods suggested in chapter 5. The actual analysis begins with an appropriate grouping of the n variables into m groups G_p ($p = 1, 2, \cdots, m$) on some *a priori* basis, by the method of B-coefficients of **7.4**, or on a purely arbitrary basis.

Since sums of variables (centroids) are involved in the multiple-group method, some basic properties of such *composite variables* will be found useful. While the individual variables z_j are in standard measure, their composites are not necessarily so; and formulas for their variances and correlations have long been known [439]. In the multiple-group method, a composite variable T_p is assumed through the cluster of n_p variables in a group G_p, namely,

$$(11.1) \qquad\qquad T_p = \sum (z_k; \quad k \in G_p) \qquad\qquad (p = 1, 2, \cdots, m).$$

Such composite variables constitute the oblique factors, which ordinarily would not have unit variances.

The calculation of variances and covariances among the factors can be expedited by the determination of certain preliminary sums of correlations. The first of these is simply the sum of the correlations of each variable z_j with all the variables in each group G_p, namely:

$$(11.2) \qquad\qquad w_{jp} = \sum (r_{jk}; \quad k \in G_p) \qquad (j = 1, 2, \cdots, n; \quad p = 1, 2, \cdots, m),$$

where the sum is on the index k which takes on all the values of the variables in group G_p. When the index k takes the value j, the "self-correlation" is assumed to be the communality, i.e., $r_{jj} = h_j^2$. Another sum which is useful in the multiple-group

236

method is

(11.3) $$W_{pq} = \sum (w_{jq}; \quad j \in G_p) \qquad (p, q = 1, 2, \cdots, m)$$

which represents the sum of correlations between all variables in group G_p with all those in group G_q (including the case where $p = q$). Of course, equation (11.3) can be expressed in terms of the original correlations, as follows:

(11.4) $$W_{pq} = \sum (r_{jk}; \quad j \in G_p, k \in G_q) \qquad (p, q = 1, 2, \cdots, m).$$

The first task is to determine the correlations among the oblique factors and the correlations (structure values) of the variables with these factors. The required correlations can be expressed concisely by means of the foregoing sums of simple correlations, but first a formula will be obtained for the variances of the oblique factors. Ordinarily the variance of a composite variable T_p would be given by:

(11.5) $$s_{T_p}^2 = n_p + 2 \sum (r_{jk}; \quad j, k \in G_p, j < k),$$

since there are n_p self-correlations of unity. However, when the "self-correlations" are replaced by communalities, this formula may be written

(11.6) $$s_{T_p}^2 = \sum (r_{jk}; \quad j, k \in G_p),$$

where it is understood that $r_{jj} = h_j^2$. Employing (11.4), the last expression becomes simply

(11.7) $$s_{T_p}^2 = W_{pp}.$$

Now, by definition the correlation between any two composite variables, T_p and T_q, is

(11.8) $$r_{T_p T_q} = \sum T_{pi} T_{qi} / N s_{T_p} s_{T_q},$$

where summation with respect to i from 1 to N is understood. The s's in the denominator have just been expressed in (11.7) in terms of the foregoing sums of simple correlations. The remainder of (11.8) may be expanded and simplified as follows:

(11.9)
$$\sum_{i=1}^{N} T_{pi} T_{qi} / N = \sum_{i=1}^{N} \left(\sum_{j \in G_p} z_{ji} \right) \left(\sum_{k \in G_q} z_{ki} \right) / N$$
$$= \sum \left(\sum_{i=1}^{N} z_{ji} z_{ki} / N; \quad j \in G_p, k \in G_q \right)$$
$$= \sum (r_{jk}; \quad j \in G_p, k \in G_q)$$
$$= W_{pq}.$$

Substituting the values from (11.7) and (11.9) into (11.8), the latter formula for the correlation between two oblique factors becomes:

(11.10) $$r_{T_p T_q} = W_{pq} / \sqrt{(W_{pp} W_{qq})}.$$

237

Next, the correlations of the variables with the factors—the oblique factor structure—can be obtained in terms of the foregoing sums of simple correlations. The structure value s_{jp} is the correlation $r_{z_j T_p}$ of a variable in standard measure with a composite variable whose variance is given by (11.7). Then, it can readily be shown that the required correlation is given by the formula:

$$(11.11) \qquad\qquad s_{jp} = w_{jp}/\sqrt{W_{pp}}.$$

To complete the solution in terms of correlated factors, the linear descriptions of the variables in terms of the factors are required as well as their correlations with the factors. The coefficients in these linear equations, i.e., the pattern values, are the coordinates with respect to the oblique (factor) axes of the points representing the variables. The factor pattern can be obtained from the known factor structure $\mathbf{S}$ and the correlations among the factors $\mathbf{\Phi}$, according to (2.44), as follows:

$$(11.12) \qquad\qquad \mathbf{P} = \mathbf{S\Phi}^{-1}$$

The bulk of work implied in this formula is the determination of the inverse of $\mathbf{\Phi}$. The square root method of **3.5** can be used to obtain the inverse and to systematically carry out the matrix multiplication to produce the pattern matrix. Actually, an alternative computing procedure is developed in **11.5** and illustrated in **11.6**.

If the analysis is to be terminated with an oblique solution then appropriate computing formulas are required for the reproduced correlations and the residuals. There are several formulas for getting the reproduced correlations directly from the component parts of an oblique solution. The basic formula (2.46), although not the most efficient one, involves the multiplication of three matrices, as follows:

$$(11.13) \qquad\qquad \mathbf{R}^\dagger = \mathbf{P\Phi P'}.$$

From the relationships between a pattern and a structure in an oblique solution (see **2.8**), this formula can be put in either of the following more convenient forms for computation:

$$(11.14) \qquad\qquad \mathbf{R}^\dagger = \mathbf{PS'} \quad \text{or} \quad \mathbf{R}^\dagger = \mathbf{SP'}.$$

In either of these forms the computation is precisely the same as in the case of an orthogonal solution, i.e., formula (2.50).

The residual matrix with m factors removed is defined by

$$(11.15) \qquad\qquad \mathbf{R}_m = \mathbf{R} - \mathbf{R}^\dagger,$$

where it is assumed that the reproduced correlations are based on the extraction of m factors by the multiple-group method.

Before considering the methods for transforming the results obtained in this section to an orthogonal solution, it is well to consider the cogent argument, presented by Guttman [175, p. 215] for accepting the oblique multiple-group solution:

> A drawback is that if rotation is actually necessary, this implies that original hypotheses about the nature of the common factors are wrong. *A posteriori* hypotheses, made after inspection of the data, may be subject to all the uncertainties and controversies which beset

any *a posteriori* theory. The results of a factor analysis would seem to be more trustworthy if the ... [grouping of the variables] is chosen according to an *a priori* psychological theory, which is then *tested* by the data. This kind of procedure carries more scientific weight than the procedure of constructing an *a posteriori* theory to fit already known facts. The latter is implied by rotation of axes (whether or not the rotation is "blind").

11.4. *The Orthogonal Solution*

Whether an orthogonal solution is desired simply for completion of the multiple-group analysis (expediting some of the computational labor) or as a stepping-stone to the rotational problem, methods for obtaining it are outlined in this section. The orthogonal solution is derived by transformation from the oblique solution described in the preceding section. After the oblique solution has been obtained, the transformation required is either from the pattern values (b_{jp}) or the structure values (s_{jp}) to the orthogonal factor weights (a_{jp}).

Of all possible transformations from oblique to rectangular coordinate axes, the special case employed in the multiple-group analysis has the following properties: the first axis of the new system coincides with the first oblique-factor axis, the second is in the plane of the first two oblique axes and orthogonal to the first, etc.* This type of transformation, for the case of only two factors, is illustrated in Figure 11.1. For the sake of simplicity, a general point is designated P instead of P_j, and its coordinates

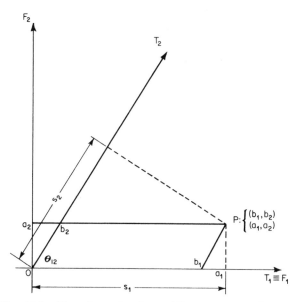

FIG. 11.1.—Transformation from oblique to rectangular axes

---

* In formal mathematics, this transformation is known as the Gram-Schmidt process and yields the orthogonalization of a matrix [385, p. 78].

are shown as (b_1, b_2) instead of (b_{j1}, b_{j2}) in the oblique reference system, and as (a_1, a_2) instead of (a_{j1}, a_{j2}) in the rectangular reference system. The point P (or the vector from the origin to P) can be represented in the common-factor space as follows (see **4.10**):

$$(11.16) \qquad\qquad z'' = b_1 T_1 + b_2 T_2,$$

or

$$(11.17) \qquad\qquad z'' = a_1 F_1 + a_2 F_2,$$

depending upon which reference system is employed. In the oblique reference system, the (orthogonal) projections on the coordinate axes are distinct from the coordinates, and are given by the structure values:

$$(11.18) \qquad\qquad s_1 = r_{zT_1} \quad \text{and} \quad s_2 = r_{zT_2}.$$

For the special type of transformation from oblique to rectangular axes with the properties listed above, the relationships between the two sets of coordinates are given by [201, p. 19]:

$$(11.19) \qquad \begin{aligned} a_1 &= b_1 + b_2 \cos \theta_{12} \\ a_2 &= b_2 \sin \theta_{12} \end{aligned}$$

where θ_{12} is the angle between the oblique axes T_1 and T_2. As noted in **4.9**, the cosine of the angle between two vectors is the correlation of the variables represented by such vectors. Hence, $\cos\theta_{12} = r$, where for simplicity r is used to designate $r_{T_1 T_2}$. Then the foregoing transformation equations may be written:

$$(11.20) \qquad \begin{aligned} a_1 &= b_1 + b_2 r \\ a_2 &= b_2 \sqrt{1 - r^2}. \end{aligned}$$

Although the example covers only two variables there is a heuristic value to expressing the transformation in matrix form:

$$(11.21) \qquad (a_{j1}\ a_{j2}) = (b_{j1}\ b_{j2}) \cdot \begin{bmatrix} 1 & 0 \\ r & \sqrt{1 - r^2} \end{bmatrix}.$$

The transformation matrix that carries the coordinates of the oblique reference system into the coordinates of the rectangular reference system can be derived from the matrix of correlations among the oblique factors. By applying the square root operation (see **3.4**) on the matrix Φ of factor correlation, the resulting "square root" matrix T' is found to be precisely the transformation matrix, as in (11.21). The general square root operation,

$$(11.22) \qquad\qquad \Phi = T'T,$$

reduces to the following explicit form for the case of two variables:

(11.23)
$$\begin{bmatrix} 1 & r \\ r & 1 \end{bmatrix} = \begin{bmatrix} 1 & 0 \\ r & \sqrt{1-r^2} \end{bmatrix} \cdot \begin{bmatrix} 1 & r \\ 0 & \sqrt{1-r^2} \end{bmatrix}.$$

The expression (11.21) is immediately generalizable to n variables and m factors, viz.,

(11.24)
$$\mathbf{A} = \mathbf{PT'},$$

where $\mathbf{A}$ and $\mathbf{P}$ are n by m matrices (a_{jp}) and (b_{jp}), respectively; and $\mathbf{T}$, a square matrix of order m, is derived by the square root operation on $\mathbf{\Phi}$. While (11.24) provides the transformation from oblique *coordinates* to the specified orthogonal coordinates, it is desirable to express the transformation in terms of the oblique *structure values*, because those are determined first in the course of the analysis. To accomplish this, substitute the expression for the oblique factor pattern matrix from (11.12) into (11.24), obtaining

(11.25)
$$\mathbf{A} = \mathbf{S\Phi}^{-1}\mathbf{T'}.$$

Then from the square root operation (11.22) on $\mathbf{\Phi}$, the foregoing equation becomes

$$\mathbf{A} = \mathbf{ST}^{-1}(\mathbf{T'})^{-1}\mathbf{T'} = \mathbf{ST}^{-1}\mathbf{I},$$

or

(11.26)
$$\mathbf{A} = \mathbf{ST}^{-1},$$

which is precisely the desired transformation from the oblique structure values to the orthogonal factor pattern. Stated another way, the transformation (11.26) to the orthogonal frame of reference (F's) is described in terms of projections (s_{jp}) on the oblique axes instead of coordinates (b_{jp}) in the original oblique reference system.

11.5. *Multiple-Group Factor Algorithm*

The methods described in the last two sections can be summarized and organized in a convenient computing form. Such a schematic form is presented in Table 11.2. The principal parts of this worksheet consist of: (1) the stub, listing the variables; (2) the heading, giving brief instructions; and (3) the body of the table proper, made up of three vertical sections with three blocks in each section. Also, at the bottom of the table, there are instructions for checking the numerical operations.

What this computing form accomplishes is the determination of both the oblique factor pattern and the orthogonal factor solution, starting with the intercorrelations among the factors and the oblique factor structure. The work is begun by recording in the first vertical section the three known matrices: (1) the $m \times m$ matrix of correlations among the factors; (2) an identity matrix of the same order; and (3) the $n \times m$ oblique factor structure.

The next step involves the application of the square root method (see **3.4**) to the first vertical section to get the middle section. The first block, of course, yields the square root matrix of the original matrix of factor correlations. The next block, obtained by applying the square root operator to the identity matrix, contains the transformation matrix $\mathbf{T}^{-1}$. In the third block, the orthogonal factor solution is determined by the same square root operation. The fact that the square root operation on the matrix $\mathbf{S}$ yields the matrix $\mathbf{A}$ can be seen from equation (11.26).

Table 11.2

Multiple-Group Factor Algorithm

	Instructions		
Variable	Original Matrices (*m* columns)	Square Root Operation $(\mathbf{T}^{-1})$ on Preceding Block (*m* columns)	Row-by-row Multiplication of Preceding Block with $\mathbf{T}^{-1}$, i.e., Postmultiplication by $(\mathbf{T}')^{-1}$ (*m* columns)
T_1 T_2 . . T_m	Factor Correlations $\boldsymbol{\Phi}$ $(\boldsymbol{\Phi} = \mathbf{T}'\mathbf{T})$	Square Root Matrix $\mathbf{T}'$ $(\boldsymbol{\Phi}\mathbf{T}^{-1} = \mathbf{T}')$	(Result is $\mathbf{I}$, except for rounding errors—may be left blank, or used as check)
T_1 T_2 . . T_m	Identity Matrix $\mathbf{I}$	Transformation Matrix $\mathbf{T}^{-1}$ $(\mathbf{IT}^{-1} = \mathbf{T}^{-1})$	Inverse of Initial Matrix $\boldsymbol{\Phi}^{-1}$ $(\mathbf{T}^{-1}(\mathbf{T}')^{-1} = \boldsymbol{\Phi}^{-1})$ (not required explicitly)
1 2 3 . *n*	Oblique Factor Structure $\mathbf{S}$	Orthogonal Factor Matrix $\mathbf{A}$ $(\mathbf{ST}^{-1} = \mathbf{A})$	Oblique Factor Pattern $\mathbf{P}$ $(\mathbf{A}(\mathbf{T}')^{-1} = \mathbf{P})$
Total	Sum of all $(2m + n)$ elements in each column		
Check	(No check in this block)	Square root operation applied to totals of preceding block	Row-by-row multiplication of totals in preceding blocks with $\mathbf{T}^{-1}$

It should be noted that the arrangement of work in Table 11.2 is transposed from that in Table 3.2. In Section **3.4**, the square root method is presented with the square root matrix below the original matrix, while here it is placed to the right. Because of this transposition of the blocks, the computing formulas of **3.4** must also be transposed. For example, the principal formulas for the values in the first three *columns* of the middle block become:

(11.27)
$$S_{j1} = \frac{r_{j1}}{S_{11}}, \qquad (j > 1)$$

(11.28)
$$S_{j2 \cdot 1} = \frac{r_{j2} - S_{j1}S_{21}}{S_{22 \cdot 1}}, \qquad (j > 2)$$

(11.29)
$$S_{j3 \cdot (2)} = \frac{r_{j3} - S_{j1}S_{31} - S_{j2 \cdot 1}S_{32 \cdot 1}}{S_{33 \cdot (2)}}, \qquad (j > 3)$$

in place of formulas in Steps 3, 5, and 7 for the successive *rows* in the arrangement of **3.4**.

Finally, the third vertical section is obtained by simple matrix multiplication. Each block (matrix) in the middle section is multiplied, row-by-row, by the transformation matrix $\mathbf{T}^{-1}$ (which is set off by the bold lines) to obtain the corresponding block in the third section. The first block need not be computed, except if desired for an additional check. The next block, which gives $\mathbf{\Phi}^{-1}$, again is not required explicitly, but results without cost as a by-product of the square root method. The required oblique factor pattern is obtained in the last block of the algorithm by postmultiplication of the orthogonal factor matrix by the transpose of the transformation matrix,* i.e.,

(11.30)
$$\mathbf{P} = \mathbf{A}(\mathbf{T}')^{-1}.$$

The fact that the row-by-row multiplication of $\mathbf{A}$ by $\mathbf{T}^{-1}$ actually yields $\mathbf{P}$, can be derived from (11.24) by postmultiplying both sides of that equation by $(\mathbf{T}')^{-1}$.

After the computations outlined in Table 11.2 have been made, it is a simple matter to get the matrix of reproduced correlations, and hence the residual matrix. Row-by-row multiplication of $\mathbf{A}$ by itself yields the matrix $\mathbf{R}^{\dagger}$ of reproduced correlations according to (2.50). An alternative procedure is row-by-row multiplication of $\mathbf{S}$ by $\mathbf{P}$ according to (11.14).

The computing procedure involving the oblique solution of **11.3**, followed by the square root method outlined in Table 11.2, will be found very efficient for factoring if an electronic computer is not available. It might still be desirable to get a multiple-group solution with the aid of a computer in some instances (e.g., to explore a specific hypothesis involving groups of variables). A computer program for triangular decomposition [353] may be very useful for such cases. In general, however, when an electronic computer is available, the principal-factor, minres, or maximum-likelihood methods would be preferred.

11.6. *Numerical Illustration*

The calculations involved in the multiple-group solution will be illustrated with a nine-variable example. The reduced correlation matrix, with the communalities

---

* As indicated in **3.2**, paragraph **18**, the row-by-row multiplication of a matrix $\mathbf{A}$ by another matrix $\mathbf{B}$ is equivalent to the conventional row-by-column multiplication of $\mathbf{A}$ by $\mathbf{B}'$.

Table 11.3

Intercorrelations of Nine Psychological Variables[a]

Variable	1	2	3	4	5	6	7	8	9
1. Word meaning	.81								
2. Sentence completion	.75	.69							
3. Odd words	.78	.72	.75						
4. Mixed arithmetic	.44	.52	.47	.91					
5. Remainders	.45	.53	.48	.82	.74				
6. Missing numbers	.51	.58	.54	.82	.74	.74			
7. Gloves	.21	.23	.28	.33	.37	.35	.35		
8. Boots	.30	.32	.37	.33	.36	.38	.45	.58	
9. Hatchets	.31	.30	.37	.31	.36	.38	.52	.67	.77

[a] Taken from K. J. Holzinger's unpublished class notes involving a study of 696 cases, 12 tests, and 4 factors.

estimated by single triads of equation (5.33), is contained in Table 11.3. As the first step in the analysis, the nine variables are placed in three groups, as follows:

$$G_1 : (1, 2, 3), \text{ verbal};$$

$$G_2 : (4, 5, 6), \text{ arithmetic};$$

$$G_3 : (7, 8, 9), \text{ spatial relations}.$$

This grouping is justified by the nature of the respective variables and verified by B-coefficients:

$$B(1, 2, 3) = 187, \quad B(4, 5, 6) = 186, \quad \text{and} \quad B(7, 8, 9) = 168.$$

The sums (11.2) of the correlations of each variable with all the variables in each group are recorded in Table 11.4. Then the sums (11.3) of these sums by groups are given in Table 11.5. From these two tables the correlations among the factors, and between the factors and the variables, can be computed readily. By use of formula (11.10), the following matrix of factor correlations is obtained:

$$\Phi = \begin{bmatrix} 1.0000 & .6511 & .4640 \\ .6511 & 1.0000 & .5324 \\ .4640 & .5324 & 1.0000 \end{bmatrix}.$$

Similarly, by application of formula (11.11), the correlations of the variables with the factors are obtained and presented in Table 11.6.

The remainder of the multiple-group analysis is performed by means of the algorithm described in 11.5. This worksheet for the nine-variable example appears in Table 11.7. The matrix Φ of correlations among the factors and the oblique factor

Table 11.4

Sums of Correlations for Variables with Groups: w_{jp}

G_p	j	w_{j1}	w_{j2}	w_{j3}
G_1	1	2.34	1.40	.82
	2	2.16	1.63	.85
	3	2.25	1.49	1.02
G_2	4	1.43	2.55	.97
	5	1.46	2.30	1.09
	6	1.63	2.30	1.11
G_3	7	.72	1.05	1.32
	8	.99	1.07	1.70
	9	.98	1.05	1.96

Table 11.5

Sums of Correlations Among Groups: W_{pq}

p \ q	1	2	3
1	6.75	4.52	2.69
2	4.52	7.15	3.17
3	2.69	3.17	4.98
$\sqrt{W_{pp}}$	2.60	2.67	2.23

Table 11.6

Oblique Factor Structure: **S**

Variable j	s_{j1}	s_{j2}	s_{j3}
1	.90	.52	.37
2	.83	.61	.38
3	.87	.56	.46
4	.55	.96	.43
5	.56	.86	.49
6	.63	.86	.50
7	.28	.39	.59
8	.38	.40	.76
9	.38	.39	.88

structure **S** of Table 11.6 provide the starting point for the square root operation and subsequent matrix multiplications performed in Table 11.7. The end products are the orthogonal factor matrix **A**, in the lower block of the middle section; and the oblique factor pattern **P**, in the lower right hand corner. After finishing this analysis, the adequacy of the solution is judged from a comparison of the matrix of reproduced correlations with the reduced correlation matrix. The reproduced correlations may be computed by row-by-row multiplication of **A** by itself, and checked by row-by-row multiplication of **S** by **P**. A comparison of the original and reproduced correlations show only one instance of a residual as high as .02. Obviously, the multiple-group solution provides an excellent fit to the observed data of Table 11.3. The adequacy of the results, of course, is independent of whether the orthogonal or the oblique solution is preferred.

Table 11.7

Computation of Orthogonal Factor Matrix A and Oblique Factor Pattern P

(Following multiple-group factor algorithm of Table 11.2)

Variable	Original Matrices			Square Root Operation T^{-1}			Row-by-row Multiplication with T^{-1}		
T_1	1.0000	a	a	1.0000			1.0000	0	0
T_2	.6511	1.0000	a	.6511	.7590		.0000	1.0000	0
T_3	.4640	.5324	1.0000	.4640	.3034	.8323	−.0000	−.0000	1.0000
T_1	1.0000	0	0	1.0000	−.8578	−.2448	1.7957	a	a
T_2	0	1.0000	0	0	1.3175	−.4803	−1.0126	1.9665	a
T_3	0	0	1.0000	0	0	1.2015	−.2941	−.5771	1.4436
	Oblique factor structures: S			Orthogonal factor matrix: A			Oblique factor pattern: P		
1	.90	.52	.37	.90	−.09	−.03	.98	−.09	−.04
2	.83	.61	.38	.83	.09	−.04	.76	.14	−.05
3	.87	.56	.46	.87	−.01	.07	.86	−.04	.08
4	.55	.96	.43	.55	.79	−.07	−.11	1.07	−.08
5	.56	.86	.49	.56	.65	.04	−.01	.84	.04
6	.63	.86	.50	.63	.60	.03	.11	.77	.04
7	.28	.39	.59	.28	.27	.45	−.06	.14	.55
8	.38	.40	.76	.38	.20	.63	.05	−.04	.76
9	.38	.39	.88	.38	.19	.77	.03	−.12	.93
Total	8.50	8.73	7.86	8.50	4.21	3.16	4.10	4.05	3.80
Check				8.50	4.21	3.17	4.12	4.03	3.80

[a] Terms above the diagonal of a symmetric matrix are deleted for simplicity. These terms, however, must be included in the totals in order for the checks to apply.

PART III

DERIVED SOLUTIONS

12
Different Solutions in Common-Factor Space

12.1. *Introduction*

In the five preceding chapters, various methods were proposed for reducing a correlation matrix to a factor matrix which in some reasonable sense reproduces the original correlations. The factor solutions could be viewed as final products, in their own right; or they could be conceived as initial products satisfying the fundamental factor theorem of reproducing the correlation matrix, and requiring further manipulation to a final form. The basic philosophy for transforming a preliminary solution into a final multiple-factor type of solution is covered in **6.1** and **6.5**. There it is made clear that once the common-factor space has been determined, an infinitude of rotations is possible from one coordinate system to another without any effect on the adequacy of solution.

The multiple-factor solution has been defined essentially in intuitive terms only, and so has not lent itself to precise mathematical formulation. This preferred type of solution rests upon the principles of "simple structure" set forth in **6.2**. Attempts to objectify these principles are made in chapters 14 and 15, thereby making possible the determination of multiple-factor solutions by analytical methods. Since these methods involve very extensive computations, their very conception had to await the development of the large electronic computers. Before considering such methods, there is a pedagogic value in reviewing the more modest techniques for obtaining a multiple-factor solution involving subjective, graphical transformations from some arbitrary initial solution. Such techniques for getting an *orthogonal* multiple-factor solution are the principal topics of this chapter, while manual methods for getting an *oblique* solution are covered in the next chapter.

Before considering the multiple-factor solution proper, the general theory of relationships among solutions in a given common-factor space is developed in **12.2**. Then graphical methods for rotating an initial solution to a multiple-factor solution are presented in **12.3**, and numerical illustrations given in **12.4**. Finally, certain

249

problems are considered in **12.5** which involve comparisons of factor solutions when either the variables or the samples are altered.

12.2. *Relationship between Two Known Solutions*

Several types of comparisons among factor solutions are of interest, both from a methodological viewpoint and from the viewpoint of establishing basic factors in a content field, such as psychology. The most obvious, of course, is a comparison of any two solutions derived from the same correlation matrix [240]. That is the subject of the present section. Other comparisons are discussed in **12.5**.

In mathematics the reference system plays a very minor role; the particular configuration of points is of prime importance, and the coordinate system is of much lesser significance. Thus, if it is desired to describe an ellipse, i.e., get an algebraic equation for the ellipse, it is quite irrelevant whether rectangular Cartesian coordinates, nonrectangular Cartesian coordinates, or polar coordinates are employed. Furthermore, the particular orientation of axes is immaterial. With each change of the coordinate system, of course, the equation of the ellipse will generally change, but the fact remains that the equation in each case describes the ellipse with respect to the given reference system.

The object of factor analysis, on the other hand, is the selection of an appropriate frame of reference, the configuration of points representing the variables being of lesser significance. Then the indeterminateness of the factor problem is obvious. In selecting a particular reference system, the unit vectors along the coordinate axes represent the factors, and, since the reference system can be rotated about its origin in an infinitude of ways in the common-factor space, there arises an infinite number of factor systems for a given body of data.

As a general procedure, it might be advisable to put any factor solution in some standard form, e.g., the canonical form of **8.8**. Then, if two independent solutions are each brought to canonical form, it will be obvious whether they are indeed alike or not (see **10.6**). When it is desired to study the relationships between two distinct factor solutions, that may be accomplished by finding a matrix of transformation which carries the coordinates of one into the other. Thus, if the first factor pattern is denoted by **A** and the second factor pattern by **B**, then the problem is to find a matrix **T** such that

(12.1)
$$\mathbf{AT} = \mathbf{B}.$$

The matrix **A** represents the coordinates a_{jp} of the n points with respect to one set of m common-factor axes, say $F_1, F_2, \cdots, F_m$; the matrix **B** represents the coordinates b_{jp} of the points with respect to a new set of axes, say $K_1, K_2, \cdots, K_m$; while the matrix **T** represents the transformation of the coordinates in **A** to those in **B**.

If the number of factors is equal to the number of variables then the solution for **T** is simply

(12.2)
$$\mathbf{T} = \mathbf{A}^{-1}\mathbf{B}.$$

Since the number of common factors is usually much smaller than the number of variables, however, the matrix **A** does not have an inverse and **T** cannot be calculated directly. It may be noted that, for any matrix **A**,

$$(12.3) \qquad (\mathbf{A'A})^{-1}(\mathbf{A'A}) = \mathbf{I},$$

and hence, if both members of (12.1) are premultiplied by $(\mathbf{A'A})^{-1}\mathbf{A'}$, there results

$$(12.4) \qquad \mathbf{T} = (\mathbf{A'A})^{-1}\mathbf{A'B}$$

This formula gives the desired matrix of transformation.

The relationships among the *factors themselves* (or the factor measurements) may also be obtained by means of the matrix **T**. In the given common-factor space the column vectors of the first and second sets of factors may be taken to be $\mathbf{f} = \{F_1 F_2 \cdots\}$ and $\mathbf{k} = \{K_1 K_2 \cdots\}$, respectively. From the definitions of the two factor patterns, and their assumed equality, it follows that

$$(12.5) \qquad \mathbf{Af} = \mathbf{Bk}.$$

Premultiplying both sides of this equation by $(\mathbf{A'A})^{-1}\mathbf{A'}$, and again employing (12.3), there results

$$(12.6) \qquad \mathbf{f} = (\mathbf{A'A})^{-1}\mathbf{A'Bk}.$$

By making use of (12.4), this expression finally simplifies to

$$(12.7) \qquad \mathbf{f} = \mathbf{Tk}.$$

This is the matrix formulation of the relationships between the F factors and the K factors.

A system of equations represented by (12.1) gives the actual transformation of coordinates between the two factor solutions. Thus the factor weights for any variable in one solution are expressed linearly in terms of the weights of the other solution. An alternative way of expressing the relationship between two factor solutions is afforded by a system of equations implied by (12.7). Thus, the contributions of the K factors to the variance of each F factor can be obtained. Also, equations (12.7) may be used to estimate the measurements of F factors from known equations of measurements of the K factors.

A detailed numerical illustration of these procedures will now be given, employing the example of thirteen psychological tests. The relationships will be developed between the multiple-factor solution of Table 12.5 and an oblique primary-factor solution for the same data (see ex. 8, chap. 13). A schematic worksheet is presented in Table 12.1 along with the specific example. The matrix of coefficients of the multiple-factor pattern is denoted by **B** and appears in the extreme right-hand block of the table, and just to the left of it is the oblique factor pattern denoted by **A**. These two solutions may be considered equivalent (or in the same common-factor space) since both solutions were obtained by transformation of a centroid solution.

After the known factor patterns are recorded in the right half of Table 12.1, the computations leading to the transformation matrix **T** are performed in the left half

Table 12.1

Transformation Between Solutions in a Fixed Common-Factor Space

A. Computing Algorithm

Calculation of Transformation Matrix		j	Known Factor Patterns					
			a_{j1}	a_{j2}	$\cdots$	b_{j1}	b_{j2}	$\cdots$
A′A Col.-by-col. multi- plication of **A** by itself	**I**	1 2 . .						
Square root method of Table 3.3 is applied to compute $(\mathbf{A'A})^{-1}$		. .		**A**			**B**	
	$(\mathbf{A'A})^{-1}$	. .						
T′ = $(\mathbf{B'A})(\mathbf{A'A})^{-1}$ Row-by-row multi- plication of (**B′A**) $(\mathbf{A'A})^{-1}$	**B′A** Col.-by-col. multi- plication of **B** by **A**	n						

B. Example of Thirteen Psychological Tests

Calculation of Transformation Matrix						j	Primary Factor Pattern[b]			Multiple-Factor Pattern[c]		
							a_{j1}	a_{j2}	a_{j3}	b_{j1}	b_{j2}	b_{j3}
1.823	−.232	−.058	1	0	0	1	.731	−.089	.142	.096	.248	.706
[a]	3.394	−.017		1	0	2	.441	.004	.004	.102	.089	.425
[a]	[a]	2.103			1	3	.721	−.090	−.142	.136	−.011	.602
						4	.508	.090	−.003	.193	.121	.516
1.350	−.172	−.043	.741	0	0							
	1.834	−.013	.069	.545	0	5	−.058	.801	.087	.702	.324	.243
		1.449	.023	.005	.690	6	.037	.809	−.051	.719	.214	.300
						7	−.068	.901	−.030	.778	.243	.237
			.554	.038	.016	8	.155	.591	.078	.562	.291	.372
			[a]	.297	.003	9	−.068	.919	−.081	.791	.198	.231
			[a]	[a]	.476							
						10	−.385	.164	.809	.119	.757	−.100
.250	.883	.070	.246	2.939	.121	11	−.039	.077	.659	.109	.651	.161
.198	.314	.962	.230	1.008	2.006	12	.073	−.177	.773	−.083	.703	.210
.950	.344	.262	1.635	.944	.490	13	.351	−.061	.594	.070	.619	.469

[a] Terms below the diagonal of a symmetric matrix are deleted for simplicity, while blanks actually denote zeros.

[b] Obtained by the graphical methods of chapter 13 in exercises 2–8 for that chapter.

[c] From Table 12.5.

of the table. First, the product $\mathbf{A'A}$ is determined and placed in the upper left block of the table; and the inverse of this product is calculated by the square root method (see **3.5**). This provides the first part of the expression (12.4) for $\mathbf{T}$. In place of the second part of (12.4), its transpose is determined (primarily for computational convenience). This product $(\mathbf{B'A})$ is recorded in the block below $(\mathbf{A'A})^{-1}$. Finally, the transpose of the desired transformation matrix (12.4) is computed in the extreme lower left corner of the table.

The actual transformation from the primary factor coordinates to the multiple-factor coordinates is given by

$$
\begin{aligned}
b_{j1} &= .250a_{j1} + .883a_{j2} + .070a_{j3}, \\
b_{j2} &= .198a_{j1} + .314a_{j2} + .962a_{j3}, \\
b_{j3} &= .950a_{j1} + .344a_{j2} + .262a_{j3},
\end{aligned}
$$

(12.8)

where the a's and b's are the coordinates in the matrices $\mathbf{A}$ and $\mathbf{B}$, respectively. It is evident from these equations that the coefficients of the first multiple factor can be described mostly in terms of the coefficients of the second primary factor; the second multiple factor in terms of the third primary factor; and the third multiple factor in terms of the first primary factor.

Similarly, by means of the matrix $\mathbf{T}$, the relationships among the factors may be exhibited as follows:

$$
\begin{aligned}
T_1 &= .250M_1 + .198M_2 + .950M_3, \\
T_2 &= .883M_1 + .314M_2 + .344M_3, \\
T_3 &= .070M_1 + .962M_2 + .262M_3,
\end{aligned}
$$

(12.9)

where the T's represent the (oblique) primary factors and the M's the (orthogonal) multiple factors. From these equations it is apparent that each of the oblique factors consists primarily of one of the multiple factors, with some slight contribution of each of the other two. For example, the factor M_3 contributes 90 per cent to the unit variance of T_1, while M_1 and M_2 contribute only 6 per cent and 4 per cent, respectively.

While the foregoing development may seem to be somewhat trivial, there was a period of time in the development of factor analysis when such relationships were not completely understood. As noted in chapter 1, it may have been the failure to recognize the fact that a given matrix of correlations could be factored in an infinite number of different ways that led to the many controversies about the "true", the "best", or the "invariant" solution for a set of data. It is now obvious that any two factorizations of a given set of data are related by (12.1), where the transformation from one to the other solution is given by (12.4).

In the problem just treated, both solutions $\mathbf{A}$ and $\mathbf{B}$ were assumed to be known, and the relationship between them (given by the transformation matrix $\mathbf{T}$) was to be determined. The general task of obtaining a derived solution, which is the subject of the entire part iii of this text, involves a somewhat different problem. The initial pattern $\mathbf{A}$ is given, and some rules about the nature of the final solution $\mathbf{B}$ are specified, and from this a matrix of transformation **T** is built up which in fact leads to **B**. If the model for **B** is specified in exact mathematical terms, there is no problem other than the computing effort in arriving at the final solution and the transformation matrix. On the other hand, if the nature of **B** is only vaguely identified, then there are many subjective solutions. This distinction will become clearer in the course of the development in the remainder of this chapter and in the following three chapters.

12.3. *Graphical Procedures for Orthogonal Multiple-Factor Solution*

Subjective procedures are proposed in this section for developing the transformation from some initial solution to a multiple-factor form of solution. The method consists, essentially, of the build-up of a series of rotations in a plane. The angle of rotation at each stage is selected by inspection of a graph and judgment as to the attainment of the objectives of simple structure (see **6.2**).

To assist in the development of orthogonal transformations, the following summary of notation will be found convenient:

$$\mathbf{A} = (a_{jp}), \text{ initial factor matrix, with factors } F_p,$$

(12.10) $$\mathbf{B} = (b_{jp}), \text{ final factor matrix, with factors } M_p,$$

$$\mathbf{T} = (\lambda_{qp}), \text{ orthogonal transformation matrix, with } \theta_{qp} \text{ the} \\ \text{angle of rotation in the plane of the original factor } p \\ \text{and the final factor } q.$$

The range of j is over the n variables, and the range of p and q is over the m factors.

When an initial factor pattern involves only two factors, the variables may be represented as points in a plane, with the coefficients of the factors as the coordinates. Then a transformation to some other form of solution implies the representation of these points with respect to the axes denoting the new factors. Such a transformation is merely a rotation of axes in this common-factor space. Thus, any point may be referred to either system of reference F_1, F_2, or M_1, M_2, as shown in Figure 12.1. For the sake of simplicity, a general point is designated P instead of P_j, and its coordinates in the original frame of reference are shown as (a_1, a_2) instead of (a_{j1}, a_{j2}), and in the new reference system as (b_1, b_2) in place of (b_{j1}, b_{j2}). The problem is to express the new b-coordinates in terms of the original a-coordinates when the reference axes are rotated through an angle θ *from* the original to the new.

The required transformation is accomplished by making use of the following property on projections of lines: the sum of the projections upon a straight line of the segments of any broken line connecting two points is equal to the corresponding sum for any other broken line connecting the same two points. Here the origin O and any point P are joined by two broken lines, namely, ORP and OSP. It follows that the projections of these broken lines along any direction are equal, i.e.,

(12.11) $$\text{Proj. } OR + \text{Proj. } RP = \text{Proj. } OS + \text{Proj. } SP.$$

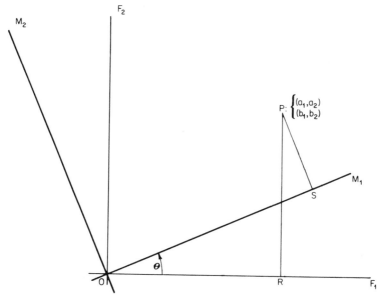

FIG. 12.1.—Rotation in a plane

If the direction is taken, first, as the positive axis of M_1 and, second, as the positive axis of M_2, the resulting expressions are

(12.12)
$$OR \cos \theta + RP \sin \theta = OS + 0,$$
$$-OR \sin \theta + RP \cos \theta = 0 + SP.$$

But the line segments are simply the coordinates, viz.,

$$OR = a_1, \quad RP = a_2 \quad \text{and} \quad OS = b_1, \quad SP = b_2.$$

Hence, the final coordinates are expressed in terms of the initial ones, resulting from the rotation of axes through the angle θ, by the following equations:

(12.13)
$$b_1 = \quad a_1 \cos \theta + a_2 \sin \theta,$$
$$b_2 = -a_1 \sin \theta + a_2 \cos \theta.$$

It should be noted that the trigonometric terms are actually the direction cosines of the new axes with respect to the old ones, and the equations (12.13) may be put in the form:

(12.14)
$$b_1 = \lambda_{11}a_1 + \lambda_{21}a_2,$$
$$b_2 = \lambda_{12}a_1 + \lambda_{22}a_2.$$

For a set of n points there would be n pairs of equations (12.14) carrying each pair of coordinates (a_{j1}, a_{j2}) into the corresponding pair (b_{j1}, b_{j2}). This transformation

255

may be put in matrix form, as follows:

(12.15)
$$(b_{j1} \quad b_{j2}) = (a_{j1} \quad a_{j2}) \cdot \begin{bmatrix} \lambda_{11} & \lambda_{12} \\ \lambda_{21} & \lambda_{22} \end{bmatrix},$$

or, in more compact and generalizable terms:

(12.16)
$$\mathbf{B} = \mathbf{AT}.$$

This expression is precisely of the same form as (12.1), but here the matrix **B** is to be derived from **A** upon the choice of the transformation matrix **T**. In the simple example of a rotation in a plane, the matrices **A** and **B** are each of order $n \times 2$ and the matrix **T** is 2×2. The elements of **T** clearly satisfy the conditions

$$\lambda_{11}^2 + \lambda_{21}^2 = 1, \qquad \lambda_{12}^2 + \lambda_{22}^2 = 1, \qquad \lambda_{11}\lambda_{12} + \lambda_{21}\lambda_{22} = 0$$

so that the transformation is orthogonal in the sense of **4.6**.

When a factor solution involves three factors, the transformation from an initial to a final pattern takes the form:

(12.17)
$$b_{j1} = \lambda_{11}a_{j1} + \lambda_{21}a_{j2} + \lambda_{31}a_{j3},$$
$$b_{j2} = \lambda_{12}a_{j1} + \lambda_{22}a_{j2} + \lambda_{32}a_{j3},$$
$$b_{j3} = \lambda_{13}a_{j1} + \lambda_{23}a_{j2} + \lambda_{33}a_{j3},$$

where the preceding notation has been extended to an additional dimension. This transformation is covered by (12.16) if the factor matrices in that expression are presumed to be of order $n \times 3$ and the transformation matrix of order 3×3. The elements of **T**, in this case, must satisfy the six independent conditions:

(12.18)
$$\lambda_{11}^2 + \lambda_{21}^2 + \lambda_{31}^2 = 1,$$
$$\lambda_{12}^2 + \lambda_{22}^2 + \lambda_{32}^2 = 1,$$
$$\lambda_{13}^2 + \lambda_{23}^2 + \lambda_{33}^2 = 1,$$
$$\lambda_{11}\lambda_{12} + \lambda_{21}\lambda_{22} + \lambda_{31}\lambda_{32} = 0,$$
$$\lambda_{11}\lambda_{13} + \lambda_{21}\lambda_{23} + \lambda_{31}\lambda_{33} = 0,$$
$$\lambda_{12}\lambda_{13} + \lambda_{22}\lambda_{23} + \lambda_{32}\lambda_{33} = 0.$$

Thus, the nine coefficients of (12.17), being subject to six conditions, afford only three degrees of freedom of rotation in ordinary space. Explicit equations for the b's in terms of the a's, involving only three independent parameters can be obtained,* but are not employed in practical analyses.

A form of transformation that is not only practical but which can be readily generalized to any number of factors will now be indicated. The principle underlying

---

* These are known as Euler's formulas, a typical one being: $a_1 = b_1(\cos \varphi \cos \psi - \sin \varphi \sin \psi \cos \theta) - b_2(\cos \varphi \sin \psi + \sin \varphi \cos \psi \cos \theta) + b_3 \sin \varphi \sin \theta$, where the first subscript j has been dropped from the a's and b's and θ, φ, ψ are angles of rotation [430, p. 42].

this method is that the result of successive orthogonal transformations is itself an orthogonal transformation, which is said to be the *product* of the successive rotations. Since a planar rotation is the simplest type, a transformation in three-space may be built up from such simpler rotations. Thus a transformation in ordinary space may involve the displacement of any two axes about the third, being, in effect, a rotation in a plane. Finally, a product of such rotations may be taken as the complete transformation.

The rotations can be arranged in a systematic order so that each axis is rotated with every other axis only once. The three rotations of pairs of axes in ordinary space may be indicated conveniently in the following manner:

Old Axes	Angle of Rotation	New Axes
$F_1 F_2$	θ_{12}	$Y_1 Y_2$
$Y_1 F_3$	θ_{13}	$M_1 Y_3$
$Y_2 Y_3$	θ_{23}	$M_2 M_3$

It will be noted that the angle of rotation is denoted by θ with subscripts corresponding to the numbers of the axes involved in the rotation. The first rotation is made in the plane of F_1 and F_2, leaving F_3 unaltered. The new axes in this plane are designated by Y_1 and Y_2. Since F_3 is perpendicular to the plane of F_1 and F_2, it is perpendicular to any line in this plane. In particular, F_3 is perpendicular to the new axis Y_1. The next rotation is made in the plane of Y_1 and F_3, leaving Y_2 unchanged. The new first axis, denoted by M_1, may be regarded as final because it is the result of rotations with each of the other axes. The last rotation transforms Y_2 and Y_3 into the final coordinate axes M_2 and M_3. It will be observed that the Y's are merely auxiliary axes and, taken alone, do not comprise a transformation from the F's with the orthogonal properties (12.18). On the other hand, both sets of axes Y_1, Y_2, F_3 and M_1, Y_2, Y_3 have these orthogonal properties, and either one may be taken, in some instances, as the final reference system. The solution ordinarily desired, however, is one based upon the complete transformation of the original axes F_1, F_2, F_3 to the final M_1, M_2, M_3.

Denoting the matrix of transformation of F_1 and F_2, leaving F_3 unchanged, by

$$(12.19) \qquad T_{12} = \begin{bmatrix} \cos\theta_{12} & -\sin\theta_{12} & 0 \\ \sin\theta_{12} & \cos\theta_{12} & 0 \\ 0 & 0 & 1 \end{bmatrix},$$

the first of the above rotations may be denoted by

$$(12.20) \qquad C = AT_{12},$$

where C is an intermediate matrix of coordinates with respect to Y_1, Y_2, F_3. The second and third rotations may be designated similarly, as follows:

$$(12.21) \qquad D = CT_{13} \quad \text{and} \quad B = DT_{23},$$

257

where **D** is another intermediate matrix, and

$$(12.22) \quad \mathbf{T}_{13} = \begin{bmatrix} \cos\theta_{13} & 0 & -\sin\theta_{13} \\ 0 & 1 & 0 \\ \sin\theta_{13} & 0 & \cos\theta_{13} \end{bmatrix}, \quad \mathbf{T}_{23} = \begin{bmatrix} 1 & 0 & 0 \\ 0 & \cos\theta_{23} & -\sin\theta_{23} \\ 0 & \sin\theta_{23} & \cos\theta_{23} \end{bmatrix}.$$

The three preceding rotations may be combined into a single transformation. Substituting the expression for **D** from the first into the second of equations (12.21) yields

$$\mathbf{B} = \mathbf{CT}_{13}\mathbf{T}_{23},$$

and substituting (12.20) for **C** in the last equation produces

$$(12.23) \qquad\qquad \mathbf{B} = \mathbf{AT}_{12}\mathbf{T}_{13}\mathbf{T}_{23}.$$

Denoting the product of the three successive rotations by

$$(12.24) \qquad\qquad \mathbf{T} = \mathbf{T}_{12}\mathbf{T}_{13}\mathbf{T}_{23},$$

the expression (12.23) reduces to (12.16). In practice this matrix **T** cannot be determined in advance, but rather, the final pattern is derived as a result of the successive rotations.

The preceding methods can be generalized to a common-factor space of m dimensions. Employing the notation (12.10) for this general case, the matrix of transformation is now

$$\mathbf{T} = \begin{bmatrix} \lambda_{11} & \lambda_{12} & \cdots & \lambda_{1m} \\ \lambda_{21} & \lambda_{22} & \cdots & \lambda_{2m} \\ \cdot & \cdot & \cdots & \cdot \\ \lambda_{m1} & \lambda_{m2} & \cdots & \lambda_{mm} \end{bmatrix},$$

and in the transformation (12.16) the initial and final factor matrices are each of order $n \times m$. The sets of λ's, by columns, are the direction cosines of the final reference axes $M_1, M_2, \cdots, M_m$ with respect to the original axes $F_1, F_2, \cdots, F_m$. These direction cosines are subject to the following set of independent conditions in order that the matrix **T** be orthogonal (see **4.6**):

$$(12.25) \qquad\qquad \sum_{r=1}^{m} \lambda_{rp}\lambda_{rq} = \delta_{pq} \qquad (p, q = 1, 2, \cdots, m; \quad p \leq q),$$

where δ_{pq} is the Kronecker delta (zero when $p \neq q$ and unity when $p = q$). Since $p \leq q$ and these indices range from 1 to m, the number of such conditions is $m(m + 1)/2$. There is a total of m^2 parameters in matrix **T**, and, since these are subject to $m(m + 1)/2$

258

restrictions, there remain

(12.26) $$m^2 - m(m+1)/2 = m(m-1)/2 = \binom{m}{2}$$

degrees of freedom of rotation in m-space.

The number of independent parameters given in (12.26) may be associated with the same number of rotations in planes. The planes in which the rotations are made are determined by all possible pairs of reference axes. Of course, since the angles of rotation are determined subjectively, there is no reason to assume that the best overall transformation has been obtained after going through the $\binom{m}{2}$ unique planar rotations. Additional rotations in any plane may be made, if desired, and the new product of all the rotations becomes the final transformation.

As in the case of three variables, the above rotations may be organized in a systematic manner. For example, when four factors are involved, the scheme outlined in Table 12.2 may be followed. After each of the partial transformations has been obtained, the complete product matrix **T** should be determined and exhibited as part of the overall results of the factor analysis. In this way, anyone reading the results can verify the course from the initial solution to the final solution. Incidentally, the matrix **T** should be checked for orthogonality in the sense of (12.25), and it may also serve to check the calculation of the final factor coefficients.

Table 12.2

Scheme for Subjective Rotations in Four Space

Old Axes	Angle of Rotation	New Axes	Orthogonal to
$F_1 F_2$	θ_{12}	$Y_1 Y_2$	$F_3 F_4$
$Y_1 F_3$	θ_{13}	$Z_1 Y_3$	$Y_2 F_4$
$Z_1 F_4$	θ_{14}	$M_1 Y_4$	$Y_2 Y_3$
$Y_2 Y_3$	θ_{23}	$Z_2 Z_3$	$M_1 Y_4$
$Z_2 Y_4$	θ_{24}	$M_2 Z_4$	$M_1 Z_3$
$Z_3 Z_4$	θ_{34}	$M_3 M_4$	$M_1 M_2$

The practical operation implied by the complete graphical method is the build-up of the transformation matrix **T** as the product of a series of rotations in planes. This involves $\binom{m}{2}$ two-dimensional plots and the matrix multiplications to get the intermediate coordinates, which is a very time consuming process. However, after many years of experience, these methods have proven quite dependable and satisfactory to many workers in factor analysis.

259

During the last two decades many attempts have been made to lighten the burden of the rotational task, and to set forth objective principles for the preferred multiple-factor solution. Some of these principles for simple structure were presented in **6.2**. In chapters 14 and 15 some of the recent developments in analytical solutions are presented. Before getting to these more sophisticated procedures, however, some indication is in order of alternatives to the complete graphical method. Such methods for getting a multiple-factor solution still require some graphical work to accomplish the rotations from the initial solution.

Because of the dependence of the simple-structure concept on subjective analysis of graphs, Thurstone has probably done more work than anyone else toward simplifying the chore of plotting graphs. As he states [477, p. 377]: "In the final acceptance or rejection of a simple-structure solution it is still the appearance of a set of graphs that determines the answer." Thurstone was among the first to seek an alternative graphical method to the two-dimensional sections as described above. In 1938, he proposed a new method for rotation [471; 477, Chap XI], consisting of three-dimensional sections, drawn in the plane of the paper however. The effect of a three-dimensional configuration in a plane is accomplished by extending the test vectors so that they all have unit projection on the first axis of the initial solution. In addition to the "method of extended vectors," Thurstone offers several other alternatives for rotation, devoting more than one-fourth of his text to the specific task of finding graphical substantiation for the simple-structure solution.

In another attempt to reduce the computational labor of rotation to simple structure, Zimmerman [549] proposes an ingenious scheme to eliminate the calculation of the numerical values of the intermediate coordinates. His procedure makes use of the principle of projection of a point from one graph to another, and involves only an ordinary drawing board, T-square, and drawing triangle. The two factor axes which are to be rotated are initially on two separate plots, with one coordinate for any point (representing a variable) projected horizontally from one plot and the other coordinate projected vertically from the second plot onto a new graph. Thus any axis can be rotated with any other without actual calculation of the numerical coordinates of the points. Only after all rotations have been made (to satisfy the appearance of simple structure), need one read and record the coordinates of the points with respect to the final axes. As a result of many rotations, and the inaccuracies of plotting, the basic relationship (2.50)—product of the factor matrix by its transpose —for the final rotated factors may not agree with that of the initial factors.

Another labor-saving approach is through the use of mechanical or electrical devices. One such machine, known as the "Factor Matrix Rotator"—conceived by Richard Gaylord and described by Harman and Harper [206]—is located in Washington, D.C., in the Army Personnel Research Office. This machine is of the analog type, that is, the readings are in the nature of displacements along a scale so that the figures have to be estimated from calibrations on the scale rather than read as precise digital values.

The initial factor weights are set into the machine by means of a series of dials; then the positions of the points representing the test are viewed as points of light on a scope (cathode ray tube). At the beginning of the work, the dials representing the transformation matrix are set for the identity transformation so that the researcher can first view the plot of the points as they appear in the initial factor solution. The axes are rotated by a simple manipulation of a dial; when desirable positions of the axes are located, the researcher can cause the appropriate elements in the transformation matrix to be reset to take the new positions into account.

Of course, the plots of points viewed on the scope are for a pair of axes at a time. An immediate advantage over hand methods arises from the fact that while a decision is being made regarding the rotation of a particular pair of axes, it is possible to view each of the remaining factor axes, in turn, with each of the two under consideration. The usual procedure employed by researchers using this machine is to view the plots in relation to all possible pairs of axes and on a schematic chart to note those planes in which rotation is most desirable and those that might be considered in order to keep the number of rotations to a minimum. When final decisions have been made about the location of factor axes to exhibit simple structure, the elements of both the transformation matrix and the final factor matrix can be obtained as fast as the experimenter can turn a dial and read a scale, since the computations are done electronically.

The Factor Matrix Rotator is designed primarily to handle problems of up to 50 tests and 12 factors and involving orthogonal rotations. Nonetheless, the machine has been applied to problems involving up to 130 tests and 24 factors. Further, it has been employed in connection with oblique transformations. However, applications beyond the basic capacity of the Rotator necessarily involve extensive additional computations off the machine.

Before leaving the subject of alternatives to the complete graphical method, it should be remembered that all of these methods arose as a result of the simple structure concept, and the lack of any real objective means of arriving at such a solution. The work of Paul Horst [251] was among the very earliest in which the transformation from an arbitrary factor matrix into a simple-structure matrix was almost completely objective. The criterion he employs is that of maximizing the ratio of the sum of squares of the "significant" factor loadings to the sum of squares of all the loadings. A variant of this method is proposed by Tucker [489], in which he gets the solution for all factors simultaneously, using graphs for the selection of subgroups of tests. A detailed discussion of analytical methods for approximating simple structure is deferred to chapters 14 and 15.

12.4. *Numerical Illustrations of Orthogonal Multiple-Factor Solutions*

In obtaining an orthogonal multiple-factor solution, the reference axes are chosen in conformity with the discussion in **6.2**. It is first necessary that the initial solution shall satisfy the criteria of the linear factor model (2.9), an orthogonal frame of reference, and parsimony of factors. Then an orthogonal rotation of such an initial pattern, in its common-factor space, will preserve these properties. The purpose of the transformation is to obtain a final pattern which also satisfies the criteria of low complexity, level contributions of factors, and hyper-planar fit; or more specifically, approximates the simple structure principles of **6.2**.

Although any initial solution with uncorrelated factors can be used to rotate to a multiple-factor pattern, the centroid solution has usually been employed in the past. The procedure is begun by plotting the points representing the variables in the plane of the first two initial factors F_1 and F_2. Since in an initial solution of the centroid form the second factor has both positive and negative weights, the points will lie in the first and fourth quadrants. The first rotation is then made through an angle θ_{12} such that all variables will have positive projections on the new axes Y_1, Y_2. Usually the angle θ_{12} so selected will be about $-45°$. Then, by applying equations of the type (12.13), the coordinates with respect to Y_1 and Y_2 are obtained. The next rotation is made in the plane of Y_1 and F_3 as indicated in the scheme exhibited in Table 12.2. Again, the angle θ_{13} is obtained by inspection of the graph. The new reference axis Z_1 should pass near a cluster of points while at the same time the other (orthogonal) axis Y_3 also should be near some other points. The variables represented by the first cluster of points will have high positive weights for the Z_1 factor, and the variables given by the second set of points will have low weights for this factor. Additional rotations may be made according to the outline given in Table 12.2. It will be evident from the following examples that the above procedure yields a final solution which approximates simple structure.

1. Eight physical variables.—The first illustration of a multiple-factor solution is based upon the two minres factors for the eight physical variables, given in Table 9.3. The coefficients in this pattern are the coordinates, with respect to the two minres axes, of the eight points representing the variables. The plot of these points is given in Figure 12.2, in which it is apparent that the points fall into two distinct clusters. If two lines, Y_1 and Y_2 were passed through these clusters of points, they would produce excellent geometric fit to the data. Such axes, however, are not orthogonal and therefore not appropriate for the present method.

If one axis is passed through a cluster and the other orthogonal to it, the standard of uncorrelated factors is met, but other standards are not well satisfied. Thus if an axis M_1' is passed through the first four points, the other axis M_2' will be far removed from the second cluster. The coefficients of such new factors would have the following properties:

Variables	Coefficients of M_1'	Coefficients of M_2'
1, 2, 3, 4	Very high	Near zero
5, 6, 7, 8	Fairly high	High

The first four variables would be of complexity one while the last four would be of complexity two. Variables 5–8 would not satisfy the criterion of low complexity for the present example involving only two factors.

In an attempt to meet the basic standards for a multiple-factor pattern, the axes M_1 and M_2 are selected so as to be about equally removed from the two clusters of points. By inspection the resulting angle of rotation is taken to be $\theta_{12} = -42°$. Another worker, of course, might select a slightly different angle. The necessary

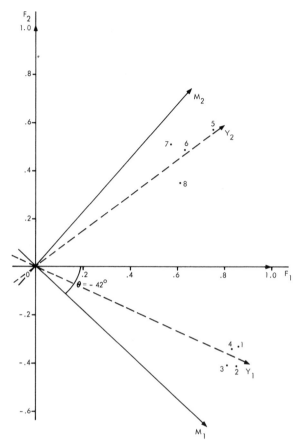

FIG. 12.2.—Rotation for eight physical variables

trigonometric functions are

$$\cos(-42°) = .7431, \quad \sin(-42°) = -.6691.$$

Substituting these values in equations (12.13), there results

(12.27)
$$\begin{cases} b_{j1} = .7431a_{j1} - .6691a_{j2}, \\ b_{j2} = .6691a_{j1} + .7431a_{j2}, \end{cases}$$

The transformation (12.27) may also be written in the equivalent form

(12.28)
$$\mathbf{B} = \mathbf{A} \begin{bmatrix} .7431 & .6691 \\ -.6691 & .7431 \end{bmatrix},$$

where $\mathbf{A}$ is the pattern matrix of Table 9.3 and $\mathbf{B}$ is the final pattern which is presented in Table 12.3.

Table 12.3

Multiple-Factor Solution for Eight Physical Variables

(Initial solution: Minres, Table 9.3)

| Variable | M_1 | M_2 | h_j^2 |
j			
1. Height	.853	.332	.838
2. Arm span	.906	.261	.889
3. Length of forearm	.874	.237	.820
4. Length of lower leg	.846	.302	.807
5. Weight	.175	.926	.888
6. Bitrochanteric diameter	.140	.788	.641
7. Chest girth	.082	.760	.584
8. Chest width	.216	.667	.492
Contribution of factor (V_p)	3.132	2.827	5.959

The pattern of Table 12.3 may be examined now to see how well it conforms to the standards for a multiple-factor solution. Since there are no sampling error formulas for this type of solution, the analyst usually must set some arbitrary level of significance. The present example is based on a large number of observations ($N = 305$), and hence even relatively small coefficients may not be insignificant. As a rough approximation, a standard error of .066 is obtained from Table B in the Appendix, for an $N = 305$ and an average correlation of .355 in the original data. If this standard error were applied to the coefficients in Table 12.3, even the smallest value might be judged significant. While the foregoing test is not strictly applicable in the present case, it nevertheless throws some doubt on the insignificance of the small values. The multiple-factor pattern for these data is therefore not a good example of this type of solution.

2. Thirteen psychological tests.—The next example is based upon the centroid pattern, given in Table 8.30, for the thirteen psychological tests, involving three factors. The transformation to a multiple-factor solution in this case is made in accordance with the scheme outlined in **12.3** for rotations in ordinary space. In Figure 12.3 the thirteen points are plotted in the plane of the first two centroid axes. The procedure in the present example differs somewhat from that employed in the preceding one. The first rotation is made in order to accomplish a leveling of the contributions of the first two factors. An angle $\theta_{12} = 50°$ is selected by inspection for this purpose. In such a rotation all points have negative projections on the second axis, designated as Y_2'. This rotation is immediately followed by reflection of the second axis, namely,

$$Y_2 = -Y_2',$$

so as to yield positive coordinates. Although many points will have appreciable loadings for both Y_1 and Y_2, this can be adjusted by subsequent rotations.

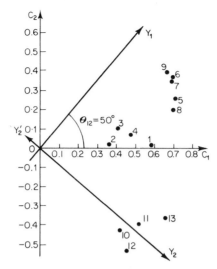

FIG. 12.3.—First rotation for thirteen psychological tests

The resulting matrix of transformation, including the reflection of the temporary second axis, takes the form:

$$\mathbf{T}_{12} = \begin{bmatrix} .6428 & .7660 \\ .7660 & -.6428 \end{bmatrix}.$$

Then, postmultiplying the first two columns of Table 8.30 by $\mathbf{T}_{12}$, yields the first two columns of Table 12.4. The numerical calculations may be checked at this stage. The new factors Y_1, Y_2, and the factor C_3 are mutually orthogonal, and their total contribution should be the same as that of the original system C_1, C_2, C_3. Thus,

$$2.981 + 3.031 + .954 = 4.620 + 1.392 + .954 = 6.966.$$

The next rotation is made in the Y_1, C_3-plane. The plot of points is presented in Figure 12.4, in which the coordinates are obtained from the first column of Table 12.4 and the third column of Table 8.30. In this transformation the first multiple-factor axis is selected. Therefore, it is important that this axis pass near a cluster of points and also be about 90° removed from a number of other points. To satisfy these require-ments, the angle $\theta_{13} = 27°$ is chosen. In this case one of the axes is reflected again to obtain positive coordinates. The transformation matrix in this plane is given by

$$\mathbf{T}_{13} = \begin{bmatrix} .8829 & .4695 \\ .4695 & -.8829 \end{bmatrix}.$$

The resulting values of M_1 and Y_3 are recorded in the appropriate columns of Tables 12.4 and 12.5.

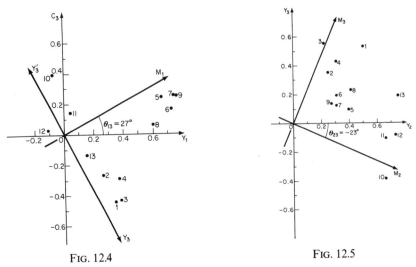

FIG. 12.4   FIG. 12.5

FIGS. 12.4–12.5.—Second and final rotations for thirteen psychological tests

The final rotation is made in the Y_2, Y_3-plane. For this transformation the last two multiple-factor axes are selected so as to pass as near as possible to clusters of points. Thus M_2 passes near points 10, 11, 12, and 13, while M_3 lies close to the points 1, 2, 3, and 4 when the angle of rotation is taken to be $\theta_{23} = -23°$. The third transformation matrix is given by

$$\mathbf{T}_{23} = \begin{bmatrix} .9205 & .3907 \\ -.3907 & .9205 \end{bmatrix}.$$

Table 12.4

Intermediate Coordinates

Test	Y_1	Y_2	Y_3
1	.344	.504	.553
2	.257	.248	.356
3	.382	.225	.558
4	.371	.313	.428
5	.665	.393	.097
6	.726	.314	.193
7	.745	.316	.123
8	.604	.413	.229
9	.762	.272	.135
10	−.077	.658	−.388
11	.046	.662	−.106
12	−.111	.729	−.081
13	.151	.753	.190
V_p	2.981	3.031	1.264

266

Table 12.5

Multiple-Factor Solution for Thirteen Psychological Tests

(Initial solution: centroid, Table 8.30)

Test j	Verbal M_1	Speed M_2	Spatial Relations M_3	Communality h_j^2
1. Visual perception	.096	.248	**.706**	.569
2. Cubes	.102	.089	**.425**	.199
3. Paper form board	.136	−.011	**.602**	.381
4. Flags	.193	.121	**.516**	.318
5. General information	**.702**	.324	.243	.657
6. Paragraph comprehension	**.719**	.214	.300	.653
7. Sentence completion	**.778**	.243	.237	.721
8. Word classification	**.562**	.291	.372	.539
9. Word meaning	**.791**	.198	.231	.718
10. Addition	.119	**.757**	−.100	.597
11. Code	.109	**.651**	.161	.462
12. Counting dots	−.083	**.703**	.210	.545
13. Straight-curved capitals	.070	**.619**	**.469**	.608
Contribution of factor (V_p)	2.670	2.292	2.005	6.967

The coefficients of the factors M_2 and M_3 are recorded in Table 12.5. The complete transformation matrix which carries the original factor weights into the final ones may be summarized, according to (12.24), as follows:

$$(12.29) \qquad \mathbf{T} = \mathbf{T}_{12}\mathbf{T}_{13}\mathbf{T}_{23} = \begin{bmatrix} .5675 & .5872 & .5771 \\ .6763 & -.7322 & .0799 \\ .4695 & .3499 & -.8127 \end{bmatrix}.$$

The numerical check on the total contribution of a factor system, which can be made after each rotation, may again be employed on the final set of factors. Thus the numbers appearing in the last line of Table 12.5 sum to 6.967, which is the same as the total contribution of the original centroid factors.

The multiple-factor pattern of Table 12.5 satisfies the standards listed above. The contributions of the factors are relatively level in comparison with other types of preferred solutions. The criteria of low complexity and good geometric fit also appear to be satisfied. For the present sample ($N = 145$) it is judged that a factor coefficient of two-tenths is insignificant. In general, the solution tends to satisfy the criteria for simple structure set forth in **6.2**. The above solution thus affords a good illustration of the multiple-factor type.

In naming the multiple factors, those variables having definitely significant weights, say, greater than four-tenths, are considered (indicated in bold face type in Table 12.5). The subgroups of tests identifying the multiple factors are the same as those employed in naming the first three group factors in the bi-factor solution of Table 7.6. The same

267

names are then assigned to the multiple factors, as indicated in Table 12.5. It may be noted that each test is essentially a measure of only one of these factors, except Test 13, which appears to be reasonable inasmuch as the test is a measure of speed of perception of simple geometric forms.

12.5. *Other Problems of Relationships between Factor Solutions*

It should be perfectly clear that many different factor solutions are possible for a given set of variables for a single sample of individuals. Not only is this evident from the several techniques for factoring a correlation matrix, developed earlier in the text, but more particularly from the considerations of transforming one solution into another (in this chapter and the three following ones). The relationships among any two solutions for a given body of data have been shown in **12.2** above.

A procedure developed by Tucker [496] for factor analysis of a three-mode matrix (individuals measured on a number of variables on several occasions) may be considered as an alternative to the comparison of ordinary factor solutions (for a group of individuals measured on a number of variables) obtained on several different occasions.

There are two additional problems that seem to be of more importance to the development of content-area (e.g., psychological) theories based upon factor analysis. Suppose the same variables (or, at least, several variables common to the two batteries) are measured for two distinct groups of individuals. What can be said about the resulting factors used in the description of the identical variables? The other problem is concerned with two distinct sets of variables (designed to measure the same traits) for which factor analyses are obtained for a single sample of individuals.

In each situation two sets of factors are obtained and the problem is to determine the extent of similarity or dissimilarity between them. Of course, factorial similarity is a matter of degree rather than coincidence. While the ultimate objective in psychology may be the formulation of some theories on the invariance of factors, the treatment in the present text is limited to an exposition of several measures for the degree of agreement between factors obtained in different solutions.

Before considering these measures, it might be well to point out some of the principal work on the "invariance" problem. Perhaps the point of departure for the present-day theoretical work in this area was the demonstration by Ahmavaara [3] of the invariance of a factor solution upon the selection of samples (satisfying certain conditions) from a population. Several other works (e.g., [24], [73], [79], [255]) have made some contributions to this area, but two papers by Meredith [365, 366] are of special significance. In the first of these, he shows that there exists a factor pattern for a given set of variables that is invariant with respect to sampling from a parent population, provided the "selection does not occur directly on the observable variables and does not reduce the rank of the system." In the second paper, Meredith develops procedures for transforming factor solutions based on different populations to conform to a single "best fitting" factor pattern, and illustrates these procedures with examples involving four groups of individuals.

268

1. Fixed variables, different samples.—Since factor analysis has been employed as a tool in the development of psychological theories, dealing with cognitive, educational, and temperamental traits, considerable interest has been directed toward the "identification" of factors from one study to another. Ideally, this problem could be solved in a manner similar to the establishment of standards for weight or mass in the physical sciences, as suggested by Mosier [372] and Young and House-holder [546]. Thus, in the field of psychological aptitudes, a "set of r independent tests is to be assigned any non-singular $r \times r$ array of factor loadings once and for all, and then future testing is to be linked to this standard by always carrying a set of r independent tests (or individuals) from each experiment to the next ..." [546, p. 51]. It is not very likely that psychologists will take this approach very seriously. Instead, they are more likely to appeal to statistical criteria for a measure of coincidence or agreement of factors obtained in one study with those of another.

Attempts to link factors of separate investigations go back to the earliest days of the development of factor analysis. Generally, rough methods of inspection and personal impressions are offered as the basis of the "identification". A good example of this approach is the report of Zachert and Friedman [548], in which they "draw inferences concerning the stability of the factor pattern" for postwar and wartime samples by noting that a given factor tends to involve the same variables with loadings of .30 or greater in each of the four samples. In notes by Barlow and Burt [24] and Leyden [341], attention is called to a variety of measures that have been proposed over the years, and to the divergent values that can be obtained with the different indices.

Since the variables are assumed to be the same in the two studies, a common statistical measure—the *root mean square*—might be used to determine the extent of agreement between corresponding factor weights. Such an index for comparing factor p of study 1 and factor q of study 2 may be put in the form:

$$(12.30) \qquad (p - q)_{rms} = \sqrt{\sum_{j=1}^{n} ({}_1 a_{jp} - {}_2 a_{jq})^2 / n,}$$

where the prefixes "1" and "2" are employed to distinguish the factor weights in the two studies. Of course, this is a very simple kind of index from which it might be difficult to ascertain what is really "good agreement", knowing that perfect agreement would yield a root mean square of zero.

The simple expedient of employing an index roughly resembling a coefficient of correlation has been used by several investigators to compare the weights of a fixed set of variables on two factors (presumed to be identical, or at least, suspected to have a high degree of relationship). Burt [58, p. 185] proposes as a proportionality criterion the "unadjusted correlation" between the two sets of factor coefficients.*
Tucker [491, p. 43] develops a *coefficient of congruence*, to study the agreement

---

* Actually, Burt compares a set of factor coefficients of twelve temperamental traits for a "general emotionality" factor with a teacher's set of independent gradings for "general emotionality."

between factors in two studies, which is precisely the same as Burt's unadjusted correlation. Again, Wrigley and Neuhaus [541] present the same formula for measuring the *degree of factorial similarity*. In the notation introduced in the last paragraph, the coefficient of congruence is simply

(12.31)
$$\varphi_{pq} = \frac{\sum\limits_{j=1}^{n} {}_{1}a_{jp} \cdot {}_{2}a_{jq}}{\sqrt{\left(\sum\limits_{j=1}^{n} {}_{1}a_{jp}^{2}\right)\left(\sum\limits_{j=1}^{n} {}_{2}a_{jq}^{2}\right)}}.$$

While this formula is similar in form to the product-moment coefficient defined in (2.7), it certainly is not a correlation—the a's are not deviates from their respective means and the summations are over the n variables instead of the number of individuals. If the n variables of study 1 are identical with those of study 2 the application of formula (12.31) is straightforward to the corresponding numbers in the two columns representing the factors p and q. If only a subset of the variables are common to the two studies, the summations in (12.31) must be understood to apply only to such variables. Since a small number of variables usually will be common to two studies, it is evident that the coefficient of congruence will be high so long as there are factor weights with like algebraic signs in the two instances. The coefficient of congruence can range in value from $+1$ for perfect agreement (or -1 for perfect inverse agreement) to zero for no agreement whatsoever.

To illustrate the calculation of (12.31), the data of Table 12.1 will be employed. While it is convenient to use the data at hand, it should be clear that a coefficient of congruence would not ordinarily be of interest for two different factor solutions of a set of variables for the same individuals. Considering the two solutions **A** and **B** as the studies "1" and "2," respectively, the only new calculations required are the denominators of (12.31), and the quotients, to get all nine coefficients of congruence; the numerators are the elements of **B′A** in Table 12.1. The results are shown in Table 12.6. Of course, the coefficients of congruence confirm the relationships among these factors discussed in **12.2**.

Table 12.6

Coefficients of Congruence between Oblique Primary and Orthogonal Multiple Factors

p	q		
	M_1	M_2	M_3
T_1	.112	.113	.855
T_2	.976	.361	.362
T_3	.051	.913	.239

In situations where factors from two studies can be matched visually, and the number of variables common to the studies is small, it can be expected that the coefficient (12.31) will be very high. Tucker [491] analyzes two studies—one involving 18 variables for a sample of Naval Recruits and the other involving 44 variables for a sample of Airmen and Soldiers—in which 10 variables are common and the six factors of the smaller study are matched with six out of the twelve factors of the larger. He accepts coefficients ranging from .999984 down to .939811 as defining congruent factors, but rejects a value of .459717 as "definitely low so that this factor will not be considered as a congruent factor" [491, p. 19].

It is generally recommended that each factor of one study be compared with all the factors of the other study, and be paired with the one with which it has the highest coefficient of congruence. This implies a considerable amount of work, for which high-speed electronic computers have been applied. While the statistical relationships between factors of different studies have certain intrinsic values, a number of workers (e.g., Cattell, Tucker, Wrigley) are even more concerned with the development of psychological theories through these means. They would employ the indices of proportionality as stepping stones to an objective basis for the matching of factors and the subsequent rotation to identical positions of the factor axes in the two studies. Tucker, for example, defines a congruent space between two studies as that spanned by their congruent factors, where the two matrices of these factor loadings are "considered as congruent if they are generally similar, with only relatively small random differences" [491, p. 18]. He then discusses the degree of confidence a psychologist might have in the representation of the same mental function by congruent factors in two studies.

Several other indices are proposed by Pinneau and Newhouse [391] for the comparison of factors based on a fixed set of variables on the same or different samples. Their "coefficient of invariance" and "coefficient of factor similarity" involve the correlation between the measurements of the factors (see chap. 16) for the individuals. This procedure follows the work of Horst [254, 255].

The measure of consistency of factors, for a fixed set of variables, from sample to sample would seem to be a classical problem in the theory of statistical sampling. However, little progress has been made toward the solution of the sampling problem in factor analysis which is the subject of this section.* Therefore the empirical approach, employing indices of proportionality of factors, which is suggested in this section seems not inappropriate at this time for the "identification" of factors across different studies.

2. Different variables, fixed sample.—Another situation where it is of interest to compare factors from different studies is when the sample of individuals is fixed but the sets of variables in two studies are different. While a statistical theory of the stability of factors under sampling variation of variables may be developed some day, the present approach to the problem is along empirical lines.

---

* Some sampling theory in factor analysis regarding the number of common factors was covered in **9.5** and **10.4**.

An important consideration to the psychologist when making a choice out of several solutions is the question of "invariance" of the particular solution. Invariance as used in the context of rotation to a preferred multiple-factor solution requires that the factorial description of a variable must remain the same when it is part of one battery or another which involves the same common factors. In this quest for basic traits in psychology, Tucker adds the requirement that "*the scores for individuals on a factor should remain invariant as the individuals are tested with different batteries which involve the factor*" [495, p. 112]. While the varimax method (see **14.4**) is proposed by Kaiser as the factorially invariant solution [293, pp. 193–98], the problem considered in the present section is concerned more with the measure of stability of factors when different variables are used.

Wrigley and Neuhaus [541] propose what appears like the most natural method for matching factors determined from two different sets of variables for the same sample of individuals. In each study the measurements of the respective factors for the individuals can be obtained by the methods of chapter 16. Then, for a given sample of individuals, the measurements of a factor p from one set of variables may be compared with the measurements of a factor q from the other set of variables in a manner similar to that above. As before, *a coefficient of congruence* can be defined for measuring the *degree of factorial similarity*, namely:

$$(12.33) \qquad \psi_{pq} = \frac{\sum\limits_{i=1}^{N} {}_1F_{pi} \cdot {}_2F_{qi}}{\sqrt{\left(\sum\limits_{i=1}^{N} {}_1F_{pi}^2\right)\left(\sum\limits_{i=1}^{N} {}_2F_{qi}^2\right)}},$$

where ${}_1F_{pi}$ is the factor measurement for individual i on a factor p for study 1, with similar interpretation for measurements of factor q of study 2. The coefficient of congruence (12.33) may range in value from -1 to $+1$ just as the index (12.31).

Assuming m_1 and m_2 factors in the two studies, there is possible a total of $m_1 \times m_2$ matchings of each factor of one study with every factor of the other. A given factor of one study may be said to be "matched with" or "congruent to" that factor of the other study with which it has the highest coefficient of congruence (12.33). If there should be any conflicts, Wrigley and Neuhaus [541] propose that the factors be paired in such a way as to make the sum of the indices (12.33) a maximum.

While the foregoing index provides a means for comparing factors obtained from different sets of variables, there is considerable interest among psychologists in bringing the factors from such studies into confluence. Specific work in this direction has been carried out by Wrigley and Neuhaus [541], Tucker [495], and Meredith [366], but is outside the scope of the present text.

13
Oblique Multiple-Factor Solutions

13.1. *Introduction*

In the early history and development of factor analysis, solutions in terms of uncorrelated factors were tacitly assumed to be the only type permissible. Then, in the 1940's the notion of correlated factors not only became acceptable, but frequently preferable to uncorrelated ones. For the field of psychology, Thurstone states the case as follows [477, p. vii]: "If we impose the restriction that the reference frame shall be orthogonal, then we are imposing the condition that the factors or parameters shall be uncorrelated in the experimental population or in the general population.... It seems just as unnecessary to require that mental traits shall be uncorrelated in the general population as to require that height and weight be uncorrelated in the general population. This admission of oblique axes has also been debated and is not yet generally accepted by students of factor theory."

The development of the different types of factor solutions in this text has been made systematically, including both orthogonal and oblique. An enumeration and properties of different types of solutions are presented in chapter 6, with methods for their calculation treated in subsequent chapters. The first oblique solution is introduced in chapter 11, although an associated orthogonal solution is also derived (to be used either as the final solution or as the starting point for the rotational process).

In the present chapter, any assumption of uncorrelated factors is discarded and procedures leading to oblique solutions are considered. It is clear that a certain simplicity of interpretation is sacrificed upon relinquishing the standard of orthogonality. This disadvantage may be offset, however, if the linear descriptions of the variables in terms of correlated factors can be made simpler than in the case of uncorrelated ones. Generally this is possible. Hence the oblique pattern proposed may not merely be an oblique multiple-factor solution satisfying the criteria for simple structure, but may actually approximate the uni-factor form.

273

An oblique solution of the type indicated may be obtained directly from clustering of variables as in chapter 11. The purpose of the present chapter is to provide a method of analysis when the direct method of chapter 11 is not applicable (although in such event the oblique solution is not very adequate). This method consists of the transformation of some initial orthogonal pattern to an oblique solution. The communalities of the variables, which are determined by the common-factor space of the preliminary solution, remain invariant under this transformation. Therefore, the entire development will be made in the common-factor space.

The geometric setting for the oblique form of solution is presented in **13.2**. This is followed by a detailed outline in **13.3** of the procedure for getting an oblique "primary factor" solution. Then an alternative approach in terms of "oblique reference axes" is developed in **13.4**. The distinction between the two types of oblique solutions is presented in **13.5**, where existing ambiguities in the literature on oblique solutions are clarified.

13.2.   *Geometric Basis for an Oblique Solution*

In **2.5** the definitions of factor patterns and structures were formulated. When the factors are uncorrelated these concepts are identical. Therefore, in the foregoing text (with the exception of chapter 11), no distinction was necessary, and the term "pattern" was used synonymously with "solution." When correlated factors are employed, however, a solution comprises both the pattern and structure. The distinction in this case can best be shown geometrically.

A pattern, in terms of common factors only, may be represented as follows:

$$(13.1) \qquad z_j'' = b_{j1} T_1 + b_{j2} T_2 + \cdots + b_{jm} T_m \qquad (j = 1, 2, \cdots, n),$$

where b's are employed to denote coefficients of correlated factors. As pointed out in **4.10**, the double prime denotes a variable projected into the common-factor space. Since the analysis of this chapter is entirely in the common-factor space, it will simplify matters to drop the primes and write the foregoing equation:

$$(13.2) \qquad z_j = b_{j1} T_1 + b_{j2} T_2 + \cdots + b_{jm} T_m \qquad (j = 1, 2, \cdots, n).$$

The coefficients may be considered as the coordinates of a point P_j with respect to the factor axes. This interpretation may be made whether the factors are represented by orthogonal or oblique axes.

For the case of two factors these ideas may be illustrated by Figure 13.1. When the correlation between the factors T_1 and T_2 is known, the unit vectors representing T_1 and T_2 are separated by an angle $\theta_{12} = \text{arc cos } r_{T_1 T_2}$. The oblique reference system is thus determined. Any variable z_j is represented by a vector, OP, whose length and direction are determined by its coordinates. Again, for the sake of simplicity, the point representing any variable z_j is designated P instead of P_j, and its coordinates are shown as (b_1, b_2) instead of (b_{j1}, b_{j2}) with respect to the two oblique axes T_1 and T_2. From the definition of general Cartesian coordinates, given in **4.8**, it may be noted that the coordinates b_1, b_2 are given by the line segments OQ and OR, respectively.

For the hypothetical variable z_j in Figure 13.1, the first coordinate is positive and greater than unity, while the second coordinate is negative and less than unity.

The length of the vector corresponding to z_j can be determined by means of formula (4.39), which in this case may be written as follows:

(13.3)
$$D^2(OP) = \sum_{p=1}^{2} \sum_{q=1}^{2} b_{jp}b_{jq} \cos \theta_{pq}$$
$$= b_{j1}b_{j1} \cos \theta_{11} + b_{j1}b_{j2} \cos \theta_{12} + b_{j2}b_{j1} \cos \theta_{21} + b_{j2}b_{j2} \cos \theta_{22}.$$

In this formula each of the angles θ_{11} and θ_{22} is equal to zero, and θ_{12} is the angle between the reference axes. Hence $\cos \theta_{11} = \cos \theta_{22} = 1$ and $\cos \theta_{12} = r_{T_1 T_2}$. The expression (13.3) then reduces to

(13.4)
$$D^2(OP) = b_{j1}^2 + b_{j2}^2 + 2b_{j1}b_{j2}r_{T_1 T_2}$$

The right-hand member is the communality h_j^2 of the variable z_j. The length of the vector is then equal to the square root of the communality, namely,

(13.5)
$$D(OP) = h_j.$$

The geometric interpretation of the correlation of a variable with a factor will be given next. Let the angle between the vector corresponding to z_j and the reference vector T_1 be denoted by ϕ. Also let the projections of the end point P upon the T_1 and T_2 axes be M and N, respectively, as indicated in Figure 13.1. From the right

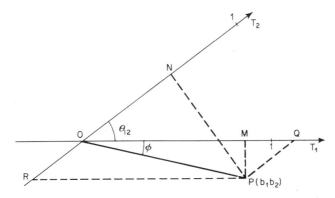

Fig. 13.1.—Distinction between coordinate and correlation in oblique reference system.

triangle OMP, it is apparent that

$$\cos \phi = \frac{D(OM)}{D(OP)}.$$

This formula reduces to

(13.6)
$$D(OM) = h_j \cos \phi$$

upon making use of (13.5). Employing the expression (4.56) for a reproduced correlation in the common-factor space, formula (13.6) can be simplified further. In the present example, one variable is z_j and the other is T_1 so that their scalar product, according to (4.56) is

(13.7) $$r'_{jT_1} = h_j h_{T_1} \cos \phi.$$

Since the length or "communality," of any factor is unity, this expression may be written in the form

(13.8) $$r_{jT_1} = h_j \cos \phi.$$

In this formula, and in all other representations of correlations of variables with factors, the prime is dropped for simplicity. Substituting (13.8) into (13.6), the projection of a vector upon a reference axis may finally be expressed as follows:

(13.9) $$D(OM) = r_{jT_1}.$$

In a similar manner it can be shown that the projection, $D(ON)$, of the vector z_j on the T_2 axis is the correlation of the variable with the second factor. Of course, the correlation between two factors is also given by the projection of either reference vector upon the other.

By referring to Figure 13.1, the distinction between a coordinate and a correlation can be seen clearly. The coordinates may be positive or negative and may be greater than one. A correlation coefficient also may be positive or negative but can never exceed unity. It may also be observed that the coordinates and correlations approach coincidence as the reference vectors approach orthogonality.

A complete solution involving correlated factors must consist of a pattern and a structure. The factor pattern may be exhibited as in equation (13.1) or, more compactly, in a table giving the coefficients of the factors. The structure usually is presented in tabular or matrix form. In addition to the pattern and structure, an oblique solution should include a table of intercorrelations of factors.

13.3. *Computing Procedures for Oblique Primary-Factor Solution*

The form of oblique multiple-factor solution developed in this section leads to a set of factors which have been called "primary" by Thurstone [477, chap. XV], when considered in the context of psychological traits. Aside from the particular application, and although arrived at somewhat differently, it is convenient to designate the oblique solution of this section as "primary-factor" to distinguish it from another form of oblique solution considered in the next section.

Starting with any initial orthogonal pattern, it is possible to transform it into an oblique primary-factor solution which, more or less, satisfies the conditions of simple structure. The procedures outlined in this section are intended for hand methods, and therefore would be useful only for small problems. However, the heuristic value goes far beyond the immediate applications.

1. Initial orthogonal pattern.—Any preliminary orthogonal solution (e.g., principal-factor, minres, maximum-likelihood) may be employed. The two minres factors for the eight physical variables, given in Table 9.3, serve as the starting point from which an oblique primary-factor solution will be derived.

2. Reduced pattern.—Since the coordinate axes representing the oblique factors will be made to pass through the centroids of clusters of variables, it is necessary to identify such groupings, say, $G_p (p = 1, 2, \cdots, m)$. These groups of variables may be established from the earlier analysis which led to the orthogonal solution, or they may be determined by the method of B-coefficients (see **7.4**); or they may be found by inspection of the initial pattern or graphs of the points. Just by inspection of Table 9.3, it is evident from the algebraic signs of the coefficients that the plot of these eight points with respect to the two minres axes would lead to a cluster in the fourth quadrant for the first four variables, and a cluster in the first quadrant for the last four. The actual plot of these points in Figure 13.2 bears this out.

To determine the directions of the oblique reference vectors, lines may be drawn by inspection from the origin through the clusters of variables. The angles which these new axes make with the old may be measured, and the transformation may thus be

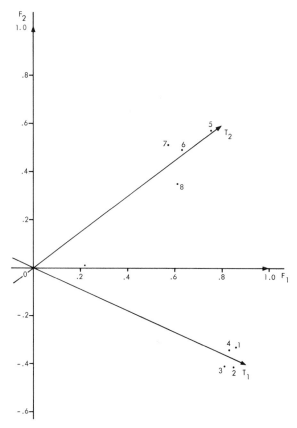

FIG. 13.2.—Oblique reference axes through clusters of points

determined. Such a procedure is completely subjective, and may be replaced by the following operational method.

A composite variable v_p is assumed through each cluster of n_p variables in group G_p. This type of variable was designated T_p in **11.3**, but it will be found more convenient in the present development to reserve T_p for the standardized form of the oblique factor. For the example, the two composite variables are defined by

$$(13.10) \qquad v_1 = z_1 + z_2 + z_3 + z_4 \quad \text{and} \quad v_2 = z_5 + z_6 + z_7 + z_8.$$

The variance of a composite variable is given by

$$(13.11) \qquad\qquad s_{v_p}^2 = \sum (r_{jk}; \quad j, k \in G_p),$$

in which there are n_p self-correlations of unity. Applying this formula to the two composite variables in (13.10), employing the correlations from Table 5.3, the resulting standard deviations are found to be

$$(13.12) \qquad\qquad s_{v_1} = 3.7465 \quad \text{and} \quad s_{v_2} = 3.4117.$$

It is now possible to express the composite variables in terms of the factors of the initial solution. The coefficients in such linear expressions are also the correlations of the composite variables with the factors (the factors in the initial solution being uncorrelated). Since the factors are standardized variables, the correlation of any composite variable v_p with a factor F is given by

$$(13.13) \qquad\qquad r_{v_p F} = \sum (r_{jF}; \quad j \in G_p)/s_{v_p},$$

where the individual correlations of the variables with the factor are, of course, the coefficients in the initial orthogonal pattern for the variables comprising the group G_p. The correlation for the first composite variable of the example with the first minres factor is calculated as follows:

$$r_{v_1 F_1} = (.856 + .848 + .808 + .831)/3.7465 = .8923,$$

where the values in the numerator are taken from Table 9.3. In a similar manner, the correlations of each of the composite variables with each of the minres factors can be obtained, and the results presented in the form of a *reduced factor pattern*, as follows:

$$(13.14) \qquad
\begin{aligned}
u_1 &= v_1/s_{v_1} = .8923F_1 - .3969F_2, \\
u_2 &= v_2/s_{v_2} = .7495F_1 + .5639F_2.
\end{aligned}$$

The standardized form of a composite variable v is indicated by u. The reduced pattern equations (13.14) have the same properties as those for individual variables.

3. Transformation matrix.—Since the oblique primary-factors are represented by the coordinate axes passing through the points corresponding to the composite variables u_p, the reduced pattern provides the basis for determining the transformation matrix. The coefficients of the reduced pattern give the coordinates of the composite points, and division by the respective distances of these points from the

278

origin produces the direction cosines of the lines through them. These lines are precisely the oblique factors T_p and hence these direction cosines with respect to the initial reference system constitute the elements of the transformation matrix.

For example, the distance of the first point from the origin is

$$\sqrt{(.8923)^2 + (-.3969)^2} = .9766,$$

according to (4.12). Then the direction cosines of T_1 with respect to the F_1 and F_2 axes are given by:

$$t_{11} = .8923/.9766 = .9137 \quad \text{and} \quad t_{21} = -.3969/.9766 = -.4064.$$

The direction cosines of the T_2 axis with respect to the orthogonal axes F_1 and F_2 are determined in a similar manner. The resulting transformation matrix may be written as follows:

(13.15)
$$\mathbf{T} = \begin{bmatrix} t_{11} & t_{12} \\ t_{21} & t_{22} \end{bmatrix} = \begin{bmatrix} .9137 & .7991 \\ -.4064 & .6012 \end{bmatrix}.$$

While this matrix is written specifically for the illustrative example, the ideas and notation are generalizable to any number of factors. The symbol $\mathbf{T}$ is used in general for the transformation matrix for any number of axes.

4. Factor correlations.—After the direction cosines of the oblique reference vectors have been obtained, the correlations among such factors can be determined. The sum of paired products of the direction cosines of two vectors gives the cosine of the angle between them, according to (4.47); and, by (4.48), this cosine is equal to the correlation between the two variables represented by the vectors. Hence, the correlation between T_1 and T_2 in the present example is

$$r_{T_1 T_2} = .9137(.7991) - .4064(.6012) = .4858.$$

The self-correlations, or variances, of the factors may be calculated in the same manner. These sums of squares by columns in the transformation matrix must be unity, and thus provide a check on the calculation of the elements of the transformation matrix.

More generally, the scalar product between any pair of vectors T_p and T_q is equal to their correlation according to (4.56) and (4.54). Such scalar products can be designated in matrix form, as follows:

(13.16)
$$\mathbf{\Phi} = \mathbf{T'T}.$$

From the correlation between factors the angle of separation of the reference vectors can be determined if desired. In the present case this angle is given by

$$\theta_{12} = \text{arc cos } .4858 = 61°.$$

5. Factor structure.—The projections of the vectors representing the variables upon the oblique primary-axes can now be determined. As indicated in (13.9), such projections are the correlations of variables with the factors, i.e., the elements of the

279

factor structure. In order to derive formulas for the structure values, Figure 13.3 has been constructed. In this figure the oblique axes T_1 and T_2 have been taken in the first quadrant of the F_1, F_2 reference system only to simplify the development, the results being the same regardless of the quadrants in which the oblique axes are located. The angles from the F_1 axis to the T_1 and T_2 axes are denoted by α and β, respectively.

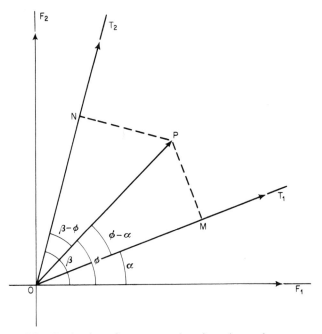

FIG. 13.3.—Derivation of structure values for primary-factor system

Any variable z_j may be represented in this figure by a point P whose coordinates (a_{j1}, a_{j2}) with respect to the original minres axes are the coefficients in the initial pattern equation. The variable may also be construed as a vector from the origin to the point P. The angle from the F_1 axis to this vector is denoted by ϕ. Then the projection of the vector upon the T_1 axis is given by

(13.17) $$D(OM) = D(OP) \cos(\phi - \alpha).$$

As noted in (13.9), the projection $D(OM)$ is equal to the correlation r_{jT_1}, and from (13.5) the length of the vector $D(OP)$ is h_j. Making these substitutions in (13.17), and expanding the cosine of the difference of two angles, this formula becomes

$$r_{jT_1} = h_j (\cos \phi \cos \alpha + \sin \phi \sin \alpha),$$
$$= (h_j \cos \phi) \cos \alpha + (h_j \sin \phi) \sin \alpha.$$

Now $h_j \cos \phi$ and $h_j \sin \phi$ are the projections a_{j1} and a_{j2} of the vector representing

280

z_j on the F_1 and F_2 axes, respectively. Then the formula finally becomes

(13.18) $$r_{jT_1} = a_{j1} \cos \alpha + a_{j2} \sin \alpha.$$

In a similar manner it can be shown that the projection $D(ON)$, of the vector representing z_j on the T_2 axis, is given by

(13.19) $$r_{jT_2} = a_{j1} \cos \beta + a_{j2} \sin \beta.$$

These results may be summarized in the following matrix form:

(13.20) $$(r_{jT_1} \quad r_{jT_2}) = (a_{j1} \quad a_{j2}) \cdot \begin{bmatrix} t_{11} = \cos \alpha & t_{12} = \cos \beta \\ t_{21} = \sin \alpha & t_{22} = \sin \beta \end{bmatrix}$$

where, in the last matrix, the elements of the first column are the direction cosines of T_1 with respect to F_1 and F_2, and those of the second column are the direction cosines of T_2. Although (13.20) was developed on the basis of Figure 13.3, this expression is true for different positions of the new axes T_1 and T_2, as, for example, that indicated in Figure 13.2.

Written in the form (13.20), the procedure for determining the elements of a structure can be generalized to problems involving more than two factors. Thus, the transformation from an initial orthogonal factor pattern **A** to the oblique structure **S** is given by:

(13.21) $$\mathbf{S} = \mathbf{AT},$$

where the transformation matrix **T** contains in its columns the direction cosines of the oblique axes with respect to the orthogonal frame of reference.

For example the minres pattern matrix of Table 9.3 is multiplied by the transformation matrix in (13.15) to get the structure values of Table 13.1. The correlations of the composite variables with the oblique factors are obtained by multiplying the reduced pattern matrix of (13.14) by the same transformation matrix. These values are presented in the reduced structure of Table 13.1.

6. Factor pattern.—To complete the solution in terms of correlated factors, the linear descriptions of the variables are required as well as their correlations with the factors. The pattern coefficients are the coordinates with respect to the oblique axes of the points representing the variables and could have been obtained directly* from the initial factor pattern. It is more convenient, however, to calculate these values after the oblique factor structure has been obtained, making use of the relationships between pattern and structure developed in **2.8**.

---

* It is possible to obtain the coordinates of the points with respect to the oblique reference system directly by transformation of the original coordinates. Since, in factor analysis, both the coordinates and the projections (i.e., the coefficients and the correlations) are desired, the present approach is suggested as the simplest and the one best adapted to systematic calculations. First the projections are obtained, and then in the next stage of the analysis the coordinates are calculated.

Table 13.1

Oblique Primary-Factor Solution for Eight Physical Variables

(Initial solution: Minres, Table 9.3)

Variable j	Structure: S		Pattern: P	
			Lankiness T_1	Stockiness T_2
	r_{jT_1}	r_{jT_2}		
1	.914	.489	.885	.059
2	.942	.430	.960	−.036
3	.904	.400	.929	−.053
4	.898	.458	.884	.028
5	.453	.943	−.007	.946
6	.377	.800	−.015	.807
7	.313	.761	−.074	.797
8	.412	.696	.097	.649
	Reduced Structure		Reduced Pattern	
u_1	.977	.474	.977	−.001
u_2	.456	.938	.000	.938

If the oblique factor pattern for the illustrative example is denoted by

$$(13.22) \qquad z_j = b_{j1} T_1 + b_{j2} T_2 \qquad (j = 1, 2, \cdots, 8),$$

the problem is to determine the coefficients b_{j1}, b_{j2}. For any variable z_j, multiply (13.22) by T_1 and T_2 in turn, sum for the N values, and divide by N. The resulting equations are

$$(13.23) \qquad \begin{aligned} r_{jT_1} &= b_{j1} & + b_{j2} r_{T_1 T_2}, \\ r_{jT_2} &= b_{j1} r_{T_2 T_1} + b_{j2}. \end{aligned}$$

There is such a pair of simultaneous equations for determining the two unknowns b_{j1}, b_{j2} for each variable z_j. In equations (13.23) the left-hand members contain the known elements of the factor structure. The correlation between the factors also is known from paragraph **4** above. Hence, the matrix of coefficients of the unknown b's is

$$\Phi = \begin{bmatrix} 1 & .4858 \\ .4858 & 1 \end{bmatrix}$$

and remains the same for all variables. The factor coefficients in this simple case may be calculated by the method of determinants; but, especially when many factors are involved, more efficient procedures are desired. Such procedures are described in **3.4**, and applied below (in Table 13.2) to the present example.

   First, the preceding results are extended to any number of variables and factors. Corresponding to the equations (13.23) for two oblique factors there is developed

Table 13.2

Calculation of a Pattern from a Structure

Schematic		Numerical Example			
Original Matrices	Computed Matrices	Original Matrices		Computed Matrices	
Factor Correlations† Φ (Assume $\Phi = Q'Q$)	Square Root Matrix Q' (Square root operation Q^{-1} on Φ)	1.0000 .4858	* 1.0000	1.0000 .4858	.8741
Identity Matrix I	Q^{-1} (Square root operation Q^{-1} on I)	1.0000 0	0 1.0000	1.0000 0	−.5558 1.1440
	$\Phi^{-1} = Q^{-1}(Q')^{-1}$ (Row-by-row multiplication of Q^{-1} by itself)			1.3089 −.6358	−.6358 1.3087
Factor Structure	Factor Pattern	.914 .942 .904 .898	.489 .430 .400 .458	.885 .960 .929 .884	.059 −.036 −.053 .028
S	P	.453 .377 .313	.943 .800 .761	−.007 −.015 −.074	.946 .807 .797
	$(P = S\Phi^{-1})$	.412 .977	.696 .474	.097 .977	.649 −.001
	(Row-to-row multiplication of S by Φ^{-1})	.456	.938	.000	.938

† The square root decomposition of Φ into $Q'Q$ should not be confused with (13.16) in which the correlations among the factors are obtained by premultiplying the transformation matrix T by its transpose.

in **2.8** the matrix relationships between the common-factor portions of an oblique pattern and structure. In a notation more suitable to this chapter equation (2.43) becomes:

(13.24) $S = P\Phi,$

which states that the factor structure **S** is equal to the pattern matrix **P** postmultiplied by the matrix Φ of factor correlations. Solving this equation explicitly for the factor pattern yields:

(13.25) $P = S\Phi^{-1}.$

While this equation can be employed to get the factor pattern from the known structure values and correlations of factors, the work implied in getting the inverse of Φ for many factors can be very substantial without the use of high-speed computers. For a small number of factors the work of computing the oblique factor pattern can best be done by using the square root method. This is illustrated for the simple example in Table 13.2. The resulting values of the factor coefficients are

283

repeated in the pattern matrix in Table 13.1, including those for the composite variables.

An alternative formula can be developed for calculating the oblique pattern, involving the initial factor pattern instead of the oblique structure. The structure is expressed in terms of the initial pattern in (13.21), and the factor correlation matrix is expressed in terms of the transformation matrix in (13.16). Making use of these relationships, formula (13.25) then becomes:

$$(13.26) \qquad\qquad \mathbf{P} = \mathbf{A}(\mathbf{T}')^{-1}.$$

This expression also involves the calculation of the inverse of a matrix of order equal to the number of factors, and hence suffers from the same limitations as the preceding formula. If one wishes to employ $\mathbf{A}$ instead of $\mathbf{S}$ for determining $\mathbf{P}$ then the worksheet of Table 11.2 will be found convenient.

7. Contributions of oblique factors.—After an oblique factor pattern has been obtained, the direct and joint contributions of these factors can be determined. The communality of a variable z_j as given by (13.2), may be expressed as follows:

$$(13.27) \qquad h_j^2 = b_{j1}^2 + b_{j2}^2 + \cdots + b_{jm}^2 + 2b_{j1}b_{j2}r_{T_1 T_2} + \cdots + 2b_{j,m-1}b_{jm}r_{T_{m-1}T_m}.$$

The terms in the right-hand member of this equation represent the portions of the communality of z_j ascribable to the respective factors. The *direct contributions* of the factors are given by the first m terms, while the *joint contributions* of the factors are furnished by the remaining terms.

In **2.4** the total contribution of a factor to the variances of all the variables was defined for the case of uncorrelated factors. When the factors are correlated, their contributions to the variances of the variables can come about through their interaction with other factors as well as through their individual impact. Thus, total contributions of oblique factors can be obtained by summing the separate contributions, as exhibited in (13.27), over all the variables. It is convenient to designate these as *total direct contributions*:

$$(13.28) \qquad\qquad V_p = \sum_{j=1}^{n} b_{jp}^2 \qquad\qquad (p = 1, 2, \cdots, m),$$

and as *total joint contributions*:

$$(13.29) \qquad\qquad V_{pq} = 2r_{T_p T_q} \sum_{j=1}^{n} b_{jp}b_{jq} \qquad (p, q = 1, 2, \cdots, m; \quad p < q).$$

These two sets of expressions can be arranged conveniently in a triangular matrix in which the direct contributions are put in the diagonal and the joint contributions in the lower part of the triangle.

In the illustrative example the total direct contributions of the two factors are given by $V_1 = 3.365$ and $V_2 = 2.611$, while the total joint contribution of these factors is $V_{12} = -.021$. The grand total of the contributions of a set of oblique factors should, of course, be equal to the total communality of the original solution. In the present example this total (5.955) agrees within a few points in the last decimal place

284

with the original value from Table 9.3. The total direct contributions of the factors account for all but a negligible amount of the total common-factor variance in the particular example.

A striking similarity may be noted between the procedures outlined in this section and those in **11.3**. The methods are quite similar, the distinction being in the data to which the methods are applied. Here the raw data are the coefficients of an initial orthogonal factor pattern, while in chapter 11 the raw data are the correlations among the variables themselves.

13.4.   *Oblique Reference Solution*

An alternative form of oblique solution is presented in this section. In an endeavor to satisfy the intuitive principles of simple structure, Thurstone [477, chap. XV] devised an ingenious procedure to guarantee a certain number of zeros in the factor solution. To this end, he introduced a reference system consisting of the normals to the coordinate hyperplanes of the primary-factor solution of the preceding section. While this procedure tends to produce the desired number of zeros, it does complicate the situation by considering a second reference system. In the remainder of this section an exposition is presented of this new "oblique reference system," and then in the following section the distinction and functional relationship between this and the "primary-factor system" is developed.

For a common-factor space of m dimensions there are, of course, m reference axes Λ_p ($p = 1, 2, \cdots, m$), each of which is normal to a coordinate hyperplane π_p (of $m - 1$ dimensions) as defined in **4.3**. In ordinary space, the hyperplanes are actual planes, and the three reference axes are normal to the three coordinate planes. For a common-factor space of only two dimensions, the hyperplane becomes a line, and its normal is another line at right-angles to it. Specifically for the example of the preceding section, the "hyperplane" π_1 in the $T_1 T_2$-plane is the space with the T_1 axis missing—in other words, the T_2 axis; and similarly the π_2 hyperplane is the T_1 axis. Then, the reference axis Λ_1 is perpendicular to π_1 ($\equiv T_2$) and Λ_2 is perpendicular to π_2 ($\equiv T_1$), as indicated in Figure 13.4. It is evident from this figure that the four points hovering close to T_1 have projections on Λ_2 very close to zero. Similarly, the variables close to T_2 have near zero projections on Λ_1.

Without drawing a three-dimensional diagram, three oblique coordinate planes π_1, π_2, and π_3 can be imagined. The normals to these planes are the reference axes Λ_1, Λ_2, and Λ_3, respectively. For each of these axes, every point in the plane to which it is orthogonal will have zero projection upon it. This will be true whether the points in the coordinate plane cluster around the intersections of these planes (T_1, T_2, and T_3) or fan out in these planes.

The generalization of these properties to any m-space is immediate. All points lying in, or close to, a hyperplane π_p will have near zero projections on the normal Λ_p to this hyperplane. It is probably this property—which guarantees the first criterion for simple structure (see **6.2**)—that led Thurstone to the choice of the reference axes. Also, by requiring that each hyperplane be "overdetermined," i.e., contain at least m points, the second criterion for simple structure is assured. Thus it can be seen why

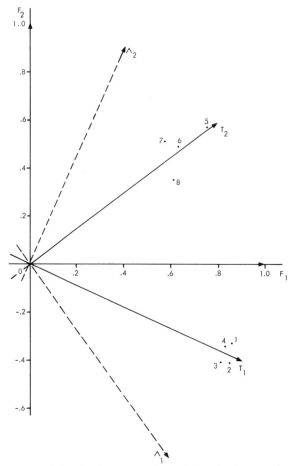

Fɪɢ. 13.4.—Distinction between primary (T) and reference (Λ) axes

Thurstone developed the oblique solution on the basis of reference axes which would be normal to geometric spaces, so that every point in such a space would have a zero projection at least on the axis at right angles to it. Concentrating on the zero projections, Thurstone plays down the factor pattern associated with the reference axes. For heuristic reasons, the complete oblique solution in terms of such reference axes will be developed here, including the factor pattern as well as the factor structure.

Just as in the preceding section, the oblique solution in terms of the new reference axes is obtained by rotation of some initial orthogonal solution. Conventionally, the transformation in this case is designated by Λ and the resulting oblique factor structure by V, while in this text A is employed for the initial matrix of coefficients of the orthogonal factors rather than F which might be confused with the factors themselves. Then in place of (13.21) there is the following equation:

(13.30) $$V = A\Lambda.$$

286

Again, as in the transformation matrix $\mathbf{T}$ of (13.21), the matrix $\mathbf{\Lambda}$ contains in its columns the direction cosines of the oblique axes (Λ_p) with respect to the orthogonal frame of reference.

Knowing the previous transformation matrix $\mathbf{T}$ it is possible to determine the desired matrix $\mathbf{\Lambda}$ without resorting to graphical methods. The elements of $\mathbf{T}$ are the direction cosines of the T-axes (passing through the clusters of variables or determined by the intersections of the coordinate hyperplanes containing a spread of the variables). These axes may be viewed as additional vectors (like the variables) in the original orthogonal reference frame. In this manner they may be considered as extensions of the factor pattern $\mathbf{A}$, just as the reduced pattern in the preceding section. Since the matrix $\mathbf{T}$ was written with the direction cosines in columns, it is necessary to take the transpose of $\mathbf{T}$ in the extension of $\mathbf{A}$. Then applying the transformation (13.30) to this continuation of $\mathbf{A}$, there results

$$(13.31) \qquad \mathbf{T'\Lambda} = \mathbf{D},$$

which is a matrix of the scalar products or correlations among vectors T_p and Λ_p ($p = 1, 2, \cdots, m$). Since Λ_p is normal to the hyperplane

$$\pi_p = OT_1 T_2 \cdots)T_p(\cdots T_m,$$

it is uncorrelated with every T-axis except T_p. Hence, the diagonal values of $\mathbf{D}$ are the correlations between corresponding Λ and T factors, while all values off the diagonal are zero, i.e., $\mathbf{D}$ is a diagonal matrix.

From the relationship (13.31), the explicit expression for the transformation matrix $\mathbf{\Lambda}$ becomes:

$$(13.32) \qquad \mathbf{\Lambda} = (\mathbf{T'})^{-1}\mathbf{D}.$$

From the previous knowledge of $\mathbf{T}$, the inverse of its transpose can be computed. However, this computation may be rather laborious because $\mathbf{T}$ is not a symmetric matrix. From the relationship (13.16), the inverse of $\mathbf{T}$ can be obtained when the inverse of the symmetric matrix $\mathbf{\Phi}$ is known. Taking the inverse of both sides of (13.16) produces

$$(13.33) \qquad \mathbf{\Phi}^{-1} = \mathbf{T}^{-1}(\mathbf{T'})^{-1}$$

and then premultiplying both sides by $\mathbf{T}$ produces the desired result:

$$(13.34) \qquad (\mathbf{T'})^{-1} = \mathbf{T\Phi}^{-1}.$$

Then $\mathbf{\Lambda}$ is obtained by normalizing the columns of this matrix, i.e., dividing each element in a column by the square-root of the sum of the squares of all the elements in that column.

After the transformation matrix $\mathbf{\Lambda}$ is determined, the initial orthogonal factor pattern is postmultiplied by it to obtain the new factor structure $\mathbf{V}$, according to (13.30). The intercorrelations of the reference factors Λ_p can be obtained by the following matrix multiplication:

$$(13.35) \qquad \mathbf{\Lambda'\Lambda} = \mathbf{\Psi},$$

where the resulting matrix is designated $\mathbf{\Psi}$ to distinguish it from the matrix $\mathbf{\Phi}$ of correlations among the factors T. Then, to complete this oblique solution, the factor pattern $\mathbf{W}$ in terms of the reference axes Λ_p is computed by either of the formulas:

$$(13.36) \qquad\qquad \mathbf{W} = \mathbf{V}\mathbf{\Psi}^{-1}$$

which corresponds to (13.25), or

$$(13.37) \qquad\qquad \mathbf{W} = \mathbf{A}(\mathbf{\Lambda'})^{-1},$$

which corresponds to (13.26).

To illustrate the foregoing, the example of eight physical variables again is employed. First, the transformation matrix $\mathbf{\Lambda}$ is required, and it is obtained by use of formula (13.32). The $(\mathbf{T'})^{-1}$ for this formula is calculated by means of (13.34) using the values for $\mathbf{T}$ and $\mathbf{\Phi}^{-1}$ from the preceding section, producing

$$(\mathbf{T'})^{-1} = \begin{bmatrix} .6879 & .4649 \\ -.9142 & 1.0452 \end{bmatrix}.$$

Then, normalizing by columns produces:

$$\mathbf{\Lambda} = \begin{bmatrix} .6012 & .4064 \\ -.7991 & .9137 \end{bmatrix},$$

as the transformation matrix to the new reference axes.

The new factor structure $\mathbf{V}$ is obtained by multiplying the original minres pattern of Table 9.3, and the reduced pattern matrix (13.14), by this transformation matrix, and the results are shown in Table 13.3. The new factor pattern $\mathbf{W}$ is calculated by

Table 13.3

Oblique Reference Solution for Eight Physical Variables

(Initial solution: Minres, Table 9.3)

Variable	Structure: V		Pattern: W	
j	$r_{j\Lambda_1}$	$r_{j\Lambda_2}$	Λ_1	Λ_2
1	.774	.052	1.046	.559
2	.839	−.032	1.078	.492
3	.813	−.045	1.034	.458
4	.773	.025	1.027	.524
5	−.005	.827	.518	1.079
6	−.014	.706	.431	.915
7	−.065	.697	.358	.871
8	.084	.567	.471	.796
	Reduced Structure		Reduced Pattern	
u_1	.854	−.000	1.118	.542
u_2	−.000	.820	.522	1.073

(13.36), using the algorithm of Table 13.2 with Ψ in place of Φ, and V in place of S. The resulting pattern W is given in Table 13.3. The correlation between Λ_1 and Λ_2, obtained from the general expression (13.35) is simply the sum of the two cross-products of the direction cosines in Λ, namely $-.4858$.*

It may also be of some interest to compute the diagonal matrix D

$$D = T'\Lambda = \begin{bmatrix} .8741 & 0 \\ 0 & .8741 \end{bmatrix},$$

giving the correlations between corresponding T and Λ factors. For the simple case of only two factors, each of these correlations is .8741.

13.5. *Relationship between Two Types of Oblique Solutions*

In the preceding two sections, the several parts that make up an oblique multiple-factor solution were outlined very explicitly for the set of T-axes and the set of Λ-axes. The T-factors of **13.3** are called *primary factors* by Thurstone, and the Λ-factors of **13.4** are merely called *reference axes*. He uses the structure of the latter system as an indication of the pattern of the former system, and thereby identifies the primary factors.

The reference axes lie in the common-factor space and are said to be bi-orthogonal to the primary factors. Certainly the reference factors of **13.4** would seem more like mathematical abstractions than the primary factors of **13.3**. The only reason for the strong interest of the Thurstone school in the simple reference structure V is its similarity to the primary-factor pattern, which is shown in (13.43) below. The bi-orthogonal system of coordinate axes may have been an ingenious idea in the 1930's, but certainly is not necessary today. This dual system—reference and primary—is presented for its historical and traditional interest; the direct approach to primary solutions (by hand methods in chapter 11 and in **13.3**, and by computer means in **15.5**) is strongly recommended.

The attempt made in the preceding sections was to clearly define and distinguish the two sets of oblique axes. It was recognized that the oblique solution is dependent upon an initial orthogonal pattern from which clustering of variables might be discerned, or else some graphical means might be necessary to locate the axes. Then the primary factors T_p were passed through these clusters of variables, and the correlations among the factors were determined. Specifically, the analysis of the variables in terms of these oblique factors was shown both by the correlations with the factors (structure S) and by the coefficients in the linear expressions in terms of the factors (pattern P). Similarly, when the analysis was made in terms of the reference axes Λ_p, both the structure V and the pattern W were displayed. It would have been quite sufficient to have a single oblique solution, consisting of the structure S and the

---

* It will be noted that this correlation is simply the negative of the correlation between the factors T_1 and T_2. From Figure 13.4 it can be seen that cos (angle between Λ_1 and Λ_2) = cos $(180° - \theta_{12}) = -\cos \theta_{12}$, so that the correlation of one set of axes is the negative of that between the other set.

pattern **P**. However, since the structure **V** has become so popular it seems important to bring into clear perspective the meaning of the apparently alternative oblique solutions. To assist in the ensuing discussion, the notation employed in the oblique solutions is summarized in Table 13.4.

Table 13.4

Notation Employed in Bi-orthogonal Oblique Solutions

Type of Solution	Factor Designation	Initial Orthog-onal Pattern	Transformation Matrix	Factor Correla-tions	Oblique Solution	
					Structure	Pattern
Sec. **13.3**	T_p (Primary)	**A**	$\mathbf{T} = (t_{qp})$	$\mathbf{\Phi}$	**S**	**P**
Sec. **13.4**	Λ_p (Reference)	**A**	$\Lambda = (\lambda_{qp})$	$\mathbf{\Psi}$	**V**	**W**

Unfortunately, the explicit designations of structure values and pattern values have not always been made in connection with oblique solutions, with a resulting state of confusion. The Thurstone school of factor analysis frequently refers to "the factor matrix **V**," implying therein the complete factor solution. This is an extremely ambiguous statement when the factors are correlated—there is no unique, single matrix! Is it the matrix of factor coefficients, or the matrix of test correlations with the factors? Both uses have been made of the term "factor matrix" in an oblique solution. The more common meaning of "the factor matrix **V**" is that defined by Thurstone [477, p. 347] as the matrix containing the projections of the test vectors on a set of oblique reference axes Λ_p, which meaning is carried in the present text.

Along with the ambiguous use of a single matrix to describe the two distinct components of an oblique solution is the equally ambiguous use of the term factor "loading." While this may be perfectly acceptable in the case of an orthogonal solution, it lacks precision of meaning in an oblique solution. Factor "loading" is not a mathematical or statistical term meaning either "correlation" or "coefficient," and hence has been used inconsistently in both senses. Even when the term is given explicit meaning in an oblique solution it can never take the place of such well-defined concepts as correlation and coefficient. Fruchter [137, p. 193] refers to the "loading" of a variable both for the *correlation with a reference axis* and for the *coefficient of a primary factor*, probably because of the relationship between the structure of the one solution and the pattern of the other, which is indicated below in (13.43).

The confusion is not simple-minded but results from some rather subtle considerations. The fact of the matter is that a mathematical relationship exists between the structure **V** and the pattern **P** (as well as between **S** and **W**). Hence, in some sense it is unnecessary to introduce **P**, because all of its properties can be inferred from **V**. While this is true, it certainly complicates the interpretation of the primary-factor pattern to have to rely on the reference-factor structure for an indication of its values, i.e., to have to look at the structure in Table 13.3 to infer the properties of the pattern in Table 13.1. Now the exact mathematical relationships will be developed.

From (13.26), the initial orthogonal factor pattern can be expressed in terms of the primary pattern,

$$(13.38) \qquad \mathbf{A} = \mathbf{PT'},$$

and from (13.30), it can also be expressed in terms of the reference structure,

$$(13.39) \qquad \mathbf{A} = \mathbf{V\Lambda}^{-1}.$$

Equating these two expressions yields:

$$(13.40) \qquad \mathbf{PT'} = \mathbf{V\Lambda}^{-1}.$$

But, from (13.32),

$$(13.41) \qquad \mathbf{\Lambda}^{-1} = \mathbf{D}^{-1}\mathbf{T'},$$

so that (13.40) becomes:

$$(13.42) \qquad \mathbf{PT'} = \mathbf{VD}^{-1}\mathbf{T'}.$$

Finally, the relationship between $\mathbf{P}$ and $\mathbf{V}$ is given by:

$$(13.43) \qquad \mathbf{P} = \mathbf{VD}^{-1} \quad \text{or} \quad \mathbf{V} = \mathbf{PD}.$$

Thus, for a given reference structure matrix and correlations between the corresponding primary and reference factors, the primary pattern matrix is determined.

In a similar fashion, the initial orthogonal factor pattern can be expressed in terms of the primary structure from (13.21), and also in terms of the reference pattern from (13.37). Then the same kind of mathematical analysis, employing the relationship (13.32) between the two transformation matrices, yields:

$$(13.44) \qquad \mathbf{S} = \mathbf{WD} \quad \text{or} \quad \mathbf{W} = \mathbf{SD}^{-1}.$$

This relationship, like (13.43), indicates that the structure of one type of oblique solution is rather simply related to the pattern of the other solution, and vice versa.

While (13.43) and (13.44) establish the exact relationships *across* the two types of oblique solutions, they do not replace the need for the clear distinction between the structure and pattern for either type of oblique solution. Of course, the structure and pattern have unique meanings, and serve rather distinct purposes, and it is in this sense that they complement each other in providing complete understanding of an oblique solution. In general, for a set of positively correlated primary factors, the factor structure will contain all positive entries, while the factor pattern will have high positive values and many values near zero (see Table 13.1). The primary-factor structure is useful in the estimation of factors (see chapter 16). On the other hand, it does not provide a very good indication of "saturation" of the variables with the factors. The primary-factor pattern gives this precisely, and thereby is most useful for identification of the factors.

By way of illustrating these points, consider variable 1 (Height) in the example of Table 13.1. From the first line of the factor structure, its correlation with the factor T_1 (Lankiness) is found to be .914 and its correlation with the factor T_2 (Stockiness), .489. However, its "saturation" with these factors can best be obtained from the linear equation:

$$z_1 = .885T_1 + .059T_2,$$

which comes from the first line of the factor pattern. The direct contributions of factors T_1 and T_2 to the variance of variable 1 are $(.885)^2 = .783$ and $(.059)^2 = .003$, respectively, while $2(.885)(.059)(.4858) = .051$ is attributable to the joint influence of the two factors. In other words, 78.3 per cent of the Height variable is attributable to the Lankiness factor, while only 0.3 per cent is attributable to the Stockiness factor and 5.1 per cent to the joint influence of these factors (leaving 15.3 per cent of the total variance of variable 1 unaccounted by the common factors).

Similar interpretations could be made of the values in Table 13.3. But actually, nobody proposes the reference axes as useful factors. The Thurstone school would exhibit the "factor matrix **V**" for purposes of identifying the factors. To this end, it is just as effective as the pattern matrix **P**, although from (13.43) it can be seen that the values in **P** are larger than those in **V** because each correlation in the diagonal matrix **D** is less than unity. However, for overall clarity and understanding, the complete primary-factor solution of Section **13.3** is recommended.

14

Analytical Methods for the Multiple-Factor Solution: Orthogonal Case

14.1. *Introduction*

The last two chapters were devoted to methods of transforming some initial factor solution to another "preferred" type of solution. The multiple-factor solutions, as developed in these chapters, are dependent in large measure on subjective judgments, and the transformations to them cannot be written explicitly from the qualitative conditions for "simple structure." Many attempts have been made to reduce the principles of simple structure to an objective form, and hence to develop an objective procedure for calculating a (simple structure) multiple-factor solution. These attempts date back to the 1930's, but it was not until 1953 that a real breakthrough was accomplished by Carroll [69].

One might wonder if objective procedures are really necessary when some of the solutions in chapter 13 (and also in chapter 11) seem so elegant even with the crude subjective procedures. These appear as choice solutions only because there were clear-cut clustering of variables into groups. Unfortunately, not all variables lend themselves to ready grouping, no matter how well an experiment is designed. Furthermore, a scientific methodology cannot be dependent on subjective operations. Now sound, objective, efficient procedures are available for determining a multiple-factor solution for any set of data. Analytical methods for transforming any initial solution to a simple-structure solution are presented in this chapter for the case of orthogonal factors and in the following chapter for the case of oblique factors.

Before developing the objective procedures a brief discussion of some semi-analytical methods is presented in **14.2**. This is done in order to provide some historical perspective to the problem of finding an analytical solution. Also in this section is developed the fundamental rationale for the analytical methods. In **14.3** and **14.4** specific procedures are presented which lead to orthogonal simple-structure solutions. Essentially the same basis—the quartimax criterion—was developed independently by four researchers, and the orthogonal solution derived therefrom is presented in **14.3** both in theory and with numerical illustrations. An alternative approach to orthogonal simple structure is developed in **14.4**, employing Kaiser's varimax criterion. This procedure not only does a better job of approximating the classical simple-structure principles, but it also tends to lead to factorially invariant solutions. Again, numerical examples are given to illustrate the methods.

While the breakthrough in the analytical rotational methods came in 1953, the new procedures could not immediately be used because of the laborious computations involved. By 1958, however, electronic computer programs were developed which made their application feasible. In presenting the analytical methods, consideration was given to separating the theory from the computing outlines, but it was decided to be somewhat inappropriate since the practical use of these methods (beyond two or three factors) is only feasible with high-speed electronic computers.

14.2. *Rationale for Analytical Methods*

As noted in chapter 12, many ingenious graphical and mechanical procedures were developed for transforming "arbitrary" factor matrices into "meaningful" factor matrices satisfying the simple structure principles of **6.2**. So long as the criteria for simple structure were stated in qualitative terms, rather than precise mathematical terms, it was to be expected that the quest for a simple structure solution could only lead to a subjective result. To get results that are independent of the particular investigator it would be necessary to rephrase the conditions for simple structure. That is precisely what has been taking place ever since the principles were first enunciated, although done indirectly or implicitly more often than by explicit attack on the principles themselves.

From the very beginning of the application of simple-structure principles, it was recognized that the procedure was more of an art than a science. In an endeavour to put the rotations on a more objective basis, the first improvements were directed toward eliminating graphical procedures. Nonetheless, arbitrary decisions were still required to determine "significant" factor loadings, "large" or "near zero" factor loadings, "subgroups" of variables, and the like. Of the many such semi-analytical solutions proposed, Horst's [251] was among the first. He follows Thurstone's early principle for simple structure, namely, that each column of the factor matrix should have a minimum number of negative values and a maximum number of nearly vanishing values. He then expresses this condition in analytical terms, as follows [251, p. 80]: "For a given factor the sum of the squares of significant factor loadings divided by the sum of the squares of all the loadings shall be a maximum." This procedure lacks complete objectivity in that a subgroup of variables with "significant" factor loadings has to be selected, and since such variables cannot be determined on statistical grounds an arbitrary operational definition is introduced.

Employing Horst's criterion as a point of departure, Tucker [489] presents a compromise procedure employing both analytical and graphical methods. In this method the positions of the trial reference axes for subgroups of variables are determined by an analytical method, while the subgroups themselves are selected subjectively employing the inter-factor graphs as guides.

Ten years later, Thurstone [478] proposed another type of near-objective procedure involving the minimization of a weighted sum of projections of the test vectors on a reference vector. The selection of the weights is on a rather arbitrary basis designed to emphasize near zero projections. The method involves simple computations and yields results closely approximating the more intuitive graphical methods.

As noted above, the first truly analytical rotation criterion for determining psychologically interpretable factors was developed by Carroll [69]. He considered Thurstone's five principles of simple structure (see **6.2**) but immediately ruled out the likelihood of a single mathematical expression embodying all these characteristics. This conscious departure was aptly stated by Kaiser [293, p. 188] as "the first attempt to break away from an inflexible devotion to Thurstone's ambiguous, arbitrary, and mathematically unmanageable qualitative rules for his intuitively compelling notion of simple structure."

In a similar attempt to objectify the definition of simple structure, Tucker [493] proposes a list of ten requirements to be satisfied by any such criteria. While his list provides another indication of the necessity to depart from Thurstone's qualitative rules, it also is dependent on subjective judgment in several places. On the basis of the objective definition of simple structure which he proposes, Tucker develops a method for the isolation of m "linear constellations" each with dimensionality $(m - 1)$ when the common-factor space is of m dimensions. His procedure yields satisfactory results primarily for "those well-designed studies in which the vectors are concentrated along all hyperplanes" [493, p. 224]. Since the emphasis in this chapter is on analytical procedures which completely avoid subjective decisions, and are applicable to any initial factor solution, Tucker's rotational method will not be treated further.

Several researchers,* working independently, almost simultaneously arrived at very similar solutions for objectifying the rotational problem in factor analysis. While three of the investigators apparently were led to their solutions by a rationale which they considered to be based on Thurstone's rules, Ferguson attempted "to develop a logical groundwork which would lead ultimately to an objective analytical solution and render explicit the meaning of such a solution" [126, p. 288]. His development centers around the concept of parsimony in factor analysis, including its philosophical kinship to the term as used in other scientific theories. This concept, with its widespread application in all aspects of the subject, provides the very foundation of factor analysis—from a simple definition of its objective to the complex considerations in the rotational problem.

Parsimony is one of the fundamental standards in selecting a preferred solution out of the infinitude of possible solutions, and is the basis of the simple-structure principles. While the notion of parsimony is implicit in much of the work in factor analysis, it does not always carry an explicit meaning. In regard to the number of factors, it is perfectly clear what is meant by parsimony. On the other hand, no such

---

* Carroll [69], draft August 1952; Saunders [416]; Neuhaus and Wrigley [379], draft August 1953; and Ferguson [126], draft July 1953.

precise meaning attaches to the notion of parsimony in the rotational problem. It was the full realization of this fact that led Ferguson to his rationale for an analytical solution to the rotational problem:

> "Since factorists in dealing with the rotational problem employ an intuitive concept of parsimony, the question can be raised as to whether the term can be assigned a precise and more explicit meaning, which will enable the rotational problem to be more clearly stated and admit the possibility of a unique and objective solution. This involves *explication* ... [which he attributes to Carnap] ... the process of assigning to a vague, ill-defined, and perhaps largely intuitive concept a precise, explicit and formal meaning ..." [126, p. 282].

Now, Thurstone's principles of simple structure were devised as an explicit expression of parsimony in factor analysis, but they do not provide *explication* in the above sense. Ferguson points out three shortcomings: (1) The conditions for simple structure cannot be represented as terms in a mathematical expression capable of manipulation; (2) the conditions are discrete rather than continuous; and (3) because of the discrete formulations in the simple-structure concept it is insufficiently general. He therefore proposes an explication of the concept of parsimony so that a unique solution to the rotational problem would result. Of course, the extent of agreement between solutions obtained by intuitive-graphical methods and by such a precise objective method would depend on the nature of the explication.

A measure of parsimony in the rotational problem can be defined in terms of the degree to which the configuration of vectors representing the variables is structured, i.e., the position of the configuration on an hypothetical continuum of all possible configurations, from the completely chaotic to the ideal configuration in which each variable is of unit complexity. As pointed out in **6.2**, the configuration of vectors serves as the vehicle to get to a particular set of reference axes. In factor analysis the structural properties of the configuration are conveyed by the frame of reference.

While there are many approaches to the problem of assigning a precise mathematical meaning to a measure of parsimony, Ferguson suggests a simple and attractive one. Starting with a single variable, represented by a point, what is the most parsimonious description of it, upon rotation of a pair of orthogonal axes? He suggests that intuitively the most parsimonious description results when one of the axes passes through the point. Approaching this ideal, it can be seen that when the reference frame is rotated so that one of the axes approaches the point, the product of the two coordinates grows smaller. Continuing this line of reasoning, Ferguson suggests that some function of the sum of products of coordinates of a set of collinear points might be used as a measure of the amount of parsimony associated with the description of these points. Finally, for the usual situation of positive and negative coordinates, he proposes (in place of the simple sum) the sum of squares of products of coordinates as a measure of parsimony. This measure, for the case of n variables and m orthogonal factors, is

$$(14.1) \qquad \sum_{j=1}^{n} \sum_{p<q=1}^{m} (a_{jp}a_{jq})^2,$$

involving $m(m-1)/2$ sums of n pairs of coordinates.

The expression (14.1) turns out to be closely related to several of the analytical procedures that were developed independently. It will be convenient to employ the following notation for the general rotational problem in terms of orthogonal factors:

$$\mathbf{A} = (a_{jp}), \text{ initial factor matrix,}$$

(14.2) $$\mathbf{B} = (b_{jp}), \text{ final factor matrix,}$$

$$\mathbf{T} = (t_{qp}), \text{ orthogonal transformation matrix,}$$

so that

(14.3) $$\mathbf{B} = \mathbf{AT}.$$

When $\mathbf{A}$ is carried into $\mathbf{B}$ by the orthogonal transformation $\mathbf{T}$, the communality of any variable is invariant, i.e.,

(14.4) $$\sum_{p=1}^{m} b_{jp}^2 = \sum_{p=1}^{m} a_{jp}^2 = h_j^2 \qquad (j = 1, 2, \cdots, n).$$

The squared communality of any variable also remains constant, namely,

(14.5) $$\left(\sum_{p=1}^{m} b_{jp}^2 \right)^2 = \sum_{p=1}^{m} b_{jp}^4 + 2 \sum_{p<q=1}^{m} b_{jp}^2 b_{jq}^2 = \text{constant.}$$

Then, summing over the n variables produces

(14.6) $$\sum_{j=1}^{n} \sum_{p=1}^{m} b_{jp}^4 + 2 \sum_{j=1}^{n} \sum_{p<q=1}^{m} b_{jp}^2 b_{jq}^2 = \text{constant.}$$

Since the sum of the two terms in this expression must always be the same, it follows that when one of these terms increases the other must decrease, and vice versa. Hence, a transformation of $\mathbf{A}$ which maximizes one of the terms in (14.6) will, at the same time, minimize the other. Formula (14.6) provides the relationship between two independent approaches to the rotational problem, as will be indicated below.

Either term of (14.6), or some function of these terms, could serve as a precise mathematical measure of parsimony. Actually, *minimization* of the second term for maximum parsimony is implied in (14.1). On the other hand, Ferguson [126, p. 286] suggests that

(14.7) $$Q = \sum_{j=1}^{n} \sum_{p=1}^{m} b_{jp}^4$$

be *maximized* for maximum parsimony of a factor structure. Of course the value of Q depends upon the factor loadings, which vary with the particular positions of the reference axes. The most parsimonious solution, in the least-square sense, would seem to require that rotation of the frame of reference which makes the value of Q a maximum for a given set of data. The theoretical limit is attained when the complexity of each variable is unity. This might be said to constitute the maximum degree of structure or organization possible for a configuration of variables.

14.3. *Quartimax Method*

Without employing the "parsimony rationale" explicitly, and each starting with an independent approach, Carroll [69], Neuhaus and Wrigley [379], and Saunders [416] arrived at criteria for objective analytical solutions closely related to the maximization of the function (14.7). In one way or another, each viewed the rotation of axes in order to arrive at simple structure as an attempt to reduce the complexity of the factorial description of the variables. The ultimate objective would be a uni-factor solution, in which each variable would be of complexity one, i.e., involve only a single common factor. An orthogonal uni-factor solution is extremely unlikely with empirical data (except for the limiting case of only a general factor for the entire set of variables, or the case of several mutually uncorrelated group factors as implied by a set of correlations as in Figure 6.1).

If a uni-factor solution were possible, the variance of each variable would result from but one factor loading; and a reasonable approach to this ideal would seem to require the maximum inequality in the distribution of the variance among the several factors for each variable in the factor pattern. In other words, the transformation desired is one which will tend to increase the large factor loadings and decrease the small ones for each variable of the original factor matrix. In this attempt to increase the inequalities among the factor loadings, the size implied is independent of algebraic sign. Since absolute values are somewhat awkward for mathematical manipulation, Neuhaus and Wrigley [379] propose that the inequalities among squares of factor loadings be maximized; or, more specifically, that the variance in the distribution of squared factor loadings should be made a maximum by the use of orthogonal transformations. Since this approach involves the maximization of fourth powers of factor loadings, Burt (in [379]) has suggested the term "quartimax" for this method. In this text the term "quartimax method" is used collectively for the several independent derivations of analytical procedures related to the maximization of the function (14.7).

In the notation of (14.2), the object of the quartimax method is to determine the orthogonal transformation $\mathbf{T}$ which will carry the original factor matrix $\mathbf{A}$ into a new factor matrix $\mathbf{B}$ for which the variance of squared factor loadings is a maximum. From the basic definition (2.4) the variance of the contributions (the squared factor loadings) of all m factors to the n variables is simply:

$$(14.8) \qquad s_{b^2}^2 = \frac{1}{mn} \sum_{j=1}^{n} \sum_{p=1}^{m} (b_{jp}^2 - \overline{b^2})^2$$

where the mean of all the squared factor loadings is

$$(14.9) \qquad \overline{b^2} = \frac{1}{mn} \sum_{j=1}^{n} \sum_{p=1}^{m} b_{jp}^2 .$$

Upon expansion and simplification, the expression (14.8) reduces to

$$(14.10) \qquad M = \frac{1}{mn} \sum_{j=1}^{n} \sum_{p=1}^{m} b_{jp}^4 - (\overline{b^2})^2 ,$$

298

which Neuhaus and Wrigley [379] designated the quartimax criterion that is to be maximized. Now, since $\overline{b^2}$ remains constant under orthogonal transformation according to (14.4), and constant terms have no effect on the maximizing process, this criterion is equivalent to the measure of parsimony (14.7), i.e., simply the maximization of the sum of fourth powers of factor loadings.

In Carroll's [69] original development of an objective procedure he focused attention on criteria 3, 4, and 5 of the simple structure principles (see **6.2**). This led him to consider the minimization of some sort of inner-product function of the columns of the final factor-structure matrix. The criterion which he proposes is that

$$(14.11) \qquad N = \sum_{p<q=1}^{m} \sum_{j=1}^{n} b_{jp}^2 b_{jq}^2$$

be a minimum. It should be noted that, for the orthogonal case, the expression (14.11) is identical with the measure of parsimony (14.1) proposed by Ferguson. Also for the orthogonal case, minimizing (14.11) is equivalent to maximizing (14.10) according to (14.6). In other words, the criterion $N = $ minimum will lead to precisely the same results as $Q = $ maximum when the rotated factors are orthogonal. However, Carroll's criterion (14.11) is not restricted to the orthogonal case. As a matter of fact, its application generally will lead to oblique factors (see **15.3**).

Again, from a fresh point of view, Saunders [416, p. 5] attempts to objectify the rotation to simple structure by maximizing "the proportion of small and large loadings, at the expense of medium-sized ones." Before considering any function of the factor loadings, he notes that the direction of scoring a test is irrelevant to simple structure, so that the algebraic signs in any column of the factor matrix may be changed without affecting the criterion. In order to deal with this sign ambiguity, and at the same time preserve the sign relationships of loadings for the same variable, he suggests that each variable be considered *twice* (as originally scored and also reflected) in the frequency distribution of factor loadings. Thus, the "doubled" distribution of factor loadings is perfectly symmetric and always has a mean of zero. Then Saunders proposes as a criterion for a simple structure solution that the kurtosis of the "doubled" frequency distribution of rotated factor loadings be a maximum. The fourth moment and second moment are easily expressed about the mean of zero, so that the kurtosis to be maximized is:*

$$(14.12) \qquad K = \sum_{j=1}^{n} \sum_{p=1}^{m} b_{jp}^4 \Big/ \left(\sum_{j=1}^{n} \sum_{p=1}^{m} b_{jp}^2 \right)^2 .$$

It will be recalled that kurtosis is a measure of the flatness or peakedness of a single-humped distribution. For the present application the special significance of this measure is that as kurtosis is increased the relative frequencies of the middle (near

---

* Since the resulting function is to be maximized, the numerical constants that arise from the number of observations and from consideration of the "doubled" frequency may be disregarded. Thus, while the notion of the "doubled" frequency was necessary to the rationale of the method, the factor loadings actually need not be reflected.

zero loadings) and tails (large loadings) of a distribution are increased at the expense of the intermediate regions. The denominator of (14.12) remains constant under orthogonal transformation according to (14.4), so that this criterion is equivalent to each of the preceding in the orthogonal case.

Since the four criteria (Q, M, N, and K) lead to identical results for an orthogonal solution, the theory in this section will be developed simply for the maximization of the sum of fourth powers of factor loadings (Q), following the procedure of Neuhaus and Wrigley [379]. The notation of (14.2) is employed, with b's representing all intermediate values resulting from rotation of the a's as well as the final factor loadings. For any variable z_j, the orthogonal transformation in the plane of factors p and q through an angle φ will carry the original coordinates (a's) into the new coordinates (b's), as follows:

$$b_{jp} = a_{jp} \cos \varphi + a_{jq} \sin \varphi$$

(14.13)

$$b_{jq} = -a_{jp} \sin \varphi + a_{jq} \cos \varphi$$

according to the basic equations of transformation in a plane (12.13). In order to measure the effect of such a transformation $\mathbf{T}_{pq}$ on the overall criterion Q, the sum of fourth powers of the new loadings of the two rotated factors is determined. This sum is defined by

$$(14.14) \qquad Q_{pq}(\varphi) = \sum_{j=1}^{n} (b_{jp}^4 + b_{jq}^4),$$

which depends on the parameter φ. The object is to determine the angle of rotation (φ_{pq} in precise notation) for any pair of factors p and q which will make the sum Q_{pq} a maximum. Then the product of the transformations of all combinations of pairs of factors produces a transformed factor matrix:

$$(14.15) \qquad \mathbf{B} = \mathbf{A}\mathbf{T}_{12}\mathbf{T}_{13}\cdots\mathbf{T}_{pq}\cdots\mathbf{T}_{(m-1),m},$$

where $p = 1, 2, \cdots, (m-1)$, and the associated $q = p+1, p+2, \cdots, m$. The complete set of $m(m-1)/2$ pairings of p and q is called a *cycle*. In each cycle of operations the value of Q for the entire matrix is as large as or larger than the preceding sum. Since the theoretical maximum of fourth powers of factor loadings cannot exceed n (even when the total unit variance of each variable is analyzed), the procedure must converge after a sufficient number of cycles.

For any rotation $\mathbf{T}_{pq}$ the angle φ which will make Q_{pq} a maximum can be determined as follows: (a) substitute the expressions for the b's from (14.13) into (14.14); (b) differentiate (14.14) with respect to φ; (c) set the derivative equal to zero; and (d) solve the equation for φ. The results [379, p. 83] can be put in the form:

$$(14.16) \qquad \tan 4\varphi = \frac{2 \sum\limits_{j=1}^{n} (2a_{jp}a_{jq})(a_{jp}^2 - a_{jq}^2)}{\sum\limits_{j=1}^{n} [(a_{jp}^2 - a_{jq}^2)^2 - (2a_{jp}a_{jq})^2]} = \frac{\nu}{\delta}.$$

When (14.14) is expanded and the terms involving φ are collected and simplified, they are found to involve $\sin 4\varphi$ and $\sin^2 2\varphi$. Since each of these terms has the period $\pi/2$ so does $Q_{pq}(\varphi)$. Therefore the solution (14.16) need only be considered for φ between $0°$ and $90°$. Actually, experience has shown that subsequent reflection of factors can be reduced by requiring φ to be between $-45°$ and $+45°$.

While any solution (14.16) yields a critical value of φ, necessary for a maximum value of Q_{pq}, such a critical value may produce a minimum, or stationary value of Q_{pq} as well. A sufficient condition for a maximum is a negative value of the second derivative of the function when the critical value is substituted in it. The conditions for a maximum can be summarized in the form:

(14.17)

$$\frac{dQ_{pq}}{d\varphi} = v \cos 4\varphi - \delta \sin 4\varphi = 0$$

$$\frac{d^2 Q_{pq}}{d\varphi^2} = -\delta \cos 4\varphi - v \sin 4\varphi < 0$$

from which it follows that

(14.18)

$$-\frac{\delta^2 + v^2}{v} \sin 4\varphi < 0.$$

Actually, the formal work of computing the second derivative can be obviated since the angle which produces a maximum can be determined from the algebraic signs of the numerator and denominator of (14.16). In the expression (14.18) the numerator is always a positive number, so the algebraic sign of the entire expression is determined completely from the simpler form:

(14.19)

$$\frac{1}{v} \sin 4\varphi > 0.$$

It follows that the numerator of (14.16) and $\sin 4\varphi$ must have the same algebraic signs if the condition (14.19) for a maximum is to be preserved. Corresponding to each

Table 14.1

Angle of Rotation

Algebraic signs in (14.16)						
Numer- ator (v) (and $\sin 4\varphi$)	Denom- inator (δ)	$\tan 4\varphi$	Sign of $\cos 4\varphi$	Resulting Quadrant of 4φ		Limits for φ
+	+	+	+	I:	$0 < 4\varphi < 90°$	$0°$ to $22.5°$
+	−	−	−	II:	$90° < 4\varphi < 180°$	$22.5°$ to $45°$
−	−	+	−	III:	$-180° < 4\varphi < -90°$	$-45°$ to $-22.5°$
−	+	−	+	IV:	$-90° < 4\varphi < 0°$	$-22.5°$ to $0°$

algebraic sign of the numerator, the denominator may be either positive or negative. The resulting four possibilities, with the angle of rotation associated with each, are set forth in Table 14.1.

The foregoing theory provides the basis for computation of the quartimax method. First $\tan 4\varphi$ is calculated from (14.16) and then, from the algebraic signs of v and δ, the angle of rotation φ is determined from Table 14.1. Then the matrix of the original (or last computed) pair of columns p and q of the factor matrix is postmultiplied by the transformation matrix

$$(14.20) \qquad \mathbf{T}_{pq} = \begin{pmatrix} \cos\varphi & -\sin\varphi \\ \sin\varphi & \cos\varphi \end{pmatrix},$$

where φ is understood to be the angle of rotation φ_{pq} in the plane of the factors p and q. The result leads to the maximum sum Q_{pq} of fourth powers of the rotated factor loadings for factors p and q. After rotation of all combinations of factors, the transformation to the final factor matrix $\mathbf{B}$ is accomplished as indicated symbolically in (14.15). The cycle of operations on all pairings of factors must be repeated as many times as necessary to assure that the Q, for the full matrix, no longer increases (to the specified number of decimal places).

In order to illustrate the quartimax method, such a solution will be calculated for the simple example of the eight physical variables. The centroid solution, taken from the first edition of this text, is repeated in Table 14.2 as the initial solution. To get the angle of rotation φ, formula (14.16) is first applied. There are essentially two types of terms in this formula—twice the products of corresponding factor loadings $(2a_{j1}a_{j2})$ and the differences of squares of factor loadings $(a_{j1}^2 - a_{j2}^2)$—and these are listed for each variable in Table 14.2. The numerator of (14.16) is twice the sum of

Table 14.2

Quartimax Solution for Eight Physical Variables

(Initial solution: Centroid)

Variable	Initial Solution		Squares		Products	Difference of squares	Final Solution	
j	a_{j1}	a_{j2}	a_{j1}^2	a_{j2}^2	$2a_{j1}a_{j2}$	$a_{j1}^2 - a_{j2}^2$	b_{j1}	b_{j2}
1	830	−.396	.6889	.1568	−.6574	.5321	.899	.196
2	.818	−.469	.6691	.2200	−.7673	.4491	.934	.131
3	.777	−.470	.6037	.2209	−.7304	.3828	.902	.105
4	.798	−.401	.6368	.1608	−.6400	.4760	.876	.172
5	.786	.500	.6178	.2500	.7860	.3678	.315	.877
6	.672	.458	.4516	.2098	.6156	.2418	.250	.774
7	.594	.444	.3528	.1971	.5275	.1557	.197	.715
8	.647	.333	.4186	.1109	.4309	.3077	.307	.660
Sum of Squares	4.4394	1.5263	2.5776	.3053	3.4247	1.1706	3.5563	2.4112

the products of these eight corresponding values, namely,

$$v = 2(-.6260) = -1.2520.$$

The sums of squares of the "products" and the "differences of squares" from the bottom row of Table 14.2 are used directly in getting the denominator of (14.16):

$$\delta = 1.1706 - 3.4247 = -2.2541.$$

Substituting these values in (14.16) yields:

$$\tan 4\varphi = \frac{-1.2520}{-2.2541} = .5554.$$

Since the numerator and denominator are both negative, the angle 4φ falls in the third quadrant according to the third line in Table 14.1. From tables of trigonometric functions it is found that $4\varphi = -150° \, 57'$ and hence the angle of rotation is $\varphi = -37° \, 44'$. The necessary elements for the transformation matrix are $\sin \varphi = -.6120$ and $\cos \varphi = .7909$, so that (14.20) may be written as

(14.21)
$$\mathbf{T} = \begin{pmatrix} .7909 & .6120 \\ -.6120 & .7909 \end{pmatrix}.$$

The expression (14.15) for the final factor matrix reduces to the simple postmultiplication of the initial factor matrix of Table 14.2 by the transformation matrix (14.21). The resulting quartimax solution appears in the last two columns of Table 14.2. The quartimax criterion for this solution is

(14.22)
$$Q = \sum_{j=1}^{8} \sum_{p=1}^{2} b_{jp}^4 = 4.091,$$

while the corresponding value for the initial solution is only 2.883. In the simple case of $m = 2$, only one cycle involving a single rotation leads to convergence.

Of course, the foregoing example of only two factors is extremely simple and does not bring out all the ramifications of the quartimax procedure, but it does show the fundamental properties of such a solution. It approximates a simple structure solution even though the small values are not as close to zero as one might like them to be. No doubt a much better approximation to simple structure could be obtained with an oblique solution (see chap. 15), but if an orthogonal solution is desired the result in Table 14.2 is the best possible in the sense of this section. It is interesting to note that the intuitive-graphical solution of Table 12.3 is very similar to the analytical solution, but it does not satisfy the quartimax criterion quite as well (see ex. 1, chap. 14).

While the indicated type of computation can be done with conventional punched-card equipment and desk calculators, the work is very laborious and time-consuming. However, it can be done most expeditiously on high-speed electronic computers. Such programs were first written for the IBM 701 (and later model machines), the Illiac, and several other electronic computers [542]. The machine procedure involves successive pairings of factors $p < q = 1, 2, \cdots, m$, and carrying through the full

$m(m - 1)/2$ transformations for each cycle. When the machine finds the angle of rotation which will give a maximal sum of fourth powers of loadings of rotated factors, it makes the transformation only if the angle is greater than some specified value (perhaps one degree; or only one minute if the computer has very large high-speed memory capacity). Cycles of operation are continued until the sum of fourth powers for the entire matrix no longer increases. The convergence is generally rapid in the first few cycles and then tends to slow down.

The application of the quartimax method to a large problem, for which an electronic computer was employed, will now be shown. Neuhaus and Wrigley [379] performed an analytical rotation on the centroid solution (which appeared in the first edition of this text) of the twenty-four psychological tests, employing the Illiac. Their results, which took about one minute of computer time, are shown in Table 14.3.* The calculation of cycles was continued until convergence of Q was obtained to the eighth decimal place. This required five cycles, but from a practical standpoint the convergence was adequate at the end of two cycles.

There is rather good agreement between the quartimax solution of Table 14.3 and the orthogonal multiple-factor solutions obtained by intuitive-graphical methods in the first edition of this text, and summarized in Table 14.6. With few exceptions, large factor loadings in one case correspond to similarly large values in the other. In the quartimax solution, the large values tend to be somewhat larger, and the small values smaller than their counterparts in either of the graphical solutions. Exceptions are especially noticeable in the third factor where there are fewer well-pronounced large loadings in the quartimax solution; and in the first factor (verbal) where even the small values are increased in the quartimax solution. This tendency toward a general factor is one of the main shortcomings, in the simple-structure sense, of the quartimax solution.

14.4. *Varimax Method*

As outlined in the last section, the emphasis in the quartimax method is on simplification of the description of each *row*, or variable, of the factor matrix. In contradistinction, Kaiser [293] places more emphasis on simplifying the *columns*, or factors, of the factor matrix in an attempt to meet the requirements for simple structure. Thus, while simplicity of each variable may be attained concurrent with a large loading on the same factor, such a general factor is precluded by the simplicity constraint on each factor.

The varimax method proposed by Kaiser [291] is a modification of the quartimax method which more nearly approximates simple structure. Following his development [293, p. 190], the simplicity of a factor p is defined as the variance of its squared loadings, i.e.

$$(14.23) \qquad s_p^2 = \frac{1}{n} \sum_{j=1}^{n} (b_{jp}^2)^2 - \frac{1}{n^2} \left(\sum_{j=1}^{n} b_{jp}^2 \right)^2 \qquad (p = 1, 2, \cdots, m).$$

---

* In 1958 an independent solution was obtained on an IBM 704 at the System Development Corporation, and it was found to agree identically with that in Table 14.3.

Table 14.3

Quartimax Solution for Twenty-Four Psychological Tests

(Initial solution: Centroid)

Test j	Verbal M_1	Speed M_2	Deduction M_3	Memory M_4
1	.369	.190	**.599**	.068
2	.245	.066	.384	.039
3	.313	.010	**.475**	.013
4	.359	.070	**.463**	−.012
5	**.806**	.135	−.016	−.039
6	**.812**	.030	.000	.055
7	**.854**	.072	−.044	−.095
8	**.660**	.202	.197	−.034
9	**.857**	−.058	−.020	.098
10	.234	**.700**	−.124	.112
11	.310	**.616**	.011	.231
12	.164	**.688**	.191	−.012
13	.350	**.569**	.323	−.082
14	.324	.190	−.026	**.424**
15	.251	.114	.101	**.448**
16	.289	.134	.372	.368
17	.285	.239	.022	**.569**
18	.215	.324	.302	**.467**
19	.276	.180	.189	.323
20	**.518**	.090	.354	.142
21	.347	.385	.347	.144
22	**.526**	.041	.295	.255
23	**.546**	.187	**.441**	.087
24	**.487**	**.432**	.101	.196
V_p	5.587	2.422	1.958	1.418

When the variance is at a maximum, the factor has the greatest interpretability or simplicity in the sense that its components (the b's) tend toward unity and zero. The criterion of maximum simplicity of a complete factor matrix is defined as the maximization of the sum of these simplicities of the individual factors, as follows:

$$(14.24) \qquad s^2 = \sum_{p=1}^{m} s_p^2 = \frac{1}{n} \sum_{p=1}^{m} \sum_{j=1}^{n} b_{jp}^4 - \frac{1}{n^2} \sum_{p=1}^{m} \left(\sum_{j=1}^{n} b_{jp}^2 \right)^2.$$

The maximization of (14.24) has been called the "raw" varimax criterion by Kaiser [293] because of his preference for an improved version which is presented below. From empirical studies he found that the "raw" varimax and the quartimax analytical methods did not meet the standard of level contributions of factors any better than the intuitive-graphical methods. Along with this tendency for the contributions of factors (V_p) to have greater dispersion in the analytical solutions, there was the tendency for the more prominent factors to have larger values in both the large and small factor loadings than their counterparts in the less prominent factors.

In the intuitive-graphical solutions such systematic bias is generally avoided, yielding level contributions of factors with more equitable distribution of high and low factor loadings.

This type of bias is attributed by Kaiser [293] to the divergent weights which implicitly are attached to the variables by the size of their communalities, namely, the square-roots of their communalities. Each variable contributes to the function (14.24) as the square of its communality. Hence, a variable with communality twice that of another will influence the rotations by four times as much. This means that a variable with communality .90 will have a weight four times that of a variable with communality .45 in determining the final solution. These relative weights are probably quite different from those intuitively assigned in graphical rotations. At Saunders' suggestion, Kaiser modified his original approach by weighting the variables equally for purposes of rotation. This is accomplished by extending the vectors representing the variables to unit length in the common-factor space, carrying out the rotations, and then bringing the vectors back to their original length.

In place of the "raw" varimax criterion (14.24), the improved standard for rotation requires that the final factor loadings be such as to maximize the function:*

$$(14.25) \qquad V = n \sum_{p=1}^{m} \sum_{j=1}^{n} (b_{jp}/h_j)^4 - \sum_{p=1}^{m} \left(\sum_{j=1}^{n} b_{jp}^2/h_j^2 \right)^2 .$$

Kaiser refers to this as the "normal" varimax criterion, but since the earlier version will not be employed in this text, the simple term "varimax" will be understood to mean (14.25). It should be noted that the adjusted correlations of variables with factors (b_{jp}/h_j) correspond to the correlations r'' of (4.55), while the original correlations (b_{jp}) correspond to the r' of (4.51) since the factors themselves are of unit length.

The computing procedure for a varimax solution is quite similar to that employed for a quartimax solution in the preceding section, but requires that (14.25) be maximized instead of (14.7). Factors are rotated two at a time according to the scheme indicated by (14.15), and the complete cycle of $m(m - 1)/2$ pairings of factors is repeated until the value of V to the specified number of decimal places no longer increases.

It will be convenient to introduce some additional notation in order to make the subsequent expressions more compact. First, the "normalized" factor loadings of a variable z_j for a particular pair of factors p and q, will be designated by

$$(14.26) \qquad \begin{aligned} x_j &= a_{jp}/h_j \\ y_j &= a_{jq}/h_j \end{aligned}$$

and the rotated loadings by X_j, Y_j, so that the transformation corresponding to

---

* Since a constant multiplier has no effect on the maximization process, the expression (14.24) was multiplied by n^2 for greater simplicity.

(14.13) may be put in the form:

(14.27)
$$(X_j \quad Y_j) = (x_j \quad y_j)\begin{pmatrix} \cos\varphi & -\sin\varphi \\ \sin\varphi & \cos\varphi \end{pmatrix},$$

where φ is the angle of rotation in the plane of the factors p and q. Since squares and cross-products of the normalized loadings are required in the computation, the following notation will be employed:

(14.28)
$$u_j = x_j^2 - y_j^2$$
$$v_j = 2x_j y_j$$
$$A = \sum u_j$$
$$B = \sum v_j$$
$$C = \sum (u_j^2 - v_j^2)$$
$$D = 2\sum u_j v_j$$

where all sums are on j from 1 to n.

The required angle of rotation is shown by Kaiser [294, p. 415] to be given by:*

(14.29)
$$\tan 4\varphi = \frac{D - 2AB/n}{C - (A^2 - B^2)/n}.$$

Just as before, the solution (14.29) which makes (14.25) a maximum need be considered only for values of φ between $-45°$ and $+45°$; and the sufficiency conditions for a maximum lead to the choice of the angle of rotation according to the values in Table 14.1.

Perhaps the best way to grasp the computing procedures is to apply them to a simple example. For this purpose, the same data of the last section will be employed. In Table 14.4 is indicated an appropriate worksheet for all the data that must be computed and recorded in the process of carrying out the analytical rotation of one pair of factors, when working with a desk calculator. The values of $2u_j v_j$ for the individual variables are not recorded since only their sum D is required, and it can be accumulated in the computer. Its value is $D = -.6930$. On the other hand, since the difference of squares, $u_j^2 - v_j^2$, cannot be accumulated on the ordinary calculator, they are recorded for each variable. Only those sums (A, B, and C) required in the calculation of φ are recorded in the last row of the table.

Substituting in formula (14.29) produces:

$$\tan 4\varphi = \frac{-.6930 - 2(3.8490)(.2809)/8}{-4.0921 - (3.8490^2 - .2809^2)/8} = \frac{-.9633}{-5.9341} = .1623$$

---

* It may be noted that expression (14.16) for the quartimax criterion is simply $\tan 4\varphi = D/C$ in terms of the notation (14.28).

Table 14.4

Computation Form for Varimax Solution: Eight Physical Variables

Variable j	Initial Solution a_{j1}	Initial Solution a_{j2}	Square root of communality h_j	Normalized loadings x_j	Normalized loadings y_j	Computing parameters u_j	Computing parameters v_j	Computing parameters $u_j^2 - v_j^2$
1	.830	−.396	.9196	.9026	−.4306	.6293	−.7773	−.2082
2	.818	−.469	.9429	.8675	−.4974	.5051	−.8630	−.4896
3	.777	−.470	.9081	.8556	−.5176	.4641	−.8857	−.5691
4	.798	−.401	.8931	.8935	−.4490	.5967	−.8024	−.2878
5	.786	.500	.9316	.8437	.5367	.4238	.9056	−.6405
6	.672	.458	.8132	.8264	.5632	.3657	.9309	−.7328
7	.594	.444	.7416	.8010	.5987	.2832	.9591	−.8397
8	.647	.333	.7277	.8891	.4576	.5811	.8137	−.3244
Sum						3.8490	.2809	−4.0921

In calculating the tangent, the numerator and denominator must be determined separately so that the algebraic signs may be noted. Then, referring to Table 14.1 for the case of both numerator and denominator negative, the angle 4φ must be in the third quadrant. From a table of trigonometric functions, $4\varphi = -170°\ 47'$, so that $\varphi = -42°\ 42'$. For this angle of rotation, $\sin \varphi = -.6782$ and $\cos \varphi = .7349$, and the transformation matrix is

$$\mathbf{T} = \begin{pmatrix} .7349 & .6782 \\ -.6782 & .7349 \end{pmatrix}.$$

Then the normalized rotated loadings are computed, according to (14.27), by postmultiplying the original normalized loadings by this matrix. The results (X_j, Y_j) appear in the first two columns of Table 14.5. Finally, the normalization is removed by multiplying each value by the appropriate h_j for the row. The resulting varimax solution appears in the last two columns of Table 14.5. The varimax criterion (14.25) for this solution is

$$V = 8[3.5331 + 3.5049] - [4.0142^2 + 3.9860^2] = 24.3012,$$

for which the necessary sums of squares and fourth-powers of rotated normalized loadings are taken from the middle two columns of Table 14.5.

A comparison of the varimax solution with the previous solutions is most enlightening. Of course, the original centroid solution is very poor from a simple structure point of view; and this is indicated by the value of only .4078 for the varimax criterion. On the other hand, the intuitive-graphical multiple-factor solution of Table 12.3 is almost as good, having a varimax criterion value of 24.27. Looked at the other way, the varimax solution of Table 14.5 comes closest to an orthogonal simple-structure solution which was arrived at intuitively in Table 12.3. The quartimax solution of Table 14.2 is also a close approximation to the desired end, but it

Table 14.5

Varimax Solution for Eight Physical Variables

(Initial solution: Centroid)

Variable j	Rotated Normalized Loadings		Squares		Final Solution	
	X_j	Y_j	X_j^2	Y_j^2	b_{j1}	b_{j2}
1	.9554	.2957	.9128	.0874	.879	.272
2	.9749	.2228	.9504	.0496	.919	.210
3	.9798	.1999	.9600	.0400	.890	.182
4	.9611	.2760	.9237	.0762	.858	.246
5	.2560	.9666	.0655	.9343	.238	.900
6	.2254	.9744	.0508	.9495	.183	.792
7	.1826	.9832	.0333	.9667	.135	.729
8	.3431	.9393	.1177	.8823	.250	.684
Sum			4.0142	3.9860		
Sum of Squares			3.5331	3.5049	3.316	2.648

does not meet the varimax criterion quite as well as the graphical method (see ex. 3, chap. 14).

As in the preceding section, the work of computing a varimax solution without the aid of high-speed electronic computers becomes prohibitive for problems involving more than a few factors. However, computer programs for the varimax rotation are available for all present-day computers, this being the most popular means of getting an orthogonal multiple-factor solution. At many computing centers, the varimax program is part of a "factor analysis package" which has the principal-factor method for the initial solution.

A varimax solution for the example of five socio-economic variables was obtained by the use of such a factor analysis program package. Starting with the correlation matrix from Table 2.2, first the principal-component solution of Table 8.1 is determined and then, specifying two factors for rotation, the varimax solution of Table 14.6 is obtained. Of course, the individual factor coefficients are altered as the result of the rotation, as is also the contribution of each of the two factors. However, the variance of each variable, and the total contribution of the two factors remain the same. Put another way, the proportion of the total variance accounted for by either set of factors is unaltered. As noted before, once the space is determined by the choice of the number of principal components, a rotation to a new basis in the same space has no effect on the lengths of the vectors representing the variables. The square of the length of each vector is its variance, according to (4.52), and is given in the last column of Table 14.6.

The varimax solution is indeed a multiple-factor solution satisfying the simple structure criteria of **6.2**. Of course, for so few variables the conditions cannot be

Table 14.6

Varimax Solution for Five Socio-Economic Variables[a]

(Initial solution: first two principal components, Table 8.1)

Variable	M_1	M_2	Variance
1	.01602	.99377	.98783
2	.94079	−.00883	.88515
3	.13702	.98006	.97930
4	.82479	.44714	.88022
5	.96821	−.00604	.93747
Contribution of factor	2.52182	2.14815	4.66997
Percent of total variance	50.4	43.0	93.4

[a] The only reason for showing five decimal places (of the computer output) is to provide a means for checking numerical calculations.

taken too literally. The factor weights of 0 or 1 in the first decimal place certainly may be viewed as essentially zero. In this sense the factor matrix exhibits one zero in each row, with the exception of variable 4; two zeros in each column; and several variables whose entries vanish in one column but not in the other. Even the exception of variable 4 is not contradictory to the set of simple-structure criteria (see number 5). Again it should be emphasized that the simple-structure criteria have compelling intuitive value but lack the precision necessary for mathematical computation. The varimax solution, on the other hand, is a precisely defined method which indeed approximates orthogonal simple structure.

An example of a varimax solution for a large problem is presented for the twenty-four psychological tests so that the varimax solution may be compared with previous ones for these data. In Table 14.7 the varimax solution is given along with the quartimax (from Table 14.3) and a subjective graphical solution (from the first edition of this text). The coefficients are recorded to two decimal places to facilitate comparison. A quick glance will immediately lead one to the intuitive conclusion that the varimax solution somehow meets the vague notions of simple structure better than either of the other two solutions. Applying each of the five criteria for simple structure (see **6.2**), it is found that both the varimax and the subjective solutions satisfy them insofar as a non-mathematical standard can be satisfied by crude judgment. On the other hand, it is quite obvious that the quartimax solution fails to satisfy the standard of having at least four zeros in each column—the first factor tending towards a general factor as noted in the previous section.

From the nature of the tests with the large weights, the following names are suggested for the factors:

M_1 : Verbal
M_2 : Speed
M_3 : Deduction
M_4 : Memory

Table 14.7

Comparison of Varimax, Quartimax, and Subjective Orthogonal
Multiple-Factor Solutions: Twenty-Four Psychological Tests

(Initial solution: Centroid)

Test j	Subjective				Quartimax				Varimax			
	M_1	M_2	M_3	M_4	M_1	M_2	M_3	M_4	M_1	M_2	M_3	M_4
1	.10	.32	.62	.20	.37	.19	.60	.07	.14	.19	.67	.17
2	.07	.15	.41	.13	.24	.07	.38	.04	.10	.07	.43	.10
3	.10	.12	.53	.13	.31	.01	.48	.01	.15	.02	.54	.08
4	.15	.18	.53	.12	.36	.07	.46	−.01	.20	.09	.54	.07
5	.75	.15	.26	.15	.81	.14	−.02	−.04	.75	.21	.22	.13
6	.72	.05	.28	.25	.81	.03	.00	.06	.75	.10	.23	.21
7	.81	.08	.27	.11	.85	.07	−.04	−.10	.82	.16	.21	.08
8	.54	.26	.38	.14	.66	.20	.20	−.04	.54	.26	.38	.12
9	.76	−.04	.29	.30	.86	−.06	−.02	.10	.80	.01	.22	.25
10	.28	.66	−.19	.14	.23	.70	−.12	.11	.15	.70	−.06	.24
11	.27	.61	−.04	.29	.31	.62	.01	.23	.17	.60	.08	.36
12	.13	.72	.09	.03	.16	.69	.19	−.01	.02	.69	.23	.11
13	.24	.63	.31	.02	.35	.57	.32	−.08	.18	.59	.41	.06
14	.23	.19	−.02	.48	.32	.19	−.03	.42	.22	.16	.04	.50
15	.11	.14	.08	.50	.25	.11	.10	.45	.12	.07	.14	.50
16	.05	.22	.34	.45	.29	.13	.37	.37	.08	.10	.41	.43
17	.15	.24	−.03	.62	.28	.24	.02	.57	.14	.18	.06	.64
18	.01	.39	.20	.52	.22	.32	.30	.47	.00	.26	.32	.54
19	.12	.22	.18	.39	.28	.18	.19	.32	.13	.15	.24	.39
20	.31	.18	.46	.29	.52	.09	.35	.14	.35	.11	.47	.25
21	.17	.46	.33	.24	.35	.38	.35	.14	.15	.38	.42	.26
22	.31	.12	.40	.40	.53	.04	.30	.26	.36	.04	.41	.36
23	.31	.29	.54	.25	.55	.19	.44	.09	.35	.21	.57	.22
24	.39	.46	.14	.31	.49	.43	.10	.20	.34	.44	.22	.34
V_p	3.43	2.92	2.68	2.36	5.59	2.42	1.96	1.42	3.50	2.44	3.08	2.36

A word about the naming of the third factor may be in order. The first four tests used to identify this factor have previously been referred to as "spatial relations" tests, involving the deduction of relations among geometric objects. All the other tests with large weights involve logical and arithmetical relations. Hence, the factor is named from the common attribute, "deduction of relations," regardless of the specific content of the tests.

The varimax solution seems to be the "best" parsimonious analytical solution in the sense that it correlates best with the intuitive concept of that term as exemplified by the graphical solution. This can be demonstrated by a numerical index of relationship among pairs of solutions. Since each of these solutions has as its goal some ideal simple structure for a given set of variables in a fixed common-factor space, it would seem quite appropriate to make direct comparisons of corresponding factor loadings.

311

The common statistical measure (used in **12.5**) that would seem to be applicable is the root mean square. For a comparison between the varimax (V) solution and the subjective (S) solution this index may be written in the simple form:

$$(14.30) \qquad (V - S)_{rms} = \sqrt{\frac{\sum (b_V - b_S)^2}{mn}}.$$

where the sum is over all mn corresponding factor loadings b_{jp} in the V-solution and b_{jp} in the S-solution. The root mean square values computed from Table 14.7 are as follows:

$$(14.31) \qquad \begin{aligned} (V - S)_{rms} &= .062, \\ (V - Q)_{rms} &= .116, \\ (Q - S)_{rms} &= .127. \end{aligned}$$

Although the scale is arbitrary, perfect agreement would be indicated by a value of zero and the relative agreement between pairs of solutions may be judged by their relative magnitudes. The varimax solution agrees almost perfectly with the subjective results, while the quartimax solution is least like the subjective; and the difference between the varimax and quartimax is almost as great as between the quartimax and the subjective.

In addition to the fact that the varimax solution tends to definitize mathematically the intuitive notion of simple structure, Kaiser [293] points out another property of this type of solution that may be of greater significance. While the weighting system introduced in the varimax method leads to results that appear more like simple structure, it may be subject to the same criticism as the intuitive-graphical methods because different sets of weights might be selected for different problems. The rationale for the varimax criterion (14.25) must be more fundamental if it is truly to provide a mathematical definition for the rotation problem. Such a basis is developed by Kaiser [293, p. 195] when he proves for a special case that the "*varimax solution is invariant under changes in the composition of the test battery.*"*

The principle of factorial invariance is stated by Thurstone [477, p. 361] as "a fundamental requirement of a successful factorial method, that *the factorial description of a test must remain invariant when the test is moved from one battery to another which involves the same common factors.*" The varimax method tends to have this invariance property; so that it permits the drawing of inferences about the factors in an (indefinite) domain of psychological content from a varimax solution based on a sample of n tests. This does not ascribe greater "psychological meaning" to the varimax factors than to factors obtained on some other basis, but it does mean that

---

* This is done by showing that the angle of rotation which maximizes (14.25) is not dependent on the number of variables in the limiting case where all variables fall into two collinear clusters. The generalization to m factors suggests virtually insuperable mathematical difficulties according to Kaiser.

varimax factors obtained in a sample will have a greater likelihood of portraying the universe varimax factors. While the general impression may be that simple structure is the "ultimate" objective of the rotational problem, Kaiser [293, p. 195] suggests that "the ultimate criterion is factorial invariance." Because the varimax solution was devised with a view to satisfying the simple structure criteria and subsequently found to show this kind of invariance, Kaiser also suggests that "Thurstone's intuition was basically on the trail of factorial invariance." Thus, the "invariance criterion" is proposed as an alternative or possible improvement to "simple structure."

An example of the tendency for the varimax criterion to lead to factorially invariant solutions is provided by Kaiser [293, pp. 196–8]. Starting with the initial centroid solution for the twenty-four psychological tests, he rotated the first five tests, then six, and so on, adding one test at a time until all twenty-four were rotated. It is in this sense that he considers the effect on the factor loadings of changes in the composition of the test battery. For the particular example, the first and third factors are essentially invariant from the outset while the second and fourth factors fluctuate some before becoming stable.

15

Analytical Methods for the Multiple-Factor Solution: Oblique Case

15.1. *Introduction*

In the last chapter the rationale for analytical solutions was presented, along with some of the historical developments. Two practical methods—albeit requiring high-speed computers—were given for the determination of multiple-factor solutions approximating simple structure under the condition that the factors be uncorrelated. The restriction of orthogonality is removed in the present chapter.

While the mathematics and the computations become more involved, there is much greater flexibility in an oblique solution. Of course, an orthogonal (or near-orthogonal) solution may result out of the more general oblique conditions if, in fact, the "best" solution should tend toward orthogonality. The conditions set forth for an oblique solution do not preclude zero correlations among the factors.

The theory and procedures which lead to oblique simple-structure solutions stem from the same objective criteria underlying the orthogonal solutions of chapter 14. Upon relaxing the restriction of orthogonality several of the criteria of chapter 14 can be adapted to produce oblique solutions. In **15.2** one form of the quartimax criterion is generalized to produce the oblimax method, involving the maximization of fourth powers of oblique structure elements. The original analytical procedure due to Carroll—the quartimin method—is developed in **15.3**. Further improvements and generalizations of that method are presented in **15.4** under the oblimin methods. In all these oblique methods a rather involved procedure is followed, wherein the desired simple structure principles for the primary factor solution are introduced in an indirect manner. Finally, in **15.5**, a direct procedure is presented for getting oblimin-like solutions. In each of these sections the theory leading to the particular oblique solution is presented and illustrated with numerical examples.

The basic concepts that arise in the analytical methods of rotation to multiple-factor solutions, both orthogonal and oblique, are listed in Table 15.1 along with the symbols employed for them in this text. This summary of concepts and notation

Table 15.1

Concepts and Notation

Concept	Notation		
	Orthogonal Case		Oblique Case
Original factors	F_p $(p = 1, 2, \cdots, m)$		F_p (orthogonal)
Original factor loadings	$\mathbf{A} = (a_{jp})$ $(j = 1, 2, \cdots, n)$		$\mathbf{A} = (a_{jp})$
Transformation matrix	$\mathbf{T} = (t_{qp})$ $(p, q = 1, 2, \cdots, m)$		$\Lambda = (\lambda_{qp})$
Final solution	$\mathbf{B} = \mathbf{AT} = (b_{jp})$		$\mathbf{V} = \mathbf{A\Lambda} = (v_{jp})$, reference structure matrix
			$\mathbf{P} = (b_{jp})$, primary pattern matrix
Final factors	M_p		T_p if primary factors
			Λ_p if reference axes
Criterion for solution:			
Quartimax	Equivalent expressions:		
	(14.7)	Q = max.	
	(14.10)	M = max.	
	(14.11)	N = min.	
	(14.12)	K = max.	
Varimax	(14.25)	V = max.	
Oblimax			(15.2) K = max.
Quartimin			(15.15) N = min.
Covarimin			(15.32) C = min.
(Oblique Varimax)			
Oblimin			(15.39) B = min.
Binormamin			(15.40) D = min.
Direct oblimin			(15.45) F = min.

should assist in distinguishing the methods in this chapter from those of the preceding chapter, and can serve as a ready reference for the basic notation employed in this chapter. Specific notation required for the development of the ensuing methods will be introduced as needed.

15.2. *Oblimax Method*

It will be recalled that four separate criteria in chapter 14 were found to be equivalent when the rotated solution is restricted to orthogonal factors. When oblique factors are permitted, the four criteria are no longer equivalent; and, as a matter of fact, each method is not immediately generalizable to the oblique case. The criterion (14.12) can be applied to the oblique case. While the criterion K = maximum is equivalent to Q = maximum in the orthogonal case (since the denominator of K is an invariant under orthogonal transformation), the full expression for K must be used in the oblique case.

The problem is to find a transformation matrix Λ which will carry an initial factor matrix $\mathbf{A}$ into a final solution $\mathbf{V}$, as in (13.30):

(15.1) $$\mathbf{V} = \mathbf{A\Lambda},$$

315

in which the elements v_{jp} of the resulting factor structure matrix $\mathbf{V}$ will satisfy the criterion $K = $ maximum, where

(15.2)
$$K = \sum_{j=1}^{n} \sum_{p=1}^{m} v_{jp}^{4} \bigg/ \left(\sum_{j=1}^{n} \sum_{p=1}^{m} v_{jp}^{2} \right)^{2}.$$

This restatement of (14.3) and (14.12) in different notation should make perfectly clear the distinction between the orthogonal and the oblique case. Also, it should be noted that in the latter case the term "loading" is used for the structure value, i.e., the correlation of the variable with the reference axis:

(15.3)
$$v_{jp} = r_{z_j \Lambda_p}.$$

An oblique solution obtained under the condition that (15.2) be a maximum will be called an "oblimax" solution.*

The development of the theory of the oblimax method will be made following the work of Pinzka and Saunders [392]. The orthogonal projections v_{jp} on an oblique reference axis Λ_p are determined in such a manner as to make

(15.4)
$$K_p = \sum_{j=1}^{n} v_{jp}^{4} \bigg/ \left(\sum_{j=1}^{n} v_{jp}^{2} \right)^{2} \qquad (p = 1, 2, \cdots, m)$$

a relative maximum under rotation in a plane. As the structure values v_{jp} are altered in successive iterations, the function (15.2) eventually attains a maximum value. Thus, while (15.4) represents the impact of maximizing the v's on a single reference axis, the criterion (15.2) represents the ultimate effect such successive maximizations have on the final solution $\mathbf{V}$. The oblimax criterion can be expressed in terms of the factor loadings of the initial solution and the direction cosines in the matrix of transformation, and thereby the latter values can be determined.

To simplify the development, the coordinates of any point in the plane of the first two factors of the original rectangular reference system are designated (a, b) instead of (a_{j1}, a_{j2}). Then the elements v_{jp} resulting from the transformation (15.1) can be expressed as follows:

(15.5)
$$v_{jp} = a\lambda_{1p} + b\lambda_{2p} \qquad (p = 1, 2, \cdots, m),$$

according to (13.20). Since the direction cosines must satisfy the conditions

(15.6)
$$\sum_{k=1}^{m} \lambda_{kp}^{2} = 1, \qquad (p = 1, 2, \cdots, m),$$

it suffices to consider the ratio of the two in (15.5) as a single unknown, $x = \lambda_{2p}/\lambda_{1p}$, and rewrite the expression in the form:†

(15.7)
$$v_{jp} = a + bx.$$

---

* This term was suggested by Saunders.

† It is tacitly assumed that $\lambda_{1p} \neq 0$, otherwise the ratio would not be defined. Of course, if $\lambda_{1p} = 0$ then $\lambda_{2p} = 1$ and the rotated axis is coincident with the second axis of the original reference frame.

Substituting (15.7) into (15.4), and without designating the factor p, the criterion to be maximized becomes:

(15.8)
$$K = \frac{\sum (a + bx)^4}{[\sum (a + bx)^2]^2},$$

where all summations are understood to extend over the n values of a and b (viz., a_{j1} and a_{j2} for $j = 1, 2, \cdots, n$). To simplify the work further, the functions of x in the numerator and denominator are designated by:

(15.9)
$$N = \sum (a + bx)^4,$$
$$D = \sum (a + bx)^2.$$

A necessary condition for the maximization of $K = N/D^2$ is the vanishing of its derivative with respect to x, namely,

(15.10)
$$K' = \frac{D^2 N' - N(2DD')}{D^4} = 0,$$

or, more simply,

(15.11)
$$f(x) = DN' - 2ND' = 0,$$

where $f(x)$ is used to designate the resulting function of x. Upon substituting the values (15.9) and their derivatives into (15.11), the resulting equation would in general be of the fifth order, but fortuitously the coefficient of x^5 is zero. Representing the quartic equation by

(15.12)
$$\alpha_4 x^4 + \alpha_3 x^3 + \alpha_2 x^2 + \alpha_1 x + \alpha_0 = 0,$$

its coefficients are given by

(15.13)
$$\alpha_4 = \sum ab \sum b^4 - \sum b^2 \sum ab^3,$$
$$\alpha_3 = \sum a^2 \sum b^4 + 2 \sum ab \sum ab^3 - 3 \sum b^2 \sum a^2 b^2,$$
$$\alpha_2 = 3 \sum a^2 \sum ab^3 \qquad\qquad - 3 \sum b^2 \sum a^3 b,$$
$$\alpha_1 = 3 \sum a^2 \sum a^2 b^2 - 2 \sum ab \sum a^3 b - \sum b^2 \sum a^4,$$
$$\alpha_0 = \sum a^2 \sum a^3 b - \sum ab \sum a^4.$$

While these coefficients appear rather imposing at first glance, a certain symmetry of form will be detected upon more careful scrutiny.

Any one of the four roots of (15.12), if real, will produce either a maximum or a minimum of K. When all four roots $x = \lambda_{2p}/\lambda_{1p}$ are real and distinct, they correspond to two relative maxima and two relative minima of K. From calculus it is known that those roots of (15.12) for which the second derivative K'' is negative make K a maximum. Differentiating $K' = f/D^3$ produces

(15.14)
$$K'' = \frac{D^3 f' - f(3D^2 D')}{D^6} = \frac{f'}{D^3}$$

where the last equality follows from $f = 0$ as stated in (15.11). Since D is a sum of squares and is always positive, the algebraic sign of K'' is the same as that of f'.

Then the sufficient condition for a maximum involves the substitution of a root of (15.12) into the derivative of the same function to note if the result is negative. Actually the derivative of (15.12) need not be determined explicitly because its behavior in the vicinity of the root can be determined from the polynomial itself. If the polynomial is increasing in the neighborhood of the root then K must be at a minimum; if decreasing, then K must be at a maximum. The sign of α_4 determines the sign of the entire polynomial as x increases without limit. Therefore, for the largest root K will be a maximum if α_4 is negative, and a minimum if α_4 is positive. Once it is known whether the largest root produces a maximum or a minimum the same information is known for each of the other roots since the roots alternate between maxima and minima.

The two roots of (15.12) that correspond to maxima yield the direction cosines of the new reference axes, and the analytical rotation is carried out accordingly. This process is repeated for all pairs of factors $p = 1, 2, \cdots, m - 1$ and $q = p + 1, p + 2, \cdots, m$, until K stabilizes at its maximum value (to a specified number of decimal places).

The oblimax method, just as all the other analytical procedures, requires a vast amount of computing and hence becomes impractical without high-speed computing facilities. Pinzka and Saunders [392, pp. 11–30] present a flow chart of the computations and outline a computer program for a hypothetical electronic computer. An oblimax program was written by Kern W. Dickman for the Illiac. Such a solution was obtained on this computer for the twenty-four psychological variables, and is exhibited in Table 15.2. The oblimax reference structure matrix V and its associated primary-factor pattern matrix P are recorded in this table from the direct output of the computer (except for the reflection of two factors and rounding to three decimal places for convenience of printing). The criterion (15.2) was $K = .02364$ for the initial centroid loadings and increased to a maximum $K = .04168$ for the structure values of the oblimax matrix V. The correlations among the reference factors and among the primary factors also are outputs of the computer.

The principal purpose of presenting Table 15.2 is to show the feasibility of an oblimax solution on a large electronic computer. It is also of interest to note that this objective solution is very similar to one that had been obtained by intuitive-graphical methods.

15.3. *Quartimin Method*

The next analytical procedure for an oblique solution is the one originally introduced by Carroll [69]. The criterion is $N = $ minimum, just as in (14.11) but without the constraint that the factors be orthogonal in the rotated solution. Carroll now suggests the name "quartimin" for this method since it involves the minimization of terms of the fourth degree, viz., the sum of cross-products of squared factor "loadings".*

---

* Of course, for an oblique solution the use of the term "loading" must be made explicit (see **13.5**), and here it stands for the structure value as given by (15.3).

Table 15.2

Oblimax Solution for Twenty-Four Psychological Tests

(Initial solution: Centroid)

Test	Reference Structure: V				Primary Pattern: P			
					Verbal	Speed	Deduction	Memory
	Λ_1	Λ_2	Λ_3	Λ_4	T_1	T_2	T_3	T_4
1	−.095	.014	.537	−.034	−.131	.018	.832	−.050
2	−.040	−.042	.353	−.023	−.056	−.056	.547	−.034
3	−.015	−.110	.454	−.060	−.021	−.146	.704	−.087
4	.020	−.048	.440	−.087	.027	−.063	.682	−.127
5	.607	.077	−.025	−.060	.839	.103	−.038	−.087
6	.601	−.052	−.015	.036	.831	−.068	−.023	.052
7	.689	.037	−.031	−.109	.952	.049	−.048	−.159
8	.365	.110	.170	−.086	.505	.146	.263	−.125
9	.655	−.146	−.031	.085	.905	−.193	−.048	.124
10	.050	.625	−.243	.085	.069	.828	−.376	.124
11	.023	.481	−.127	.187	.032	.636	−.196	.271
12	−.132	.596	.090	−.079	−.182	.789	.139	−.115
13	−.011	.466	.250	−.165	−.016	.618	.387	−.239
14	.099	.032	−.144	.405	.137	.043	−.223	.589
15	−.013	−.065	−.016	.417	−.018	−.086	−.024	.607
16	−.109	−.077	.261	.298	−.150	−.101	.404	.434
17	−.008	.029	−.136	.541	−0.11	.039	−.211	.786
18	−.201	.090	.145	.397	−.277	.120	.224	.577
19	−.020	.015	.087	.278	−.028	.020	.135	.404
20	.151	−.065	.298	.076	.208	−.087	.462	.110
21	−.046	.223	.250	.066	−.064	.296	.387	.095
22	.168	−.134	.224	.198	.232	−.177	.347	.287
23	.119	.022	.381	.003	.165	.029	.590	.004
24	.165	.289	−.006	.146	.228	.382	−.009	.212

Factor	Correlations Among Factors							
1	1.000	−.094	−.413	−.207	1.000	.494	.661	.579
2		1.000	−.253	−.315		1.000	.590	.598
3			1.000	−.342			1.000	.663
4				1.000				1.000

A transformation of the form (15.1) will produce a quartimin solution if the elements v_{jp} of the resulting factor structure matrix $\mathbf{V}$ are made to satisfy the criterion $N = $ minimum, where

$$(15.15) \qquad N = \sum_{p<q=1}^{m} \sum_{j=1}^{n} v_{jp}^2 v_{jq}^2.$$

This criterion can be expressed in terms of the initial factor loadings and the direction cosines in the matrix of transformation. For any row j of $\mathbf{A}$ and any column p of Λ

319

the resulting element of $\mathbf{V}$, according to (15.1), is

$$(15.16) \qquad v_{jp} = \sum_{k=1}^{m} a_{jk}\lambda_{kp},$$

so that (15.15) can be expressed in the form:

$$(15.17) \qquad N = \sum_{p<q=1}^{m}\sum_{j=1}^{n}\left(\sum_{k=1}^{m} a_{jk}\lambda_{kp}\right)^{2}\left(\sum_{k=1}^{m} a_{jk}\lambda_{kq}\right)^{2}.$$

It would appear that by conventional calculus methods, the elements of the trans-formation matrix could be determined such that the expression (15.17) is a minimum. As Carroll [69, p. 26] points out, however, the resulting equations would be so complex as not to be readily soluble. Instead, Carroll reaches a solution by iterative methods—systematically varying values of λ_{qp} until the value of N attains a minimum under the m conditions (15.6).*

The iterative solution is accomplished by a systematic process permitting the values in one column of Λ to vary while the remaining columns are fixed. If the column vector for which the values are going to be changed is designated

$$\Lambda_{x} = \{\lambda_{1x}, \lambda_{2x}, \cdots, \lambda_{mx}\},$$

then it is appropriate to designate by N_{x} the value of the criterion N when it changes as a function of Λ_{x}, namely:

$$(15.18) \qquad N_{x} = \sum_{j=1}^{n}\left[v_{jx}^{2}\sum_{p=1}^{m} v_{jp}^{2}\right], \qquad\qquad (p \neq x).$$

Now, for any variable j the sum of squares of structure values which is independent of x may be designated by:

$$(15.19) \qquad w_{j} = \sum_{p=1}^{m} v_{jp}^{2}, \qquad\qquad (p \neq x),$$

so that the criterion (15.18) becomes:

$$(15.20) \qquad N_{x} = \sum_{j=1}^{n} w_{j}v_{jx}^{2}.$$

It will simplify the following development to employ matrix algebra. The column vector $\mathbf{V}_{x}$ of the structure matrix $\mathbf{V}$ which results from a change in Λ_{x} is, according to (15.1),

$$(15.21) \qquad \mathbf{V}_{x} = \mathbf{A}\Lambda_{x}.$$

Hence, corresponding to the sum of squared structure values is

$$(15.22) \qquad \mathbf{V}_{x}'\mathbf{V}_{x} = \Lambda_{x}'\mathbf{A}'\mathbf{A}\Lambda_{x}$$

---

* These conditions merely state that each reference vector is of unit length, while the additional restriction that $\Lambda'\Lambda = \mathbf{I}$ would impose orthogonality on the solution; but in that case the simpler, equivalent solution of **14.3** would be employed.

and the entire expression (15.20) becomes:

(15.23)
$$N_x = \Lambda'_x A' W A \Lambda_x$$

where W is a diagonal matrix of the n scalars w_j. Define a new matrix

(15.24)
$$C = A' W A,$$

so that (15.23) may be written

(15.25)
$$N_x = \Lambda'_x C \Lambda_x.$$

The problem, then, is to minimize (15.25) under the condition

(15.26)
$$\Lambda'_x \Lambda_x = 1$$

corresponding to (15.6) for the reference vector x. This can be accomplished by the method of Lagrange's multipliers, yielding the characteristic equation of C, namely:

(15.27)
$$\begin{vmatrix} (c_{11} - N_x) & c_{12} & \cdots & c_{1m} \\ c_{21} & (c_{22} - N_x) & \cdots & c_{2m} \\ \cdot & \cdot & \cdots & \cdot \\ c_{m1} & c_{m2} & \cdots & (c_{mn} - N_x) \end{vmatrix} = 0.$$

Any latent root of this m^{th} order linear equation will make the determinant vanish; and, in order to minimize N_x, the smallest latent root is selected. Then the elements of the latent vector associated with this root are the desired solutions λ_{px}. When the smallest N_x is determined from equation (15.27), it is substituted into the following set of homogeneous linear equations (from which the condition (15.27) was derived):

(15.28)
$$\begin{aligned} (c_{11} - N_x)\lambda_{1x} + \quad c_{12}\lambda_{2x} + \quad \cdots \quad + \quad c_{1m}\lambda_{mx} &= 0, \\ c_{21}\lambda_{1x} + (c_{22} - N_x)\lambda_{2x} + \quad \cdots \quad + \quad c_{2m}\lambda_{mx} &= 0, \\ \cdot \quad\quad\quad\quad\quad\quad\quad\quad\quad\quad\quad &, \\ c_{m1}\lambda_{1x} + \quad c_{m2}\lambda_{2x} + \quad \cdots \quad + (c_{mm} - N_x)\lambda_{mx} &= 0. \end{aligned}$$

The resulting solutions λ_{px} are all proportional to one arbitrary solution, and by applying the condition (15.26) the direction cosines for the new axis are obtained which will make the criterion N_x a minimum.

The theory of the quartimin method, as outlined above, clearly implies a tremendous amount of computing. The work involved in preparation for the iterations, determining C, and the large number of iterations that are usually required, indicate that only with the capability of a high-speed electronic computer is a quartimin rotation feasible. The only practical exception is the case of only two common factors.

More will be said about computer programs for the quartimin method in 15.4. To illustrate the preceding theory, however, a simple numerical example will be employed; and to make comparisons possible, the example of the eight physical variables again is used. The centroid solution for this example is taken as the initial solution **A** and appears in Table 15.3.

Table 15.3

Quartimin Solution for Eight Physical Variables

(Initial solution: Centroid)

Variable j	Initial Solution: **A**		Elements of **W** for First Two Iterations		Structure: **V**	
	a_{j1}	a_{j2}	$x = 1$ $w_j = a_{j2}^2$	$x = 2$ $w_j = a_{j1}^2$	v_{j1}	v_{j2}
1	.830	−.396	.1568	.6889	.783	.046
2	.818	−.469	.2200	.6691	.838	−.024
3	.777	−.470	.2209	.6037	.817	−.044
4	.798	−.401	.1608	.6368	.770	.027
5	.786	.500	.2500	.6178	.007	.814
6	.672	.458	.2098	.4516	−.020	.723
7	.594	.444	.1971	.3528	−.050	.673
8	.647	.333	.1109	.4186	.072	.601

The object of the iteration process is successively to alter the values of the transformation matrix

(15.29)
$$\Lambda = \begin{bmatrix} \lambda_{11} & \lambda_{12} \\ \lambda_{21} & \lambda_{22} \end{bmatrix}$$

in such a manner as to reduce the value of N, as given by (15.17), to a minimum. The process is begun by arbitrarily selecting the first column to be the vector Λ_x for which the values λ_{11}, λ_{21} are going to be changed. Having designated $x = 1$, the values (15.19) are determined next. These w_j values are simply the respective a_{j2}^2 for the first iteration, and are also given in Table 15.3. The diagonal matrix **W** is made up of these elements. Then the matrix multiplications in (15.24) are carried out to produce:

$$C = \begin{bmatrix} .8561 & -.0294 \\ -.0294 & .3053 \end{bmatrix}.$$

The minimization process leads to the characteristic equation

$$\begin{vmatrix} (.8561 - N_x) & -.0294 \\ -.0294 & (.3053 - N_x) \end{vmatrix} = 0,$$

or

$$N_x^2 - 1.1614N_x + .2605 = 0,$$

322

from which the smallest root is found to be $N_x = .3038$. For this value of N_x, equations (15.28) become

$$.5523\lambda_{11} - .0294\lambda_{21} = 0,$$

$$-.0294\lambda_{11} + .0015\lambda_{21} = 0.$$

From the first of these equations,

$$\lambda_{21} = \frac{.5523}{.0294}\lambda_{11}$$

and, upon applying the condition (15.6), viz.,

$$\frac{.305035}{.000864}\lambda_{11}^2 + \lambda_{11}^2 = 1$$

there results $\lambda_{11}^2 = .002824$, and hence $\lambda_{21}^2 = .997176$. The direction cosines of the new position of the first reference axis are $\lambda_{11} = .0531$ and $\lambda_{21} = .9986$, while the second axis remains unchanged. The impact of this first transformation is to reduce the value of N from .8561 for the initial solution to .3038.

The second iteration is made by taking the second column of (15.29) to be the vector Λ_x and using the new values of the first column for the remainder of the transformation matrix. In this case, a new matrix $\mathbf{C}$ is set up, for which the characteristic equation is

$$\begin{vmatrix} (.8245 - N_x) & .0605 \\ .0605 & (.3037 - N_x) \end{vmatrix} = 0.$$

The least root of this equation is $N_x = .2968$, a slight drop from the previous value of .3038. Proceeding as before in applying the condition (15.6), the new direction cosines for the second reference axis are found to be $\lambda_{12} = -.1139$ and $\lambda_{22} = .9935$.

After seven iterations the value of N is found to be stable at $N = .0065$. These iterations changed the values of the elements in the transformation matrix until the following were reached:

$$\begin{pmatrix} .4756 & -.5432 \\ .8797 & .8396 \end{pmatrix}.$$

The signs of the second column are reflected and the two columns are interchanged in order to present the final results in the same order as previously. The transformation matrix may then be written:

(15.30)
$$\Lambda = \begin{pmatrix} .5432 & .4756 \\ -.8396 & .8797 \end{pmatrix}.$$

Postmultiplying the initial solution $\mathbf{A}$ by this matrix produces the factor structure of the quartimin solution in Table 15.3.

The quartimin structure **V** is very similar to both the intuitive-graphical solution in Table 13.3 and to the oblimax solution (which was given in the first edition of this text), the difference between corresponding elements being no greater than .003 in either case. In spite of the close agreements the differences among these solutions stem from fundamental differences in the basis underlying each one. It is of interest to note that the oblimax criterion for the quartimin solution of Table 15.3 is $K = .12890$. Of course this cannot be quite as large as the maximum value, $K = .12891$, for the oblimax solution (although the difference is only in the fifth decimal place). Theoretically the present solution is not as good as the one obtained according to the oblimax criterion. On the other hand, the quartimin criterion for Table 15.3 is $N = .0065$ while a similar computation for the oblimax solution yields $N = .0068$. In the same sense, the present solution is better than the oblimax solution according to the quartimin criterion. While the foregoing differences were rather academic, real pronounced differences can be expected in situations where the clusters are not so well-defined as in the simple example of eight physical variables.

15.4. *Oblimin Methods*

In the preceding section an approximation to a simple-structure solution was obtained by minimizing the expression (15.15) involving terms of the fourth degree. Carroll [71] has generalized his original criterion to a whole class of methods for oblique transformations to simple structure which involve minimization of certain expressions. This class of methods, involving oblique factors and a minimizing criterion, is designated by the term "oblimin." Carroll arrived at the general class of oblimin solutions from a consideration of his quartimin criterion and Kaiser's oblique version of the varimax criterion [291].

The criterion for the latter solution, which Kaiser [293] considers the most obvious way of relaxing the restriction of orthogonality in his original varimax method, is the minimization of the function :*

$$(15.31) \qquad C^* = \sum_{p<q=1}^{m} \left(n \sum_{j=1}^{n} v_{jp}^2 v_{jq}^2 - \sum_{j=1}^{n} v_{jp}^2 \sum_{j=1}^{n} v_{jq}^2 \right),$$

i.e., minimization of the covariances of squared elements of the factor structure **V**. In the orthogonal case the criterion (14.24) is equivalent to (15.31). Just as (14.24) is replaced by (14.25), so Kaiser [293, p. 198] suggests replacing (15.31) by

$$(15.32) \qquad C = \sum_{p<q=1}^{m} \left[n \sum_{j=1}^{n} (v_{jp}^2/h_j^2)(v_{jq}^2/h_j^2) - \sum_{j=1}^{n} v_{jp}^2/h_j^2 \sum_{j=1}^{n} v_{jq}^2/h_j^2 \right],$$

involving "normalized loadings." This implies the normalization by rows of the initial factor matrix, carrying through the transformation in terms of the extended vectors, and then reducing the matrix **V** thus obtained to the original-length vectors by multiplying the elements in rows of **V** by the square root of the respective communalities.

* Also called the "covarimin" criterion by Carroll [70].

Both Kaiser and Carroll have found from empirical investigations that neither the quartimin nor the covarimin methods work very well. The trouble is that the latter procedure is almost invariably biased toward factor axes which are too orthogonal, while the former procedure is just as biased in the opposite direction of factor axes which are too highly correlated. Since covarimin tends to be "too orthogonal" and quartimin "too oblique," Carroll [70] proposed the following "biquartimin" criterion as a compromise:

$$(15.33) \qquad B^* = N + C^*/n = \text{minimum},$$

where N is defined in (15.15) and C^* in (15.31). In the last term, the full covarimin expression including division by n is retained, whereas it had been dropped as immaterial to the minimization of (15.31). The rationale for (15.33) is the simultaneous minimization of two quantities, each of which has a valid justification.

Subsequently, Carroll [71] generalized this simple sum of the two separate criteria to permit varying weights of the "quartimin" and "covarimin" components. This is accomplished by introducing variable parameters α and β as follows

$$(15.34) \qquad B^* = \alpha N + \beta C^*/n = \text{minimum}.$$

Then, substituting the criteria N and C^* from (15.15) and (15.31), the new criterion becomes

$$(15.35) \qquad B^* = \sum_{p<q=1}^{m} \left\{ \alpha \sum_{j=1}^{n} v_{jp}^2 v_{jq}^2 + \beta \left[n \sum_{j=1}^{n} v_{jp}^2 v_{jq}^2 - \sum_{j=1}^{n} v_{jp}^2 \sum v_{jq}^2 \right] \right/ n \right\}.$$

Multiplying the entire expression (15.35) by n (which has no effect on the minimum of B^*), and combining terms, produces the following:

$$(15.36) \qquad B^* = \sum_{p<q=1}^{m} \left[(\alpha + \beta) \left(n \sum_{j=1}^{n} v_{jp}^2 v_{jq}^2 \right) - \beta \sum_{j=1}^{n} v_{jp}^2 \sum_{j=1}^{n} v_{jq}^2 \right].$$

Dividing this expression by the sum of the weights and setting

$$(15.37) \qquad \gamma = \beta/(\alpha + \beta),$$

the general oblimin criterion is given by:

$$(15.38) \qquad B^* = \sum_{p<q=1}^{m} \left(n \sum_{j=1}^{n} v_{jp}^2 v_{jq}^2 - \gamma \sum_{j=1}^{n} v_{jp}^2 \sum_{j=1}^{n} v_{jq}^2 \right).$$

When the analysis is carried through for "normalized loadings," the final oblimin criterion may be expressed by:

$$(15.39) \qquad B = \sum_{p<q=1}^{m} \left[n \sum_{j=1}^{n} (v_{jp}^2/h_j^2)(v_{jq}^2/h_j^2) - \gamma \sum_{j=1}^{n} v_{jp}^2/h_j^2 \sum_{j=1}^{n} v_{jq}^2/h_j^2 \right] = \text{min}.$$

It will be noted that the covarimin criterion (15.31) is a special instance of (15.38) corresponding to the value $\gamma = 1$ of the arbitrary parameter.* Similarly, the quartimin

* Or in terms of normalized elements, (15.32) is a special instance of (15.39).

criterion (15.15) is another special instance of (15.38), namely, when $\gamma = 0$. Also when $\alpha = \beta = 1$, or $\gamma = .5$ from (15.37), the biquartimin criterion results. These special instances of the general oblimin criterion are summarized as follows:

$$\text{Quartimin:} \quad \gamma = 0; \qquad \text{most oblique.}$$

$$\text{Biquartimin:} \quad \gamma = .5; \qquad \text{less oblique.}$$

$$\text{Covarimin:} \quad \gamma = 1; \qquad \text{least oblique.}$$

Of course, any other value between zero and unity may be selected for γ with a corresponding variation in the criterion (15.39) and the oblimin solution resulting therefrom. Based upon empirical evidence, Carroll [71, p. 3] suggests "that results will be most generally satisfactory when γ is set equal to $\frac{1}{2}$."

Another analytical procedure involving oblique factors and a minimizing criterion is due to Kaiser and Dickman [303], and called "binormamin" by Dickman [97, p. 81]. Although it is not a special case of the class of oblimin solutions (15.39), it has many similarities in its formal expression, namely:*

$$(15.40) \quad D = \sum_{p<q=1}^{m} \left[\sum_{j=1}^{n} (v_{jp}^2/h_j^2)(v_{jq}^2/h_j^2) \middle/ \left(\sum_{j=1}^{n} v_{jp}^2/h_j^2 \right)\left(\sum_{j=1}^{n} v_{jq}^2/h_j^2 \right) \right] = \min.$$

This criterion resulted from Kaiser's attempt to resolve the undetermined parameter γ in the oblimin class of solutions. Essentially the criterion (15.40) provides a solution which corrects for the "too oblique" bias of the quartimin criterion and the "too orthogonal" bias of the covarimin criterion without arbitrarily taking $\gamma = \frac{1}{2}$ of the biquartimin solution. In comparing their criterion with the biquartimin, Kaiser and Dickman [303, pp. 6–7] argue that apparently the advantage of one or the other depends on the nature of the data under consideration: if the data are particularly simple, or extremely complex, criterion (15.40) is better; but if the data are moderately complex then criterion (15.39) is superior.

Actually, there has not been sufficient experience with these new analytical methods to judge whether one or another method is so effective as to justify the exclusion of all others. Kaiser and Dickman summarize their exploration by indicating examples of the two extremes: their worst result being for Thurstone's box problem [477, p. 136] and their best for the twenty-four psychological tests. In the first case, they tend to get slightly negative loadings for the well-established zeros, and somewhat higher intercorrelations among the primary factors than the intercorrelations of the underlying three dimensions of the boxes. On the other hand, the correspondence between their analytical solution for the twenty-four psychological tests and the subjective-graphical solution is almost uncanny. Kaiser and Dickman conclude that the degree of simplicity of structure inherent in the data accounts for these results. An example of a binormamin solution is given later, but a detailed mathematical development involving the criterion (15.40) is not included.

---

* In order to avoid confusion with the oblimax criterion, the symbol "D" is employed here instead of the symbol "K" used by Kaiser and Dickman.

Returning to the class of oblimin solutions given by the criterion (15.39), it is obvious that the task of computing such a factor solution is extremely difficult. Since there is little likelihood that the general oblimin methods will be employed with desk calculators, detailed steps for such calculations are not presented. An efficient computer program has been prepared by Carroll [71]—written in FORTRAN for the IBM 704 originally, but since adapted to the IBM 7094, IBM System 360, and other computers—and a general indication will be given of the form of these calculations.

Somewhat similar to the computing procedure described in **15.3**, Carroll found the most practicable procedure (even for large matrices) to be the successive modification of the transformation matrix Λ and the reference structure matrix V until it meets the condition (15.39). The process is begun by selecting one column of the matrix V, say V_x, and altering its values (with the elements in the remaining $(m - 1)$ columns unchanged) until a minimum value is obtained for the following expression:

$$(15.41) \qquad B_x = \sum_{\substack{q=1 \\ (q \neq x)}}^{m} \left[n \sum_{j=1}^{n} (v_{jx}^2/h_j^2)(v_{jq}^2/h_j^2) - \gamma \sum_{j=1}^{n} v_{jx}^2/h_j^2 \sum_{j=1}^{n} v_{jq}^2/h_j^2 \right].$$

This operation on a single column is designated a "minor cycle" of the iterations. A set of m minor cycles, one for each of the m columns of V, is called a "major cycle."

For each minor cycle, the core of the electronic computations involves the solution of a characteristic equation, yielding the algebraically smallest eigenvalue and corresponding eigenvector of a non-symmetric matrix [71, pp. 4–6]. From such an eigenvector is derived a column of the transformation matrix and the desired V_x of the structure matrix, while the eigenvalue is the required minimum value of (15.41). The iterative process is continued, taking successive values of x until a major cycle is accomplished. The computer program involves successive major cycles until a satisfactory degree of convergence is attained. This is measured by the amount of change in the total value of the criterion (15.39), consisting of the sum of the m values (15.41) obtained in each major cycle; or more precisely, by the amount of change in the individual values (15.41).

To illustrate the oblimin solutions the set of eight physical variables is again used for the first example. The minres solution of Table 9.3 was taken as the initial matrix **A**, and three different values of the parameter γ were employed to get the factor structure matrices of Table 15.4, on an IBM 7094 computer. It will be recalled that the quartimin solution for the same example was also computed by desk calculator methods in the last section (but employing a centroid initial solution), and the structure matrix appears in Table 15.3. Of course there are some differences in structure values (the largest being .034) since the two solutions are based on different initial matrices, but also because the first employed the criterion (15.15) while the second used the normalized form (15.39) with $\gamma = 0$. Of the three solutions in Table 15.4, the covarimin less clearly satisfies the simple structure principles than either of the others. On the other hand, it may be considered the simplest because the covarimin factors are uncorrelated in this example. While the well-defined zero weights in the quartimin structure may make it appear more desirable than the

Table 15.4

Three Oblimin Solutions for Eight Physical Variables

(Initial solution: Minres, Table 9.3)

Variable j	Quartimin ($\gamma = 0$) Reference Structure		Biquartimin ($\gamma = .5$) Reference Structure		Covarimin ($\gamma = 1$) Reference Structure	
	v_{j1}	v_{j2}	v_{j1}	v_{j2}	v_{j1}	v_{j2}
1	.775	.051	.825	.154	.872	.278
2	.840	−.033	.884	.074	.921	.204
3	.814	−.046	.854	.056	.887	.181
4	.774	.024	.821	.126	.864	.248
5	−.003	.826	.105	.872	.233	.913
6	−.012	.706	.080	.744	.189	.778
7	−.064	.697	.024	.728	.129	.753
8	.086	.567	.165	.610	.258	.652
Criterion (15.39) Initial value Final value	11.621 .068		5.414 −2.848		−.793 −6.601	
Correlation between primary factors	.485		.275		.000	

biquartimin solution, the latter has the advantage of lower correlation between the primary factors. All things considered, the biquartimin solution appears to be the "best."

Another, more practical, application of the oblimin procedure was made to the example of twenty-four psychological tests. For a problem of this magnitude electronic computations become imperative. Starting with the centroid solution and an initial criterion value of $B = 9.33$, seven major cycles for a total of 610 iterations later (but only a few minutes) produced the biquartimin reference structure of Table 15.5 with a final minimum criterion of $B = -4.17$. This structure matrix V is in terms of the original lengths of the test vectors, although they were first normalized and after the rotations were accomplished they were shrunken again.

The output of the computer also includes: (1) the transformation matrix Λ that carries the initial matrix A into V; (2) the matrix $\Psi = \Lambda'\Lambda$ containing the correlations among the reference factors Λ_p; (3) the matrix $\Phi = T'T$ containing the correlations among the primary factors T_p; and (4) a matrix of numbers which can easily be transformed into factor measurements (see 16.7). From the first three of these matrices the primary factor pattern can be obtained to complete the oblique solution. The primary factor pattern P may be determined from the structure V by employing the relationship (13.43). What is needed, first, is the diagonal matrix D of correlations between corresponding Λ and T factors. This is defined in (13.31) and involves the transformation matrix T from the initial solution to the primary-factor structure.

328

Table 15.5

Biquartimin Solution for Twenty-Four Psychological Tests

(Initial solution : Centroid)

Test	Reference Structure : V				Primary Pattern: P			
	Λ_1	Λ_2	Λ_3	Λ_4	Verbal T_1	Speed T_2	Deduction T_3	Memory T_4
1	.014	.094	.598	.051	.015	.103	**.666**	.058
2	.028	.007	.392	.029	.031	.008	**.436**	.033
3	.067	−.052	.498	.000	.074	−.057	**.555**	.000
4	.106	.011	.490	−.022	.117	.012	**.545**	−.025
5	.675	.110	.075	−.008	**.748**	.120	.083	−.009
6	.670	−.016	.089	.084	**.742**	−.018	.099	.095
7	.755	.063	.068	−.061	**.836**	.069	.076	−.069
8	.449	.159	.256	−.019	**.497**	.174	.285	−.021
9	.722	−.111	.079	.130	**.800**	−.122	.087	.146
10	.080	.650	−.186	.132	.089	**.711**	−.208	.149
11	.074	.525	−.054	.245	.082	**.574**	−.060	.276
12	−.072	.641	.132	−.011	−.080	**.701**	.146	−.012
13	.074	.524	.307	−.082	.082	**.573**	.341	−.092
14	.135	.070	−.069	.437	.149	.077	−.076	**.492**
15	.029	−.019	.052	.452	.032	−.021	.058	**.508**
16	−.032	−.007	.330	.359	−.035	−.008	**.368**	**.404**
17	.034	.079	−.053	.579	.038	.086	−.059	**.652**
18	−.130	.161	.217	.460	−.144	.176	.242	**.518**
19	.035	.066	.151	.324	.039	.072	.168	**.365**
20	.240	−.002	.378	.143	.265	−.002	**.421**	.161
21	.038	.289	.318	.141	.042	**.316**	**.353**	.159
22	.250	−.071	.311	.258	.277	−.078	**.346**	.291
23	.223	.095	.464	.085	.247	.104	**.516**	.095
24	.234	.341	.082	.211	.260	**.373**	.091	.237

Factor	Correlations Among Factors							
1	1.000	−.120	−.233	−.216	1.000	.262	.341	.337
2		1.000	−.172	−.233		1.000	.295	.338
3			1.000	−.192			1.000	.329
4				1.000				1.000

But, from formula (13.31), it follows that

$$(15.42) \qquad\qquad T' = D\Lambda^{-1},$$

which states that T' is obtainable from Λ^{-1} by normalizing its rows. The inverse of the non-symmetric transformation matrix Λ may involve considerable computations. To simplify the process, the symmetric matrix Ψ of correlations among the reference factors Λ_p is set up, namely :

$$(15.43) \qquad\qquad \Psi = \Lambda'\Lambda,$$

329

and its inverse can be obtained by the square-root method of **3.5**. Then the desired inverse of Λ follows simply from the matrix product:

$$(15.44) \qquad \Lambda^{-1} = \Psi^{-1}\Lambda'.$$

Finally, the algebraic factors required to normalize the rows of Λ^{-1} are the values for the principal diagonal of **D**.

For the example of twenty-four psychological tests, the matrices Λ^{-1} and **D** are obtained in ex. 9, chap. 15. The proportionality factors necessary for calculating the primary pattern are contained in the matrix:

$$\mathbf{D}^{-1} = \begin{bmatrix} 1.1075 & 0 & 0 & 0 \\ 0 & 1.0939 & 0 & 0 \\ 0 & 0 & 1.1128 & 0 \\ 0 & 0 & 0 & 1.1251 \end{bmatrix}.$$

Applying formula (13.43), the primary pattern of Table 15.5 is obtained.

The objective solution of Table 15.5 may be compared with the solution obtained by subjective graphical methods, and also with the oblimax solution of Table 15.2. There is a striking similarity between the biquartimin and each of the other two solutions. The biquartimin factors have smaller intercorrelations than either those arrived at by graphical methods or those determined by the oblimax method. The relative contributions of the factors to the total communality of 11.383 appear to be somewhat different. The complete analysis of the contributions of the bi-quartimin factors is presented in Table 15.6. These analytically determined factors

Table 15.6

Total Contributions of Biquartimin Primary Factors

Factor	T_1	T_2	T_3	T_4
T_1	3.070	—	—	—
T_2	.172	2.039	—	—
T_3	.581	.251	2.465	—
T_4	.267	.340	.364	1.839

Grand total = 11.388

have a greater variation in their direct contributions than those obtained sub-jectively by passing the primary factors through the points representing composite variables. In other words, there is a greater tendency toward level contributions of factors determined by intuitive-graphical methods.

Since the calculation of an analytical oblique solution for a problem of twenty-four variables and four factors can be obtained in a matter of minutes on an electronic computer, several additional solutions to the one in Table 15.5 were determined. Without presenting the detailed tables, certain interesting properties will be noted. As an empirical test of convergence, two biquartimin solutions were obtained, once starting with the centroid solution and then again starting with the varimax solution (Table 14.6). The results were almost identical, with a maximum difference for any element of the final structure matrix **V** being less than .01.

Two other oblimin solutions were computed, for $\gamma = 0$ and $\gamma = 1$, each time starting with the same centroid solution. Of course these solutions turned out to be quite different from the biquartimin solution of Table 15.5 since they were designed to satisfy different criteria. One striking difference was that the quartimin ($\gamma = 0$) solution contained forty-one small negative entries while the covarimin ($\gamma = 1$) solution did not contain a single negative entry. While it would require too much space to show these solutions, some of the statistics associated with them are presented in Table 15.7. Either of the transformation matrices given in this table may be applied to the centroid pattern to get a corresponding oblimin reference structure by using (15.1). From the correlations among the primary factors, it will be noted that the quartimin factors are most highly correlated, the covarimin factors are least correlated, while the biquartimin factors are between these extremes. It was empirical evidence of this type, coupled with its own rationale, that led Carroll to the development of the biquartimin criterion.

Table 15.7

Some Statistics for the Quartimin and Covarimin Solutions for Twenty-Four Psychological Tests

Factor	Quartimin Solution ($\gamma = 0$)				Covarimin Solution ($\gamma = 1$)			
	1	2	3	4	1	2	3	4
	Transformation Matrix Λ							
Λ_1	.234	.201	.170	.160	.671	.545	.631	.599
Λ_2	−.588	−.376	.499	.434	−.378	.625	−.576	.536
Λ_3	−.714	.737	−.530	.425	.514	−.386	−.458	.246
Λ_4	.301	−.525	−.665	.778	−.378	−.405	.246	.542
	Correlations Among Primary Factors							
T_1	1.000	.680	.564	.653	1.000	−.037	−.304	−.080
T_2		1.000	.604	.655		1.000	−.020	−.339
T_3			1.000	.724			1.000	−.044
T_4				1.000				1.000
Number of iterations	1,218				121			
Criterion								
Initial	132.22				− 12.69			
Final	4.03				− 21.92			

The final application of the oblimin methods is to the problem of eight political variables for which the method of **15.2** broke down. The oblimin methods applied to the same difficult problem lead to satisfactory results. First, the quartimin method of **15.3** is applied, using a desk calculator, and after six iterations the criterion stabilizes at the minimum $N = .1819$ (from an original value of $N = .4344$ for the initial principal-factor solution). The resulting structure is the first one exhibited in Table 15.8. Alongside of this solution is a corresponding one obtained on an IBM 704, but in which normalized loadings were employed in the course of the calculations.

Table 15.8

Three Oblimin Solutions and Binormamin Solution for Eight Political Variables

(Initial solution: Principal-Factor, Table 8.18)

Var-iable j	Quartimin ($\gamma = 0$) Solutions*				Covarimin ($\gamma = 1$) Solution‡		Biquartimin ($\gamma = .5$) Solution				Binormamin Solution			
	On Desk Calculator†		On Electronic Computer											
	Structure **V**		Structure **V**				Structure **V**		Pattern **P**		Structure **V**		Pattern **P**	
	Λ_1	Λ_2	Λ_1	Λ_2	T_1	T_2	Λ_1	Λ_2	T_1	T_2	Λ_1	Λ_2	T_1	T_2
1	.63	.09	.71	.14	.74	−.04	.74	.09	.77	.09	.73	.12	.79	.12
2	.90	.23	.98	.30	1.00	.05	1.00	.23	1.04	.24	1.00	.27	1.07	.28
3	.64	−.07	.78	−.01	.86	−.22	.84	−.06	.87	−.06	.82	−.03	.87	−.03
4	−.44	.32	−.62	.26	−.76	.46	−.71	.32	−.74	.33	−.68	·29	−.73	.31
5	−.37	−.70	−.20	−.69	−.03	−.71	−.09	−.70	−.09	−.73	−.13	−.70	−.13	−.74
6	.51	−.25	.68	−.19	.80	−.39	.76	−.24	.79	−.25	.74	−.21	.79	−.23
7	.08	.72	−.15	.68	−.36	.79	−.29	.71	−.30	.74	−.24	.70	−.26	.74
8	−.43	.40	−.64	.34	−.80	.55	−.75	.39	−.78	.40	−.72	.36	−.77	.39
$r_{T_1 T_2}$	−.63		−.47		−.00		−.26				−.35			

* In order to save space, only the reference structures are exhibited. The primary factor pattern for the first solution is given by $\mathbf{P} = 1.291\mathbf{V}$ while the corresponding relationship for the second solution is $\mathbf{P} = 1.134\mathbf{V}$.

† This solution is the only one not based on normalized loadings.

‡ Because this oblique varimax solution actually resulted in an orthogonal frame of reference the Λ- and T-axes coincide; and the four otherwise distinct matrices—reference structure, reference pattern, primary structure, and primary pattern—all collapse into a single matrix involving orthogonal factors.

Two additional oblimin solutions—the covarimin ($\gamma = 1$) and the biquartimin ($\gamma = .5$)—for the eight political variables were also obtained on an IBM 704 and are shown in Table 15.8. Again, it will be noted that the quartimin factors tend to be highly correlated, the covarimin factors tend toward orthogonality (actually so in this case), while the biquartimin factors assume some intermediate positions. Any one of these solutions is a better approximation to simple structure than the one attempted by graphical methods (in first edition of this text). The results of the biquartimin solution are exhibited in Figure 15.1. Of course, after obtaining the results of the analytical solutions it is easy to see wherein the original intuitive judgments could be improved upon—and this kind of rationalization is to be expected if the objective definition of simple structure is indeed a good explication of the intuitive concept.

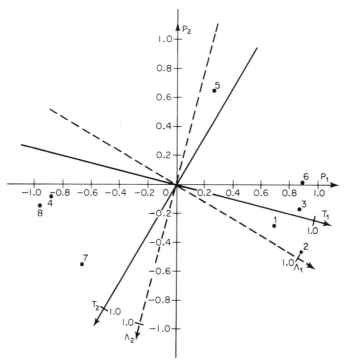

Fig. 15.1.—Biquartimin factors for eight political variables

An oblique solution for the difficult example of eight political variables was also obtained by applying the binormamin criterion (15.40). This solution is shown at the extreme right of Table 15.8, and as far as meeting the simple structure principles it does about as good a job as any of the oblimin solutions, coming closest to the biquartimin form. With regard to the degree of obliqueness, its primary factors are a little more correlated than those of the biquartimin solution but less than the quartimin.

While the entire class of oblimin solutions is infinite, depending on the value of the parameter γ, three particular forms have been singled out: the quartimin for $\gamma = 0$, the covarimin for $\gamma = 1$, and the biquartimin for $\gamma = .5$. In addition, there is the binormamin solution based upon the criterion (15.40), and a fifth major form is the oblimax solution. An important consideration in making a choice of form of solution is the degree of correlation among the primary factors. All five of these methods were employed in the analysis of the eight physical variables, the eight political variables, and the twenty-four psychological variables. From these empirical studies, the covarimin criterion was found to lean very strongly toward orthogonality; the quartimin criterion was found to produce primary factors which were highly correlated; the biquartimin criterion led to an intermediate position but tending toward the lower correlations; and the binormamin criterion also led to an intermediate position but somewhat higher than the biquartimin factors. The oblimax criterion also leads to primary factors which are highly correlated like the quartimin factors. From the viewpoint of showing least bias toward orthogonality or obliqueness, either the biquartimin or the binormamin solutions are most satisfactory. As noted earlier, the superiority of either of these solutions over the other is apt to stem from the inherent nature of the data rather than from a theoretical difference.

It should be noted that the problem of analytical rotation in the orthogonal case is essentially resolved. Several very competent methods are available in chapter 14 and chances are that they can be little improved upon. On the other hand analytical methods for the oblique case are fundamentally different and still in a developmental state. An important new development is presented in the next section.

Since the trend is toward oblique simple structure, Schmid and Leiman [420] became concerned with the difficulties that may arise in the psychological interpretation of oblique factors. They propose a method for transforming such a solution into an orthogonal one, still preserving simplicity but involving a larger number of orthogonal factors. Their model of an hierarchical factor solution is a natural extension of the bi-factor solution, including subgroups of the group factors. Unlike the bi-factor method, or Burt's [61] group-factor method which involves the successive grouping of variables according to their sign pattern in a centroid solution, the hierarchical solution proposed by Schmid and Leiman depends upon successively obtained higher-order factor solutions. These higher-order solutions are the factorizations of the matrices of correlations among the oblique factors. If an oblique simple-structure type solution can be obtained at each level then their procedure can be used to recast the several higher-order factors into an orthogonal hierarchical factor pattern.

15.5. *Direct Oblimin*

As noted in **13.5**, the bi-orthogonal system of coordinate axes—reference and primary—played an important role in the development of oblique primary-factor solutions. Now the computational capabilities are available to make obsolete this rather awkward approach. An important breakthrough was made by Jennrich and Sampson [279] when they derived an analytical procedure to go directly from an initial to a primary-factor pattern. Their procedure also involves a parameter, different values of which lead to a whole class of oblimin-like solutions. Because a primary-factor pattern is obtained directly, without involving an intermediate reference structure, and because the method involves oblique factors and a minimizing criterion, it is designated "direct oblimin" in keeping with the previous names. Jennrich and Sampson use the term "simple loadings."

The general procedure for getting a simple structure solution has been to maximize, as in (15.2), or minimize, as in (15.15) or (15.39), some function of the reference structure elements. The ultimate objective is to make the primary-factor pattern satisfy the simple structure principles. Since the reference-factor structure and the primary-factor pattern are simply related by (13.43), it follows that the latter will look simple if the former does. This property has permitted the indirect approach of simplifying the reference structure to be used as a basis for getting the desired primary-factor solution.

The point of departure in the Jennrich and Sampson approach is to seek a simple structure solution directly by minimizing a function of the primary-factor-pattern coefficients. Thus, in place of the criterion (15.38) that involves the structure values, the corresponding function for the direct oblimin method may be expressed in the form:

$$(15.45) \qquad F(\mathbf{P}) = \sum_{p<q=1}^{m} \left(\sum_{j=1}^{n} b_{jp}^2 b_{jq}^2 - \frac{\delta}{n} \sum_{j=1}^{n} b_{jp}^2 \sum_{j=1}^{n} b_{jq}^2 \right),$$

where $\mathbf{P}$ is the primary-factor-pattern matrix with elements b_{jp}. In order to avoid confusion with the (indirect) oblimin methods of the preceding section, the parameter δ is employed in the present section instead of γ, which Jennrich uses. Of course, the original factor loadings a_{jp} may be normalized by rows, i.e., divided by h_j, and the transformation to the final matrix $\mathbf{P}$ may be carried through in terms of the extended vectors. The original lengths are restored at the end of the process by multiplying the final b_{jp} by h_j. In any event, the direct oblimin solution is obtained by minimizing $F(\mathbf{P})$ in (15.45). It will be recalled from (13.26) that

$$(15.46) \qquad\qquad \mathbf{P} = \mathbf{A}(\mathbf{T}')^{-1},$$

so that the problem amounts to finding a transformation matrix $\mathbf{T}$ that will minimize $F(\mathbf{A}(\mathbf{T}')^{-1})$ under the side condition

$$(15.47) \qquad\qquad \operatorname{diag}(\mathbf{T}'\mathbf{T}) = \mathbf{I}.$$

In the paper by Jennrich and Sampson [279], the mathematical development is presented for the simplest case—what might be called the "direct quartimin," when $\delta = 0$ in (15.45)—and comparisons are made with the biquartimin solutions for two practical problems. The mathematical details actually are given for one elementary rotation (involving only two primary factors), from which the generalization of the process is readily evident. Rotations of this type are performed systematically using all possible pairs of factors until $F(\mathbf{P})$ converges.

A FORTRAN IV subroutine which implements the direct oblimin procedures has been written by Jennrich and Sampson, and has been adapted by the author [202] in FORTRAN II for use on Philco 2000 and in FORTRAN IV for use on IBM 7044. In this program, the criterion for convergence is

$$(15.48) \qquad\qquad (F_{i-1} - F_i)/F_0 \leq \epsilon,$$

where i is the iteration number and ϵ is usually .00001. Actually, the function mini-mized in the subroutine is twice that in (15.45); the sum over the factors in the sub-routine is only restricted to $p \neq q$, and since the terms are symmetric in p and q the resulting sum is twice what it would be if these indices were not permitted to be inter-changed. The output of the program is an oblique factor solution satisfying the principles of simple structure, more or less. The solution consists of the factor pattern, the correlations among the factors, and the factor structure (all of these, of course, refer to the primary-factor solution).

When applying the direct oblimin criterion (15.45), it is possible for the minimum of $F(\mathbf{P})$ to approach $-\infty$ if positive values of δ are employed. Specifically, Jennrich has demonstrated (in a private communication to the author) that $F(\mathbf{P})$ approaches $-\infty$ if and only if $\delta > \frac{4}{5}$. For practical purposes, it is recommended that the value of δ in (15.45) be zero or negative (to be distinguished from the range of zero to one for γ in the indirect oblimin methods). When δ is zero, the factors are most oblique (even higher correlations among the factors can be obtained for positive fractional values of δ). For negative values of δ the factors become less oblique as δ gets smaller.

The last mentioned property is immediately evident from the three direct oblimin solutions shown in Table 15.9—the correlation between the two factors goes down as the value of δ decreases. Other properties may also be determined from a study of this table, and from supplementary data obtained by running this problem for values of δ from -100 to $+1$. First, of course, it is of interest to see how the various direct solutions compare with the oblimin solutions of the preceding section. For

Table 15.9

Three Direct Oblimin Factor Patterns for Eight Physical Variables

(Initial solution: Minres, Table 9.3)

Variable j	$\delta = 0$		$\delta = -.5$		$\delta = -70$	
	T_1	T_2	T_1	T_2	T_1	T_2
1	.883	.065	.866	.115	.819	−.411
2	.956	−.029	.933	.027	.802	−.498
3	.926	−.045	.902	.010	,762	−.491
4	.882	.035	.863	.085	.792	−.427
5	.005	.940	.061	.918	.804	.490
6	−.006	.803	.042	.784	.678	.424
7	−.065	.793	−.017	.770	.618	.448
8	.104	.646	.140	.637	.640	.286
Criterion (15.45)						
Initial value	1.453		2.228		110.071	
Final value	.036		.968		108.597	
Correlation between primary factors	.471		.373		.002	

$\delta = 0$, the solution is very similar to that of the quartimin, for which the reference structure is given in Table 15.4 and the primary factor pattern is provided in the answer to ex. 8, chap. 15. The differences between respective factor coefficients are only in the third decimal place. For $\delta = -1$ to $\delta = -4$, the resulting direct oblimin solutions are roughly like the biquartimin, with the correlation between the primary factors ranging from .337 to .285 and all factor coefficients being positive and forming the two very distinct clusters.

Experimentation was continued with different values of δ for the problem of eight physical variables. By the time δ gets down to -6.5, the resulting factor pattern has "returned" to the form of the initial minres solution (the first factor coefficients agree within .001 while the second factor coefficients differ by three units in the second decimal place). The correlation between the primary factors is .044 as contrasted with the zero correlation in the minres case. Even when the correlation is reduced to .002 (for $\delta = -70$ to $\delta = -100$), the resulting factor pattern is not materially different from that obtained for $\delta = -6.5$. Specifically, the first axis goes through the cluster of all the points and the second is essentially at right angle to it, just as in the case of the minres solution. For no value of δ was a solution found that could be said to be similar to the covarimin (reference structure given in Table 15.4) with its features of zero correlation between the primary factors and all positive factor coefficients. The direct oblimin solutions for large negative values of δ satisfy the condition of near zero correlation while the solution for $\delta = -4$ satisfies the property of positive factor coefficients, but no single value of δ produced all the features of the covarimin solution. Before leaving this problem, a couple of positive values of δ were tried also. For $\delta = .5$, the correlation between the factors reached .748 and the factor coefficients did not satisfy the simple structure principles nearly as well as for the $\delta = 0$ solution in Table 15.9. Finally, just as an empirical test it was found that for $\delta = 1$ the function in (15.45) did in fact become very large negatively before the calculations in the computer were stopped.

The behavior of the direct oblimin method was also explored for the problem of twenty-four psychological tests. This was done both with an initial minres solution and an initial centroid solution. Because of space limitations, only one complete solution is presented, in Table 15.10, but conclusions will be drawn from all of the experimental work. As a general observation, the direct oblimin solution in this table is quite similar to the biquartimin solution of Table 15.5 although the two solutions were obtained by different methods and were based on different initial matrices. The correlations among the direct oblimin factors are consistently, but only slightly, larger than the corresponding correlations of the biquartimin solution (Table 15.5), but not as large as the correlations among the quartimin factors (Table 15.7).

As δ increases negatively, it seems that the resulting factor pattern tends to return to the form of the original input and the correlations among the factors tend toward zero. The ultimate results did not appear, however, up to $\delta = -95$. No negative δ produced a solution with as high correlations among the factors as the (indirect) quartimin. When δ was permitted to be positive—experimenting with δ from .1 to

Table 15.10

Direct Oblimin Solution ($\delta = 0$) for Twenty-Four Psychological Tests

(Initial solution: Minres, $m = 4$)

Test j	Primary Structure: S				Primary Pattern: P			
	r_{jT_1}	r_{jT_2}	r_{jT_3}	r_{jT_4}	Verbal T_1	Speed T_2	Deduction T_3	Memory T_4
1	.353	.331	.731	.344	.008	.113	**.680**	.035
2	.234	.170	.478	.198	.029	.026	**.458**	−.001
3	.283	.104	.574	.244	.053	−.095	**.564**	.039
4	.364	.202	.577	.232	.149	.014	**.523**	−.037
5	.793	.345	.365	.347	**.760**	.107	.009	−.011
6	.816	.225	.383	.412	**.785**	−.069	.024	.103
7	.849	.283	.361	.284	**.872**	.041	.009	−.096
8	.674	.361	.481	.345	**.547**	.131	.211	−.012
9	.857	.208	.376	.404	**.850**	−.094	.004	.085
10	.289	.829	.048	.308	.118	**.856**	−.273	.045
11	.336	.617	.251	.503	.074	**.493**	−.045	**.305**
12	.190	.734	.294	.259	−.084	**.734**	.124	−.029
13	.359	.621	.515	.292	.069	**.519**	**.359**	−.070
14	.318	.199	.177	.591	.126	−.032	−.095	**.588**
15	.244	.186	.220	.554	.022	−.029	.005	**.554**
16	.265	.205	.501	.596	−.083	−.069	**.357**	**.518**
17	.284	.333	.198	.631	.031	.122	−.086	**.606**
18	.220	.449	.406	.554	−.136	.267	.221	**.425**
19	.282	.279	.335	.438	.049	.096	.162	**.319**
20	.523	.252	.529	.449	**.304**	−.016	**.323**	.204
21	.361	.528	.503	.386	.061	**.376**	**.329**	.092
22	.511	.274	.516	.445	.290	.017	**.308**	.199
23	.545	.377	.627	.425	.279	.125	**.433**	.096
24	.511	.588	.346	.465	.294	**.421**	.026	.175

Factor	Correlations Among Factors				
T_1	1.000	.316	.432	.414	Criterion (15.45):
T_2		1.000	.296	.374	Initial value, 5.221
T_3			1.000	.387	Final value, 1.740
T_4				1.000	

.5 in .1 increments—it was found that for $\delta = .4$ the resulting solution was most nearly like the quartimin. The correlations among the factors for these two solutions are shown in the top blocks of Table 15.11.

Unlike the preceding example, for the twenty-four psychological tests the direct oblimin solution with $\delta = 0$ does not approximate the quartimin but comes closer to the biquartimin. Actually, the solution for $\delta = -.5$ is a better approximation to the biquartimin than that produced by $\delta = 0$. The correlations among the factors for each of these solutions, as well as those of the biquartimin factors are exhibited in Table 15.11. The actual 96 factor coefficients for the biquartimin and each of these

338

Table 15.11

Comparison of Direct and Indirect Oblimin Factor Correlations:
Twenty-Four Psychological Tests, Four Factors

(Initial solution: Centroid)

	Direct Oblimin					Indirect Oblimin			
Factor	T_1	T_2	T_3	T_4	Factor	T_1	T_2	T_3	T_4
	$\delta = .4$					Quartimin $(\gamma = 0)$			
T_1	1.000	.646	.712	.717	T_1	1.000	.680	.564	.653
T_2		1.000	.633	.701	T_2		1.000	.604	.655
T_3			1.000	.673	T_3			1.000	.724
T_4				1.000	T_4				1.000
	$\delta = 0$					Biquartimin $(\gamma = .5)$			
T_1	1.000	.313	.434	.405	T_1	1.000	.262	.341	.337
T_2		1.000	.313	.412	T_2		1.000	.295	.338
T_3			1.000	.376	T_3			1.000	.329
T_4				1.000	T_4				1.000
	$\delta = -.5$					Covarimin $(\gamma = 1)$			
T_1	1.000	.270	.379	.335	T_1	1.000	-.037	-.304	-.080
T_2		1.000	.280	.364	T_2		1.000	-.020	-.339
T_3			1.000	.329	T_3			1.000	-.044
T_4				1.000	T_4				1.000

Average Correlation: $\bar{r}$

δ	$\bar{r}$	δ	$\bar{r}$	δ	$\bar{r}$	γ	$\bar{r}$	Type
.5	.841	.2	.443	-.5	.326	0	.647	Quartimin
.4	.680	.1	.400	-10	.283	.5	.317	Biquartimin
.3	.524	0	.375	-95	.031	1	-.137	Covarimin

direct oblimin solutions were compared, yielding mean differences of .0114 and
.0155 for $\delta = -.5$ and $\delta = 0$, respectively; and for the more important coefficients
(i.e., $a_{jp} > .300$), these mean differences are .0109 and .0147, respectively.

Further experimentation with the 24-variable problem was conducted for values
of δ from -10 to -95 in increments of -5. First, it should be noted that the process
failed to converge within the limit of 100 iterations (for $\delta = 0$ it only required about
a dozen iterations for convergence), and the criterion function (15.45) was very large
for these values of δ and changed very little in successive iterations. As noted before,
the factor correlations decrease as δ becomes larger negatively. The first instance
where all the factor correlations are zero in the first decimal place is for $\delta = -25$.
In this sense, that solution is like the covarimin; but just as in the case of the 8-variable

339

example, it appears to be more like the original centroid pattern than the intended covarimin form with all positive factor coefficients and very low factor correlations.

Direct oblimin solutions, with $\delta = 0$, are presented for two additional problems, but without any discussion or comparison with the indirect methods. These are the solutions for the five socio-economic variables in Table 15.12 and for the eight political variables in Table 15.13.

Table 15.12

Direct Oblimin Solution ($\delta = 0$) for Five Socio-Economic Variables

(Initial solution: Minres, Table 9.2)

Variable j	Primary Structure: S		Primary Pattern: P	
	r_{jT_1}	r_{jT_2}	T_1	T_2
1	.120	.997	−.073	1.011
2	.870	.089	.886	−.080
3	.242	.978	.057	.967
4	.826	.490	.761	.344
5	.982	.082	1.003	−.110

Factor	Factor Correlations		Criterion (15.45):
T_1	1.000	.191	Initial value, .976
T_2		1.000	Final value, .138

Table 15.13

Direct Oblimin Solution ($\delta = 0$) for Eight Political Variables

(Initial solution: Principal-Factor, Table 8.18)

Variable j	Primary Structure: S		Primary Pattern: P	
	r_{jT_1}	r_{jT_2}	T_1	T_2
1	.735	−.102	.772	.127
2	.964	−.024	1.050	.288
3	.886	−.288	.878	−.027
4	−.839	.518	−.751	.295
5	.130	−.703	−.086	−.729
6	.266	−.454	.802	−.215
7	−.521	.815	−.305	.724
8	−.904	.610	−.792	.374

Factor	Factor Correlations		Criterion (15.45):
T_1	1.000	−.297	Initial value, .743
T_2		1.000	Final value, .452

From the theoretical developments and the empirical investigations, certain tentative conclusions can be drawn regarding the direct oblimin methods. First, it becomes quite evident that no simple relationship exists between the direct and the indirect methods. That is not to say that striking agreements cannot be found between results obtained by the two approaches, but merely that there is not a very simple way of saying what value of δ in the direct method will lead to an equivalent result for a given γ in the indirect method. Secondly, there is no compelling reason to accept the three special instances of the indirect oblimin—quartimin ($\gamma = 0$), biquartimin ($\gamma = .5$), and covarimin ($\gamma = 1$)—as superior to direct oblimin. In some sense, the direct oblimin is superior, not only because of its greater simplicity but because of the wider range of oblique solutions that are possible. However, this very flexibility may detract from the direct method. It may be advisable, in due course of time, to recommend certain "preferred" values of δ that may be expected to have special properties, depending on the number of variables, number of factors, and perhaps other parameters.

PART IV

FACTOR MEASUREMENTS

16

Measurement of Factors

16.1. *Introduction*

There are two basic problems with which factor analysis is concerned. The first of these deals with the methods for obtaining the linear resolution of a set of variables in terms of hypothetical factors. Most of the preceding work has been devoted to the solution of this problem. The results are the several different orthogonal and oblique solutions. The second problem is concerned with the description of the factors in terms of the observed variables, and is the subject matter of the present chapter.

While there has been much research, and new theory and computing techniques for determining the factor weights of the variables in terms of the factors, there has not been a corresponding effort directed toward the expression of the factors in terms of the variables. The limited work on factor measurements since the early 1940's includes theoretical papers by Kestelman [314] and Heerman [221], a brief note by Thomson [464], a comparison with approximate methods by Baggaley and Cattell [19], such applications as reported by Wenger, Holzinger, and Harman [508] and Selvin [426], and several computer programs.

Methods for expressing the hypothetical constructs—the factors—in terms of the observed variables are developed in this chapter. First, the need for "estimation" rather than determining factor measurements directly is discussed in **16.2**. This is followed, in **16.3**, by the special situation for the measurement of principal components. Then various means are considered for estimating factor measurements when the classical factor analysis model is employed. The best prediction, in the least-square sense, is that obtained by ordinary regression methods. In **16.4** the linear regression of any factor on the n observed variables is obtained by the usual method. This is followed by an approximation method, which employs composite variables, in order to reduce the laborious task of the complete regression method. Another approach is presented in **16.7** which is superior to either of the preceding because it is more rapid and usually gives results as accurate as the complete estimation method. In

345

effect, the "short method" replaces the observed correlations of variables by those reproduced (or computed) from the factor solution.

Two other methods, which at present do not seem to be as practical as the preceding ones, also are given. In **16.8** a regression method is presented in which the sum of the squares of the unique factors is minimized. This method produces estimates of factors which are usually quite different from those given by any of the other methods. The final method for describing the factors in terms of the variables involves the mathematical solution of a set of equations rather than the statistical estimation by regression. Hence the factors themselves, instead of estimates of them, are obtained. Unfortunately, however, this solution is in terms of "ideal" variables (not the observed ones) and therefore cannot be employed in a practical way.

16.2. *Direct Solution versus Estimation*

To facilitate the development of the theory and methods of this chapter, as well as to bring together many of the concepts of the previous chapters, a summary of the relevant matrix notation is presented in Table 16.1. Because it is practically impossible to use a separate and distinct symbol for each new concept, and to retain the particular symbol every place that it occurs, the intent of the table is to call attention to the specific uses of the notation and to provide a ready reference source. In addition to the basic concepts in this table, other definitions will be made, as needed, in the course of the development of the various procedures.

A set of n variables can be analyzed either (a) in terms of common factors only, by inserting unities in the diagonal of $\mathbf{R}$; or (b) in terms of common and unique factors, by inserting communalities in the diagonal of $\mathbf{R}$. These two approaches, of course, correspond to the component analysis and the classical factor analysis models, respectively, as first presented in **2.3**. In the first instance $\mathbf{R}$ is a Gramian matrix, generally of rank n, and the factor solution

$$(16.1) \qquad\qquad \mathbf{z} = \mathbf{Af}$$

is in terms of n common factors. Since $\mathbf{A}$ is a square non-singular matrix, in this instance, it will have an inverse. Then the required factor measurements are given simply by:

$$(16.2) \qquad\qquad \mathbf{f} = \mathbf{A}^{-1}\mathbf{z}.$$

This solution is determined exactly, is unique, and involves no "estimation."

However, when the factor model involves common and unique factors the solution is not so simple. Then the total number of factors exceeds the number of variables, and an inverse does not exist for the factor matrix $\mathbf{M}$. The generally accepted procedure, in this case, is to resort to the "best fit" in the least squares sense. Such methods are developed in the ensuing sections.

Kestelman [314] proves that even when the total number of factors exceeds the number of variables, exact numerical specifications can be found for the factors (but not unique values) such that

$$\mathbf{FF'} = \mathbf{I},$$

Table 16.1

Notation for Matrices Frequently Used

Matrix	Order	Definition and Use
R	$n \times n$	Matrix of observed correlations among the n variables.
R†	$n \times n$	Matrix of reproduced correlations from a factor solution with communalities in the principal diagonal. When there can be no confusion, the dagger may be dropped.
R† + **D**^{2}	$n \times n$	Matrix of reproduced correlations with unities in diagonal.
Z $\equiv (z_{ji})$	$n \times N$	Matrix of N measurements on each of the n variables.
z $\equiv \{z_j\}$	$n \times 1$	Column vector of the n variables.
F $\equiv (F_{pi})$	$m \times N$	Matrix of N measurements on each of the m common factors.
f $\equiv \{F_p\}$	$m \times 1$	Column vector of the m common factors.
u $\equiv \{U_j\}$	$n \times 1$	Column vector of the n unique factors.
M $\equiv$ (**A**|**D**)	$n \times m + n$	Complete pattern matrix.
A	$n \times m$	General matrix of common-factor coefficients. Also, initial orthogonal solution when transformation to oblique solution is involved.
D	$n \times n$	Matrix of unique-factor coefficients. Also matrix for unique-factor portion of factor structure.
S	$n \times m$	Factor structure matrix. Only the common-factor portion is usually of interest; both the common and unique portions may be represented by (**S**|**D**).
Φ	$m \times m$	General matrix of correlations among a set of oblique common factors.
Ψ	$m \times m$	Matrix of correlations among common factors when these are reference axes and have to be distinguished from the primary factors.
P	$n \times m$	Primary-factor pattern matrix (in oblique factor analysis an initial principal-factor solution is designated **A** rather than **P**).
S	$n \times m$	Primary-factor structure matrix (in oblique factor analysis this is not mistaken for a general factor structure matrix).
V	$n \times m$	Reference-factor structure matrix.
W	$n \times m$	Reference-factor pattern matrix.

i.e., the factor measurements are in standard form and uncorrelated. He also indicates that such theoretical measurements are not necessarily superior, from a statistical standpoint, to the correlated estimates obtained by regression methods.

The concern with the fact that the regression methods lead to correlated estimates of factor measurements is taken up by Heerman [221]. He develops two procedures for transforming the least-squares estimates of orthogonal factors so as to produce uncorrelated measurements. These he calls "orthogonal approximations." He also derives "univocal estimates" of orthogonal factors that have the property of not correlating with any of the factors except those they were designed to estimate. Of course, in making any of these transformations there is bound to be a loss in the validity of the estimators—the regression methods determine estimates that give the "best" fit according to the least-squares principle. However, in considering alternative advantages of uncorrelated factor measurements and lack of correlations with other factors, Heerman argues that "it would appear that the orthogonal estimators represent something of a compromise between the maximum validity of least-squares estimators and the purity of the univocal estimators" [221, p. 172].

16.3. *Measurement of Principal Components*

When the analysis is in terms of principal components then the factor measurements can be obtained directly. Not only does the inverse of the factor matrix exist when all n components have been obtained, so that the factor measurements are given by (16.2), but actually it is not necessary to calculate the inverse of the factor matrix. Furthermore, in the more practical situation when only a few of the larger components are used, the simplified procedure still applies.

In the factor model (16.1) it need not be assumed that A is square, but can be of order $n \times m$. Premultiplying both sides of (16.1) by A' produces

$$A'z = A'Af,$$

and solving for f explicitly, the final result is

$$(16.3) \qquad\qquad f = (A'A)^{-1}A'z = \Lambda_m^{-1}A'z,$$

where Λ_m is the diagonal matrix of the m eigenvalues retained, corresponding to (8.22). From this expression, or the equivalent algebraic form:

$$(16.4) \qquad\qquad F_p = \sum_{j=1}^{n} \frac{a_{jp}}{\lambda_p} z_j \qquad\qquad (p = 1, 2, \cdots, m),$$

it is clear that the principal components are described mathematically as linear combinations of the variables, with no question of statistical estimation. The coefficients in the equation for any principal component in terms of the variables are obtained simply by dividing its "factor loadings" by its eigenvalue. This property was first derived by Hotelling [259, sec. 8] and generalized more recently by Kaiser [298].

To illustrate the foregoing, consider the principal component solution of Table 8.1 for the five socio-economic variables. The necessary eigenvalues are the square roots of the variances in the second to last row of that table. Then dividing the numbers in the columns by the respective eigenvalue produces the required coefficients. For example, the resulting equation in the case of the second component (P_2) is:

$$F_2 = 1.0809z_1 - .7302z_2 + .9731z_3 - .1398z_4 - .7482z_5.$$

Another important property of component analysis is that the measurements of any rotated components can also be obtained more simply than in the case of classical factor analysis. Consider a rotation of the principal component solution (say, to the varimax form) by means of the transformation

$$(16.5) \qquad\qquad B = AT,$$

where A is the initial matrix of coefficients of the principal components, B is the corresponding matrix for the rotated component solution, and T is the matrix of

348

transformation. The new solution may be represented by

(16.6) $z = Bg$

where g is used to distinguish the new column vector from the original f. Then, pre-multiplying both sides of (16.6) by B' and solving for g produces

(16.7) $g = (B'B)^{-1}B'z$.

Again using the five socio-economic variables for illustration, the rotated varimax components are given in Table 14.6. The matrix B can be read from this table, as follows (actually, its transpose for printing convenience):

$$B' = \begin{pmatrix} .0160 & .9408 & .1370 & .8248 & .9682 \\ .9938 & -.0088 & .9801 & .4471 & -.0060 \end{pmatrix}.$$

Simple computations produce:

$$B'B = \begin{pmatrix} 2.5218 & .5048 \\ .5048 & 2.1481 \end{pmatrix} \quad \text{and} \quad (B'B)^{-1} = \begin{pmatrix} .4161 & -.0978 \\ -.0978 & .4885 \end{pmatrix}.$$

Then, equation (16.7) can be applied to get the equation for each of the rotated components, namely:

$$G_1 = -.0905z_1 + .3923z_2 - .0388z_3 + .2995z_4 + .4035z_5,$$

$$G_2 = .4839z_1 - .0963z_2 + .4654z_3 + .1378z_4 - .0976z_5.$$

The measurements of these (varimax) components for the sample of $N = 12$ entities (census tracts) were computed on a Philco 2000 computer and are presented in Table 16.2. The rotated components are designated by M's instead of G's because that was

Table 16.2

Measurements of Varimax Components: Five Socio-Economic Variables

(Solution of Table 14.6)

Case	M_1	M_2
1	1.20	-.03
2	-.66	-1.38
3	-1.26	-.77
4	1.11	-.80
5	.94	-.76
6	-1.23	.55
7	-.17	-1.55
8	-.44	.73
9	.32	.91
10	1.58	1.03
11	-.95	.96
12	-.45	1.11

the notation used in chapter 14. To check any of these values by hand methods, the standard scores for the variables would first have to be calculated from Table 2.1 and then substituted in the above equations. Alternatively, these equations could be transformed to raw score form and the values from Table 2.1 used directly.

While the above procedure, which led to (16.7), is relatively simple, there is still another approach for getting the measurements of rotated components. From (16.1) and (16.6) it follows that

$$(16.8) \qquad\qquad \mathbf{f} = \mathbf{Tg},$$

which relationship between the two sets of components corresponds to (12.7). Premultiplying by $\mathbf{T'}$, and remembering that $\mathbf{T'T} = \mathbf{I}$ for an orthogonal transformation, this relationship becomes

$$(16.9) \qquad\qquad \mathbf{g} = \mathbf{T'f},$$

and, upon substituting (16.3) for $\mathbf{f}$,

$$(16.10) \qquad\qquad \mathbf{g} = \mathbf{T'\Lambda}_m^{-1}\mathbf{A'z}.$$

Now, the transformation matrix itself can be expressed in the form

$$(16.11) \qquad\qquad \mathbf{T} = \mathbf{\Lambda}_m^{-1}\mathbf{A'B},$$

which corresponds to (12.4) and which can be obtained directly from (16.5). Finally, substituting (16.11) into (16.10), the formula for the rotated components becomes:

$$(16.12) \qquad\qquad \mathbf{g} = \mathbf{B'A\Lambda}_m^{-2}\mathbf{A'z}.$$

Either (16.7) or this formula yields the equations for the rotated components. The difference between these two expressions is that the former employs the eigenvalues of $\mathbf{B'B}$, involving the rotated matrix, while the latter uses the initial factor matrix. Thus, (16.7) may actually require more computations if m is of fair size because the matrix to be inverted is not diagonal as it is in (16.12). The results of applying formula (16.12) to the example of five socio-economic variables are identical to those obtained above; the computations are left as an exercise.

16.4. *Complete Estimation Method*

The remainder of this chapter deals primarily with the classical factor analysis model (2.9). In this and the following two sections, conventional regression methods are employed to obtain estimates of factor measurements. The linear regression of any factor F_p on the n variables may be expressed in the form:

$$(16.13) \qquad\qquad \bar{F}_p = \beta_{p1}z_1 + \beta_{p2}z_2 + \cdots + \beta_{pn}z_n \qquad\qquad (p = 1, 2, \cdots, m).$$

From the general theory of multivariate regression, it follows that the normal equation for determining the β's are

$$(16.14) \quad \begin{cases} \beta_{p1} + r_{12}\beta_{p2} + \cdots + r_{1n}\beta_{pn} = s_{1p}, \\ r_{21}\beta_{p1} + \beta_{p2} + \cdots + r_{2n}\beta_{pn} = s_{2p}, \\ \cdot \quad \cdot \quad \cdot \quad \cdot \quad \cdot \quad \cdots \quad \cdot \quad \cdot \quad \cdot \quad \cdot \\ r_{n1}\beta_{p1} + r_{n2}\beta_{p2} + \cdots + \beta_{pn} = s_{np}, \end{cases}$$

where $s_{jp} = r_{z_jF_p}$. The coefficients of the unknown β's are the elements of the symmetric matrix of observed correlations. Thus, any factor can be estimated when the correlations of the variables with the factor and the correlations among the variables themselves are known.

The formal solution of equations (16.14) can best be indicated by considering the matrix:

$$(16.15) \quad \mathbf{\Delta} = \begin{bmatrix} 1 & s_{1p} & s_{2p} & \cdots & s_{np} \\ s_{1p} & 1 & r_{12} & \cdots & r_{1n} \\ s_{2p} & r_{21} & 1 & \cdots & r_{2n} \\ \cdots & \cdots & \cdots & \cdots & \cdots \\ s_{np} & r_{n1} & r_{n2} & \cdots & 1 \end{bmatrix},$$

consisting of the observed correlation matrix $\mathbf{R}$ bordered by the correlations of the variables with the particular factor. Then the unknowns in (16.14) are given by:

$$(16.16) \quad \beta_{pj} = -|\mathbf{\Delta}_{jp}|/|\mathbf{R}| \qquad (j = 1, 2, \cdots, n),$$

where the fixed denominator is the determinant of the observed correlation matrix and $|\mathbf{\Delta}_{jp}|$ is the cofactor of s_{jp} in $\mathbf{\Delta}$. It should be noted that the determinants $|\mathbf{\Delta}_{jp}|$ also can be expressed in terms of the cofactors of the original correlation matrix $\mathbf{R}$. Thus the values (16.6) may be written explicitly in the form

$$(16.17) \quad \beta_{pj} = (s_{1p}|\mathbf{R}_{1j}| + s_{2p}|\mathbf{R}_{2j}| + \cdots + s_{np}|\mathbf{R}_{nj}|)/|\mathbf{R}|,$$

where $|\mathbf{R}_{kj}|$ is the cofactor of r_{kj} in $\mathbf{R}$.

Substituting (16.17) into (16.13) and employing the more compact matrix designations, the estimate of any one of the factors F_p may be put in the form:

$$(16.18) \quad \bar{F}_p = \mathbf{s}_p'\mathbf{R}^{-1}\mathbf{z}, \qquad (p = 1, 2, \cdots, m)$$

where $\mathbf{s}_p$ is the column vector $\{s_{1p} s_{2p} \cdots s_{np}\}$ taken from column p of the factor structure $\mathbf{S}$. By considering all m factors and the N measurements of each variable, the measurements of all the factors can be expressed compactly, as follows:

$$(16.19) \quad \bar{\mathbf{F}} = \mathbf{S}'\mathbf{R}^{-1}\mathbf{Z}.$$

While the foregoing development employed the factor structure, it is possible to estimate the factors by use of the factor pattern instead. Substituting the expression

(2.43) for the structure in terms of the pattern, equation (16.19) becomes

(16.20) $$\bar{\mathbf{F}} = \mathbf{\Phi A'R}^{-1}\mathbf{Z},$$

in which $\mathbf{\Phi}$ is the matrix of correlations among the factors. When the factors are uncorrelated, $\mathbf{\Phi}$ in (16.20) is the identity matrix, and the matrix equation for the prediction of such factors becomes

(16.21) $$\bar{\mathbf{F}} = \mathbf{A'R}^{-1}\mathbf{Z} \qquad \text{(uncorrelated factors)}$$

which is also immediately evident from (16.19) since the pattern and structure coincide. If the factors are correlated, of course the distinction between a pattern and a structure is of paramount importance.

A measure of the accuracy of estimating a factor F_p by means of equation (16.13) is given by the coefficient of multiple correlation R_p. Several important and useful formulas involving R_p will be developed next. The normal equations (16.14) may be written in the condensed form

(16.22) $$\sum (F_{pi} - \bar{F}_{pi})z_{ji} = 0 \qquad (j = 1, 2, \cdots, n),$$

where the summation extends over the N observations of each variable. In the following development, summation on i from 1 to N will be understood although the i is omitted. Since the set of residuals $(F_p - \bar{F}_p)$ is orthogonal to each of the n sets of numbers z_j, it is orthogonal to any linear combination of these z_j. In particular, the set $\bar{F}_p$ is such a linear combination, and hence

$$\sum (F_p - \bar{F}_p)\bar{F}_p = 0,$$

which, upon dividing through by N, reduces to

(16.23) $$s_{F_p}r_{F_p\bar{F}_p} = s_{\bar{F}_p}^2,$$

since F_p is in standard form. The coefficient of multiple correlation of F_p in terms of $z_1, z_2, \cdots, z_n$ is defined to be the simple correlation coefficient of F_p and $\bar{F}_p$. The expression (16.23) may finally be written in the form

(16.24) $$R_p = r_{F_p\bar{F}_p} = s_{\bar{F}_p}.$$

This formula shows that the standard deviation of the factor estimates is equal to the coefficient of multiple correlation.

A simple formula for calculating R_p may be obtained by multiplying both sides of (16.13) by F_p, summing for the N individuals, and dividing by N. The result is

$$s_{\bar{F}_p}r_{F_p\bar{F}_p} = \beta_{p1}s_{1p} + \beta_{p2}s_{2p} + \cdots + \beta_{pn}s_{np},$$

where the symbol for the sample standard deviation ($s_{\bar{F}}$) should not be confused with the symbol for a factor structure element (s_{jp}). Then, according to (16.24),

(16.25) $$R_p^2 = \beta_{p1}s_{1p} + \beta_{p2}s_{2p} + \cdots + \beta_{pn}s_{np}.$$

While (16.25) is the simplest formula for computing the multiple correlation, another form can be derived with other useful features. To this end, multiply the first of equations (16.14) by β_{p1}, the second by β_{p2}, etc., obtaining

$$\beta_{p1}s_{1p} = \beta_{p1}^2 \qquad + \beta_{p1}\beta_{p2}r_{12} + \cdots + \beta_{p1}\beta_{pn}r_{1n},$$

(16.26)

$$\cdot \quad \cdot \quad \cdot \quad \cdot \quad \cdot \quad \cdot \quad \cdot \quad \cdot \quad \cdots \quad \cdot \quad \cdot \quad \cdot$$

$$\beta_{pn}s_{np} = \beta_{pn}\beta_{p1}r_{n1} + \beta_{pn}\beta_{p2}r_{n2} + \cdots + \beta_{pn}^2.$$

Adding these equations, and employing (16.25), there results

(16.27)
$$R_p^2 = \sum_{j=1}^n \beta_{pj}^2 + 2 \sum_{j<k=1}^n \beta_{pj}\beta_{pk}r_{jk}.$$

This formula, although not so simple as (16.25) for computing R_p, illustrates an important property. Any product term $\beta_{pj}s_{jp}$ in (16.25) measures the *total* (*direct* and *indirect*) contribution of the corresponding variable X_j to R_p^2, or the importance of that variable as a "determiner" of F_p. The resolution of the total contribution of any variable into its direct and indirect effect upon F_p is indicated in (16.26). Thus, while $\beta_{p1}s_{1p}$ represents the total portion of R_p^2 which is due to X_1, the right-hand member of the first of equations (16.26) shows that this is composed of the direct contribution (β_{p1}^2) of X_1 and of the indirect contribution $(\beta_{p1}\beta_{pk}r_{1k})$ of X_1 through its correlations with each of the other variables X_k ($k = 2, 3, \cdots, n$). It may be noted that the indirect or joint contribution of any two variables is distributed equally between them.

In the preceding section involving component analysis it was demonstrated that the principal components (or orthogonal rotations of them) are linear combinations of the original variables involving no estimation. One immediate implication of this is that the multiple correlation for any principal component must be precisely unity. It must also be unity for any rotation of the principal components. On the other hand, when the analysis is in terms of classical factor analysis then the multiple correlation will be less than one for each factor. The extent of this reduction can be seen from the following analysis.

Suppose the factor coefficients have been estimated by the principal-factor method of **8.2**; that is, the columns of factor loadings are appropriately normalized eigenvectors of $\mathbf{R} - \mathbf{D}^2$, where $\mathbf{R}$ is the full correlation matrix and $\mathbf{D}^2$ is the diagonal uniqueness matrix. Designating the eigenvalues by λ_p and the corresponding unit-length eigenvectors by $\boldsymbol{\alpha}_p$, it follows from (8.15) that

(16.28) $\qquad\qquad (\mathbf{R} - \mathbf{D}^2)\boldsymbol{\alpha}_p = \lambda_p\boldsymbol{\alpha}_p \qquad\qquad (p = 1, 2, \cdots, m)$

and

(16.29) $\qquad\qquad \boldsymbol{\alpha}_p'\boldsymbol{\alpha}_p = 1.$

The column vector $\mathbf{a}_p$ of factor coefficients is scaled according to (8.14) as follows:

(16.30) $\qquad\qquad \mathbf{a}_p = \sqrt{\lambda_p}\boldsymbol{\alpha}_p.$

Now, let $\boldsymbol{\beta}_p$ be the column vector of regression coefficients for the estimation of F_p from $z_1, \cdots, z_n$. Also let $\mathbf{s}_p$ designate the column vector of correlations of the

353

variables with factor F_p. Then, the expression (16.17) for the regression coefficients can be put in the following matrix form:

$$(16.31) \qquad \boldsymbol{\beta}_p = \mathbf{R}^{-1}\mathbf{s}_p = \mathbf{R}^{-1}\mathbf{a}_p,$$

where the last equality follows from the fact that the structure elements are identical with the pattern coefficients in the case of an orthogonal factor solution. The expression (16.25) for the multiple correlation similarly can be put in matrix form, as follows:

$$(16.32) \qquad R_p^2 = \mathbf{s}_p'\boldsymbol{\beta}_p.$$

Substituting the value for $\boldsymbol{\beta}_p$ from (16.31), the last expression becomes

$$(16.33) \qquad R_p^2 = \mathbf{a}_p'\mathbf{R}^{-1}\mathbf{a}_p,$$

or, making use of (16.30),

$$(16.34) \qquad R_p^2 = \sqrt{\lambda_p}\mathbf{\alpha}_p'\mathbf{R}^{-1}\mathbf{\alpha}_p\sqrt{\lambda_p} = \mathbf{\alpha}_p'\mathbf{R}^{-1}(\lambda_p\mathbf{\alpha}_p),$$

where the last equality follows from the fact that λ_p is a scalar. Then, according to the basic relationship (16.28), the last equation can be put in the form

$$R_p^2 = \mathbf{\alpha}_p'\mathbf{R}^{-1}(\mathbf{R} - \mathbf{D}^2)\mathbf{\alpha}_p$$

$$= \mathbf{\alpha}_p'(\mathbf{I} - \mathbf{R}^{-1}\mathbf{D}^2)\mathbf{\alpha}_p$$

$$= \mathbf{\alpha}_p'\mathbf{\alpha}_p - \mathbf{\alpha}_p'\mathbf{R}^{-1}\mathbf{D}^2\mathbf{\alpha}_p,$$

and, finally

$$(16.35) \qquad R_p^2 = 1 - \mathbf{\alpha}_p'\mathbf{R}^{-1}\mathbf{D}^2\mathbf{\alpha}_p,$$

by use of (16.29). This indicates the extent to which the multiple correlation is reduced from unity when the factor solution includes uniqueness variance. On the other hand, when the correlation matrix with ones in the diagonal is factored, then $\mathbf{D}^2 = \mathbf{0}$ and the multiple correlation is exactly one for each principal component.

16.5. *Numerical Illustrations of Complete Estimation Method*

It is apparent that the estimation of factor measurements involves considerable computation. The general formula (16.19) requires the inverse of a matrix of order n, which can be a very laborious task as n becomes large. Hence, the complete estimation method is practical only with large computers. An example of such computer results is given, as well as a more detailed illustration of the work on a desk calculator, for a manageable set of data.

To better grasp the nature of the estimation, the hand procedures will be taken up first. While the determinantal method was employed to get formula (16.16) for the regression coefficients, in practical applications the more efficient methods of chapter 3 are employed for the solution of systems of linear equations. Since each set of normal equations (16.14) for estimating the successive common factors involves the same matrix of coefficients, all the factors can be estimated simultaneously.

Table 16.3

Estimation of Factors: Square Root Method*

Variable	Independent Variables 1	2	3	4	5	6	7	8	Dependent Variables P_1	P_2	T_1	T_2	Total	Check
1	1.000	.846	.805	.859	.473	.398	.301	.382	.858	−.328	.919	.484	6.997	
2	*	1.000	.881	.826	.376	.326	.277	.415	.849	−.414	.943	.435	6.760	
3	*	*	1.000	.801	.380	.319	.237	.345	.810	−.412	.907	.399	6.472	
4	*	*	*	1.000	.436	.329	.327	.365	.825	−.339	.893	.454	6.776	
5	*	*	*	*	1.000	.762	.730	.629	.747	.561	.455	.932	7.481	
6	*	*	*	*	*	1.000	.583	.577	.637	.507	.374	.813	6.625	
7	*	*	*	*	*	*	1.000	.539	.561	.488	.312	.740	6.095	
8	*	*	*	*	*	*	*	1.000	.619	.371	.412	.724	6.378	
1	1.000	.846	.805	.859	.473	.398	.301	.382	.858	−.328	.919	.484	6.997	
2		.533	.375	.186	−.045	−.020	.042	.172	.231	−.256	.311	.048	1.577	1.577
3			.460	.086	.035	.013	−.046	−.059	.071	−.113	.110	−.019	.539	.538
4				.469	.075	−.022	.138	.021	.083	.000	.077	.066	.908	.907
5					.876	.655	.663	.521	.391	.809	.028	.800	4.744	4.743
6						.641	.052	.138	.070	.162	−.006	.154	1.213	1.211
7							.666	.088	.033	.071	−.002	.066	.922	.922
8								.723	.052	.116	−.002	.117	1.005	1.006
$\beta_{P_1 \cdot j}$	.178	.311	.120	.117	.306	.090	.040	.072	.963	.885	.960	.923	$= R_p^2$	
$\beta_{P_2 \cdot j}$	−.261	−.265	−.246	−.119	.606	.211	.085	.160	.981	.941	.980	.961	$= R_p$	
$\beta_{T_1 \cdot j}$	.275	.388	.206	.158	.042	−.008	−.003	−.003						
$\beta_{T_2 \cdot j}$	−.043	.131	−.069	.022	.609	.199	.078	.162						

* The schematic form of Table 3.2 is the basis for this table.

355

Furthermore, this means that several sets of factors, obtained by different methods of analysis, can be predicted at the same time. In the first example, the two principal factors and two oblique factors are estimated for the eight physical variables. The complete work, by the square root method, is shown in Table 16.3. The observed correlations come from Table 5.3; the correlations of the variables with the principal factors P_1 and P_2 come from Table 8.12; and the correlations of the variables with the oblique factors T_1 and T_2 come from a factor structure based on a centroid solution which is very similar to the factor structure in Table 13.1 based on a minres solution. The arrangement of the work in Table 16.3 follows the schematic form of Table 3.2, but in place of a single dependent variable there are the four factors to be estimated. After the square root operation is applied, yielding the blocks below the known correlations, the regression coefficients are calculated by means of formulas of the type (3.27). Thus the last regression coefficient for each factor is given by:

$$\beta_{P_18} = .052/.723, \quad \beta_{P_28} = .116/.723, \quad \beta_{T_18} = -.002/.723, \quad \beta_{T_28} = .117/.723;$$

the next to last is given by:

$$\beta_{P_17} = [.033 - .088(.072)]/.666, \qquad \beta_{P_27} = [.071 - .088(.160)]/.666,$$

$$\beta_{T_17} = [-.002 - .088(-.003)]/.666, \quad \beta_{T_27} = [.066 - .088(.162)]/.666;$$

and so on until the first regression coefficients are obtained. In addition to the regression weights, the square of the multiple correlation for each factor estimate is obtained by applying formula (16.25). The results of these calculations, and the multiple correlations themselves, are recorded in the lower right corner of Table 16.3.

The values of the regression coefficients in the equations predicting the oblique factors T_1 (Lankiness) and T_2 (Stockiness) as given in Table 16.3, may be written explicitly as follows:

$$(16.36) \quad \begin{cases} \overline{T}_{1i} = .275z_{1i} + .388z_{2i} + .206z_{3i} + .158z_{4i} + .042z_{5i} \\ \qquad - .008z_{6i} - .003z_{7i} - .003z_{8i}, \\ \overline{T}_{2i} = -.043z_{1i} + .131z_{2i} - .069z_{3i} + .022z_{4i} + .609z_{5i} \\ \qquad + .199z_{6i} + .078z_{7i} + .162z_{8i}. \end{cases}$$

The measurements of these factors for a particular individual i are obtained by substituting the appropriate standardized values in the above equations. The subscript i has been included in these equations to indicate clearly that values are substituted for the variables in order to get particular estimates of the factors. In general, however, the secondary subscript is dropped for simplicity.

The prediction of the above factors will now be illustrated for two individuals whose measurements for the eight variables are given in Table 16.4. The original observations X_{ji} are changed to standardized values z_{ji} by applying formula (2.5). The means and standard deviations required for this change also are given in Table 16.4. Upon substituting the values z_{ji} into equations (16.36), the following results are

356

obtained:

Factor measurements for Case 1: $\bar{T}_{11} = -0.26$, $\bar{T}_{21} = 1.78$;

Factor measurements for Case 2: $\bar{T}_{12} = 1.21$, $\bar{T}_{22} = 0.53$.

It can be seen from the eight standardized values for each girl in Table 16.4 that the first is of the stocky type and the second is tall or lanky. While the original values reveal these facts, they can be indicated more simply by the above factor measurements. Although the estimated factors are not in standard form, their standard deviations (.980 and .961) are nearly the same, and so the estimated values are reasonably comparable. The measurements for the first girl indicate clearly that she is almost two standard deviations above the mean in the factor "Stockiness" and slightly below the average in "Lankiness." The second girl is a less extreme type— being less lanky than the other girl is stocky and also being above average in "Stockiness."

Table 16.4

Means and Standard Deviations of Eight Physical Variables,* and Values for Two Girls

Variable	Mean	Standard Deviation	Case 1		Case 2	
j	$\bar{X}_j$	s_j	X_{j1}	z_{j1}	X_{j2}	z_{j2}
1. Height	63.96 in.	2.09 in.	63.98 in.	0.01	66.34 in.	1.14
2. Arm span	64.25 in.	2.50 in.	63.19 in.	−0.42	66.89 in.	1.06
3. Length of forearm	17.10 in.	.67 in.	16.89 in.	−0.31	17.99 in.	1.33
4. Length of lower leg	19.62 in.	.86 in.	19.09 in.	−0.62	20.71 in.	1.27
5. Weight	119.22 lb.	15.19 lb.	149.25 lb.	1.98	125.5 lb.	0.41
6. Bitrochanteric diameter	12.27 in.	.66 in.	13.15 in.	1.33	12.44 in.	0.26
7. Chest girth	31.21 in.	1.91 in.	34.37 in.	1.65	32.52 in.	0.69
8. Chest width	9.92 in.	.67 in.	10.87 in.	1.42	10.55 in.	0.94

* For 305 fifteen-year old girls.

In the foregoing illustrations standardized values were employed in the direct application of equations (16.36). The calculations of the standardized values for many variables for a large sample of individuals is laborious. The work can be greatly reduced by formally expressing the equations of estimation in terms of observed values by the use of formula (2.5). Thus, in general, an equation of the form (16.13) may be written as follows:

(16.37)
$$F_p = \frac{\beta_{p1}}{\sigma_1} X_1 + \frac{\beta_{p2}}{\sigma_2} X_2 + \cdots + \frac{\beta_{pn}}{\sigma_n} X_n - C,$$

where*

(16.38)
$$C = \frac{\beta_{p1}}{\sigma_1} \bar{X}_1 + \frac{\beta_{p2}}{\sigma_2} \bar{X}_2 + \cdots + \frac{\beta_{pn}}{\sigma_n} \bar{X}_n.$$

* The notation for the mean value of a variable should not be confused with the use of a bar over a factor to designate its prediction by regression methods.

It should be noted that an estimated factor is not in standard form. Such a variable, however, has a mean of zero and a standard deviation which is equal to the coefficient of multiple correlation as shown by (16.24).

The values of the factors estimated by equation (16.13), or (16.37), include both positive and negative numbers. If it is desired to eliminate the negative values, a transformation can be made to an arbitrary positive scale. This can be accomplished by standardizing the values $\bar{F}_{pi}$ given by (16.37) and equating this variable to an arbitrary variable in standard form. Thus if the arbitrary variable Y is assigned a mean of 50 and standard deviation of 10, the required transformation can be written in the form

$$(16.39) \qquad\qquad \bar{Y}_p = 10\bar{F}_p/R_p + 50,$$

where the multiple correlation coefficient has been substituted for the standard deviation of the estimated factor according to (16.24). Such transformations have been found especially useful in psychological studies employing factor estimates [245, 508].

An illustration of the proportions of the variance of one of the above estimated factors due to the eight physical variables will now be given. The direct and indirect contributions of these variables on the prediction of the factor $T_1 =$ Lankiness are indicated in Table 16.5. Each entry in the table proper represents the total indirect

Table 16.5

Proportions of Variance of Computed T_1 Due to the Independent Variables

Variable	1	2	3	4	5	6	7	8	Total Contribution $\beta_{1j}s_{j1}$
1	—	—	—	—	—	—	—	—	.253
2	.182	—	—	—	—	—	—	—	.369
3	.090	.140	—	—	—	—	—	—	.184
4	.075	.102	.051	—	—	—	—	—	.141
5	.011	.013	.007	.006	—	—	—	—	.020
6	−.002	−.002	−.001	−.001	−.001	—	—	—	−.003
7	−.001	−.001	−.000	−.001	−.000	.000	—	—	−.002
8	−.000	−.001	−.000	−.000	−.000	.000	.000	—	−.001
Direct contribution	.076	.153	.041	.025	.002	.000	.000	.000	
Indirect contribution	.177	.216	.143	.116	.018	−.003	−.002	−.001	$R_1^2 = .961$

contribution $(2\beta_{1j}\beta_{1k}r_{jk})$ of variables X_j and X_k. The total indirect contribution of any variable is equal to one-half of the sum in the row and column representing that variable and is given in the last row of the table. The direct contributions (β_{1j}^2) are given in the row preceding the last. The total contribution $(\beta_{1j}s_{j1})$ of each variable is presented in the last column of the table. Of course, the sum of the direct and indirect contributions of each variable must be equal to its total contribution. Finally, the sum of the entries in the last column (or last two rows) is equal to the square of the multiple correlation.

Since it is a well known fact that adding variables to a regression equation can only increase a multiple correlation, one might wonder about the small negative numbers in the last column of Table 16.5. No doubt these are spurious, insignificant values that have arisen from the rather involved mathematical computations. Because of the limited number of decimal figures retained in the calculations, no significance should be attached to the values appearing in the third decimal place as a result of a matrix inversion.

One practical use of the contributions of variables to the variance of a factor is to measure their relative importance for predictive purposes. In building a psychological test, for example, many items might be analyzed by factorial methods, and then the question might arise about the "importance" of the different items. A simple measure of validity is the correlation of an item with the factor. However, a much better indicator is the total contribution of an item to the variance of the computed factor. The correlation of an item with the factor does not reflect sufficiently the indirect contributions of the item through its correlations with each of the other items. Returning to the example of eight physical variables, this point might be made by comparing the importance of variable 1 (Height) with variable 5 (Weight) as to their effect on the prediction of factor T_1 (Lankiness). Their correlations with the factor are .92 and .46, respectively; while their total contributions to the prediction of the factor are .25 and .02, respectively. While one would not take direct ratios of these pairs of numbers, nonetheless it seems that the large difference in the proportions of the variance of the estimated factor make the latter numbers much more meaningful in judging the relative importance of the two variables.

Table 16.6

Coefficients of Regression Equations for Prediction of
Direct Oblimin ($\delta = 0$) Factors: Five Socio-Economic Variables

(Solution of Table 15.12)

Factor	Coefficients of Variables					Constant
	1	2	3	4	5	
	Standard Form					
T_1	−.5874	−.0666	.6742	.0730	.9136	
T_2	1.1214	.1407	−.1369	.0201	−.0639	
	Raw Score Form					
T_1	−.0002	−.0373	.0005	.0006	.0001	−2.2912
T_2	.0003	.0787	−.0001	.0002	−.0000	−2.5289

As indicated above, the measurement of factors by the complete estimation method is feasible only with an electronic computer, except for small problems. Just as an illustration, such computations were carried out in an **IBM 7094** for two oblique factors for the five socio-economic variables. The factors considered are those determined by the direct oblimin method in Table 15.12. The coefficients for the estimation equations are given in Table 16.6, both for the variables in standard form and in raw score form. Also the estimated measurements of the two oblique factors for each of the twelve census tracts are presented in Table 16.7. It should be remembered that the values in this table have been estimated, according to the least-squares principle, while the values in Table 16.2 are exact measurements of the rotated principal components.

Table 16.7

Measurements of Direct Oblimin ($\delta = 0$) Factors:
Five Socio-Economic Variables

(Solution of Table 15.12)

Case	$\bar{T}_1$	$\bar{T}_2$
1	1.38	−.14
2	−1.10	−1.51
3	−1.36	−.93
4	1.15	−.63
5	1.09	−.62
6	−.83	.40
7	−.40	−1.44
8	−.43	.85
9	.10	1.16
10	1.35	1.10
11	−.72	.89
12	−.22	.88

16.6. *Approximation Method*

Several approximations for estimating common factors have been proposed [194] to reduce the order of the matrix whose inverse is required. Such methods involve the grouping of certain variables into composites. The simplest procedure is as follows: Combine the respective subsets of variables which best measure the factors and employ formula (16.19) in which all the symbols now stand for the corresponding reduced matrices. This approximation method is best adapted to the case of many variables which fall into a relatively small number of distinct subgroups. In applying this formula to an example including, say, m subgroups, the $m \times m$ matrix of correlations among the composite variables is used in the place of **R**. Then the major portion of the calculations is greatly reduced. The effect of this procedure is to give all variables of a subgroup equal weight.

If it is desired to give varying weights to some of the individual variables, the preceding method can be modified slightly. For example, if the first four variables of a set are the best measures of the first common factor, they may be used individually, while all other variables are grouped into composites, for the estimation of this factor. The matrix whose inverse is required then consists of the intercorrelations of the first four variables and the $(m - 1)$ composite variables. When the second, and successive, factors, are estimated, the corresponding variables which best measure them are retained, while all other variables are grouped into composites.

To illustrate the approximation method, the eight physical variables are again employed. Grouping the variables as in (13.10), and using the standard deviations of (13.12), the composite variables may be written as follows:

$$u_1 = v_1/s_{v_1} = (z_1 + z_2 + z_3 + z_4)/3.7465,$$

$$u_2 = v_2/s_{v_2} = (z_5 + z_6 + z_7 + z_8)/3.4117.$$

The correlation between these composites can be calculated by means of formula (11.10), employing the correlations of the original variables from Table 5.3 to get

$$r_{v_1 v_2} = 5.686/12.782 = .4448.$$

The estimate of the first oblique factor T_1, for example, can be made from the regression equation

$$\overline{T}_1 = \beta_{11}u_1 + \beta_{12}u_2.$$

The normal equations (16.14) in this case are

$$\beta_{11} + .4448\beta_{12} = .977,$$

$$.4448\beta_{11} + \beta_{12} = .455,$$

where the correlations of the composite variables with T_1 are taken from the reduced structure. Solving these equations for the β's and substituting the results in the regression equation, produces

$$\overline{T}_1 = .9656u_1 + .0255u_2.$$

This equation cannot be used for estimating individual values of T_1 unless the values of the composite variables are computed. Instead, by substituting the expressions for u_1 and u_2, this equation becomes

$$\overline{T}_1 = .258(z_1 + z_2 + z_3 + z_4) + .007(z_5 + z_6 + z_7 + z_8),$$

illustrating the fact that all variables of a subgroup are given equal weight by the approximation method. For the two girls, considered before, the values of the first factor are $\overline{T}_{11} = -.30$ and $\overline{T}_{12} = 1.25$. The discrepancies between these values and those previously obtained are due to the grouping of the variables. While the preceding illustration makes possible direct comparison with the complete estimation method, one would not ordinarily use the approximation method when only eight variables are involved.

16.7. *Short Method*

While the method of the preceding section involves much less work than the complete estimation method, it is a somewhat crude approximation only. In the attempt to more nearly replicate the results of complete regression but with reduced labor, Ledermann [337] developed a "shortened method" for estimating factors by regression, and Harman [197] generalized the method to the case of oblique factors. To the extent that the factor solution is adequate (i.e., the residuals vanish), the results of the shortened method will approach those of the complete estimation method. In effect, the method to be developed in this section is a complete regression method applied to reproduced correlations rather than observed correlations. By making the assumption that the reproduced correlations are equal to the observed correlations, there derives the great advantage of replacing the nth order matrix of correlations by a matrix of order m (the number of common factors). Since the number of such factors usually is small by comparison to the number of variables, the labor of computing the inverse matrix is greatly reduced.

Stated explicitly, the assumption made in this section is that

$$(16.40) \qquad\qquad \mathbf{R}^\dagger + \mathbf{D}^2 = \mathbf{R},$$

i.e., the reproduced correlations, with ones in the diagonal, are set equal to the observed correlations. To avoid unnecessarily awkward notations, $\mathbf{R}$ will be employed for the correlations resulting from a factor analysis. Then, according to (2.47), this matrix can be expressed as follows:

$$(16.41) \qquad \mathbf{R} = (\mathbf{A}\ \mathbf{D})\begin{pmatrix}\mathbf{\Phi} & \mathbf{O}\\ \mathbf{O} & \mathbf{I}\end{pmatrix}\begin{pmatrix}\mathbf{A}'\\ \mathbf{D}\end{pmatrix} = (\mathbf{A}\mathbf{\Phi}\ \mathbf{D})\begin{pmatrix}\mathbf{A}'\\ \mathbf{D}\end{pmatrix} = \mathbf{A}\mathbf{\Phi}\mathbf{A}' + \mathbf{D}^2.$$

This relation will now be used in simplifying formula (16.20) for the estimation of the m common factors, permitted to be oblique in order to cover the most general case. Premultiplying both sides of (16.41) by $\mathbf{A}'\mathbf{D}^{-2}$ there arises*

$$(16.42) \qquad \mathbf{A}'\mathbf{D}^{-2}\mathbf{R} = \mathbf{A}'\mathbf{D}^{-2}(\mathbf{A}\mathbf{\Phi}\mathbf{A}' + \mathbf{D}^2) = (\mathbf{A}'\mathbf{D}^{-2}\mathbf{A}\mathbf{\Phi} + \mathbf{I})\mathbf{A}'.$$

Then, defining the following $m \times m$ matrix,

$$(16.43) \qquad\qquad \mathbf{K} = \mathbf{A}'\mathbf{D}^{-2}\mathbf{A}\mathbf{\Phi},$$

the expression (16.42) can be put in the form:

$$(16.44) \qquad\qquad (\mathbf{I} + \mathbf{K})\mathbf{A}' = \mathbf{A}'\mathbf{D}^{-2}\mathbf{R}.$$

Now, premultiplying both members of this equation by $(\mathbf{I} + \mathbf{K})^{-1}$ and postmultiplying by $\mathbf{R}^{-1}$, it becomes

$$(16.45) \qquad\qquad \mathbf{A}'\mathbf{R}^{-1} = (\mathbf{I} + \mathbf{K})^{-1}\mathbf{A}'\mathbf{D}^{-2}.$$

---

* Throughout this and the following section it is tacitly assumed that none of the uniquenesses vanishes. For an excellent treatment of the contrary case see Guttman [172].

Then, substituting this expression for $\mathbf{A'R}^{-1}$ in (16.20), there finally results

(16.46) $$\bar{\mathbf{f}} = \boldsymbol{\Phi}(\mathbf{I} + \mathbf{K})^{-1}\mathbf{A'D}^{-2}\mathbf{z},$$

where only the column vectors for the factors and variables are represented instead of the complete matrices for the N individuals. Although this formula may appear to be more complex than (16.20), it is actually much simpler to apply. Aside from inverting the squares of the unique-factor coefficients, the only matrix whose inverse must be calculated is of order m.

For the estimation of common factors by the short method, it is convenient to write formula (16.46) in another form. Premultiply both sides of this equation by $[\boldsymbol{\Phi}(\mathbf{I} + \mathbf{K})^{-1}]^{-1}$ to get

(16.47) $$(\mathbf{I} + \mathbf{K})\boldsymbol{\Phi}^{-1}\bar{\mathbf{f}} = \mathbf{A'D}^{-2}\mathbf{z}.$$

It will be observed that the resulting matrix on each side of (16.47) is of order $m \times 1$. This matrix equation represents a system of m algebraic equations, obtained by setting the corresponding elements equal to each other. The matrices in the right-hand member of (16.47) are quite simple, but the expression on the left appears to be rather complex. The latter may be put in a more convenient form by substituting the definition of $\mathbf{K}$, producing

(16.48) $$(\mathbf{I} + \mathbf{K})\boldsymbol{\Phi}^{-1} = (\mathbf{I} + \mathbf{A'D}^{-2}\mathbf{A}\boldsymbol{\Phi})\boldsymbol{\Phi}^{-1} = (\boldsymbol{\Phi}^{-1} + \mathbf{A'D}^{-2}\mathbf{A}).$$

Finally, the system of m equations for estimating the common factors may be written in the matrix form:

(16.49) $$\bar{\mathbf{f}} = \mathbf{L}^{-1}\mathbf{A'D}^{-2}\mathbf{z},$$

where

(16.50) $$\mathbf{L} = \boldsymbol{\Phi}^{-1} + \mathbf{J} \quad \text{and} \quad \mathbf{J} = \mathbf{A'D}^{-2}\mathbf{A}.$$

In case the common factors are uncorrelated, $\boldsymbol{\Phi}$ is the identity matrix, and formula (16.49) reduces to

(16.51) $$\bar{\mathbf{f}} = (\mathbf{I} + \mathbf{J})^{-1}\mathbf{A'D}^{-2}\mathbf{z} \qquad \text{(uncorrelated factors)}$$

The recommended procedure in applying formula (16.51) to a numerical problem is as follows: Divide each element of the jth row of $\mathbf{A}$ by d_j^2; this gives the matrix $\mathbf{D}^{-2}\mathbf{A}$, which occurs in $\mathbf{J}$ and the transpose of which also occurs in the right-hand member of (16.51). Then multiply $\mathbf{A}$ by $\mathbf{D}^{-2}\mathbf{A}$, column by column,* to get the $m \times m$ matrix $\mathbf{J}$. Finally, add unity to each diagonal element of $\mathbf{J}$ to complete the determination of the m equations represented by (16.51). Then the solution for the common factors can be carried out by the square root method of **3.4**.

The procedure for estimating a set of correlated factors by means of (16.49) is quite similar to the preceding. After the matrix $\mathbf{J}$ is determined, it must be added to

---

* As noted in **3.2**, paragraph **18**, this is the same as the conventional row-by-column multiplication of $\mathbf{A'}$ by $\mathbf{D}^{-2}\mathbf{A}$.

Φ^{-1} instead of the identity matrix. The procedure for calculating the inverse of a matrix is given in **3.5**.

A compact procedure for estimating factors by the short method, employing the square root method with a desk calculator, is outlined in Table 16.8 and illustrated with a numerical example. In order to demonstrate the most general case, the worksheet is set up to determine the regression coefficients for oblique factors. The primary-factor pattern in this table was obtained from a centroid solution and therefore is slightly different from that obtained in Table 13.1, which was derived from a minres solution. In Table 16.8, **P** is used to designate the oblique factor pattern, in place of the general symbol **A** of the formulas above. This is done to emphasize that the primary-factor system of oblique factors rather than the reference factors are the ones being estimated.

Table 16.8

Short Method of Estimating Factors by Regression

A. Computing Algorithm

Variable	Supplementary Matrices		Variables in Basic Matrices			
	$T_1 \cdots T_m$	$T_1 \cdots T_m$	1	2 · · · · · · · · · · · · ·		n
T_1 $\vdots$ T_m	Φ	**I**	**P′** (Transpose of factor pattern of factors for which regression equations are desired)			
	Square root method of Table 3.3 is applied to compute Φ^{-1}		Uniquenesses from diagonal matrix $\mathbf{D}^2$ (From initial orthogonal solution even if **P** is oblique)			
			Diagonal of **D** (Square roots of preceding numbers)			
T_1 $\vdots$ T_m		Φ^{-1}	$\mathbf{P'D}^{-1}$ (Entries in **P′** divided by number in corresponding column of preceding line)			
J is obtained by row-by-row multiplication of $\mathbf{P'D}^{-1}$ by itself	$\mathbf{L} = \Phi^{-1} + \mathbf{J}$ (Let $\mathbf{L} = \mathbf{E'E}$)		$\mathbf{C'} = \mathbf{P'D}^{-2}$ (Entries in **P′** divided by uniqueness for corresponding variable)			
Square root of matrix **L** applied to entire table (Operator $\mathbf{EL}^{-1}$)	**E**		$\mathbf{EL}^{-1}\mathbf{C'}$ (Square root operator applied to preceding matrix **C′**)			
T_1 $\vdots$ T_m			$\mathbf{B'} = \mathbf{L}^{-1}\mathbf{C'}$ (Back solution, using formulas of type (3.27), computing the last line first and working up)			

Table 16.8 (*continued*)

B. Example of Eight Physical Variables
(*Oblique Primary-Factor Solution*)

Variable	Supplementary Matrices				Variables in Basic Matrices							
	T_1	T_2	T_1	T_2	1	2	3	4	5	6	7	8
T_1	1.000	.484	1.000	0	.894	.956	.932	.879	.005	−.025	−.060	.080
T_2	*	1.000	0	1.000	.051	−.027	−.052	.029	.930	.825	.769	.685
	1.000	.484	1.000	0	.154	.111	.175	.202	.132	.339	.450	.471
		.875	−.553	1.143	.392	.333	.418	.449	.363	.582	.671	.686
T_1			1.306	−.632	2.281	2.871	2.230	1.958	.014	−.043	−.089	.117
T_2			*	1.306	.130	−.081	−.124	.065	2.562	1.418	1.146	.999
			23.542	−.731	5.805	8.613	5.326	4.351	.038	−.074	−.133	.170
			*	12.218	.331	−.243	−.297	.144	7.045	2.434	1.709	1.454
			4.852	−.151	1.196	1.775	1.098	.897	.008	−.015	−.027	.035
				3.492	.147	.007	−.041	.080	2.018	.696	.488	.418
T_1					.248	.366	.226	.186	.020	.003	−.001	.011
T_2					.042	.002	−.012	.023	.578	.199	.140	.120

The plan of computations in Table 16.8 was developed under the premise that the *reference structure* matrix **V** is the key component of the oblique simple-structure solution but that measurements of the *primary factors* are desired. In this type of multiple-factor analysis the sequence of calculations usually is as follows (see **13.5**):

1. **A**, initial orthogonal solution;
2. Λ, transformation matrix to reference structure;
3. **V**, reference structure in rotated simple-structure solution;
4. **Φ**, correlations among primary factors;
5. **D**, diagonal matrix required to normalize the rows of Λ^{-1} (not to be confused with the matrix of unique-factor coefficients);
6. $\mathbf{P} = \mathbf{VD}^{-1}$, primary-factor pattern in rotated simple-structure solution (can also be obtained by transformation of the initial orthogonal solution, viz., $\mathbf{P} = \mathbf{A(T')}^{-1}$, where $\mathbf{T'} = \mathbf{D\Lambda}^{-1}$);
7. $\mathbf{S} = \mathbf{P\Phi}$, primary-factor structure in rotated simple-structure solution.

After an oblique factor structure matrix **V** is obtained by the methods of chapters 13 or 15, it is converted to a primary-factor pattern **P** to provide the basic data for Table 16.8. Then the entries in this pattern are divided by the square-roots of the respective uniquenesses to obtain the matrix in the right-hand portion of the table, while the inverse of the matrix **Φ** of correlations among the factors is calculated in the left-hand portion. Next, the matrix **L** is determined on the left, and the matrix **C′** alongside it on the right. Application of the square root of matrix **L** to the entire

Table 16.9

Short Method of Estimating Factors, Including Calculation of R^{-1}

A. Computing Algorithm

Variable	Supplementary Matrices		Variables in Basic Matrices		
	$T_1 \cdots T_m$	$T_1 \cdots T_m$	1 2 . . . . n		
T_1 . . T_m	Φ	I	P' (Transpose of factor pattern of factors for which regression equations are desired)		
	Square root method of Table 3.3 is applied to compute Φ^{-1}		Uniquenesses from diagonal matrix D^2 (From initial orthogonal solution even if P is oblique)		
			Diagonal of D (Square roots of preceding numbers)		
T_1 . . . T_m		Φ^{-1}	$P'D^{-1}$ (Entries in P' divided by number in corresponding column of preceding line)		
J is obtained by row-by-row multiplication of $P'D^{-1}$ by itself	$L = \Phi^{-1} + J$ (Let $L = E'E$)		$C' = P'D^{-2}$ (Entries in P' divided by uniqueness for corresponding variable)		
Square root of matrix L applied to entire table (Operator EL^{-1})		E	$EL^{-1}C'$ (Square root operator applied to preceding matrix C')		
			Diagonal of D^{-2} (Reciprocals of uniquenesses)		
1 . . . n			$R^{-1} = D^{-2} - CL^{-1}C'$ (Compute $CL^{-1}C'$ by column-by-column multiplication of $EL^{-1}C'$ by itself, and subtract from D^{-2}) Actually inverse of $(R^{\dagger} + D^2)$ as approximation to R^{-1}		
T_1 . . . T_m			$S' = \Phi P'$ (Column-by-column multiplication of Φ and P')		
T_1 . . . T_m			$B' = S'R^{-1}$ (Row-by-row multiplication of S' and R^{-1})		

Table 16.9—Continued

B. Example of Eight Physical Variables

(Oblique Primary-Factor Solution)

Variable	Supplementary Matrices				Variables in Basic Matrices							
	T_1	T_2	T_1	T_2	1	2	3	4	5	6	7	8
T_1	1.000	.484	1.000	0	.894	.956	.932	.879	.005	−.025	−.060	.080
T_2	*	1.000	0	1.000	.051	−.027	−.052	.029	.930	.825	.769	.685
		1.000	.484	1.000	0	.154	.111	.175	.202	.132	.339	.450	.471
			.875	−.553	1.143	.392	.333	.418	.449	.363	.582	.671	.686
T_1			1.306	−.632	2.281	2.871	2.230	1.958	.014	−.043	−.089	.117
T_2			*	1.306	.130	−.081	−·124	.065	2.562	1.418	1.146	.999
			26.542	−.731	5.805	8.613	5.326	4.351	.038	−.074	−.133	.170
			*	12.218	.331	−.243	−.297	.144	7.045	2.434	1.709	1.454
			4.852	−.151	1.196	1.775	1.098	.897	.008	−.015	−.027	.035
				3.492	.147	.007	−.041	.080	2.018	.696	.488	.418
					6.494	9.009	5.714	4.950	7.576	2.950	2.222	2.123
1					5.042	−2.124	−1.307	−1.085	−.306	−.084	−.039	−.103
2					*	5.858	−1.949	−1.593	−.028	.022	.045	−.065
3					*	*	4.507	−.982	.074	.045	.050	−.021
4					*	*	*	4.139	−.169	−.042	−.015	−.065
5					*	*	*	*	3.504	−1.404	−.985	−.844
6					*	*	*	*	*	2.465	−.340	−.290
7					*	*	*	*	*	*	1.983	−.203
8					*	*	*	*	*	*	*	1.947
T_1					.919	.943	.907	.893	.455	.374	.312	.412
T_2					.484	.435	.399	.454	.932	.813	.740	.724
T_1					.251	.365	.229	.182	.023	.004	.002	.013
T_2					.045	−.003	−.001	.019	.577	.202	.140	.121

table yields $\mathbf{EL}^{-1}\mathbf{C}'$ in the right-hand block. Now, from (16.49) the matrix of β-coefficients may be written in the form:

$$(16.52) \qquad\qquad \mathbf{B}' = \mathbf{L}^{-1}\mathbf{C}',$$

in which $\mathbf{C}'$ as defined in Table 16.8 corresponds to $\mathbf{A}'\mathbf{D}^{-2}$ of (16.49). In order to get the right-hand member of (16.52) from $\mathbf{EL}^{-1}\mathbf{C}'$ it is only necessary to premultiply this expression by $\mathbf{E}^{-1}$. Without actually calculating the inverse of the triangular matrix $\mathbf{E}$, the desired result can be accomplished by applying formulas of the type (3.27).

367

The last two lines of Table 16.8B contain the β-weights for the equations giving $\overline{T}_1$ and $\overline{T}_2$ in terms of the standardized variables. By comparison with equations (16.36) obtained by complete regression, it will be noted that the agreement is excellent, minor discrepancies being due to the fact that the correlations computed from the factor pattern are not exactly equal to the corresponding observed correlations. The coefficients of multiple correlation, $R_1 = .981$ and $R_2 = .960$, indicate that the present method for predicting T_1 and T_2 are just as reliable as the equations (16.36), for which $R_1 = .980$ and $R_2 = .961$. For the two girls whose measurements on the eight physical variables are given in Table 16.4 the values of the factors, as estimated by the short method, are

$$\overline{T}_{11} = -0.27, \quad \overline{T}_{21} = 1.80,$$

$$\overline{T}_{12} = 1.23, \quad \overline{T}_{22} = 0.52,$$

which are practically identical with the values previously obtained.

It should be remembered that the method developed in this section is dependent upon the vanishing of the residuals resulting from the factor analysis. If the condition (16.40) is satisfied only approximately then the β-weights and multiple correlations produced by the short method will approach the actual values as the residuals approach zero. Dwyer [108, p. 216] suggests that the multiple correlation resulting from the use of the factor solution will generally differ in absolute value from the actual multiple R determined from the observed correlations by an amount approximately equal to the average of the absolute residual error.

In the procedure just outlined the results of the factor analysis were employed to obviate the calculation of $\mathbf{R}^{-1}$ required in the basic formula (16.19) of the complete regression method. It is also possible to obtain an approximation to $\mathbf{R}^{-1}$ via the factor analysis, and then to get the regression weights by this formula. The computing algorithm for this purpose is presented in Table 16.9A, and the procedure is illustrated for the example of eight physical variables in Table 16.9B. The work through the square root of matrix $\mathbf{L}$ is identical to that in Table 16.8. The remaining manipulations in Table 16.9 lead to an approximation of $\mathbf{R}^{-1}$ and the calculations of the β's by (16.19). Since this formula calls for the correlations of the variables with the primary factors, such a factor structure is computed toward the bottom of Table 16.9.

An alternative procedure, in which $\mathbf{P}$ and $\mathbf{S}$ are not obtained explicitly, is employed by Carroll [63] in an IBM 704 computer program (and subsequently adapted to later model computers) to get "factor score coefficients" by the short method. The output of this program must be multiplied by the matrix $\mathbf{D}$ to get the actual β-weights. If a high-speed electronic computer is available, the determination of factor measurements by the short method is certainly very practical and is the recommended procedure.

While the worksheet of Table 16.9 is designed primarily for determining factor measurements by the short method, there is inherent in this table a technique for much more general statistical application. The reference is to the potential for a simplified method of inverting a matrix, which operation is frequently required in statistical work. For example, in multiple regression analysis involving n variables, the inverse of a correlation matrix of order n is required. If a factor solution (*any* factor solution) involving only m (much less than n) common factors were obtained, considerable savings could be realized by employing the method of Table 16.9. Ordinarily an orthogonal factor solution would be employed. Then the worksheet would be simplified since the identity matrix $\mathbf{I}$ would replace $\boldsymbol{\Phi}^{-1}$ and only the second square root operation would be involved. For further developments in the utilization of factor analysis in multiple and partial regression the reader is referred to Dwyer [108] and Creager [90].

16.8. Estimation by Minimizing Unique Factors

An alternative to the ordinary regression method for estimating factors has been proposed by Bartlett [25]. Whereas in the previous methods the sum of the squares of discrepancies between the true and estimated factors over the range of individuals is minimized, now the sum of squares of the unique factors over the range of variables will be minimized. This method is in harmony with Bartlett's principle that unique factors should be introduced only in order to explain discrepancies between observed values and postulated general or group factors.

To indicate how the theory is developed, consider the case of only two common factors with the following factor pattern:

$$(16.53) \qquad z_j = a_{j1}F_1 + a_{j2}F_2 + d_jU_j \qquad (j = 1, 2, \cdots, n).$$

The explicit expression for the unique factor of any variable z_j is

$$(16.54) \qquad U_j = (z_j - a_{j1}F_1 - a_{j2}F_2)/d_j,$$

and the sum of the squares of all such factors may be denoted by the function

$$(16.55) \qquad U(F_1, F_2) = \sum_{j=1}^{n} U_j^2 = \sum_{j=1}^{n} (z_j - a_{j1}F_1 - a_{j2}F_2)^2/d_j^2.$$

Then to minimize the sum of squares of the unique factors over the range of variables, it is necessary that the partial derivatives of the function U with respect to F_1 and F_2 vanish, i.e.,

$$\begin{cases} \dfrac{\partial U}{\partial F_1} = 2\sum \dfrac{1}{d_j^2}(z_j - a_{j1}F_1 - a_{j2}F_2)a_{j1} = 0, \\[2mm] \dfrac{\partial U}{\partial F_2} = 2\sum \dfrac{1}{d_j^2}(z_j - a_{j1}F_1 - a_{j2}F_2)a_{j2} = 0, \end{cases}$$

where the summations extend from $j = 1$ to $j = n$. These equations may be put in the form

$$(16.56) \qquad \begin{cases} \left(\sum \dfrac{a_{j1}^2}{d_j^2}\right)\bar{F}_1 + \left(\sum \dfrac{a_{j1}a_{j2}}{d_j^2}\right)\bar{F}_2 = \sum \dfrac{a_{j1}}{d_j^2} z_j, \\[3mm] \left(\sum \dfrac{a_{j2}a_{j1}}{d_j^2}\right)\bar{F}_1 + \left(\sum \dfrac{a_{j2}^2}{d_j^2}\right)\bar{F}_2 = \sum \dfrac{a_{j2}}{d_j^2} z_j, \end{cases}$$

where bars have been placed on the F's to distinguish the estimates of the factors

369

from the true factors. This pair of simultaneous equations can be solved for the two unknowns, $\bar{F}_1$ and $\bar{F}_2$, by the methods of chapter 3.

The foregoing development can be generalized to the case of m factors. The set of equations (16.56), written in matrix form, then becomes:

$$(16.57) \qquad\qquad \mathbf{J}\bar{\mathbf{f}} = \mathbf{A}'\mathbf{D}^{-2}\mathbf{z},$$

in which the matrix $\mathbf{J}$ is defined in (16.50). Although formula (16.57) is not a special case of formula (16.49), it may be noted that if the term $\mathbf{\Phi}^{-1}$ is dropped from the matrix $\mathbf{L}$ in that formula it becomes identical with (16.57). The computations required in the application of formula (16.57) are the same as that described for the short method, except that nothing is added to the matrix $\mathbf{J}$. The general computing scheme of Table 16.8 is applicable in a simplified version, in which $\mathbf{\Phi}^{-1}$ is not employed and $\mathbf{J}$ replaces $\mathbf{L}$.

The calculation of factor estimates according to formula (16.57) is presented in Table 16.10, both schematically and for the same numerical example employed in

Table 16.10

Estimation by Minimization of Unique Factors

A. Computing Algorithm

Variable	Supplementary Matrices		Basic Matrices	
	T_1 · · · · · · T_m		1 2 · · · · · · · · · · · · · · · n	
T_1 . . . T_m			$\mathbf{P}'$ (Transpose of factor pattern of factors for which prediction equations are desired)	
			Uniquenesses from diagonal matrix $\mathbf{D}^2$ (From initial orthogonal solution even if $\mathbf{P}$ is oblique)	
			Diagonal of $\mathbf{D}$ (Square roots of preceding numbers)	
T_1 . . . T_m			$\mathbf{P}'\mathbf{D}^{-1}$ (Entries in $\mathbf{P}'$ divided by number in corresponding column of preceding line)	
	$\mathbf{J}$ (Row-by-row multiplication of $\mathbf{P}'\mathbf{D}^{-1}$ by itself) (Let $\mathbf{J} = \mathbf{S}'\mathbf{S}$)		$\mathbf{C}' = \mathbf{P}'\mathbf{D}^{-2}$ (Entries in $\mathbf{P}'$ divided by uniqueness for corresponding variable)	
	$\mathbf{S}$ (Square root of matrix $\mathbf{J}$)		$\mathbf{S}\mathbf{J}^{-1}\mathbf{C}'$ (Square root operator applied to preceding matrix $\mathbf{C}'$)	
T_1 . . . T_m			$\mathbf{\Gamma}' = \mathbf{J}^{-1}\mathbf{C}'$ (Back solution, using formulas of type (3.27), computing the last line first and working up)	

the previous sections. The data through the matrix $\mathbf{C'}$ are identical to that employed in the short method. The supplementary matrix to the left of $\mathbf{C'}$, however, is simply $\mathbf{J}$ instead of the matrix $\mathbf{L}$ of the preceding tables. Then the square root of matrix $\mathbf{J}$ operating on $\mathbf{C'}$ produces $\mathbf{SJ^{-1}C'}$. If this expression is premultiplied by $\mathbf{S^{-1}}$ there results the matrix of coefficients of the variables in the prediction equations for the factors as given by (16.57), namely:

$$(16.58) \qquad\qquad \mathbf{\Gamma' = J^{-1}C'},$$

in which the coefficients are designated by γ's to distinguish them from the conventional regression coefficients, and $\mathbf{C'}$ as defined in Table 16.10 corresponds to $\mathbf{A'D^{-2}}$ of (16.57). As before, it is not necessary to calculate the inverse of the square root matrix since the same effect can be accomplished by the back solution of the square root method outlined in Step 9 of **3.4**.

The γ-coefficients of the standardized variables for estimating the common factor by (16.57) are given in the last two lines of Table 16.10B. For the two girls previously considered, estimates of the factor measurements follow:

$$\overline{T}_{11} = -0.35, \quad \overline{T}_{21} = 2.03;$$
$$\overline{T}_{12} = 1.28, \quad \overline{T}_{22} = 0.56.$$

Table 16.10 (*continued*)

B. Example of Eight Physical Variables
(*Oblique Primary-Factor Solution*)

Variable	Supplementary Matrices		Basic Matrices							
	T_1	T_2	1	2	3	4	5	6	7	8
T_1			.894	.956	.932	.879	.005	−.025	−.060	.080
T_2			.051	−.027	−.052	.029	.930	.825	.769	.685
			.154	.111	.175	.202	.132	.339	.450	.471
			.392	.333	.418	.449	.363	.582	.671	.686
T_1			2.281	2.871	2.230	1.958	.014	−.043	−.089	.117
T_2			.130	−.081	−.124	.065	2.562	1.418	1.146	.999
	22.236	−.099	5.805	8.613	5.326	4.351	.038	−.074	−.133	.170
	*	10.912	.331	−.243	−.297	.144	7.045	2.434	1.709	1.454
	4.716	−.020	1.231	1.826	1.129	.923	.008	−.016	−.028	.036
		3.302	.108	−.063	−.083	.049	2.134	.737	.517	.441
T_1			.261	.387	.239	.196	.004	−.002	−.005	.008
T_2			.033	−.019	−.025	.015	.646	.223	.157	.134

The reliability of prediction can be judged by the appropriate standard error or multiple correlation coefficient. It should be noted, however, that formula (16.25) does not yield the required multiple correlation for the present method. If formula (16.25) is applied, the resulting "multiple correlation" will be found to be equal to unity. This follows from the fact that the common factors are estimated under the condition that the unique factors are minimized, and the uniqueness is the standard error of estimate in a pattern equation.

Bartlett [25, p. 100] proposes as a measure of the "information (reciprocal of the error variance)" for any factor p, the expression

$$(16.59) \qquad |\mathbf{J}|/|\mathbf{J}_{pp}|,$$

where $|\mathbf{J}_{pp}|$ is the minor of the element in row and column p of $|\mathbf{J}|$. From this expression, a measure of "multiple correlation" for the prediction of a factor p by the method discussed in this section may be put in the form:

$$(16.60) \qquad R_p^2 = 1 - |\mathbf{J}_{pp}|/|\mathbf{J}|.$$

This form corresponds to the multiple correlation for the conventional regression estimate of a factor p (shown for the orthogonal case by Dwyer [108, p. 229]), namely:

$$(16.61) \qquad R_p^2 = 1 - |\mathbf{L}_{pp}|/|\mathbf{L}|,$$

where $\mathbf{L}$ is defined in (16.50) and $|\mathbf{L}_{pp}|$ is the minor of the element in row and column p of $|\mathbf{L}|$.

The multiple correlations for the factors estimated in Table 16.10B, as given by formula (16.60) are

$$R_1 = 1 - 10.912/242.629 = .977,$$

$$R_2 = 1 - 22.236/242.629 = .953.$$

These values are practically identical to those obtained by the complete estimation method or the short method. For the particular example it may be concluded that, statistically, the different methods for estimating factors are equally good. For other data the method of this section may lead to radically different results than the conventional regression methods (compare exercises 2 or 6 with 13). The choice of the method of this section instead of one of the other methods must be made on the basis of the principle of prediction which is involved.

The estimates of the common factors by means of formula (16.57) provide an alternative solution to any of the regression estimates of the preceding sections. Bartlett pointed out that the principle of estimation adopted in this section does not completely agree with the solution that has usually been employed, although the difference does not affect the relative weights assigned to the variables in estimating a single general factor. When several common factors are involved, however, the discrepancy between equations (16.49) and (16.57) is even more serious. Bartlett [25] states: "One point of view appears to have been to consider all the persons with different possible factorial make-ups that would give rise to the observed test scores

372

of a particular person, whereas I have regarded the test scores as a sample of all possible scores that might have arisen for that person according to the different values of specific [unique] factors he may happen to have."

16.9. *Factor Measurements by Ideal Variables*

While on the subject of factor measurements, one more procedure will be indicated. It is possible to get a mathematical solution for the factors in terms of the variables (z_j'') in the common-factor space. To this end write (16.1) in the form:

$$(16.62) \qquad\qquad \mathbf{z}^* = \mathbf{Af},$$

where $\mathbf{z}^*$ is the column vector $\{z_1'' \; z_2'' \cdots z_n''\}$ of the variables projected into the common-factor space. The factors may be determined as linear combinations of the hypothetical variables (z_j'') much as was done in **16.3** for the case of principal components. Pre-multiplying (16.62) by $\mathbf{A}'$ and designating the diagonal matrix of m eigenvalues by

$$(16.63) \qquad\qquad \mathbf{\Lambda}_m = \mathbf{A}'\mathbf{A}$$

as in (8.22), the explicit solution for $\mathbf{f}$ becomes:

$$(16.64) \qquad\qquad \mathbf{f} = \mathbf{\Lambda}_m^{-1}\mathbf{A}'\mathbf{z}^*.$$

This result is very similar to (16.3) for principal components except for the fact that the observed variables are replaced by "ideal" variables in the present case.

To illustrate the present method, formula (16.64) will be applied to the example of eight physical variables. The matrix $\mathbf{A}$ of coefficients of the common factors T_1 and T_2 is the matrix $\mathbf{P}$ of Table 16.8. The matrix $\mathbf{\Lambda}_m$ and its inverse follow:

$$\mathbf{\Lambda}_2 = \begin{bmatrix} 3.365 & -.011 \\ -.011 & 2.613 \end{bmatrix}, \quad \mathbf{\Lambda}_2^{-1} = \begin{bmatrix} .297 & .001 \\ .001 & .383 \end{bmatrix},$$

The inverse matrix may be computed by the method outlined in **3.5**, or, for the simple case of a second-order matrix, directly from the definition of an inverse in **3.2**, paragraph **22**. The only calculation remaining is the multiplication by $\mathbf{A}'$, producing the following expressions for the factors:

$$T_1 = .266z_1'' + .284z_2'' + .277z_3'' + .261z_4'' + .002z_5'' - .007z_6'' - .017z_7'' + .024z_8'',$$

$$T_2 = .020z_1'' - .009z_2'' - .019z_3'' + .012z_4'' + .356z_5'' + .316z_6'' + .294z_7'' + .262z_8''.$$

These equations give the descriptions of the two oblique factors (not their estimates) in terms of the "common-factor portions" of the original variables. The values of the variables z_j'' are not known, and hence cannot be applied directly to obtain the measurements of the factors for the individuals. By replacing each z_j'' by z_j, however, an approximation can be obtained. Denoting such approximations by double primes, the measurements for the two girls previously studied become:

$$\text{Case 1:}\ \ T_{11}'' = -.036,\ T_{21}'' = 1.98;$$

$$\text{Case 2:}\ \ T_{12}'' = \ \ 1.31,\ \ T_{22}'' = 0.68.$$

These values are different from those obtained by the complete estimation method

373

or the short method, as should be expected. Their being of the same order of magnitude is due to the relatively small uniqueness, so that the ideal variables are not too far removed from the observed variables. Also, it is almost unfortunate that the eight physical variables constitute such a simple, well-structured set of data for which many different approaches lead to nearly equivalent results.

*   *   *

Certain consequences of the factor analysis model should be noted. The fundamental assumption that the observed variables are linear functions of the factor variables implies that certain kinds of data (e.g., color of eyes, nationality) cannot be studied in the framework of factor analysis. A corollary condition is that all observed variables must be linearly related to one another. In general if factor-analysis methods were to be applied to qualitative or non-linear data, new equations would have to be derived to fit the data. Hence, the first step to take in a factor analysis is to make certain that the n observed variables are linearly related. Very often this is not done because of the implied labor. At least a visual inspection if not a formal statistical check should be made for each pair of observed variables. If non-linearity appears, then at least one of the non-linear pair is not a linear function of the factors.

Sometimes factor analysis is applied to non-linearly related variables, provided their relationships are monotonic. This is done with the belief that a straight line is always a good approximation to a monotonic function. Under this premise, most of the variance will be explained by the common-factor coefficients, even though a portion may be lost due to the inadequate fit of a straight line to a curve. Hence, while the factor analysis model may not be appropriate in a strict sense, it may be very useful in explaining the correlations and extracting as much variance as possible by means of the factors.

A purely statistical restriction is the requirement that each observed variable be normally distributed. While considerable latitude might be allowed, nevertheless a variable which is distinctly non-normal should not be included in the analysis. It must be remembered that the n variables are presumed to have a multivariate normal distribution in the mathematical developments leading to the large sample χ^2 tests of **9.5** and **10.4**. In other words, the powerful statistical methods of chapters 9 and 10 will lead to sound conclusions provided the basic assumptions are met.

Factor analysis has made tremendous progress in recent years. Much of this modern development is included in the text. However, what has been presented certainly is not all there is to say about factor analysis. Some of the omitted areas are: (a) applications of factor analysis in general; (b) specific applications toward construction of theories in the behavioral sciences, such as the works of Ahmavaara [4], Burt [60], Cattell [76], Henrysson [226], Stephenson [449], and Vernon [499]; (c) inverted factor techniques as expounded principally by Cattell and Stephenson; and image analysis of Guttman [176]. This book is intended to provide the logical foundation and to build the theories and computing procedures for the major methods of factor analysis.

The new computing techniques, the objective procedures for determining simple-structure solutions, and the statistical tests of hypotheses are largely responsible for bringing modern factor analysis out of the abyss of a psychological fetish to the heights of a respected branch of statistical multivariate analysis.

PART V

PROBLEMS AND EXERCISES

Problems

CHAPTER 2

1. Why are each of the following types of factors postulated:
   (a) common, (b) unique, (c) specific, (d) error?

2. Why are all variables and factors taken to be in standard form?

3. Write equations (2.9) for $n = 5$ and $m = 2$.

4. (a) What elements of these equations must be calculated in obtaining a factor solution?
   (b) How many of these elements are there to be determined in the case of exercise 3?

5. (a) Write the contributions of the common factors to the variance of z_1 in the following pattern equation:

   $$z_1 = .5F_1 + .8F_2 + .33U_1$$

   (b) Write the contributions of the common factors to the variance of z_2 in exercise 3.

6. Obtain the total contributions of the common factors in exercise 3.

7. What is the communality of z_1 in exercise 5?

8. Why cannot the communality of a variable exceed its reliability?

9. In the following table there are eight exercises in which two quantities are given and the remaining three can be determined therefrom. Complete the table.

377

Variance Component	a	b	c	d	e	f	g	h
Specificity	.10	.15	.20	.25				
Error variance	.20				.05	.10		
Communality		.75			.60		.50	
Uniqueness			.35			.45		.30
Reliability				.85			.75	.90

Exercises 10–25 are based upon the data of Table I.

Table I
Coefficients of Two Uncorrelated Common Factors

Variable	F_1	F_2
1	.7	.3
2	.8	0
3	.7	0
4	.8	.6
5	.6	.5
6	.5	0
7	.6	.4
8	.7	.6

10. Calculate the communality of variable 8.

11. Which variable has the highest communality?

12. Which variable has the lowest communality?

13. Calculate the uniqueness of variable 1.

14. Which variable has the lowest uniqueness?

15. Which variable has the highest uniqueness?

16. Is a general factor present in this solution?

17. Is a group factor present in this solution?

18. Find the total contributions of F_1 and F_2.

19. What per cent of the total variance is attributable to each of the common factors?

20. What per cent of the total communality is attributable to each of the common factors?

21. If the reliability of variable 5 is .84, write the complete linear description of this variable, including the specific and error factors.

378

22. Calculate the index of completeness of factorization for variable 5.

23. What is the complexity of variable 1? Of variable 2?

24. Calculate the correlations r'_{12}, r'_{14}, r'_{25}, r'_{26}.

25. Are any of the reproduced correlations equal to zero?

CHAPTER 3

Evaluate the determinants in exercises 1–6:

1. $\begin{vmatrix} 5 & 3 \\ 2 & 4 \end{vmatrix}$
   2. $\begin{vmatrix} 3 & 4 \\ -2 & 6 \end{vmatrix}$
   3. $\begin{vmatrix} 4 & -2 \\ -7 & 3 \end{vmatrix}$

4. $\begin{vmatrix} 4 & 3 & 4 \\ 2 & 1 & 5 \\ 1 & 5 & 3 \end{vmatrix}$
   5. $\begin{vmatrix} 3 & -2 & 4 \\ 8 & 5 & -3 \\ 1 & 2 & 1 \end{vmatrix}$
   6. $\begin{vmatrix} 1 & 2 & 1 \\ 0 & 1 & 2 \\ 1 & 3 & 3 \end{vmatrix}$

Find the ranks of the matrices in exercises 7–9:

7. $\mathbf{A} = \begin{bmatrix} -4 & 2 & -6 \\ 6 & -3 & 9 \end{bmatrix}$
   8. $\mathbf{B} = \begin{bmatrix} 1 & 2 & 1 \\ 0 & 1 & 2 \\ 1 & 3 & 3 \end{bmatrix}$
   9. $\mathbf{C} = \begin{bmatrix} .81 & .54 & .72 \\ .54 & .40 & .54 \\ .72 & .54 & .73 \end{bmatrix}$

10. Are the matrices **B** and **C** singular or nonsingular?

11. Which of the matrices **A**, **B**, **C** is symmetric?

12. Postmultiply the matrix **A** by the matrix **B**. What is the rank of the product matrix?

13. Write the transpose of: (a) the pattern matrix of ex. 3, chap. 2; (b) the pattern matrix of Table I.

14. Assume the following pattern (with uncorrelated factors):

$$z_1 = .5F_1 + .8F_2 + .33U_1$$
$$z_2 = .8F_1 + .3F_2 \qquad\qquad + .52U_2$$
$$z_3 = .6F_1 + .6F_2 \qquad\qquad\qquad + .53U_3$$
$$z_4 = .7F_1 + .4F_2 \qquad\qquad\qquad\qquad + .59U_4$$
$$z_5 = .7F_1 + .7F_2 \qquad\qquad\qquad\qquad\qquad + .14U_5$$

   (a) Calculate the matrix $\mathbf{R}^\dagger$ of reproduced correlations (to 2 decimal places) by means of equation (2.50).
   (b) Interpret the diagonal elements.

15. Assume the following factor solution:

$$z_1 = .80F_1 + .60F_2$$
$$z_2 = .73F_1 + .68F_2$$
$$z_3 = .87F_1 + .49F_2$$
$$z_4 = .51F_1 + .86F_2$$
$$z_5 = .64F_1 + .77F_2$$

(a) Calculate $\mathbf{R}^\dagger$.
(b) Interpret the diagonal elements.

16. For the numerical examples:

$$\mathbf{A} = \begin{bmatrix} 1 & 2 \\ 3 & 4 \end{bmatrix} \quad \text{and} \quad \mathbf{B} = \begin{bmatrix} 0 & 1 \\ 2 & 3 \end{bmatrix},$$

show that:
(a) $\mathbf{AB} \neq \mathbf{BA}$, i.e., multiplication of matrices is not commutative;
(b) $|\mathbf{AB}| = |\mathbf{A}| \cdot |\mathbf{B}|$, i.e., the determinant of the product of two square matrices is equal to the product of their determinants;
(c) $|\mathbf{AB}| = |\mathbf{BA}|$, i.e., the determinant of the product of two square matrices is independent of the order of multiplication of the matrices.

17. Compute the product matrices $\mathbf{AB}$, $\mathbf{BA}$, $\mathbf{A'B}$, $\mathbf{BA'}$, $\mathbf{B'A}$, $\mathbf{AB'}$, $\mathbf{A'B'}$, $\mathbf{B'A'}$ when the individual matrices are given by:

$$\mathbf{A} = \begin{bmatrix} 1 & 2 & 3 \\ 0 & 1 & 4 \\ 0 & 0 & 1 \end{bmatrix} \quad \text{and} \quad \mathbf{B} = \begin{bmatrix} 6 & 0 & 0 \\ 7 & 8 & 0 \\ 7 & 4 & 2 \end{bmatrix}.$$

Verify, with these particular examples, that multiplication of matrices is not commutative. Also verify the theorem on the transpose of products of matrices, viz., $(\mathbf{AB})' = \mathbf{B'A'}$, $(\mathbf{A'B})' = \mathbf{B'A}$, etc.

18. For the matrices of the preceding exercise, obtain the values of the determinants $|\mathbf{A}|$, $|\mathbf{B}|$, $|\mathbf{AB}|$, and $|\mathbf{BA}|$.

19. Given the following two matrices:

$$\mathbf{C} = \begin{bmatrix} 2 & 4 & 6 \\ 3 & 1 & 2 \end{bmatrix} \quad \text{and} \quad \mathbf{D} = \begin{bmatrix} 9 & 1 \\ 3 & 2 \\ 2 & 7 \end{bmatrix}.$$

(a) Compute the product matrices $\mathbf{CD}$ and $\mathbf{DC}$.
(b) Are the determinants of the resulting matrices equal?

20. Show that the product (in either order) of a matrix by its transpose is a symmetric matrix.

380

21. The determinant of the inverse of a matrix is equal to the reciprocal of the determinant of the matrix, i.e.,

$$|\mathbf{A}^{-1}| = \frac{1}{|\mathbf{A}|}.$$

Demonstrate this theorem in the following two instances:

(a) $\mathbf{A} = \begin{bmatrix} a & b \\ c & d \end{bmatrix}$

(b) $\mathbf{A} = \begin{bmatrix} 2 & 1 & 1 & 2 \\ 1 & 2 & 1 & 0 \\ 3 & 1 & 1 & 1 \\ 0 & 0 & 3 & 0 \end{bmatrix}.$

22. Calculate the inverse of the matrix

$$\begin{bmatrix} 1.000 & .693 & .216 \\ .693 & 1.000 & .295 \\ .216 & .295 & 1.000 \end{bmatrix}$$

by the square root method indicated in Table 3.3, and check the results by (3.14).

23. Compute the inverse of the matrix in ex. 21 (b), employing the square root method of Table 3.3 and check the result by comparing the value of its determinant with that obtained in ex. 21. (Hint: Use idea of ex. 20.)

CHAPTER 4

1. (a) Construct a 2-dimensional rectangular Cartesian coordinate system and plot the following points: $(1, 2)$, $(0, 4)$, $(3, 0)$, $(-2, 5)$, $(-3, 0)$, $(2, -2)$, $(-3, -1)$, $(0, -4)$.
   (b) Plot the points whose coordinates are given in (a) with respect to a reference system in which the axes form an angle of $45°$.

2. In a non-homogeneous Cartesian coordinate system in a 5-dimensional Euclidean space, how many of each of the following occur:
   (a) coordinate axes, (b) coordinate hyperplanes, (c) planes through pairs of axes, (d) three-flats through sets of three axes?

3. In a rectangular coordinate system, plot the points $P:(3, 4)$ and cP for $c = 2, 3$. What is the relationship among these three points?

4. Determine the linear combination of the two points $P_1:(1, 3)$ and $P_2:(2, 4)$ for $t_1 = 3, t_2 = -2$. Plot these three points.

5. Determine the linear combination of the three points $P_1:(1, 3, 4)$, $P_2:(2, 1, 5)$, and $P_3:(3, -2, -1)$ for $t_1 = 2, t_2 = -3$, and $t_3 = 1$.

6. Show that the three points $P_1:(1, 2)$, $P_2:(3, 4)$, $P_3:(5, 1)$ are linearly dependent by employing the conditions (4.3). Express the coordinates of P_3 explicitly as linear combinations of the coordinates of P_1 and P_2.

7. (a) By use of Theorem 4.1 determine the number of linearly independent points in the set of four points of exercise 5.

   (b) What is the smallest space containing these four points?

   (c) For the set of three points of exercise 6, how many are linearly independent and what is the smallest space containing them?

8. Given two points $P_1:(3, 4)$ and $P_2:(4, 1)$ in a rectangular Cartesian coordinate system, find (a) $D(OP_1)$, (b) $D(OP_2)$, (c) $D(P_1 P_2)$.

9. Write equations (4.22) for the rotation about the origin:
   (a) in the plane; (b) in ordinary space.

10. (a) In a rectangular coordinate system, find the direction cosines of the straight line through the origin and the point $P:(4, 3)$.

    (b) Find the sum of the squares of the direction cosines.

11. (a) In a four dimensional rectangular coordinate system, find the direction cosines of a line through the origin and the point $P:(.4, .2, .1, -.2)$.

    (b) Find the sum of the squares of the direction cosines.

12. Find the angle between the line of exercise 11 and the line going through the origin and the point $Q:(.5, .6, .4, .2)$.

13. Find the scalar product of the two vectors of exercise 12.

14. (a) Given two points $P_1:(0, 4)$ and $P_2:(3, 0)$ in a reference system in which the axes form an angle of 60°, find $D(P_1 P_2)$.

    (b) Find the distance between two points with the preceding coordinates in a rectangular reference system.

    (c) Plot these points employing the same horizontal line for the first axis in each case and the same origin. Verify the distances.

Exercises 15–19 are based upon the data of Table II.

Table II

Values of Two Variables for Three Individuals

Individual i	X_{1i}	X_{2i}
1	1	2
2	5	2
3	6	8

15. Exhibit the point representation and also the vector representation of the data.

16. Obtain the lengths of the vectors representing the variables.

382

17. Calculate the direction cosines of these vectors.

18. (a) Find the angle of separation of these vectors.
    (b) Determine the coefficient of correlation by use of formula (4.48).

19. Check the value of the correlation coefficient by employing the standardized values in formula (2.7).

Exercises 20–22 are based upon the data of Table I.
20. Are the two columns of the pattern matrix linearly independent?

21. What is the rank of the reproduced correlation matrix $\mathbf{R}^\dagger$ (determined in ex. 25, chap. 2)?

22. What subset of variables would give a correlation matrix of rank one?

Exercises 23–25 are based upon the data of Table III.

Table III

Coefficients of Two Uncorrelated Common Factors

Variable	F_1	F_2
1	.86	.43
2	.48	.24
3	.70	.35
4	.50	.25
5	.64	.32
6	.56	.28

23. Plot the points representing the six variables in the common factor space.

24. (a) Are the two columns of the pattern matrix linearly independent?
    (b) Do all the second order minors vanish?
    (c) Why can these six variables be described in terms of only one common factor?

25. Obtain a factor solution in terms of only one common factor, calculating the factor weights: (a) from the plot of exercise 23; (b) by employing formula (4.52).

26. Given the following portion of an orthogonal factor pattern:

$$z_1'' = .4F_1 + .2F_2 + .1F_3 - .2F_4,$$

$$z_2'' = .5F_1 + .6F_2 + .4F_3 + .2F_4.$$

Calculate:
(a) the correlation corrected for uniqueness;
(b) the reproduced correlation, as the scalar product of the two vectors in the common-factor space;
(c) the reproduced correlation, as the cosine of the angle between the two vectors in the total factor space.

383

CHAPTER 5

1. In a properly designed experiment with expected relationships among the correlations (i.e., not arbitrary or independent), how would you use Table 5.2 to find the smallest number of variables required to determine:
   (a) four factors,
   (b) six factors?

2. Why is it not desirable to employ only eleven variables to determine six factors?

Exercises 3–6 are based upon the data of Table IV, Set A:

Table IV

Intercorrelations of Two Sets of Five Variables

Variable	Set A					Set B				
	1	2	3	4	5	1	2	3	4	5
1		.48	.56	.32	.40		.64	.78	.67	.91
2	.48		.42	.24	.30	.64		.66	.68	.77
3	.56	.42		.28	.35	.78	.66		.66	.84
4	.32	.24	.28		.20	.67	.68	.66		.77
5	.40	.30	.35	.20		.91	.77	.84	.77	

3. Show that the five variables can be described in terms of only one common factor by employing the conditions (5.9).

4. (a) Calculate the communality of the first variable by means of equations (5.8).
   (b) Why are the numerical values of the six distinct expressions of (5.8) exactly equal?

5. For a given variable, how many different (a) tetrads and (b) triads are there?

6. Obtain the coefficients of the common factor.

7. Assume a matrix of correlations among five variables, with unknown communalities h_j^2 ($j = 1, \cdots, 5$). Equations (5.9) constitute five linearly independent conditions that the correlations must satisfy if the five variables are to be described in terms of only one common factor. Equations (5.9) were obtained as a result of formally solving for h_1^2. Obtain an equivalent set of equations by solving for h_2^2, and show that they are linear combinations of equations (5.9).

Exercises 8–13 are based upon the data of Table IV, Set B:
8. Test the set of correlations to see if the five variables can be described in terms of only one common factor:
   (a) Calculate the communalities under the assumption that the rank of the correlation matrix is one.

(b) Write the factor pattern.

(c) Calculate the matrix of reproduced correlations.

(d) Calculate the residuals.

9. Show that the intercorrelations of the five variables satisfy the condition (5.15) exactly.

10. Calculate the communalities under the assumption that the rank of the correlation matrix is two.

11. Obtain a solution in terms of two common factors. Hint: Select one of the factor coefficients, say, a_{11}, arbitrarily.

12. Check that the correlations are reproduced exactly by the solution of exercise 11.

13. Discuss the relative merits of the solutions in exercises 8 and 11 considering the data (a) as exact, (b) as observations subject to fluctuations of sampling.

14. Check that the rank of the correlation matrix in Table V can appropriately be assumed to be equal to two.

Table V

Intercorrelations of Six Physical Variables for 305 Girls

Variable	1	2	3	4	5	6
1. Height						
2. Length lower leg	.859					
3. Sitting height	.740	.451				
4. Weight	.473	.436	.507			
5. Chest girth	.301	.327	.327	.730		
6. Chest depth	.201	.227	.211	.611	.484	

15. Calculate the communalities of the variables in Table V by means of formula (5.19).

16. Calculate the communalities for the eight political variables of Table 8.17.

17. Why are communalities put in the principal diagonal of a correlation matrix?

18. Make an outline of various methods that may be employed in estimating communalities, and comment on their relative merits.

19. The communalities of the five fictitious variables of Table IV, Set B were computed under the assumption of unit rank in exercise 8, and under the assumption of rank 2 in exercise 10. Compare these values with the "arbitrary estimates" given by:

(a) the highest correlation for each variable;

(b) the average correlation; and
(c) the single triad, formula (5.33).
Also compare these values with the "complete estimates" given by:
(d) the first centroid factor, formula (5.36).

20. Determine the estimates of communality (a), (b), (c), and (d), as in exercise 19, for the six physical variables of Table V and compare with the communalities computed in exercise 15, under the assumption of rank 2.

21. Compute the *SMC*'s for the example of eight physical variables. Their inter-correlations are given in Table 5.3 and the inverse of the correlation matrix is computed in ex. 3, chap. 16. Compare these *SMC*'s with the communalities determined in Table 5.4.

22. Employing the approximation to $\mathbf{R}^{-1}$ for the eight physical variables shown in Table 16.9, calculate the *SMC*'s for these variables. How do these results compare with those determined from the actual $\mathbf{R}^{-1}$ in exercise 21?

CHAPTER 6

1. The following questions are intended to be provocative and for general class discussion.
   (a) Why can a set of variables be interpreted in terms of a factorial solution involving correlated or uncorrelated factors?
   (b) What are some advantages in employing uncorrelated factors?
   (c) How may several workers arrive at the same factorial solution for a given matrix of correlations?
   (d) How can one judge the relative significance of the factors of a given solution.
   (e) Why would the uni-factor solution be the most desirable form? Why is this form not likely to be obtained with observed data?
   (f) Why is a more complex solution than the uni-factor type likely to furnish a more satisfactory description of observed data?
   (g) Why is the multiple-factor solution formulated so as not to include a general factor?
   (h) How may the selectivity of the sample affect the intercorrelations of a set of variables, and the subsequent factorial analysis?
   (i) Can a new variable be added to a given set without changing the factorial solution of the original portion?
   (j) When new variables are added to a set for which a factorial solution has been obtained, is any one of the preferred forms likely to be more "invariant" than the others?
   (k) How would you justify the co-existence of several preferred solutions for a given body of data? How would you make a choice among them?

2. Give illustrations, other than those in the text, in which bipolar factors furnish more convenient interpretations than those with all positive coefficients.

3. (a) What happens to the factorial composition of a variable when its scale is reversed?

   (b) What is the effect on the reproduced correlations when all the coefficients of any factor are multiplied by -1?

CHAPTER 7

Exercises 1–2 are based upon the correlations among the variables 5, 6, 7, 8, 9 in Table 7.4:

1. Assume rank one for the matrix of correlations, and calculate a "two-factor" pattern by means of formula (7.10).

2. (a) Compute the residuals.

   (b) Check the significance of these residuals, by use of Table A in Appendix (justifying the assumption of exercise 1).

3. Obtain another permissible solution (with more than one common factor) for the correlation matrix of Table 7.2 which led to the Heywood case.

4. Consider a set of ten variables $(z_1, z_2, \cdots, z_{10})$ grouped as follows:

$$G_1 = (1, 2, 3,), \quad G_2 = (4, 5, 6, 7,), \quad G_3 = (8, 9, 10,).$$

Use the set theory notations of (7.11) to express the following:

(a) variable 6 is included in group 2;

(b) the system of elements consisting of variables 1, 2, 3 and 8, 9, 10;

(c) the sum of the first 100 values of variable 5.

Exercises 5–13 are based upon the data of Table VI.

Table VI

Intercorrelations of Twelve Psychological Tests for 355 Pupils

Variable	1	2	3	4	5	6	7	8	9	10	11	12
1. Perception of brightness												
2. Counting dots	.690											
3. Straight and curved letters	.596	.655										
4. Speed in simple code	.515	.557	.600									
5. Verbal completion	.421	.397	.386	.255								
6. Understanding paragraphs	.350	.300	.252	.200	.611							
7. Reading vocabulary	.376	.349	.329	.258	.642	.576						
8. General information	.405	.448	.351	.310	.660	.545	.738					
9. Arithmetic proportions	.342	.381	.284	.241	.407	.428	.435	.478				
10. Permutations-combinations	.325	.377	.324	.286	.359	.407	.392	.385	.460			
11. Mechanical ability I	.260	.285	.255	.252	.321	.370	.408	.379	.406	.384		
12. Mechanical ability II	.165	.200	.146	.145	.162	.236	.303	.285	.278	.213	.398	

Source: K. J. Holzinger, [234, No. 9, Table 2].

387

5. From the definition in **7.4**, calculate the following B-coefficients and interpret the results: (a) B (1, 2, 3); (b) B (1, 6, 12).

6. Starting with the B-coefficient of exercise 1(a), determine B (1, 2, 3, 4) by means of the following steps:
   (a) Denote the sums in the calculation of B (1, 2, 3) by S_3 and T_3.
   (b) Add test 4 to the group and determine L_4 by formula (7.18).
   (c) Calculate S_4 and T_4 by means of (7.19) and (7.20).
   (d) Employing the results of (c), calculate B (1, 2, 3, 4) by means of formula (7.16).

7. Allocate the twelve tests to appropriate groups, employing the B-coefficient technique as outlined in Table 7.5.

8. Make a bi-factor pattern plan, using the groups determined in the last exercise.

9. Write formula (7.25) for the determination of the general-factor coefficient for the first variable: (a) in the set theory notation, (b) in the conventional summation notation, indicating the limits, (c) in expanded form, indicating the individual correlations.

10. Calculate the general-factor coefficients.

11. Obtain the general-factor residuals and check the satisfactoriness of the pattern plan.

12. (a) Calculate the group-factor coefficients, and write the complete factor pattern.
    (b) Determine the communalities.

13. Obtain the final residuals and test the adequacy of the solution.

Exercises 14–18 are based upon the data of Table VII.

Table VII

Correlations and Portion of Bi-Factor Solution for
Five Physical Variables for 305 Girls

Variable	Correlations (r_{jk})					General Factor F_0	Residuals ($\dot{r}_{jk}$)				
	1	2	3	4	5		1	2	3	4	5
1. Height						.691					
2. Arm span	.846					.591	.438				
3. Length of forearm	.805	.881				.581	.404	.538			
4. Length of lower leg	.859	.826	.801			.598	.446	.473	.454		
5. Sitting height	.740	.497	.494	.451		.674	.274	.099	.102	.048	

Source: Frances Mullen [375, p. 20].

14. In a study [375] involving 17 physical variables the five variables of Table VII were found to belong together according to their B-coefficient, and a bi-factor pattern was postulated with a general physical (or growth) factor F_0 and a group factor F_1 through these variables. Given the general-factor coefficients and the residuals, determine whether the original hypothesis of a single group factor for the five variables is warranted. Proceed as follows:
    (a) Compute the B-coefficients of variable 5 with each of the other four variables, one at a time, employing the residuals.
    (b) Compute the B-coefficients of variable 5 with all combinations of the other four variables, two at a time.
    (c) Compute the B-coefficients of variable 5 with all combinations of the other four variables, three at a time.
    (d) Compute B (1, 2, 3, 4).
    (e) What conclusion may be drawn from the contrast of (d) and the preceding B-coefficients?

15. Test the statistical significance of the general-factor residuals for variable 5, employing an average correlation $r = .355$ (based on all 17 variables in [375, p. 20]) and $N = 305$.

16. Formulate a revised pattern plan for the five variables, based upon the findings in exercises 14 and 15.

17. Determine the new group-factor coefficients.

18. Assuming a doublet factor for variables 1 and 5, and allowing one standard error for chance error, why cannot the remaining variance be divided equally between the two variables?

CHAPTER 8

Exercises 1–8 are based upon the data of Table V, and employ the computing procedures of **8.5**.

1. Employing the communalities which were determined in ex. 15, chap. 5, write the complete correlation matrix and determine the first set of trial values.

2. Square the matrix of correlations as many times as necessary, determining a set of trial values at each stage, until the successive trial values agree to within 5 units in the third decimal place.

3. Calculate the coefficients of the first principal factor by means of **8.5**, paragraph 3.

4. Find the matrix of first-factor residuals.

5. Determine the best set of trial values for the calculation of the second-factor coefficients, following the procedure of paragraph **5**.

6. Compute the coefficients of the second principal factor.

7. Calculate the second-factor residuals, and decide whether they may be considered as final residuals.

8. Check the properties (8.23) of the principal-factor solution.

9. Compute the principal-factor solution for the six hypothetical variables of Table 5.5, employing the "actual" communalities of Table 5.6. What is exceptional about the six eigenvalues?

10. Obtain the first two principal factors for the eight physical variables example of Table 5.3, employing the SMC's (determined in ex. 21, chap. 5) for the diagonal values of the correlation matrix. Compare the results with the solution in Table 8.12 for which communalities were employed.

Exercises 11–17 are based upon the data of Table V and employ the computing procedures of **8.9**, paragraph **2**.

11. Put the communalities which were determined in ex. 15, chap. 5 in the principal diagonal of the correlation matrix, calculate the sums $S_j (j = 1, \cdots, 6)$, and then compute the total T of these sums.

12. Calculate the coefficients of the first centroid factor and apply the check (8.71).

13. Calculate the products of the first-factor coefficients, and determine the first-factor residuals. Check that the sum of all the residuals for each variable is zero.

14. Reflect the variables with a large number of negative signs in the residual matrix, following the procedure of Table 8.25.

15. Calculate the coefficients of the second centroid factor, and apply the checks.

16. Calculate the second-factor residuals, and decide whether they may be considered as final residuals.

17. Summarize the results of the analysis, showing the complete centroid pattern and the degree to which the centroid factors account for the original communality assumed in exercise 11.

18. Check the properties (8.61) for the foregoing centroid solution. Why are the variables reflected in the computation of the second and later centroid axes?

19. Compare the centroid solution of exercise 17 with the principal-factor solution obtained in exs. 3, 6. Comment on the extent of agreement for this six variable problem and what might be expected in larger problems.

20. Contrast the properties (8.23) of a principal-factor solution with the properties (8.61) of a centroid solution.

CHAPTER 9

1. Starting with the objective function (9.9) for the sum of squares of residual correlations with a fixed variable j, derive a formula for the minres solution for the case of $m = 1$ (i.e., a single common factor).

2. For the five hypothetical variables of Table 7.2:
   (a) Obtain a minres solution in terms of one factor, using the formulas derived in the preceding exercise.
   (b) Compare the minres solution (after 3 iterations) with the original Heywood solution, in terms of the residuals and of the size of the objective function.

3. For the problem of five socio-economic variables, apply the asymptotic χ^2 test to determine the significance of one, two, and three factors at the .1%, 1%, and 5% levels. While the illustrative example actually contains only 12 cases, and the approximations made in arriving at the statistic (9.31) assumed a large sample, nonetheless as an exercise apply the tests for $N = 12, 50, 100, 200$. (The necessary determinants were produced by a computer as follows: $|\mathbf{R}| = .0016908$ for the original correlations; and $|\mathbf{R}_1^\dagger| = .1273853$, $|\mathbf{R}_2^\dagger| = .0023976$, $|\mathbf{R}_3^\dagger| = .0016908$ for the reproduced correlations for minres solutions with $m = 1, 2, 3$, respectively.)

4. Obtain a minres solution, with $m = 2$, for the six hypothetical variables of Table 5.5.

CHAPTER 10

1. For the binomial distribution

$$f(X;p) = p^X(1 - p)^{1 - X} \qquad\qquad (X = 0, 1)$$

involving samples of size N, a particular set of observations $X_1, X_2, \cdots X_N$ consists of a sequence of zeros and ones. Suppose that in a sample of $N = 100$ a total of 18 successes were noted. Determine the following for this case:
   (a) The likelihood function L (i.e., the joint distribution of the sample values).
   (b) The logarithm (to base e) of L.
   (c) The derivative of $\log L$ with respect to p.
   (d) The maximum-likelihood estimator $\hat{p}$.

Exercises 2 and 3 are based on the data of Table 7.1, and employ the computing procedures of **10.5**.

2. Since Spearman used these data to demonstrate the two-factor theory, it is reasonable to hypothesize a single common factor and to take the general-factor coefficients from Table 7.1 as first approximations for the calculation of maximum-likelihood estimates. Set up a worksheet in the form of Table 10.3, but for $m = 1$, and determine: (a) the first iteration; (b) additional iterations, as necessary, to obtain convergence of the factor weights.

3. Test the hypothesis of $m = 1$, proceeding as follows:
   (a) calculate the reproduced correlations and residuals, and determine the sum for formula (10.29);
   (b) complete the calculation of U_1;
   (c) determine the number of degrees of freedom;
   (d) for this number of degrees of freedom, what value of χ^2 produces a probability of $P = .01$?
   (e) how does the actual U_1 compare with this value?
   (f) what conclusion may be drawn regarding the hypothesis?

4. For the five socio-economic variables the observed correlations are given in Table 2.2 and the maximum-likelihood solution, under the hypothesis of $m = 2$, is in Table 10.7. Test this hypothesis, organizing your work as in Tables 10.4 and 10.5.

Exercises 5–8 are based on the data of Table V. Although it is reasonable to assume two common factors for these data (see ex. 14, chap. 5), other assumptions are made for the sake of exercise.

5. Obtain a maximum-likelihood solution under the assumption $m = 1$, employing the coefficients of the first principal factor (ex. 3, chap. 8) as first approximations.

6. Since the natural choice of ex. 5 for first approximations to the maximum-likelihood loadings led to lengthy computations, start with the following trial values to see how soon convergence is obtained:

Exercise	1	2	3	4	5	6
a	1.000	.800	.700	.600	.500	.400
b	.900	.700	.600	.500	.400	.300
c	.950	.850	.750	.500	.350	.250

(In order to get the full value of the convergence problem indicated in exs. 5 and 6, without requiring the laborious calculations on the part of each student, it is suggested that teams be formed and the work shared.)

7. Test the hypothesis of $m = 1$.

8. Assume $m = 2$ and take as starting values the principal-factor coefficients from exs. 3 and 6, chap. 8, to set up a worksheet like Table 10.3 and carry through one complete iteration.

9. If a computer and a suitable program are available, obtain a maximum-likelihood solution for $m = 2$ starting with the first two principal components rather than the principal factors of the preceding exercise.

10. Obtain maximum-likelihood estimates of factor loadings for the eight physical variables, whose correlation matrix is given in Table 10.2, under the assumption

that $m = 2$ and employing the principal-factor coefficients for the initial set of trial values.

11. Test the hypothesis of the preceding example.

12. If N were 120 instead of 305 for the same correlations for the eight physical variables would the hypothesis of $m = 2$ be rejected? How about the hypothesis of $m = 3$?

13. Suppose N were only 100 instead of 305, what conclusions could be drawn about the significance of 2 or 3 common factors for the eight physical variables?

CHAPTER 11

Exercises 1–7 are designed for practice in applying the multiple-group method, and are based on the data for the eight physical variables:

1. Set up the reduced correlation matrix by employing the correlations from Table 5.3 and the communalities from Table 5.4. Assume the previously determined grouping of variables:

$$G_1 : (1, 2, 3, 4), \text{ lankiness}; \qquad G_2 : (5, 6, 7, 8), \text{ stockiness}.$$

Determine the sums (11.1) and record them in the form of Table 11.4.

2. Obtain the sums (11.3) of correlations between groups, as in Table 11.5, and calculate the standard deviations of the composite variables according to (11.7).

3. Calculate the correlation between the two oblique factors, T_1 and T_2, by means of (11.10).

4. Determine the oblique factor structure, the elements of which are given by (11.11).

5. Obtain the oblique factor pattern and the orthogonal factor matrix by setting up a worksheet like Table 11.2 and following the instructions given therein.

6. Compute the reproduced correlations by employing the orthogonal factor matrix and check the results by using the oblique structure and pattern.

7. Show the residuals. Are these residuals of the order of magnitude of final residuals of previous solutions? What percent of the original communality assumed in exercise 1 is accounted for by two multiple-group factors?

8. Develop in detail the formula (11.5), or (11.6), for the variance of T_1, assuming three variables in G_1.

CHAPTER 12

1. Determine the transformation matrix $\mathbf{T}$ in (12.1) for the twenty-four psychological tests when $\mathbf{A}$ is the biquartimin pattern (Table 15.5) and $\mathbf{B}$ is the quartimax pattern (Table 14.3).

2. Employing the transformation equation (12.1), calculate b_{11}, b_{12}, b_{13}, b_{14}, b_{53}, $b_{24,4}$ and compare the results with the original values in Table 14.3.

3. The multiple-factor solution (Table 12.5) for the thirteen psychological tests was obtained by graphical methods, considering two factors at a time, as described in **12.3**. Check the coefficients for z_1 and z_{13} in the multiple-factor pattern of Table 12.5 by applying the complete transformation matrix (12.29) to the original centroid pattern of Table 8.30.

4. When a multiple-factor solution is obtained by intuitive-graphical methods it is not expected that a particular solution obtained by one worker could be replicated by another, or by the same individual at another time. As exercises in applying the methods of **12.3**, the eight, thirteen, and twenty-four variable examples can be employed, with independent graphing and calculations, and checked against the results obtained in the text.

5. Rotate the minres solution of ex. 4, chap. 9 to "simple structure" by the hand methods of **12.3**. Compare the results with the direct solution of Table 5.8.

CHAPTER 13

1. Compare the primary-factor solution (Table 13.1) for the eight physical variables with the multiple-group solution given in the table of ex. 5, chap. 11.

Exercises 2–9 are designed for practice in obtaining a primary-factor solution according to the outline in **13.3**, and employ the thirteen psychological tests with the initial centroid solution of Table 8.30.

2. Available information about these data (chap. 7) suggest the three composite variables:

$$v_1 = z_1 + z_2 + z_3 + z_4$$

$$v_2 = z_5 + z_6 + z_7 + z_8 + z_9$$

$$v_3 = z_{10} + z_{11} + z_{12} + z_{13}$$

Calculate the standard deviations of these composite variables.

3. Express the composite variables (standardized) in terms of the factors of the initial solution.

4. Determine the distances of the three composite points from the origin.

5. Obtain the transformation matrix from the centroid factors (C_p) to the primary factors (T_p).

6. Calculate the correlations among the primary factors by use of formula (13.16).

7. Obtain the primary-factor structure by applying (13.21).

8. Obtain the primary-factor pattern by using the computing algorithm of Table 13.2.

9. Determine the contributions of the primary factors according to formulas (13.28) and (13.29).

10. Develop formula (13.37) starting with (13.36).

11. Set up a worksheet like Table 13.2 and show the detailed calculations for the pattern **W** of the oblique reference solution of Table 13.3.

CHAPTER 14

1. Compute the sum of fourth powers of the factor loadings for the eight physical variables in the graphical solution of Table 12.3, and compare with the value for the analytical solution of Table 14.2.

2. (a) Using the principal-factor solution (Table 8.18) for the eight political variables as the initial matrix **A**, compute the quartimax solution.
   (b) Compare the quartimax criterion of the final solution with that of the initial solution.

3. Compute the varimax criterion V for the quartimax solution for the eight physical variables (Table 14.2), and compare the result with the values for the graphical solution (Table 12.3) and the varimax solution (Table 14.5).

4. (a) Starting with the principal-factor solution for the eight political variables (Table 8.18), compute the corresponding varimax solution.
   (b) Compare the varimax criterion for the initial and the final solutions.

5. Compute the root mean square values for the differences between the following pairs of solutions for the eight physical variables:

   (a) Varimax and Subjective
   (b) Varimax and Quartimax
   (c) Quartimax and Subjective.

CHAPTER 15

1. Compute the oblimax criterion K for the centroid solution of the eight physical variables (initial solution **A** in Table 15.3).

2. Show that the value of the quartimin criterion N for the factor structure of Table 13.3 does not differ significantly from the value for the quartimin solution of Table 15.3, although the minres solution served as the starting point for the former while the centroid solution was used in the latter.

3. The quartimin solution (obtained on a desk calculator) for the eight political variables is shown in Table 15.8. The initial matrix **A** is the principal-factor solution of Table 8.18. Determine the final quartimin solution through the following procedures of **15.3**:
   (a) Select the first column (i.e., $x = 1$) of the transformation matrix Λ to initiate the iteration process and determine the values w_j for $p \neq 1$.

(b) Employing the values from (a) for the diagonal matrix **W**, determine the matrix **C** according to (15.24).

(c) Write the characteristic equation and solve for the least root N_x $(x = 1)$.

(d) Obtain the values of λ_{11} and λ_{21}.

(e) Determine the new elements v_{j1} resulting from the first iteration.

(f) Select $x = 2$ for the second iteration and repeat the process (a)–(e), arriving at new elements v_{j2}.

(g) Perform as many iterations as necessary, alternating between $x = 1$ and $x = 2$, until the value of N converges (to the minimum of $N = .1819$ as indicated in the text). Write the final transformation matrix.

(h) Verify a few entries in the final structure matrix **V** by applying (15.1) with the transformation matrix determined in (g).

4. Calculate the following matrices for determining the primary-factor pattern corresponding to the structure **V** in Table 15.3:

(a) The inverse of the transformation matrix given in (15.30).

(b) The transformation matrix **T**.

(c) The diagonal matrix **D**.

(d) The primary-factor pattern **P**.

Also calculate:

(e) The correlation between the two primary factors.

Problems 5–7 are based on the first two principal components (see Table 8.1) for the five socio-economic variables as the initial factor matrix **A**, and certain results produced by a computer.

5. Get the quartimin primary-factor pattern corresponding to the reference structure matrix

$$
\mathbf{V} = \begin{bmatrix}
-.0954 & .9857 \\
.9359 & -.1142 \\
.0264 & .9585 \\
.7695 & .3519 \\
.9628 & -.1145
\end{bmatrix},
$$

and the transformation matrix

$$
\mathbf{\Lambda} = \begin{pmatrix}
.7515 & .4758 \\
-.6597 & .8795
\end{pmatrix}.
$$

6. Get the biquartimin primary-factor pattern corresponding to the reference structure matrix

$$
\mathbf{V} = \begin{bmatrix}
-.0366 & .9909 \\
.9399 & -.0669 \\
.0850 & .9697 \\
.8000 & .3954 \\
.9672 & -.0658
\end{bmatrix},
$$

and the transformation matrix

$$\Lambda = \begin{pmatrix} .7893 & .5196 \\ -.6140 & .8544 \end{pmatrix}.$$

7. Determine the common-factor variance of variable 1 from the primary-factor pattern found in ex. 5 and compare it with the value from the initial factor matrix **A**.

8. The quartimin reference structure for the eight physical variables is given in Table 15.4. This solution, based on the minres initial matrix of Table 9.3, was produced by a computer which also gave the transformation matrix

$$\Lambda = \begin{pmatrix} .6032 & .4052 \\ -.7976 & .9142 \end{pmatrix}.$$

Obtain the quartimin primary-factor pattern corresponding to this reference structure.

9. The reference structure **V** in Table 15.5 was computed on an electronic computer. One of the outputs of the computer program is the transformation matrix:

$$\Lambda = \begin{bmatrix} .3520 & .2699 & .3684 & .2944 \\ -.6047 & .5822 & -.3846 & .5051 \\ -.6432 & -.4960 & .6839 & .3712 \\ .3109 & -.5849 & -.4985 & .7214 \end{bmatrix}.$$

(a) Obtain the inverse of **Λ**. First apply the square root method of **3.5** to the symmetric matrix

$$\Psi = \Lambda'\Lambda$$

to get Ψ^{-1}, and then the desired result follows from (15.44).

(b) Determine the diagonal matrix **D**, i.e., the normalizing factors of the rows of Λ^{-1}.

(c) Determine the transformation matrix T for the primary-factor solution.

Problems 10–13 are based on the 3-variable example employed by Jennrich and Sampson [279] for which they assume the following initial pattern matrix (in terms of orthogonal factors):

$$A = \begin{bmatrix} .960 & .140 \\ .480 & .070 \\ -.560 & .300 \end{bmatrix}.$$

10. Get the value of the criterion (15.45) for the initial factor pattern for each of the following values of the parameter δ:

$$0, -.5, -1, -5, .1, .5, .8, 1.$$

11. Normalize matrix **A** by rows, and determine the value of the criterion function for $\delta = 0$ in this case.

397

12. Plot the three variables with reference to the orthogonal common-factor axes. What is special about these points?

13. For $\delta = 0$, a computer produced the following factor pattern:

j	b_{j1}	b_{j2}
1	.97015	.00000
2	.48508	.00000
3	.00000	.63530

The correlation between the primary factors is $-.80411$.
(a) What is the value of the criterion function for this solution?
(b) Determine the primary-factor structure for this solution.

Problems 14–15 are based on the minres solution (Table 9.2) for the five socio-economic variables as the initial factor matrix **A**.

14. Compute the criterion (15.45) for **A**, with $\delta = 0$.

15. Normalize matrix **A** by rows and, for $\delta = 0$, determine the initial value of the criterion function and the final value after the function has been minimized. Show the complete direct oblimin ($\delta = 0$) solution. (This exercise requires the use of a computer, and may be useful as a test case.)

CHAPTER 16

1. In **16.3** the measurements of the rotated varimax components for the five socio-economic variables were obtained by use of (16.7). The same results can be obtained by use of (16.12); show the computations leading to the two equations by means of the latter formula.

2. From the fictitious data presented by Holzinger [239, p. 130], the following table is derived (with $r_{F_1 F_2} = .5$):

Variable j	Intercorrelations			Structure		Pattern		Uniqueness
	1	2	3	r_{jF_1}	r_{jF_2}	F_1	F_2	a_j^2
1	1.00	.81	.87	.90	.60	.8	.2	.16
2	*	1.00	.83	.85	.65	.7	.3	.21
3	*	*	1.00	.95	.55	.9	.1	.09

Obtain the complete estimates of the two oblique factors (use the square root method, following the procedure of Table 16.3). Also determine the multiple correlations.

3. In the complete estimation method of **16.4** the inverse of a matrix of observed correlations is required. For the example of eight physical variables, the square

root method is applied in Table 16.3 to yield the necessary regression weights. Employing the square root matrix S (assuming $R = S'S$) of Table 16.3, obtain R^{-1}.

4. Employing the matrix equation (16.18), show the explicit formula for the prediction of T_2 in the factor analysis of the eight physical variables (use R^{-1} computed in ex. 3). How does the result compare with the second of equations (16.36)?

5. Prove that the matrix L, defined in (16.50), is a symmetric matrix.

6. Apply the short method, using the algorithm of Table 16.8, to estimate the two factors of the fictitious data in exercise 2. Also determine the multiple correlations.

7. Verify the calculations of the β-coefficients in the last two rows of Table 16.8 by determining E^{-1} and carrying out the multiplication $E^{-1}(EL^{-1}C')$.

8. The quartimin solution for the eight physical variables consists of the reference structure (in Table 15.3) and the primary-factor pattern which was determined in ex. 4, chap. 15. Starting with this factor pattern and correlation of .483 between the primary factors, compute the regression weights for these factors by the short method using the worksheet of Table 16.8.

9. A by-product of the computer program for the oblimin solutions of **15.4** is a matrix of numbers which can easily be converted to the factor measurements as estimated by the short method. For the four biquartimin factors (Table 15.5) for the twenty-four psychological tests, the computer output the following "factor score coefficients":

	1	2	3	4	5	6	7	8	9	10	11	12
T_1	−.042	−.013	−.013	−.006	.230	.222	.339	.089	.324	.024	.010	−.036
T_2	.015	−.009	−.032	−.011	.056	−.035	.038	.056	−.135	.330	.229	.297
T_3	.291	.113	.169	.170	−.022	−.012	−.035	.086	−.030	−.147	−.069	.044
T_4	−.011	−.004	−.020	−.034	−.044	.047	−.117	−.046	.125	.059	.124	−.053

	13	14	15	16	17	18	19	20	21	22	23	24
T_1	−.009	.019	−.004	−.030	−.002	−.053	−.006	.024	−.016	.029	.020	.039
T_2	.249	.005	−.026	−.029	.003	.034	.002	−.023	.089	−.054	.017	.124
T_3	.137	−.051	−.002	.108	−.060	.071	.031	.131	.106	.101	.206	−.003
T_4	−.111	.188	.185	.155	.317	.234	.118	.049	.040	.117	.014	.090

(a) Convert these numbers to regression coefficients by premultiplying the above matrix by D (determined in ex. 9, chap. 15).

(b) How could the multiple correlations be computed for the prediction of the four biquartimin factors?

10. Why are the coefficients in the equation derived in exercise 4 different from the values in the last line of Table 16.9?

11. Compare the approximation to $\mathbf{R}^{-1}$ as given by $(\mathbf{R}^{\dagger} + \mathbf{D}^2)^{-1}$ in Table 16.9 with the actual $\mathbf{R}^{-1}$ determined in exercise 3.

12. Prove that the matrix of coefficients given by (16.58) when postmultiplied by the factor-structure matrix produces the matrix of correlations among the factors, viz.,

$$\mathbf{\Gamma'S} = \mathbf{\Phi}.$$

13. (a) Apply the method of **16.8** to estimate the two factors of the fictitious data in exercise 2.
    (b) Compute the "multiple correlations" by means of formula (16.60).

14. Verify the relationship proven in exercise 12 for the matrix of coefficients determined in exercise 13.

Answers

CHAPTER 2

1. Discussion in **2.4**.

2. For computational convenience.

3. $z_1' = a_{11}F_1 + a_{12}F_2 + d_1 U_1,$
$z_2' = a_{21}F_1 + a_{22}F_2 \qquad\qquad + d_2 U_2,$
$z_3' = a_{31}F_1 + a_{32}F_2 \qquad\qquad\qquad + d_3 U_3,$
$z_4' = a_{41}F_1 + a_{42}F_2 \qquad\qquad\qquad\qquad + d_4 U_4,$
$z_5' = a_{51}F_1 + a_{52}F_2 \qquad\qquad\qquad\qquad\qquad\quad d_5 U_5.$

4. (a) The a's and d's; (b) 15.

5. (a) .25, .64; (b) a_{21}^2, a_{22}^2.

6. $a_{11}^2 + a_{21}^2 + a_{31}^2 + a_{41}^2 + a_{51}^2$ and $a_{12}^2 + a_{22}^2 + a_{32}^2 + a_{42}^2 + a_{52}^2$.

7. $h_1^2 = .89$.

8. Reliability $= 1 - e^2 = h^2 + b^2 \geq h^2$.

9. The given quantities are $\times$'d out.

Variance Component	Formula	a	b	c	d	e	f	g	h
Specificity	$b^2 = d^2 - e^2$	$\times$	$\times$	$\times$	$\times$	.35	.35	.25	.20
Error variance	$e^2 = 1 - r = d^2 - b^2$	$\times$	.10	.15	.15	$\times$	$\times$	.25	.10
Communality	$h^2 = 1 - d^2$	.70	$\times$	.65	.60	$\times$	.55	$\times$	.70
Uniqueness	$d^2 = 1 - h^2 = b^2 + e^2$	.30	.25	$\times$	.40	.40	$\times$	.50	$\times$
Reliability	$r = 1 - e^2$	.80	.90	.85	$\times$	.95	.90	$\times$	$\times$

10. $h_8^2 = .85$.

11. z_4 (since $h_4^2 = 1.00$).

12. z_6 (since $h_6^2 = .25$).

13. $d_1^2 = 42$.

14. z_4 (since $d_4^2 = 0$).

15. z_6 (since $d_6^2 = .75$).

16. Yes, F_1.

17. Yes, F_2.

18. $\sum\limits_{j=1}^{8} a_{j1}^2 = 3.72,\ \sum\limits_{j=1}^{8} a_{j2}^2 = 1.22.$

19. 46.50% and 15.25%.

20. 75.3% and 24.7%.

21. $z_5 = .6F_1 + .5F_2 + .48S_5 + .4E_5.$

22. $C_5 = 72.6\%.$

23. 2, 1.

24. $r'_{12} = .56,\ r'_{14} = .74,\ r'_{25} = .48,\ r'_{26} = .40.$

25. No.

CHAPTER 3

1. 14.   2. 26.   3. -2.   4. -15.   5. 139.   6. 0.

7. 1.   8. 2.   9. 2.   10. Singular.   11. **C**.   12. 1.

13. (a)
$$\mathbf{A'} = \begin{bmatrix} a_{11} & a_{21} & a_{31} & a_{41} & a_{51} \\ a_{12} & a_{22} & a_{32} & a_{42} & a_{52} \end{bmatrix}$$

(b)
$$\mathbf{A'} = \begin{bmatrix} .7 & .8 & .7 & .8 & .6 & .5 & .6 & .7 \\ .3 & 0 & 0 & .6 & .5 & 0 & .4 & .6 \end{bmatrix}$$

14 (a)
$$\mathbf{R}^\dagger = \begin{bmatrix} .89 & .64 & .78 & .67 & .91 \\ .64 & .73 & .66 & .68 & .77 \\ .78 & .66 & .72 & .66 & .84 \\ .67 & .68 & .66 & .65 & .77 \\ .91 & .77 & .84 & .77 & .98 \end{bmatrix}$$

15. (a)
$$\mathbf{R}^\dagger = \begin{bmatrix} 1.00 & .99 & .99 & .92 & .97 \\ .99 & 1.00 & .97 & .96 & .99 \\ .99 & .97 & 1.00 & .87 & .93 \\ .92 & .96 & .87 & 1.00 & .99 \\ .97 & .99 & .93 & .99 & 1.00 \end{bmatrix}$$

16. (a)
$$\mathbf{AB} = \begin{bmatrix} 4 & 7 \\ 8 & 15 \end{bmatrix}, \quad \mathbf{BA} = \begin{bmatrix} 3 & 4 \\ 11 & 16 \end{bmatrix};$$

(b) $|\mathbf{AB}| = 4,\ |\mathbf{A}| \cdot |\mathbf{B}| = (-2)(-2)$;   (c) $|\mathbf{AB}| = 4,\ |\mathbf{BA}| = 4$.

17.

$$\mathbf{AB} = \begin{bmatrix} 41 & 28 & 6 \\ 35 & 24 & 8 \\ 7 & 4 & 2 \end{bmatrix} \qquad \mathbf{BA} = \begin{bmatrix} 6 & 12 & 18 \\ 7 & 22 & 53 \\ 7 & 18 & 39 \end{bmatrix}$$

$$\mathbf{A'B} = \begin{bmatrix} 6 & 0 & 0 \\ 19 & 8 & 0 \\ 53 & 36 & 2 \end{bmatrix} \qquad \mathbf{BA'} = \begin{bmatrix} 6 & 0 & 0 \\ 23 & 8 & 0 \\ 21 & 12 & 2 \end{bmatrix}$$

$$\mathbf{B'A} = \begin{bmatrix} 6 & 19 & 53 \\ 0 & 8 & 36 \\ 0 & 0 & 2 \end{bmatrix} \qquad \mathbf{AB'} = \begin{bmatrix} 6 & 23 & 21 \\ 0 & 8 & 12 \\ 0 & 0 & 2 \end{bmatrix}$$

$$\mathbf{B'A'} = \begin{bmatrix} 41 & 35 & 7 \\ 28 & 24 & 4 \\ 6 & 8 & 2 \end{bmatrix} \qquad \mathbf{A'B'} = \begin{bmatrix} 6 & 7 & 7 \\ 12 & 22 & 18 \\ 18 & 53 & 39 \end{bmatrix}$$

18. $|\mathbf{A}| = 1, \qquad |\mathbf{B}| = 96, \qquad |\mathbf{AB}| = |\mathbf{BA}| = 96.$

19. (a)

$$\mathbf{CD} = \begin{bmatrix} 42 & 52 \\ 34 & 19 \end{bmatrix}, \qquad \mathbf{DC} = \begin{bmatrix} 21 & 37 & 56 \\ 12 & 14 & 22 \\ 25 & 15 & 26 \end{bmatrix}.$$

(b) No, since $|\mathbf{CD}| = -970$ and $|\mathbf{DC}| = 0.$

20. Suppose the given matrix is $\mathbf{A}$ and let $\mathbf{B} = \mathbf{AA'}$, then

$$\mathbf{B'} = (\mathbf{AA'})' = (\mathbf{A'})'(\mathbf{A})' = \mathbf{AA'} = \mathbf{B}.$$

Similarly, if $\mathbf{C} = \mathbf{A'A}$, then $\mathbf{C'} = (\mathbf{A'A})' = \mathbf{A'A} = \mathbf{C}$. Since the matrix $\mathbf{B}$ (or $\mathbf{C}$) is equal to its transpose, the product (in either order) of any matrix by its transpose is symmetric according to the definition in **3.2**, paragraph **14**.

21. (a) $|\mathbf{A}| = ad - bc, \qquad \mathbf{A}^{-1} = \begin{bmatrix} d/|\mathbf{A}| & -b/|\mathbf{A}| \\ -c/|\mathbf{A}| & a/|\mathbf{A}| \end{bmatrix},$

$$|\mathbf{A}^{-1}| = \frac{ad - bc}{(ad - bc)^2} = \frac{1}{ad - bc} = \frac{1}{|\mathbf{A}|}.$$

(b)

$$|\mathbf{A}| = 21, \qquad \mathbf{A}^{-1} = \begin{bmatrix} -6/21 & -3/21 & 12/21 & -1/21 \\ 3/21 & 12/21 & -6/21 & -3/21 \\ 0 & 0 & 0 & 7/21 \\ 15/21 & -3/21 & -9/21 & -1/21 \end{bmatrix},$$

$$|\mathbf{A}^{-1}| = \frac{3 \cdot 3 \cdot 3 \cdot 1}{21 \cdot 21 \cdot 21 \cdot 21} \begin{vmatrix} -2 & -1 & 4 & -1 \\ 1 & 4 & -2 & -3 \\ 0 & 0 & 0 & 7 \\ 5 & -1 & -3 & -1 \end{vmatrix}$$

$$= \frac{-7}{7 \cdot 7 \cdot 7 \cdot 21}[-2(-14) - 1(7) + 5(-14)] = \frac{(-1)(-49)}{49.21} = \frac{1}{21}.$$

22.

R	I	1	.693	.216	1	0	0
		*	1	.295		1	0
		*	*	1			1
S	$(S')^{-1}$	1	.693	.216	1	0	0
			.721	.202	−.961	1.387	0
				.955	−.023	−.293	1.047
	R^{-1}				1.924	−1.326	−.024
					*	2.010	−.307
					*	*	1.096

Check:

$$RR^{-1} = \begin{bmatrix} 1.000 & .001 & -.000 \\ * & 1.001 & -.000 \\ * & * & 1.000 \end{bmatrix}.$$

23. First obtain a symmetric matrix by multiplying the given matrix by its transpose, namely:

$$B = AA' = \begin{bmatrix} 10 & 5 & 10 & 3 \\ 5 & 6 & 6 & 3 \\ 10 & 6 & 12 & 3 \\ 3 & 3 & 3 & 9 \end{bmatrix}.$$

Apply the method of Table 3.3 to the matrix **B** to obtain

$$B^{-1} = \begin{bmatrix} .612 & .021 & -.511 & -.041 \\ .021 & .367 & -.184 & -.068 \\ -.511 & -.184 & .594 & .034 \\ -.041 & -.068 & .034 & .136 \end{bmatrix}.$$

But $B^{-1} = (AA')^{-1} = (A')^{-1}A^{-1}$. Therefore premultiplying B^{-1} by A' yields A^{-1}, as follows:

$$A^{-1} = \begin{bmatrix} -.288 & -.143 & .576 & -.048 \\ .143 & .571 & -.285 & -.143 \\ -.001 & .000 & .001 & .333 \\ .713 & -.142 & -.428 & -.048 \end{bmatrix}.$$

Check: $|A^{-1}| = .048$.

CHAPTER 4

2. (a) 5; (b) 5; (c) $\binom{5}{2} = 10$; (d) $\binom{5}{3} = 10$.

3. The three points $P:(3, 4)$, $2P:(6, 8)$, and $3P:(9, 12)$ lie on a line.

4. $P(3, -2):(-1, 1)$.

5. $P(2, -3, 1):(-1, 1, -8)$.

6. $x_{31} = -8.5x_{11} + 4.5x_{21}$,
   $x_{32} = -8.5x_{12} + 4.5x_{22}$.

7. (a) 3; (b) Ordinary space; (c) 2, a plane.

8. (a) 5; (b) $\sqrt{17}$; (c) $\sqrt{10}$.

9. (a) $y_{j1} = \alpha_{11}x_{j1} + \alpha_{12}x_{j2}$,
   $y_{j2} = \alpha_{21}x_{j1} + \alpha_{22}x_{j2}$,
   where $\alpha_{1k}\alpha_{1l} + \alpha_{2k}\alpha_{2l} = \delta_{kl}$. When

$$\begin{aligned} \alpha_{11} &= \cos\theta & \alpha_{12} &= \sin\theta \\ \alpha_{21} &= -\sin\theta & \alpha_{22} &= \cos\theta \end{aligned}$$

it can be verified by (4.24) that the conditions for an *orthogonal transformation* are satisfied.

(b) $y_{j1} = \alpha_{11}x_{j1} + \alpha_{12}x_{j2} + \alpha_{13}x_{j3}$,
$y_{j2} = \alpha_{21}x_{j1} + \alpha_{22}x_{j2} + \alpha_{23}x_{j3}$,
$y_{j3} = \alpha_{31}x_{j1} + \alpha_{32}x_{j2} + \alpha_{33}x_{j3}$.

10. (a) $\lambda_1 = .8$, $\lambda_2 = .6$; (b) 1.

11. (a) $\lambda_1 = .8$, $\lambda_2 = .4$, $\lambda_3 = .2$, $\lambda_4 = -.4$; (b) 1.

12. $\phi = 44° 41'$. 13. $P \cdot Q = .32$.

14. (a) $D(P_1P_2) = \sqrt{13} = 3.6$; (b) $D(P_1P_2) = \sqrt{25} = 5$.

16. $\rho_1 = 3.74$, $\rho_2 = 4.90$.

17. $\lambda_{11} = -.802$, $\lambda_{12} = .267$, $\lambda_{13} = .535$;
    $\lambda_{21} = -.408$, $\lambda_{22} = -.408$, $\lambda_{23} = .816$.

18. (a) $\phi_{12} = 49°$; (b) $r_{12} = \cos\phi_{12} = .655$.

20. Yes, matrix is of rank 2. 21. 2. 22. Variables 2, 3, and 6.

24. (a) No; (b) Yes; (c) By Theorem 4.6.

25. (b) $a_{10} = .96$, $a_{20} = .54$, $a_{30} = .78$, $a_{40} = .56$, $a_{50} = .72$, $a_{60} = .63$.

26. (a) $r''_{12} = .71$ by formula (4.54); (b) $r'_{12} = .32$ by formula (4.56);
    (c) $r'_{12} = .32$.

CHAPTER 5

1. (a) Read across in row $m = 4$ to the first positive entry, and the number $n = 8$ at the head of that column is the minimum number of variables required for the determination of 4 factors;
   (b) $n = 11$.

4. (a) $h_1^2 = .64$;
   (b) Rank of the matrix is one mathematically, not just statistically.

5. (a) 15; (b) 6.   6. .8, .6, .7, .4, .5.

7. There are six linear equations for the solution of h_2^2, namely,

$$h_2^2 = \frac{r_{21}r_{23}}{r_{13}} = \frac{r_{21}r_{24}}{r_{14}} = \frac{r_{21}r_{25}}{r_{15}} = \frac{r_{23}r_{24}}{r_{34}} = \frac{r_{23}r_{25}}{r_{35}} = \frac{r_{24}r_{25}}{r_{45}}.$$

On eliminating h_2^2, the consistency conditions may be put in the form:

(i) $r_{23}r_{14} - r_{24}r_{13} = 0,$
(ii) $r_{23}r_{15} - r_{25}r_{13} = 0,$
(iii) $r_{12}r_{34} - r_{24}r_{13} = 0,$
(iv) $r_{12}r_{35} - r_{25}r_{13} = 0,$
(v) $r_{23}r_{45} - r_{24}r_{35} = 0.$

To show that these equations are linear combinations of those in (5.9), note that equations (i) and (ii) are equivalent to (5.9_1) and (5.9_2), respectively; equation (iii) is the difference of (5.9_1) and (5.9_3); and equation (iv) is the difference of (5.9_2) and (5.9_4). To show that (v) is linearly dependent on (5.9), substitute $r_{13} = r_{14}r_{23}/r_{24}$, obtained from (5.9_1), into (5.9_5). The result is

$$r_{14}r_{23}r_{45} - r_{14}r_{35}r_{24} = 0,$$

which reduces to (v) by factoring out r_{14}.

8. (a) $h_1^2 = .7620$ (b) $a_{11} = .87$
       $h_2^2 = .6163$ $a_{21} = .79$
       $h_3^2 = .7289$ $a_{31} = .85$
       $h_4^2 = .6351$ $a_{41} = .80$
       $h_5^2 = .9530$ $a_{51} = .98$

(c)   (d)

	1	2	3	4
1				
2	.69			
3	.75	.67		
4	.70	.63	.68	
5	.85	.77	.83	.78

	1	2	3	4
1				
2	−.05			
3	.03	−.01		
4	−.03	.05	−.02	
5	.06	.00	.01	−.01

10. .89, .73, .72, .65, .98.

11. One solution is the factor pattern given in ex. 14, chap. 3.

15. .718, .494, .414, .945, .546, .363.

16. .52, 1.00, .78, .82, .36, .80, .63, .97.

17. According to the "common-factor" model set forth in (2.9).

19.

Variable	Assumed Rank		Arbitrary Estimate			Complete Estimate
	1	2	(a)	(b)	(c)	(d)
1	.76	.89	.91	.75	.84	.81
3	.62	.73	.77	.69	.68	.65
3	.73	.72	.84	.74	.72	.75
4	.64	.65	.77	.70	.68	.67
5	.95	.98	.91	.82	.98	.93

20.

Variable	Ex. 15	(a)	(b)	(c)	(d)
1	.718	.859	.515	1.409	.644
2	.494	.859	.460	.524	.545
3	.414	.740	.447	.793	.484
4	.942	.730	.551	.922	.664
5	.546	.730	.434	.578	.459
6	.363	.611	.347	.405	.301

21. Employing formula (5.38), and using the diagonal elements of the matrix $\mathbf{R}^{-1}$ in the answer to ex. 3, chap. 16, the SMC's are:

.816, .849, .800, .788, .749, .605, .563, .477.

22. Employing the approximation to $\mathbf{R}^{-1}$, the resulting SMC's are:

.802, .829, .778, .758, .715, .594, .496, .486.

In every instance except variable 8, the SMC's computed from the approximation to $\mathbf{R}^{-1}$ are lower than the corresponding values determined in exercise 21. The differences range from one to three units in the second decimal place except for variable 7 for which the approximate solution is .067 less than the actual solution.

CHAPTER 6

2. A few examples follow: friendliness—hostility; active—inactive; impulsiveness —restraint; demonstrative—inhibitive; dominance—submissiveness; heat— cold; difficulty—ease; radicalism—conservatism.

3. (a) Its factor weights are changed in sign;   (b) No effect.

CHAPTER 7

1.   2. (a)

Variable	F_0
5	.809
6	.811
7	.854
8	.680
9	.840

Variable	5	6	7	8	9
5					
6	−.034				
7	−.035	.029			
8	.031	−.021	.042		
9	.043	.033	−.032	−.036	

4. (a) $6 \in G_2$;   (b) $(z_j; j \in G_p, p = 1, 3)$;   (c) $\sum (z_{5i}; i = 1, 2, \cdots, 100)$.

5. (a) $B(1, 2, 3) = 186$;   (b) $B(1, 6, 12) = 69$.

6. (a) $S_3 = 1.941$, $T_3 = 9.380$;   (b) $L_4 = 1.672$;
   (c) $S_4 = 3.613$, $T_4 = 9.655$;   (d) $B(1, 2, 3, 4) = 200$.

7. $G_1 = (1, 2, 3, 4)$, $G_2 = (5, 6, 7, 8)$, $G_3 = (9, 10, 11, 12)$.

9. (a) $a_{10}^2 = \sum (r_{1j}r_{1k}; \ j \in G_2, k \in G_3) / \sum (r_{jk}; \ j \in G_2, k \in G_3)$.

(b) $a_{10}^2 = \sum\limits_{k=9}^{12} \sum\limits_{j=5}^{8} r_{1j}r_{1k} \bigg/ \sum\limits_{k=9}^{12} \sum\limits_{j=5}^{8} r_{jk}$.

10 and 12.

Variable		Common Factors			Communality
j	F_0	F_1	F_2	F_3	h_j^2
1	.543	.555			.603
2	.568	.624			.712
3	.481	.650			.654
4	.405	.564			.482
5	.653		.519		.696
6	:610		.342		.489
7	.688		.506		.729
8	.736		.382		.688
9	.636			.223	.454
10	.613			.245	.436
11	.537			.380	.433
12	.347			.435	.310

11 and 13. The general-factor residuals are below the diagonal and the final residuals are above.

Variable	1	2	3	4	5	6	7	8	9	10	11	12
1		.036	−.026	−.018								
2	.382		−.024	−.025								
3	.335	.382		.038								
4	.295	.327	.405									
5	.066	.026	.072	−.009		.036	−.070	−.019				
6	.019	−.046	−.041	−.047	.213		−.017	−.035				
7	.002	−.042	−.002	−.021	.193	.156		.039				
8	.005	.030	−.003	.012	.179	.096	.232					
9	−.003	.020	−.022	−.017	−.008	.040	−.003	.010		.015	−.021	−.040
10	−.008	.029	.029	.038	−.041	.033	−.030	−.066	.070		−.038	−.107
11	−.032	−.020	−.003	.035	−.030	.042	.039	−.016	.064	.055		.047
12	−.023	.003	−.021	.004	−.065	.024	.064	.030	.057	.000	.212	

14. (a) $B(5, 1) = 107$, $B(5, 2) = 32$, $B(5, 3) = 34$, $B(5, 4) = 16$.
 (b) $B(5, 1, 2) = 81$, $B(5, 1, 3) = 77$, $B(5, 1, 4) = 78$, $B(5, 2, 3) = 71$, $B(5, 2, 4) = 55$, $B(5, 3, 4) = 54$.
 (c) $B(5, 1, 2, 3) = 87$, $B(5, 1, 2, 4) = 79$, $B(5, 1, 3, 4) = 74$, $B(5, 2, 3, 4) = 73$.
 (d) $B(1, 2, 3, 4) = 164$.
 (e) In the set of five variables, there is no doubt that 1, 2, 3, 4 belong together, while variable 5 does not group with any of the others; except that variables 5 and 1 belong together to about the same extent to which they belong with the other three variables.

15. $\sigma_{\dot{r}} = .074$ from Table A in Appendix.
 For $\dot{r}_{51}$: $.274/.074 = 3.70$, $P = 1 - \alpha = .0002$ from Table C in Appendix.
 For $\dot{r}_{52}$: $.099/.074 = 1.34$, $P = .1802$.
 For $\dot{r}_{53}$: $.102/.074 = 1.38$, $P = .1676$.
 For $\dot{r}_{54}$: $.048/.074 = 0.65$, $P = .5092$.
 The probability P for the residual $\dot{r}_{51} = .274$ indicates that the observed value would be exceeded in less than a fraction of one per cent in sampling from a true value of zero; and hence it may be concluded that the true value of this residual is different from zero. The probabilities for the other three residuals are each greater than .05, the standard level of significance usually recommended, so that the deviations of these values from zero may be attributed to chance errors.

16.

Variable	F_0	F_1	D_1
1	a_{10}	a_{11}	d_{11}
2	a_{20}	a_{21}	—
3	a_{30}	a_{31}	—
4	a_{40}	a_{41}	—
5	a_{50}	—	d_{51}

409

17. $a_{11} = .616$, $a_{21} = .732$, $a_{31} = .689$, $a_{41} = .679$.

18. Since $\sigma_{\hat{i}} = .074$, to divide the remaining variance between the two variables means that

$$d_{11} = d_{51} = \sqrt{.274 - .074} = .447.$$

If this value were taken for d_{11}, then the communality for the first variable would be:

$$h_1^2 = .691^2 + .616^2 + .447^2 = 1.057,$$

an impossible value if there is to be a real unique factor.

CHAPTER 8

1.

j	S_j	$\alpha_{j1}^{(1)}$
1	3.292	.889
2	2.794	.755
3	2.650	.716
4	3.702	1.000
5	2.715	.733
6	2.097	.566

2. Squaring the correlation matrix once, but without actually calculating the elements of $\mathbf{R}^4$, the trial values are found to stabilize, viz.,

j	$S_j^{(2)}$	$T_j^{(2)}$	$\alpha_{j1}^{(2)}$	$S_j^{(4)}$	$T_j^{(4)}$	$\alpha_j^{(4)}$
1	9.715	9.714	.893	—	85.637	.898
2	8.381	8.381	.770	—	73.679	.773
3	8.000	8.000	.735	—	70.285	.737
4	10.881	10.880	1.000	—	95.331	1.000
5	7.971	7.971	.733	—	69.801	.732
6	6.193	6.192	.569	—	54.177	.568

3.

j	α_{j1}	γ_{j1}	α_{j1}	a_{j1}	Supplementary Calculations
1	.898	2.662	.8987	.793	$\lambda_1 = 2.962$, $\sum \alpha_{j1}^2 = 3.8084$
2	.773	2.290	.7731	.682	
3	.737	2.185	.7377	.651	$\sqrt{2.962/3.8084} = .8819$
4	1.000	2.962	1.0000	.882	
5	.732	2.169	.7321	.646	$a_{j1} = .8819\,\alpha_{j1}$
6	.568	1.683	.5682	.501	
					$\sum a_{j1}^2 = 2.964$

4.

$$\mathbf{R}_1 = \begin{bmatrix} .089 & .318 & .224 & -.226 & -.211 & -.196 \\ .318 & .029 & .007 & -.166 & -.114 & -.115 \\ .224 & .007 & -.010 & -.067 & -.094 & -.115 \\ -.226 & -.166 & -.067 & .167 & .160 & .169 \\ -.211 & -.114 & -.094 & .160 & .129 & .160 \\ -.196 & -.115 & -.115 & .169 & .160 & .112 \end{bmatrix}$$

5.

j	S_{j1}	$\alpha_{j2}^{(1)}$	$S_j^{(2)}$	$\lambda_1 E_{j1}$	$S_{j1}^{(2)}$	$\alpha_{j2}^{(2)}$
1	$-.002$	.036	9.715	9.757	$-.042$	1.00
2	$-.041$	.745	8.381	8.397	$-.016$	.38
3	$-.055$	1.000	8.000	8.012	$-.012$	.29
4	.037	$-.673$	10.881	10.856	.025	$-.60$
5	.030	$-.545$	7.971	7.953	.018	$-.43$
6	.015	$-.273$	6.193	6.167	.026	$-.62$

6.

j	α_{j2}	α'_{j2}	α_{j2}	α'_{j2}	α_{j2}	$\cdots$	α_{j2}	a_{j2}	Supplementary Calculations
1	1.00	.623	1.000	After seven			1.000	.508	$\lambda_2 = 0.914, \quad \sum \alpha_{j2}^2 = 3.5368$
2	.38	.551	.884	more itera-			.712	.362	
3	.29	.340	.546	tions			.477	.243	$\sqrt{.914/3.5368} = .5084$
4	$-.60$	$-.582$	$-.934$				$-.832$	$-.423$	
5	$-.43$	$-.532$	$-.854$				$-.750$	$-.381$	$a_{j2} = .5084\,\alpha_{j2}$
6	$-.62$	$-.513$	$-.823$				$-.740$	$-.376$	$\sum a_{j2}^2 = .914$

7.

$$\mathbf{R}_2 = \begin{bmatrix} -.169 & .134 & .101 & -.011 & -.017 & -.005 \\ .134 & -.102 & -.081 & -.013 & .024 & .021 \\ .101 & -.081 & -.069 & .036 & -.001 & -.024 \\ -.011 & -.013 & .036 & -.012 & -.001 & .010 \\ -.017 & .024 & -.001 & -.001 & -.016 & .017 \\ -.005 & .021 & -.024 & .010 & .017 & -.029 \end{bmatrix}$$

8. $\sum a_{j1}^2 = 2.964 = \lambda_1, \quad \sum a_{j2}^2 = .914 = \lambda_2, \quad \sum a_{j1} a_{j2} = .000.$

9.

Variable	P_1	P_2
1	.8600	$-.0169$
2	.8341	$-.1559$
3	.8646	$-.3773$
4	.5776	.3956
5	.4950	.3391
6	.3300	.2261

The two largest eigenvalues are $\lambda_1 = 2.8704$ and $\lambda_2 = .4896$, while the remaining four are zero. This property follows from the fact that the reduced correlation matrix (with communality) is of rank 2, mathematically.

10.

Variable	P_1	P_2
1	.857	−.317
2	.846	−.398
3	.810	−.402
4	.832	−.335
5	.728	.537
6	.627	.494
7	.567	.516
8	.607	.360
Contribution of factor	4.410	1.461

This solution agrees very closely with the solution in Table 8.12, with corresponding factor coefficients differing by less than .02 in the case of the first factor, and by less than .03 for the second factor. The total common-factor variance accounted for in Table 8.12 is 5.966 while the present solution (with minimal values of communalities) accounts for 5.871.

11 and 12.

j	S_j	a_{j1}	Supplementary Calculations
1	3.292	.793	$T = 17.250$
2	2.794	.673	$\sqrt{T} = 4.153$
3	2.650	.638	$a_{j1} = S_j/4.153$
4	3.702	.892	
5	2.715	.654	$D_1 = \sum a_{j1} = 4.155 = \sqrt{T}$
6	2.097	.505	
Total	17.250	4.155	

13 and 15. The first-factor residuals, $_1r_{jk}$, are in the principal diagonal and below it; the values above the diagonal are those after reflection of variables (exercise 14) and are used in calculating the second-factor coefficients in exercise 15.

Variable	−1	−2	−3	4	5	6	Supplementary Calculations
1	.089	.325	.234	.234	.218	.199	
2	.325	.041	.022	.164	.113	.113	
3	.234	.022	.007	.062	.090	.111	
4	−.234	−.164	−.062	.149	.147	.161	
5	−.218	−.113	−.090	.147	.118	.154	
6	−.199	−.113	−.111	.161	.154	.108	
Total	−.003	−.002	.000	−.003	−.002	.000	
S_{j1}	1.299	.778	.526	.917	.840	.846	$T_1 = 5.206$
$\varepsilon_j S_{j1}$	−1.299	−.778	−.526	.917	.840	.846	$\sqrt{T_1} = 2.282$
a_{j2}	−.569	−.341	−.230	.402	.368	.371	$D_2 = .001$, $\sum \varepsilon_j a_{j2} = 2.281 = \sqrt{T_1}$

14.

Variable	Variable Reflected	No. neg. before refl.	No. negatives after reflection		
			1	2	3
1	—	3	2	1	0
2	—	3	4	1	0
3	—	3	4	5	0
4		3	2	1	0
5		3	2	1	0
6		3	2	1	0
Total		18	16	10	0
Difference			2	6	10

16. Second factor residuals, $_2r_{jk}$:

Variable	1	2	3	4	5	6
1	−.235					
2	.131	−.075				
3	.103	−.056	−.046			
4	−.005	−.027	.030	−.013		
5	−.009	.012	−.005	−.001	−.017	
6	.012	.014	−.026	.012	.017	−.030

17.

Variable	Common-Factor Coefficients		Communality		
	C_1	C_2	Original (1)	Calculated (2)	(1) − (2)
1	.793	−.569	.718	.953	−.235
2	.673	−.341	.494	.569	−.075
3	.638	−.230	.414	.460	−.046
4	.892	.402	.945	.957	−.012
5	.654	.368	.546	.563	−.017
6	.505	.371	.363	.393	−.030
Total	4.155	.001	3.480	3.895	−.415
Contribution of factor	2.967	.928	—	—	—
Percent of total orig. comm.	85.3	26.7	—	111.9	−11.9

CHAPTER 9

1. For the simple case of $m = 1$ formula (9.9) becomes

$$f_j = \sum_{\substack{k=1 \\ k \neq j}}^{n} (r_{jk} - a_k b_j)^2 \qquad (j \text{ fixed})$$

Then, expanding the quadratic, this becomes

$$f_j = l_j b_j^2 - 2Q_j b_j + C_j$$

or, by completing the square,

$$f_j = l_j \left(b_j - \frac{Q_j}{l_j} \right)^2 + K_j$$

where

$$l_j = \sum a_k^2, \quad Q_j = \sum r_{jk} a_k, \quad C_j = \sum r_{jk}^2, \quad \text{and} \quad K_j = C_j - \frac{Q_j^2}{l_j}$$

and it is understood that all summations extend over the range $k = 1$ to n but not equal to j. From the last formula for f_j it is seen that its minimum value occurs when $b_j = Q_j/l_j$. Thus, the minres solution is given by:

$$b_j = \frac{Q_j}{l_j} \quad \text{if} \quad \left| \frac{Q_j}{l_j} \right| \leq 1,$$

$$b_j = 1 \quad \text{if} \quad \left| \frac{Q_j}{l_j} \right| > 1.$$

2. (a) Denoting the original loadings by a_j and the minres loadings by b_j with a superscript for the iteration number, the solutions are given in the following table:

j	a_j	$b_j^{(1)}$	$b_j^{(2)}$	$b_j^{(3)}$
1	1.05	1.000	1.000	1.000
2	.90	.918	.913	.912
3	.80	.810	.809	.809
4	.70	.706	.707	.707
5	.60	.604	.605	.605

(b) For the Heywood solution (with the communality of the first variable being greater than one) all the residuals vanish and the objective function is precisely zero. The minres solution yields an $f = .004441$ from the residuals in the following table:

j	1	2	3	4	5
1					
2	.033				
3	.031	−.018			
4	.028	−.015	−.012		
5	.025	−.012	−.009	−.008	

3.

m	U_m for N equal to:				v	χ^2			Action regarding null hypothesis
	12	50	100	200		0.1%	1%	5%	
1	47.5	211.8	427.9	860.1	10	29.6	23.2	18.3	Reject at all levels, all N.
2	3.8	17.1	34.6	69.6	6	22.5	16.8	12.6	For $N = 12$, accept at all levels; for $N = 50$, accept at 0.1% level, reject at 5% level; for $N > 50$, reject at all levels.
3	0	0	0	0	3	16.3	11.3	7.8	Accept at all levels, all N.

4.

j	F_1	F_2	h_j^2
1	.860	−.017	.740
2	.834	−.156	.720
3	.865	−.377	.890
4	.577	.396	.490
5	.495	.339	.360
6	.330	.226	.160
Variance	2.870	.490	3.360

415

CHAPTER 10

1. (a) $L = \prod_{i=1}^{N} f(X_i;\ p) = \prod_{i=1}^{N} p^{X_i}(1-p)^{1-X_i} = p^{\Sigma X_i}(1-p)^{N-\Sigma X_i}$

In the example, $N = 100$ and $\sum X_i = 18$, so that the likelihood function becomes: $L = p^{18}(1-p)^{82}$.

(b) $\log L = 18 \log p + 82 \log (1-p)$

(c) $\dfrac{d(\log L)}{dp} = \dfrac{18}{p} - \dfrac{82}{1-p}$

(d) $18(1-\hat{p}) - 82\hat{p} = 0$, $\hat{p} = 0.18$.

2. (a)

First Iteration for Maximum-Likelihood Estimates of General-Factor Weights for Five Psychological Tests of Table 7.1

Line	Instruction	1	2	3	4	5
1	a_{j1}	.707	.673	.604	.554	.398
2	$d_j^2 = 1 - a_{j1}^2$	.5002	.5471	.6352	.6931	.8416
3	L_1/L_2	1.413	1.230	.951	.799	.473
4	RL_3	2.847	2.727	2.402	2.259	1.611
5	$L_4 - L_1$	2.140	2.054	1.798	1.705	1.213
6	$a_{j1} = L_5/\sqrt{L_3 \cdot L_5}$	.706	.677	.593	.562	.400
7	$d_j^2 = 1 - L_6^2$	.5016	.5417	.6484	.6842	.8400

The uniquenesses are in line 2 of the above table, and the first iteration is contained in lines 3–7. The square-root of the inner product of the vectors in line 3 and line 5 is $\sqrt{L_3 \cdot L_5} = 3.033$.

(b) The convergence is considered satisfactory after four iterations when four of the five weights have stabilized to three decimal places, and the coefficient for test 2 differs by one unit in the third decimal place from its preceding value. The maximum-likelihood estimates of the five coefficients are: .705, .682, .587, .566, .399.

3. (a) The work can be organized conveniently as in Tables 10.4 and 10.5, and the required sum is

$$\sum_{j<k=1}^{5} \bar{r}_{jk}^2/d_j^2 d_k^2 = .007626.$$

(b) $U_1 = 757(.007626) = 5.77.$ (c) $v = 5.$ (d) $\chi^2 = 15.1.$

(e) The calculated U_1 is well below the χ^2 required for the 1 % significance level.

(f) The hypothesis stands unrejected, i.e., on the basis of random sampling a fit as bad or worse than that observed can be expected in about 1 out of 2 cases ($P = .46$) if the real description of the data were actually in terms of a single common factor.

4. In order to provide a means for checking numerical calculations, the data are presented to five decimal places (certainly, with no implications of such degree of accuracy). The reproduced correlations are given in the upper triangle and the residuals in the lower triangle of the following table:

Variable	1	2	3	4	5
1		.01118	.97243	.43866	.02195
2	−.00143		.11660	.71458	.86422
3	.00002	.03768		.52000	.13429
4	.00021	−.02317	−.00528		.76768
5	.00046	−.00115	−.01236	.00997	

For $N = 12$, the resulting statistic (10.29) is $U_2 = 2.21306$. From (10.28), the number of degrees of freedom is one and the associated χ^2 is 3.841 at the .05 level of significance. The hypothesis of 2 common factors would be accepted since U_2 is less than χ^2. (It should be remembered that this was merely an exercise; the large-sample test certainly should not be applied to cases of $N < 100$).

5. Starting with the coefficients of the first principal factor (ex. 3, chap 8) it took 36 iterations for convergence. To assist the reader, some of the intermediate results are shown in addition to the final factor weights.

Trial	1	2	3	4	5	6
Initial	.793	.682	.651	.882	.646	.501
1st iteration	.735	.678	.674	.843	.669	.535
5th iteration	.764	.698	.687	.795	.643	.508
10th iteration	.862	.784	.727	.691	.533	.407
20th iteration	.966	.867	.727	.527	.363	.254
30th iteration	.980	.865	.734	.506	.339	.233
Final	.984	.864	.736	.499	.330	.226

7. It should be immediately obvious upon computing the residuals that at least a second common factor is necessary to explain the correlations. Simply as an exercise in applying formula (10.29), it is found that

$$\sum_{j<k=1}^{6} (\bar{r}_{jk}^2/d_j^2 d_k^2) = 1.477737$$

and that $U_1 = 450.7$ since $N = 305$. This tremendously large value of χ^2 falls off Table D for $v = 9$ degrees of freedom. Without question the hypothesis is rejected, and at least a second factor should be sought for an adequate fit to the correlations.

8. First Iteration for Maximum-Likelihood Estimates of Two Factors for Six Physical Variables of Table V

Line	Instruction	1	2	3	4	5	6
1	a_{j1}	.793	.682	.651	.882	.646	.501
2	a_{j2}	.508	.362	.243	−.423	−.381	−.376
3	$d_j^2 = 1 - a_{j1}^2 - a_{j2}^2$	.1131	.4038	.5172	.0431	.4375	.6076
4	L_1/L_3	7.011	1.689	1.259	20.464	1.477	.825
5	L_2/L_3	4.492	.896	.470	−9.814	−.871	−.619
6	RL_4	19.683	17.872	18.241	26.737	19.889	16.102
7	$L_6 - L_1$	18.890	17.190	17.590	25.855	19.243	15.601
8	$a_{j1} = L_7/\sqrt{L_4 \cdot L_7}$	.688	.626	.641	.942	.701	.568
9	RL_5	.581	.262	−1.193	−8.074	−6.536	−5.831
10	$L_9 - L_2$	.073	−.100	−1.436	−7.651	−6.155	−5.455
11	$L_{10} - (L_5 \cdot L_8)L_8$	4.376	3.815	2.573	−1.760	−1.771	−1.903
12	$a_{j2} = L_{11}/\sqrt{L_5 \cdot L_{11}}$	.658	.573	.387	−.265	−.266	−.286
13	$d_j^2 = 1 - L_8^2 - L_{12}^2$	.0937	.2798	.4394	.0424	.4378	.5956

The method broke down after eleven iterations when the uniqueness of the first variable became negative. With an electronic computer the process would be started over again, with a different set of initial values—perhaps the first maximum-likelihood factor obtained in ex. 5, and some arbitrary values for the second factor based upon the residuals determined in ex. 7.

9. The maximum-likelihood solution obtained by use of the program [204] on a Philco 2000, after 100 iterations, is given in the following table:

j	a_{j1}	a_{j2}	h_j^2
1	.999	−.009	.999
2	.860	.028	.740
3	.742	.170	.580
4	.486	.847	.953
5	.311	.683	.564
6	.210	.600	.404
Variance	2.665	1.575	4.240

10.

Variable	Initial Values		After 1 Iteration		After 2 Iterations		After 3 Iterations	
j	a_{j1}	a_{j2}	a_{j1}	a_{j2}	a_{j1}	a_{j2}	a_{j1}	a_{j2}
1	.858	−.328	.890	−.210	.894	−.183	.894	−.182
2	.849	−.414	.886	−.325	.895	−.300	.896	−.301
3	.810	−.412	.855	−.313	.864	−.290	.866	−.291
4	.825	−.339	.863	−.237	.871	−.210	.871	−.209
5	.747	.561	.675	.648	.657	.670	.656	.663
6	.637	.507	.574	.573	.556	.586	.554	.577
7	.561	.488	.506	.573	.491	.592	.490	.587
8	.619	.371	.566	.404	.553	.413	.551	.403

11. For $n = 8$ and $m = 2$, the number of degrees of freedom is $v = 13$. The sum of squared residuals divided by the product of uniquenesses is

$$\sum_{j<k=1}^{8} \bar{r}_{jk}^2/d_j^2 d_k^2 = .263,$$

and for $N = 305$, formula (10.29) gives $U_2 = 80.2$. Since this value is so much in excess of $\chi^2 = 27.7$, corresponding to the 1 % level of significance, the hypothesis is rejected. An interpretation from the viewpoint of goodness of fit may be put this way : corresponding to $\chi^2 = 80.2$ with $v = 13$, the accompanying probability is $P < .001$; that is, in less than 1 out of 1000 trials, in random sampling, can a fit as bad or worse than that observed be expected if the real description of the data were actually in terms of two common factors. Clearly the actual fit is a bad one, and another hypothesis is indicated.

12. For $m = 2$ and $v = 13$, when $N = 120$, then

$$U_2 = 120 \, (.263) = 31.6.$$

This value is still in excess of the critical value of 27.7, and the hypothesis would be rejected. However, for $m = 3$ and $v = 7$, $U_3 = 120(.151) = 18.1$ is just below the $\chi^2 = 18.5$ which produces a probability $P = .01$, and it may be said that three common factors are just significant at the 1 % level in describing the correlations of Table 10.2 (if they were based on only 120 cases).

13. For $m = 2$ and $v = 13$, when $N = 100$, then

$$U_2 = 100(.263) = 26.3.$$

Since this value is just below that required to produce $P = .01$, the hypothesis would not be rejected, i.e., two factors would suffice at the 1 % level. Of course, if 3 factors were obtained then the $U_3 = 15.1$ for $v = 7$ would certainly be significant at the 1 % level (actually $P = .04$ for this χ^2).

CHAPTER 11

1.

G_p	j	w_{j1}	w_{j2}
G_1	1	3.352	1.554
	2	3.434	1.394
	3	3.304	1.281
	4	3.301	1.457
G_2	5	1.665	2.993
	6	1.372	2.569
	7	1.142	2.436
	8	1.507	2.247

2.

q / p	1	2
1	13.391	5.686
2	5.686	10.245
s_q	3.659	3.201

3. $r_{T_1 T_2} = 5.686/(3.659)(3.201) = .4855.$

4. The factor structure appears as the 8 × 2 matrix in the lower left corner of the answer to ex. 5.

5. The oblique factor pattern is the 8 × 2 matrix, calculated in the right-hand block of the table, while the orthogonal factor matrix is obtained in the middle block.

Variable	Original Matrices		Square Root Operation		Row-by-Row Multiplication with T^{-1}	
T_1	1.0000	*	1.0000		1.0000	0
T_2	.4855	1.0000	.4855	.8742	−.0000	1.0000
T_1	1.0000	0	1.0000	−.5554	1.3085	*
T_2	0	1.0000	0	1.1439	−.6353	1.3085
1	.916	.485	.916	.046	.890	.053
2	.939	.435	.939	−.024	.952	−.027
3	.903	.400	.903	−.044	.927	−.050
4	.902	.455	.902	.020	.891	.023
5	.455	.935	.455	.817	.001	.935
6	.375	.803	.375	.710	−.019	.812
7	.312	.761	.312	.697	−.075	.797
8	.412	.702	.412	.574	.093	.657
Total	7.699	7.461	7.699	4.259	5.333	4.873
Check			7.699	4.259	5.334	4.872

6. The reproduced correlations in the table were obtained by row-by-row multiplication of the orthogonal factor matrix **A** by itself. These numbers may be checked by row-by-row multiplication of the oblique structure **S** by the oblique pattern **P**,

or in reverse order.

Variable	1	2	3	4	5	6	7	8
1	.841							
2	.859	.882						
3	.825	.849	.817					
4	.827	.846	.814	.814				
5	.454	.408	.375	.427	.875			
6	.376	.335	.307	.352	.751	.645		
7	.318	.276	.251	.295	.711	.612	.583	
8	.404	.373	.347	.383	.656	.562	.529	.499

7. The residuals are recorded in the table. Without applying any approximate statistical tests (see ex. 12, chap. 8) it seems reasonable to conclude that these residuals are random deviations around zero. Two multiple-group factors account for 99.93 % of the original communality of 5.960.

Variable	1	2	3	4	5	6	7	8
1	.001							
2	−.013	−.001						
3	−.020	.032	.000					
4	.032	−.020	−.013	.001				
5	.019	−.032	.005	.009	−.003			
6	.022	−.009	.012	−.023	.011	.002		
7	−.017	.001	−.014	.032	.019	−.029	.001	
8	−.022	.042	−.002	−.018	−.027	.015	.010	.003

8. $s_{T_1}^2 = \sum T_{1i}^2/N = \sum (z_{1i} + z_{2i} + z_{3i})^2/N$

$$= \sum z_{1i}^2/N + \sum z_{2i}^2/N + \sum z_{3i}^2/N + 2(\sum z_{1i}z_{2i}/N + \sum z_{1i}z_{3i}/N + \sum z_{2i}z_{3i}/N)$$

$$= s_1^2 + s_2^2 + s_3^2 + 2(r_{12} + r_{13} + r_{23})$$

$s_{T_1}^2 = \sum_{j,k=1}^{3} r_{jk}$, where $r_{jj} = 1$ or $r_{jj} = h_j^2$ depending on the model.

CHAPTER 12

1.
$$T = \begin{bmatrix} .990 & .016 & -.130 & -.044 \\ .257 & .961 & .076 & -.012 \\ .456 & .112 & .878 & .026 \\ .386 & .250 & .109 & .881 \end{bmatrix}$$

2. $b_{11} = .367$, $b_{12} = .188$, $b_{13} = .597$, $b_{14} = .067$,
$b_{53} = -.016$, $b_{24,4} = .195$.

3. $b_{11} = .096$, $b_{12} = .248$, $b_{13} = .706$;
$b_{13,1} = .070$, $b_{13,2} = .619$, $b_{13,3} = .469$.

These values agree perfectly with those obtained in Table 12.5 (by successive rotations in a plane).

5. It should be noted that variables 4, 5, 6 fall on a straight line. Hence, one axis can be passed through these three points and the other at right angles to it. The direction of the second axis may have to be reversed in order to make the algebraic signs of the factor loadings agree with those in Table 5.8.

CHAPTER 13

1. There is generally close agreement between corresponding values in the two solutions, with a number being identical. The largest discrepancy in structure values is .008 and the largest in pattern coefficients is .011.

2. $S_{v_1} = 2.843$, $S_{v_2} = 4.214$, $S_{v_3} = 3.147$.

3. $u_1 = .6535C_1 + .0735C_2 - .5012C_3$
$u_2 = .8448C_1 + .3759C_2 + .2330C_3$
$u_3 = .6841C_1 - .5697C_2 + .1405C_3$

4. $D(Ou_1) = .8268$, $D(Ou_2) = .9536$, $D(Ou_3) = .9013$.

5.
$$\mathbf{T} = \begin{bmatrix} .7904 & .8859 & .7590 \\ .0889 & .3942 & -.6321 \\ -.6062 & .2443 & .1559 \end{bmatrix}.$$

6.
$$\boldsymbol{\Phi} = \mathbf{T'T} = \begin{bmatrix} 1.000 & .587 & .449 \\ .587 & 1.000 & .461 \\ .449 & .461 & 1.000 \end{bmatrix}$$

7.
$$\mathbf{S} = \mathbf{CT} = \begin{bmatrix} .743 & .406 & .430 \\ .445 & .264 & .204 \\ .604 & .324 & .157 \\ .559 & .386 & .266 \\ .451 & .807 & .429 \\ .489 & .807 & .339 \\ .447 & .846 & .355 \\ .537 & .717 & .420 \\ .435 & .841 & .311 \\ .075 & .311 & .712 \\ .302 & .357 & .677 \\ .316 & .222 & .724 \\ .582 & .419 & .723 \end{bmatrix}$$

8. The primary-factor pattern $\mathbf{P}$ for these data is exhibited as the matrix $\mathbf{A}$ in Table 12.1.

9. The total direct contributions are given in the diagonal and the total joint contributions below the diagonal of the table:

Factor	T_1	T_2	T_3
T_1	1.823		
T_2	−.272	3.394	
T_3	−.052	−.015	2.103

The grand total of the contributions is 6.981 as compared with the centroid total communality of 6.966.

10.
$$\mathbf{W} = \mathbf{V\Psi}^{-1}$$
$$= \mathbf{V(\Lambda'\Lambda)}^{-1} \quad \text{from (13.35)}$$
$$= \mathbf{V\Lambda}^{-1}\mathbf{(\Lambda')}^{-1} \quad \text{from (3.16)}$$
$$= \mathbf{A(\Lambda')}^{-1} \quad \text{from (13.30).}$$

CHAPTER 14

1. $Q = 3.983$ for the graphical solution of Table 12.3 (for a graphical solution based on a centroid pattern, which was given in the first edition of this text, $Q = 4.061$), while the maximum $Q = 4.091$ is for the quartimax solution of Table 14.2.

2. (a) Quartimax solution for eight political variables:

j	b_{j1}	b_{j2}
1	.74	.10
2	.97	.25
3	.89	−.05
4	−.83	.30
5	.11	−.70
6	.86	−.23
7	−.50	.70
8	−.89	.38

(b) $Q = 4.040$ for the quartimax solution; $Q = 4.009$ for the principal-factor solution.

3. $V = 23.61$ for quartimax solution; $V = 23.75$ for graphical solution; $V = 24.30$ for varimax solution.

4. (a) Varimax solution for eight political variables:

j	b_{j1}	b_{j2}
1	.74	.08
2	1.00	.00
3	.85	.26
4	−.73	−.50
5	−.06	.70
6	.78	.43
7	−.31	−.81
8	−.77	−.59

(b) $V = 9.58$ for principal-factor solution; $V = 15.95$ for varimax solution.

5. (a) $(V - S)_{rms} = .040$;   (b) $(V - Q)_{rms} = .052$;   (c) $(Q - S)_{rms} = .091$.

CHAPTER 15

1. $K = .0810$.

3. (a)

j	$w_j = a_{j2}^2$
1	.0784
2	.2304
3	.0289
4	.0081
5	.4225
6	.0001
7	.3136
8	.0225

(b) $C = \begin{bmatrix} .4344 & .0799 \\ .0799 & .3375 \end{bmatrix}$

(c) $N_1^2 - .7719N_1 + .1402 = 0$;
$N_1 = .2924$.

(d) $\lambda_{11} = .4904$, $\lambda_{21} = -.8715$

(e)

j	v_{j1}
1	.5824
2	.8499
3	.5748
4	−.3531
5	−.4292
6	.4277
7	.1644
8	−.3401

(f)

j	$w_j = v_{j1}^2$	v_{j2}
1	.3392	−.0695
2	.7223	−.2064
3	.3304	.0876
4	.1247	−.3394
5	.1842	.7030
6	.1829	.2657
7	.0270	−.7262
8	.1157	−.4199

$C = \begin{bmatrix} 1.3451 & -.3478 \\ -.3479 & .2925 \end{bmatrix}$

$N_2^2 - 1.6376N_2 + .2724 = 0$
$N_2 = .1879$
$\lambda_{12} = .2878$, $\lambda_{22} = .9576$.

(g) $\Lambda = \begin{bmatrix} .5784 & -.2659 \\ -.8158 & -.9640 \end{bmatrix}$

4. (a) $\Lambda^{-1} = \begin{bmatrix} 1.0030 & -.5422 \\ .9574 & .6194 \end{bmatrix}$ (b) $T = \begin{bmatrix} .8797 & .8396 \\ -.4755 & .5432 \end{bmatrix}$

(c) $D = T'\Lambda = \begin{bmatrix} .877 & .000 \\ .000 & .877 \end{bmatrix}$

(d) $P' = D^{-1}V' = \begin{bmatrix} .893 & .955 & .931 & .878 & .008 & -.023 & -.057 & .082 \\ .052 & -.027 & -.050 & .031 & .928 & .824 & .767 & .685 \end{bmatrix}$

(e) $r_{T_1 T_2} = .4803.$

5. $\Lambda^{-1} = \begin{pmatrix} .9022 & -.4881 \\ .6767 & .7709 \end{pmatrix}.$

The matrix for normalizing the rows of Λ^{-1} is:

$$D = \begin{pmatrix} .97488 & 0 \\ 0 & .97488 \end{pmatrix}, \quad \text{and} \quad D^{-1} = \begin{pmatrix} 1.02577 & 0 \\ 0 & 1.02577 \end{pmatrix}.$$

The primary-factor pattern is given by:

$$P = VD^{-1} = \begin{bmatrix} -.0979 & 1.0111 \\ .9600 & -.1171 \\ .0271 & .9832 \\ .7893 & .3610 \\ .9876 & -.1175 \end{bmatrix}.$$

6. $\Lambda^{-1} = \begin{pmatrix} .8601 & -.5231 \\ .6181 & .7945 \end{pmatrix}; \quad D = \begin{pmatrix} .9934 & 0 \\ 0 & .9934 \end{pmatrix}; \quad D^{-1} = \begin{pmatrix} 1.0066 & 0 \\ 0 & 1.0066 \end{pmatrix};$

$$P = VD^{-1} = \begin{bmatrix} -.0368 & .9974 \\ .9461 & -.0673 \\ .0856 & .9761 \\ .8053 & .3980 \\ .9736 & .0662 \end{bmatrix}.$$

7. From the solution of ex. 5, the first variable may be expressed as follows:

$$z_1' = -.0979T_1 + 1.0111T_2 + .1104U_1,$$

and its common-factor variance is given by

$$h_1^2 = (-.0979)^2 + (1.0111)^2 + 2(-.0979)(1.0111)r_{T_1 T_2}$$

where the correlation between the two oblique factors is required. This may be obtained by use of (15.42),

$$T' = D\Lambda^{-1} = \begin{pmatrix} .8795 & -.4758 \\ .6597 & .7515 \end{pmatrix},$$

and then from (13.16) it follows that $r_{T_1 T_2} = .2226.$ Hence,

$$h_1^2 = .0096 + 1.0223 - .0441 = .9878.$$

This value is precisely the same as the sum of the squares of the coefficients of the first two principal components for variable 1.

8.
$$\Lambda^{-1} = \begin{pmatrix} 1.0452 & -.4633 \\ .9119 & .6897 \end{pmatrix}; \quad D = \begin{pmatrix} .8746 & 0 \\ 0 & .8747 \end{pmatrix}; \quad D^{-1} = \begin{pmatrix} 1.1446 & 0 \\ 0 & 1.1434 \end{pmatrix};$$

$$P = 1.144V = \begin{bmatrix} .886 & .058 \\ .961 & -.038 \\ .931 & -.053 \\ .885 & .027 \\ -.004 & .945 \\ -.013 & .807 \\ -.073 & .797 \\ .099 & .648 \end{bmatrix}.$$

9. (a)
$$\Lambda^{-1} = \begin{bmatrix} .7956 & -.5068 & -.5031 & .2891 \\ .6893 & .5767 & -.3975 & -.4806 \\ .8223 & -.3133 & .5514 & -.3999 \\ .7842 & .4695 & .2755 & .5955 \end{bmatrix}.$$

(b)
$$\begin{bmatrix} .9029 & 0 & 0 & 0 \\ 0 & .9142 & 0 & 0 \\ 0 & 0 & .8986 & 0 \\ 0 & 0 & 0 & .8888 \end{bmatrix}.$$

(c) **T** is determined by use of (15.42):

$$T = \begin{bmatrix} .7183 & .6302 & .7389 & .6970 \\ -.4576 & .5272 & -.2815 & .4173 \\ -.4542 & -.3634 & .4955 & .2449 \\ .2610 & -.4394 & -.3594 & .5293 \end{bmatrix}.$$

10. $F_0 = .0474, \quad F_{-.5} = .0754, \quad F_{-1} = .1033, \quad F_{-5} = .3271$
$F_{.1} = .0418, \quad F_{.5} = .0194, \quad F_{.8} = .0026, \quad F_1 = -.0085.$

11.

j	a_{j1}/h_j	a_{j2}/h_j
1	.9895	.1443
2	.9895	.1443
3	-.8815	.4722

$F_0 = .2140$ for normalized **A**.

12. The first two variables are represented by two collinear points with the origin. An "obvious" oblique solution would consist of an axis through the first two variables and another through the third variable, which would make an obtuse angle with the first axis.

426

13. (a) $F_0 = 0$.

(b) The structure matrix is obtained by postmultiplying the pattern matrix by the factor correlation matrix, according to (2.43). The result is

$$\begin{bmatrix} .97015 & -.78011 \\ .48508 & -.39005 \\ -.51085 & .63530 \end{bmatrix}.$$

14. $F_0 = .83956$. The computer program calculates the sum over the factors only under the constraint that the indices for the factors be different. Formula (15.45) requires that one index always be less than the other. Hence, the computer output, $F_0 = 1.679149$, is just twice that calculated by (15.45).

15. In terms of the expression (15.45), but with each b_{jp} replaced by b_{jp}/h_j, the initial value is .976 and the final value is .138. The complete direct oblimin $(\delta = 0)$ solution consists of the following:

j	Factor Pattern		Factor Structure	
	b_{j1}	b_{j2}	r_{jT_1}	r_{jT_2}
1	−.07316	1.01078	.12028	.99678
2	.88580	−.08021	.87045	.08931
3	.05653	.96704	.24160	.97786
4	.76056	.34397	.82638	.48953
5	1.00303	−.10971	.98203	.08224
			Factor Correlations	
T_1			1.	.19137
T_2			.19137	1.

CHAPTER 16

1. In formula (16.12) the matrix $\mathbf{A}$ consists of the first two principal components from Table 8.1, the matrix $\mathbf{B}$ comes from Table 14.6, and the matrix $\mathbf{\Lambda}_m$ is the diagonal matrix of the first two eigenvalues retained. The key parts of the computations include:

$$\mathbf{B'A} = \begin{pmatrix} 2.35810 & -1.02656 \\ 1.64172 & 1.47451 \end{pmatrix},$$

$$\mathbf{\Lambda}_2^2 = \begin{pmatrix} 8.25591 & 0 \\ 0 & 3.22799 \end{pmatrix},$$

$$\mathbf{B'A\Lambda}_2^{-2} = \begin{pmatrix} .28562 & -.31801 \\ .19885 & .45678 \end{pmatrix}.$$

Finally, postmultiplying the last matrix by $\mathbf{A'}$ produces the identical values for the coefficients of the z's as those arrived at in the text by use of (16.7).

2. $\bar{F}_1 = .26z_1 + .14z_2 + .60z_3, \quad R_1 = .96,$
$\bar{F}_2 = .31z_1 + .53z_2 - .16z_3, \quad R_2 = .67.$

3. Following the instructions in Table 3.3, place the identity matrix to the right of **R**, apply the square root operation of Table 16.3 to this identity matrix, and then column-by-column multiplication of the resulting matrix yields:

$$\mathbf{R}^{-1} = \begin{bmatrix} 5.444 & -2.080 & -.374 & -2.432 & -.845 & -.385 & .515 & .277 \\ -2.080 & 6.632 & -3.362 & -1.005 & 1.004 & .019 & -.355 & -.881 \\ -.374 & -3.362 & 5.007 & -.912 & -.446 & -.096 & .394 & .267 \\ -2.432 & -1.005 & -.912 & 4.728 & -.245 & .424 & -.430 & .075 \\ -.845 & 1.004 & -.446 & -.245 & 3.984 & -1.559 & -1.485 & -.654 \\ -.385 & .019 & -.096 & .424 & -1.559 & 2.529 & -.131 & -.391 \\ .515 & -.355 & .394 & -.430 & -1.485 & -.131 & 2.289 & -.253 \\ .277 & -.881 & .267 & .075 & -.654 & -.391 & -.253 & 1.913 \end{bmatrix}.$$

4. $\bar{T}_2 = (.484 \quad .435 \quad .399 \quad .454 \quad .932 \quad .813 \quad .740 \quad .724)\mathbf{R}^{-1}\{z_1 \, z_2 \cdots z_8\}$
$= -.042z_1 + .131z_2 - .069z_3 + .021z_4 + .612z_5 + .199z_6 + 0.77z_7$
$+ .162z_8.$

The result is identical with the second equation in (16.36) except for trivial differences in the third decimal place.

5. To prove that **L** is a symmetric matrix it is sufficient to show that its transpose is equal to the matrix itself, namely,

$$\mathbf{L}' = (\boldsymbol{\Phi}^{-1} + \mathbf{A}'\mathbf{D}^{-2}\mathbf{A})' = (\boldsymbol{\Phi}^{-1})' + (\mathbf{A})'(\mathbf{D}^{-2})'(\mathbf{A}')' = \boldsymbol{\Phi}^{-1} + \mathbf{A}'\mathbf{D}^{-2}\mathbf{A} = \mathbf{L},$$

since $\boldsymbol{\Phi}$ (and hence $\boldsymbol{\Phi}^{-1}$) is symmetric, as is also the diagonal matrix $\mathbf{D}^{-2}$.

6. $\bar{F}_1 = .26z_1 + .13z_2 + .62z_3, \quad R_1 = .96,$
$\bar{F}_2 = .31z_1 + .54z_2 - .16z_3, \quad R_2 = .67.$

7. $\mathbf{E}^{-1} = \begin{bmatrix} .2061 & .0089 \\ 0 & .2864 \end{bmatrix}.$

8. $\mathbf{B}' = \begin{bmatrix} .248 & .367 & .226 & .185 & .020 & .003 & -.001 & .011 \\ .042 & .000 & .011 & .023 & .578 & .200 & .140 & .120 \end{bmatrix}.$

This answer is based upon a computer output which produced the quartimin reference structure of Table 15.3, and therefore may vary slightly from the results that will be obtained by the method suggested in the exercise.

9. (a) $\mathbf{B}' = \begin{bmatrix} -.038 & -.012 & \cdots & .035 \\ .014 & .008 & \cdots & .113 \\ .261 & .102 & \cdots & -.003 \\ -.010 & -.004 & \cdots & .080 \end{bmatrix}.$

(b) By formula (16.25), employing the primary-structure values (which would have to be determined); or by formula (16.27) involving the complete correlation matrix.

10. The computations in Table 16.9 are based on an approximation to $\mathbf{R}^{-1}$ while the coefficients in exercise 3 were determined from the actual $\mathbf{R}^{-1}$ for the observed correlations. The two sets of values would agree perfectly if the residual matrix were the null matrix.

11. Of course the individual entries in these two 8×8 matrices differ considerably since they were derived by very intricate and distinct computations starting from different initial values. Each inverse when multiplied by the original matrix upon which it is based, either $\mathbf{R}$ or $(\mathbf{R}^{\dagger} + \mathbf{D}^2)$, will produce the identity matrix. But since the original matrices differ to the extent that the residual matrix does not vanish, the respective inverses must differ. Nonetheless, reasonable approximations to some of the desired statistics can be made from the approximate $\mathbf{R}^{-1}$ given in Table 16.9 (see ex. 22, chap. 5).

12. $\mathbf{\Gamma'S} = \mathbf{J}^{-1}\mathbf{C'S}$, postmultiplying (16.58) by $\mathbf{S}$,
$\quad = \mathbf{J}^{-1}\mathbf{C'P\Phi}$, substituting for $\mathbf{S}$ from (2.43),
$\quad = \mathbf{J}^{-1}\mathbf{P'D}^{-2}\mathbf{P\Phi}$, substituting for $\mathbf{C'}$ from its definition,
$\quad = \mathbf{J}^{-1}\mathbf{J\Phi}$, from the definition of $\mathbf{J}$,
$\quad = \mathbf{\Phi}$.

13. (a) $\bar{F}_1 = .065z_1 - .530z_2 + 1.465z_3$,
$\quad \bar{F}_2 = 1.337z_1 + 3.820z_2 - 4.155z_3$.

(b) $R_1 = \sqrt{1 - .790/3.113} = .864$,

$R_2 = \sqrt{1 - 15.333/3.113} =$ imaginary; the measure of information is only $3.113/15.333 = .203$ instead of a value greater than unity.

14.
$$\mathbf{\Gamma'S} = \begin{bmatrix} .065 & -.530 & 1.465 \\ 1.337 & 3.820 & -4.155 \end{bmatrix} \begin{bmatrix} .90 & .60 \\ .85 & .65 \\ .95 & .55 \end{bmatrix},$$

$$= \begin{bmatrix} 1.000 & .500 \\ .500 & 1.000 \end{bmatrix}.$$

APPENDIX

Statistical Tables

The sampling distribution of statistics arising in factor analysis has been largely neglected during the rapid development of descriptive procedures. An early exception was the work of Spearman and Holzinger [443] on the sampling error of tetrad differences. When Hotelling [259] presented the general theory and computing procedures for the principal-factor method, he also included discussions of the sampling errors of the roots of the characteristic equation and of the sampling of variables from a hypothetical infinite population of such variables. In 1940 came the next major contribution to the statistical theory of factor analysis, when Lawley [320] introduced the maximum likelihood methods into factor analysis.

Because of the lack of precise sampling error formulas for factor coefficients and residuals, approximation procedures were developed by Holzinger and Harman [243, pp. 122–36]. Without repeating this development here, nor giving the details of the various assumptions, the principal results are presented in the first two tables. The basic assumption is that the individual correlations may be replaced by the mean (r) of the set. Additional assumptions which led to the approximations tabled were out of consideration of computational labor. For each successive approximation the sampling error formulas generally became smaller. Knowing that the sampling errors are probably under-estimated, a more stringent level of significance should be required. In Table A the standard error of a residual (with one factor removed) is given for samples from $N = 20$ to $N = 500$ for an average correlation from $r = .10$ to $r = .75$. For the same range of values of N and r, the standard error of a factor coefficient a is given in Table B.

Tables C and D contain more conventional statistical information. Areas under the normal curve are given in Table C where the frequency or probability of occurrence $(\frac{1}{2}\alpha)$ in the interval from the mean to a deviate x/s is shown for values of x/s from 0 to 4 by steps of .02. Then the probability of exceeding a deviation of $\pm x/s$ is given by $P = 1 - \alpha$.

In Table D the χ^2 distribution is presented for a few selected values of P, where

$$P(\chi^2) = \int_0^{\chi^2} \frac{(\chi^2)^{(v-2)/2} e^{-\chi^2/2} \, d(\chi^2)}{2^{v/2}[(v-2)/2]!}$$

and for the number of degrees of freedom v from 1 to 30. The value of P is the probability that on random sampling a value of χ^2 would be obtained as great as, or greater than, the value actually obtained.

433

Table A

Standard Errors of Residuals with One Factor Removed

$$\sigma_{\tilde{r}} = (1 - r)\sqrt{(5 + 8r + 2r^2)/2N}$$

r / N	.10	.15	.20	.25	.30	.35	.40	.45	.50	.55	.60	.65	.70	.75
20	.343	.336	.327	.317	.305	.292	.277	.261	.244	.225	.205	.184	.161	.138
30	.280	.274	.267	.258	.249	.238	.226	.213	.199	.184	.167	.150	.132	.112
40	.243	.237	.231	.224	.215	.206	.196	.185	.172	.159	.145	.130	.114	.097
50	.217	.212	.207	.200	.193	.184	.175	.165	.154	.142	.130	.116	.102	.087
60	.198	.194	.189	.183	.176	.168	.160	.151	.141	.130	.118	.106	.093	.079
70	.183	.180	.175	.169	.163	.156	.148	.139	.130	.120	.110	.098	.086	.074
80	.172	.168	.163	.158	.152	.146	.138	.130	.122	.113	.103	.092	.081	.069
90	.162	.158	.154	.149	.144	.137	.131	.123	.115	.106	.097	.087	.076	.065
100	.154	.150	.146	.142	.136	.130	.124	.117	.109	.101	.092	.082	.072	.062
110	.146	.143	.139	.135	.130	.124	.118	.111	.104	.096	.087	.078	.069	.059
120	.140	.137	.133	.129	.124	.119	.113	.107	.099	.092	.084	.075	.066	.056
130	.135	.132	.128	.124	.120	.114	.109	.102	.096	.088	.080	.072	.063	.054
140	.130	.127	.124	.120	.115	.110	.105	.099	.092	.085	.078	.070	.061	.052
150	.125	.123	.119	.116	.111	.106	.101	.095	.089	.082	.075	.067	.059	.050
160	.121	.119	.116	.112	.108	.103	.098	.092	.086	.080	.073	.065	.057	.049
170	.118	.115	.112	.109	.105	.100	.095	.090	.084	.077	.070	.063	.055	.047
180	.114	.112	.109	.106	.102	.097	.092	.087	.081	.075	.068	.061	.054	.046
190	.111	.109	.106	.103	.099	.095	.090	.085	.079	.073	.067	.060	.052	.045
200	.109	.106	.103	.100	.096	.092	.088	.083	.077	.071	.065	.058	.051	.044
250	.097	.095	.092	.090	.086	.082	.078	.074	.069	.064	.058	.052	.046	.039
300	.089	.087	.084	.082	.079	.075	.071	.067	.063	.058	.053	.047	.042	.036
350	.082	.080	.078	.076	.073	.070	.066	.062	.058	.054	.049	.044	.039	.033
400	.077	.075	.073	.071	.068	.065	.062	.058	.054	.050	.046	.041	.036	.031
450	.072	.071	.069	.067	.064	.061	.058	.055	.051	.047	.043	.039	.034	.029
500	.069	.067	.065	.063	.061	.058	.055	.052	.049	.045	.041	.037	.032	.028

Note: r is the average value in the correlation matrix.

Table **B**

Standard Errors of Factor Coefficients

$$\sigma_a = \tfrac{1}{2}\sqrt{(3/r - 2 - 5r + 4r^2)/N}$$

N \ r	.10	.12	.14	.16	.18	.20	.22	.24	.26	.28	.30	.35	.40	.45	.50	.55	.60	.65	.70	.75
20	.587	.530	.485	.448	.417	.390	.366	.345	.326	.309	.293	.258	.227	.201	.177	.155	.134	.115	.097	.079
30	.479	.433	.396	.366	.340	.318	.299	.282	.266	.252	.239	.210	.186	.164	.144	.126	.110	.094	.079	.065
40	.415	.375	.343	.317	.295	.276	.259	.244	.231	.218	.207	.182	.161	.142	.125	.109	.095	.081	.068	.056
50	.371	.335	.307	.283	.264	.247	.232	.218	.206	.195	.185	.163	.144	.127	.112	.098	.085	.073	.061	.050
60	.339	.306	.280	.259	.241	.225	.211	.199	.188	.178	.169	.149	.131	.116	.102	.089	.077	.066	.056	.046
70	.314	.283	.259	.239	.223	.208	.196	.184	.174	.165	.157	.138	.122	.107	.094	.083	.072	.061	.052	.042
80	.293	.265	.242	.224	.208	.195	.183	.173	.163	.154	.146	.129	.114	.100	.088	.077	.067	.057	.048	.040
90	.277	.250	.229	.211	.196	.184	.173	.163	.154	.146	.138	.121	.107	.095	.083	.073	.063	.054	.046	.037
100	.262	.237	.217	.200	.186	.174	.164	.154	.146	.138	.131	.115	.102	.090	.079	.069	.060	.051	.043	.035
110	.250	.226	.207	.191	.178	.166	.156	.147	.139	.132	.125	.110	.097	.086	.075	.066	.057	.049	.041	.034
120	.240	.216	.198	.183	.170	.159	.150	.141	.133	.126	.120	.105	.093	.082	.072	.063	.055	.047	.039	.032
130	.230	.208	.190	.176	.163	.153	.144	.135	.128	.121	.115	.101	.089	.079	.069	.061	.053	.045	.038	.031
140	.222	.200	.183	.169	.158	.147	.138	.130	.123	.117	.111	.097	.086	.076	.067	.058	.051	.043	.036	.030
150	.214	.193	.177	.164	.152	.142	.134	.126	.119	.113	.107	.094	.083	.073	.065	.056	.049	.042	.035	.029
160	.207	.187	.171	.158	.147	.138	.129	.122	.115	.109	.104	.091	.080	.071	.062	.055	.047	.041	.034	.028
170	.201	.182	.166	.154	.143	.134	.126	.118	.112	.106	.100	.088	.078	.069	.061	.053	.046	.039	.033	.027
180	.196	.177	.162	.149	.139	.130	.122	.115	.109	.103	.098	.086	.076	.067	.059	.052	.045	.038	.032	.026
190	.190	.172	.157	.145	.135	.126	.119	.112	.106	.100	.095	.084	.074	.065	.057	.050	.044	.037	.031	.026
200	.186	.168	.153	.142	.132	.123	.116	.109	.103	.098	.093	.081	.072	.064	.056	.049	.042	.036	.031	.025
250	.166	.150	.137	.127	.118	.110	.104	.098	.092	.087	.083	.073	.064	.057	.050	.044	.038	.032	.027	.022
300	.151	.137	.125	.116	.108	.101	.095	.089	.084	.080	.076	.067	.059	.052	.046	.040	.035	.030	.025	.020
350	.140	.127	.116	.107	.100	.093	.088	.083	.078	.074	.070	.062	.054	.048	.042	.037	.032	.027	.023	.019
400	.131	.118	.108	.100	.093	.087	.082	.077	.073	.069	.065	.058	.051	.045	.040	.035	.030	.026	.022	.018
450	.124	.112	.102	.094	.088	.082	.077	.073	.069	.065	.062	.054	.048	.042	.037	.033	.028	.024	.020	.017
500	.117	.106	.097	.090	.083	.078	.073	.069	.065	.062	.059	.052	.045	.040	.035	.031	.027	.023	.019	.016

Note: r is the average value in the correlation matrix.

Table C

Area under the Normal Curve

$$\tfrac{1}{2}\alpha = \frac{1}{\sqrt{2\pi s}} \int_{0}^{x/s} e^{-\frac{1}{2}(x/s)^2}\, dx$$

x/s	$\tfrac{1}{2}\alpha$	x/s	$\tfrac{1}{2}\alpha$	x/s	$\tfrac{1}{2}\alpha$	x/s	$\tfrac{1}{2}\alpha$	x/s	$\tfrac{1}{2}\alpha$
.00	.0000	.80	.2881	1.60	.4452	2.40	.4918	3.20	.4993
.02	.0080	.82	.2939	1.62	.4474	2.42	.4922	3.22	.4994
.04	.0160	.84	.2995	1.64	.4495	2.44	.4927	3.24	.4994
.06	.0239	.86	.3051	1.66	.4515	2.46	.4931	3.26	.4994
.08	.0319	.88	.3106	1.68	.4535	2.48	.4934	3.28	.4995
.10	.0398	.90	.3159	1.70	.4554	2.50	.4938	3.30	.4995
.12	.0478	.92	.3212	1.72	.4573	2.52	.4941	3.32	.4995
.14	.0557	.94	.3264	1.74	.4591	2.54	.4945	3.34	.4996
.16	.0636	.96	.3315	1.76	.4608	2.56	.4948	3.36	.4996
.18	.0714	.98	.3365	1.78	.4625	2.58	.4951	3.38	.4996
.20	.0793	1.00	.3413	1.80	.4641	2.60	.4953	3.40	.4997
.22	.0871	1.02	.3461	1.82	.4656	2.62	.4956	3.42	.4997
.24	.0948	1.04	.3508	1.84	.4671	2.64	.4959	3.44	.4997
.26	.1026	1.06	.3554	1.86	.4686	2.66	.4961	3.46	.4997
.28	.1103	1.08	.3599	1.88	.4699	2.68	.4963	3.48	.4997
.30	.1179	1.10	.3643	1.90	.4713	2.70	.4965	3.50	.4998
.32	.1255	1.12	.3686	1.92	.4726	2.72	.4967	3.52	.4998
.34	.1331	1.14	.3729	1.94	.4738	2.74	.4969	3.54	.4998
.36	.1406	1.16	.3770	1.96	.4750	2.76	.4971	3.56	.4998
.38	.1480	1.18	.3810	1.98	.4761	2.78	.4973	3.58	.4998
.40	.1554	1.20	.3849	2.00	.4772	2.80	.4974	3.60	.4998
.42	.1628	1.22	.3888	2.02	.4783	2.82	.4976	3.62	.4999
.44	.1700	1.24	.3925	2.04	.4793	2.84	.4977	3.64	.4999
.46	.1772	1.26	.3962	2.06	.4803	2.86	.4979	3.66	.4999
.48	.1844	1.28	.3997	2.08	.4812	2.88	.4980	3.68	.4999
.50	.1915	1.30	.4032	2.10	.4821	2.90	.4981	3.70	.4999
.52	.1985	1.32	.4066	2.12	.4830	2.92	.4982	3.72	.4999
.54	.2054	1.34	.4099	2.14	.4838	2.94	.4984	3.74	.4999
.56	.2123	1.36	.4131	2.16	.4846	2.96	.4985	3.76	.4999
.58	.2190	1.38	.4162	2.18	.4854	2.98	.4986	3.78	.4999
.60	.2257	1.40	.4192	2.20	.4861	3.00	.4987	3.80	.4999
.62	.2324	1.42	.4222	2.22	.4868	3.02	.4987	3.82	.4999
.64	.2389	1.44	.4251	2.24	.4875	3.04	.4988	3.84	.4999
.66	.2454	1.46	.4279	2.26	.4881	3.06	.4989	3.86	.4999
.68	.2517	1.48	.4306	2.28	.4887	3.08	.4990	3.88	.4999
.70	.2580	1.50	.4332	2.30	.4893	3.10	.4990	3.90	.5000
.72	.2642	1.52	.4357	2.32	.4898	3.12	.4991	3.92	.5000
.74	.2703	1.54	.4382	2.34	.4904	3.14	.4992	3.94	.5000
.76	.2764	1.56	.4406	2.36	.4909	3.16	.4992	3.96	.5000
.78	.2823	1.58	.4429	2.28	.4913	3.18	.4993	3.98	.5000

Table D

Distribution of χ^2 for Selected Probabilities P and Degrees of Freedom v

v \ P	.99	.98	.95	.90	.80	.70	.50	.30	.20	.10	.05	.02	.01	.001
1	.000	.001	.004	.016	.064	.148	.455	1.074	1.642	2.706	3.841	5.412	6.635	10.827
2	.020	.040	.103	.211	.446	.713	1.386	2.408	3.219	4.605	5.991	7.824	9.210	13.815
3	.115	.185	.352	.584	1.005	1.424	2.366	3.665	4.642	6.251	7.815	9.837	11.345	16.268
4	.297	.429	.711	1.064	1.649	2.195	3.357	4.878	5.989	7.779	9.488	11.668	13.277	18.465
5	.554	.752	1.145	1.610	2.343	3.000	4.351	6.064	7.289	9.236	11.070	13.388	15.086	20.517
6	.872	1.134	1.635	2.204	3.070	3.828	5.348	7.231	8.558	10.645	12.592	15.033	16.812	22.457
7	1.239	1.564	2.167	2.833	3.822	4.671	6.346	8.383	9.803	12.017	14.067	16.622	18.475	24.322
8	1.646	2.032	2.733	3.490	4.594	5.527	7.344	9.524	11.030	13.362	15.507	18.168	20.090	26.125
9	2.088	2.532	3.325	4.168	5.380	6.393	8.343	10.656	12.242	14.684	16.919	19.679	21.666	27.877
10	2.558	3.059	3.940	4.865	6.179	7.267	9.342	11.781	13.442	15.987	18.307	21.161	23.209	29.588
11	3.053	3.609	4.575	5.578	6.989	8.148	10.341	12.899	14.631	17.275	19.675	22.618	24.725	31.264
12	3.571	4.178	5.226	6.304	7.807	9.034	11.340	14.011	15.812	18.549	21.026	24.054	26.217	32.909
13	4.107	4.765	5.892	7.042	8.634	9.926	12.340	15.119	16.985	19.812	22.362	25.472	27.688	34.528
14	4.660	5.368	6.571	7.790	9.467	10.821	13.339	16.222	18.151	21.064	23.685	26.873	29.141	36.123
15	5.229	5.985	7.261	8.547	10.307	11.721	14.339	17.322	19.311	22.307	24.996	28.259	30.578	37.697
16	5.812	6.614	7.962	9.312	11.152	12.624	15.338	18.418	20.465	23.542	26.296	29.633	32.000	39.252
17	6.408	7.255	8.672	10.085	12.002	13.531	16.338	19.511	21.615	24.769	27.587	30.995	33.409	40.790
18	7.015	7.906	9.390	10.865	12.857	14.440	17.338	20.601	22.760	25.989	28.869	32.346	34.805	42.312
19	7.633	8.567	10.117	11.651	13.716	15.352	18.338	21.689	23.900	27.204	30.144	33.687	36.191	43.820
20	8.260	9.237	10.851	12.443	14.578	16.266	19.337	22.775	25.038	28.412	31.410	35.020	37.566	45.315
21	8.897	9.915	11.591	13.240	15.445	17.182	20.337	23.858	26.171	29.615	32.671	36.343	38.932	46.797
22	9.542	10.600	12.338	14.041	16.314	18.101	21.337	24.939	27.301	30.813	33.924	37.659	40.289	48.268
23	10.196	11.293	13.091	14.848	17.187	19.021	22.337	26.018	28.429	32.007	35.172	38.968	41.638	49.728
24	10.856	11.992	13.848	15.659	18.062	19.943	23.337	27.096	29.553	33.196	36.415	40.270	42.980	51.179
25	11.524	12.697	14.611	16.473	18.940	20.867	24.337	28.172	30.675	34.382	37.652	41.566	44.314	52.620
26	12.198	13.409	15.379	17.292	19.820	21.792	25.336	29.246	31.795	35.563	38.885	42.856	45.642	54.052
27	12.879	14.125	16.151	18.114	20.703	22.719	26.336	30.319	32.912	36.741	40.113	44.140	46.963	55.476
28	13.565	14.847	16.928	18.939	21.588	23.647	27.336	31.391	34.027	37.916	41.337	45.419	48.278	56.893
29	14.256	15.574	17.708	19.768	22.475	24.577	28.336	32.461	35.139	39.087	42.557	46.693	49.588	58.302
30	14.953	16.306	18.493	20.599	23.364	25.508	29.336	33.530	36.250	40.256	43.773	47.962	50.892	59.703

This table is taken from R. A. Fisher and Frank Yates, *Statistical Tables for Biological, Agricultural and Medical Research*, and is published with the kind permission of the authors and publishers.

Bibliography

Included in the bibliography are not only all the books and papers to which references are made in the text, but also certain other works that may be useful to the researcher and student. The items have been culled from the vast literature on the basis of their relevance to the theory or technique of factor analysis. Practical applications are not included unless they were used in the text. The following abbreviations are employed.

AJP = American Journal of Psychology

AMM = American Mathematical Monthly

Ann. Math. = Annals of Mathematics

Ann. Math. Stat. = The Annals of Mathematical Statistics

Ann. N.Y. Acad. Sci. = Annals of the New York Academy of Sciences

Biom. = Biometrika

BJEP = British Journal of Educational Psychology

BJ Math. Stat. Psych. = British Journal of Mathematical and Statistical Psychology
(former designations: BJP Stat. Sec.; BJ Stat. Psych.)

BJP = British Journal of Psychology

Ed. Psych. Measurement = Educational and Psychological Measurement

J. AMA = Journal of the American Medical Association

J. ASA = Journal of the American Statistical Association

J. ACM = Journal of the Association for Computing Machinery

JEP = Journal of Educational Psychology

J. Exp. Ed. = Journal of Experimental Education

J. Roy. Stat. Soc. = Journal of the Royal Statistical Society

J. Soc. Psych. = Journal of Social Psychology

Phil. Trans. Roy. Soc. = Philosophical Transactions of the Royal Society of London, Series A

Psych. = Psychometrika

439

Psych. Bull. = *Psychological Bulletin*
Psych. Rep. = *Psychological Reports*
Psych. Rev. = *Psychological Review*
Proc. Edin. M.S. = *Proceedings of the Edinburgh Mathematical Society*, Second
        Series
Proc. Nat. Acad. Sci. = *Proceedings of the National Academy of Sciences*
Proc. Roy. Soc. Edin. = *Proceedings of the Royal Society of Edinburgh*
Proc. Roy. Soc. Lon. = *Proceedings of the Royal Society of London*, Series A
Rev. Ed. Res. = *Review of Educational Research*
SM = *Scientific Monthly*
Trans. AMS = *Transactions of the American Mathematical Society*

1. ADCOCK, C. J. A note on cluster-directed analysis. *Psych.,* **17** (1952), 249–53.
2. ADKINS, DOROTHY C., and SAMUEL B. LYERLY. *Factor analysis of reasoning tests.* Chapel Hill: U. of North Carolina Press, 1952. Pp. iv + 122.
3. AHMAVAARA, YRJÖ. The mathematical theory of factorial invariance under selection. *Psych.,* **19** (1954), 27–38.
4. ———. On the unified factor theory of mind. *Annales Akademiae Scientiarum Fennicae,* Ser. B. **106**. Helsinki, 1957. Pp. 176.
5. AITCHISON, J., and S. D. SILVEY. Maximum-likelihood estimation procedures and associated tests of significance. *J. Roy. Stat. Soc.,* B, **22** (1960), 154–71.
6. AITKEN, A. C. *Determinants and matrices.* Second edition. Edinburgh: Oliver and Boyd, 1942. Pp. vii + 135.
7. ALBERT, A. A. *Introduction to algebraic theories.* Chicago: U. of Chicago Press, 1941. Pp. vii + 137.
8. ———. The matrices of factor analysis. *Proc. Nat. Acad. Sci.,* (1944), 90–95.
9. ———. The minimum rank of a correlation matrix. *Proc. Nat. Acad. Sci.,* (1944), 144–46.
10. ALKER, HAYWARD. Dimensions of conflict in the general assembly. *Amer. Polit. Sci. Rev.,* **58** (1964), 642–57.
11. ANDERSON, T. W. *An introduction to multivariate statistical analysis.* New York: John Wiley & Sons, Inc., 1958. Pp. 374.
12. ———. Asymptotic theory for principal-component analysis. *Ann. Math. Stat.,* **34** (1963), 122–48.
13. ———. The use of factor analysis in the statistical analysis of multiple time series. *Psych.,* **28** (1963), 1–25.
14. ANDERSON, T. W., and H. RUBIN. Statistical inference in factor analysis. *Proc. of the Third Berkeley Symp. on Math. Statistics and Probability,* **5** (1956), 111–50.
15. ANDREWS, T. G. Statistical studies in allergy. II: A factorial analysis. *J. of Allergy,* **19** (1948), 43–46.
16. APOSTOL, T. M. *Mathematical analysis: A modern approach to advanced calculus.* Reading, Mass.: Addison-Wesley Publishing Co., 1957. Pp. xii + 553.

17. AUBERT, EUGENE J., IVER A. LUND, and ALBERT J. THOMASELL. Some objective six-hour predictions prepared by statistical methods. *J. of Meteorology*, **16** (1959), 436–46.

18. BAEHR, MELANY E. A comparison of graphic and analytic solutions for both oblique and orthogonal simple structures for factors of employee morale. *Psych.*, **28** (1963), 199–209.

19. BAGGALEY, A., and R. B. CATTELL. A comparison of exact and approximate linear function estimates of oblique factor scores. *BJ Stat. Psych.*, **9** (1956), 83–86.

20. BANACHIEWICZ, T. Méthode de résolution numerique des équations linéaires, du calcul de déterminants et des inverses et de réduction des formes quadratiques. *Bull. Int. Acad. Polonaise des Sciences et Lettres*, (1938), 393–404.

21. ———. An outline of the Cracovian algorithm of the method of least squares. *Astronomical Journal*, **50** (1942), 38–41.

22. BANKS, CHARLOTTE, and CYRIL BURT. The reduced correlation matrix. *BJ Stat. Psych.*, **7** (1954), 107–17.

23. BARGMANN, R. Factor analysis program for 7090, preliminary version. Internal document, 28–126 (1963). Yorktown Heights, N.Y.: IBM Research Center.

24. BARLOW, J. A. and C. BURT. The identification of factors from different experiments. *BJ Stat. Psych.*, **7** (1954), 52–56.

25. BARTLETT, M. S. The statistical conception of mental factors. *BJP*, **28** (1937), 97–104.

26. ———. The general canonical correlation distribution. *Ann. Math. Stat.*, **18** (1947), 1–17.

27. ———. Internal and external factor analysis. *BJP Stat. Sec.*, **1** (1948), 73–81.

28. ———. Tests of significance in factor analysis. *BJP Stat. Sec.*, **3** (1950), 77–85.

29. ———. A further note on tests of significance in factor analysis. *BJP Stat. Sec.*, **4** (1951), 1–2.

30. ———. The effect of standardization on a χ^2 approximation in factor analysis. *Biom.*, **38** (1951), 337–44.

31. ———. Factor analysis in psychology as a statistician sees it. *Uppsala Symposium on Psychological Factor Analysis*. Uppsala: Almqvist & Wiksell (1953), 23–34.

32. ———. A note on the multiplying factors for various χ^2 approximations. *J. Roy. Stat. Soc.*, B, **16** (1954), 296–98.

33. ———. *Essays on probability and statistics*. New York: John Wiley & Sons, Inc., 1962. Pp. viii + 127.

34. BECHTOLDT, HAROLD P. An empirical study of the factor analysis stability hypothesis. *Psych.*, **26** (1961), 405–32.

35. BENOIT, COMMANDANT. Note sur une méthode de résolution des équations normales. *Bull. Géodésique*, (1924), 67–77.

36. BERNYER, G. Psychological factors: Their number, nature, and identification. *BJ Stat. Psych.*, **10** (1957), 17–27.

37. BERRY, BRIAN J. L. A method for deriving multi-factor uniform regions. *Polish Geographical Review (Przeglad Geogrficzny)*, **33** (1961), 263–79.

38. ———. Basic patterns of economic development. In Norton Ginsburg, *Atlas of economic development*. Chicago: U. of Chicago Press, (1961), 110–19.

39. BLACK, MICHAEL S. Institute for Juvenile Research statistical package (IJRPAC). IBM 7094 program. Chicago: U. of Chicago Computation Center, 1965.

40. BLACK, T. P. The probable error of some boundary conditions in diagnosing the presence of group and general factors. *Proc. Roy. Soc. Edin.*, **49** (1929), 72–77.

41. BLISS, G. A. Mathematical interpretations of geometrical and physical phenomena. *AMM*, **40** (1933), 472–80.

42. *BMD: Biomedical computer programs.* Los Angeles: U. of California, Health Sciences Computing Facility, School of Medicine, 1964. Pp. 585.

43. BODEWIG, E. *Matrix calculus.* New York: Interscience Publishers, Inc., 1956.

44. BOLDT, ROBERT F. Least-squares factoring to fit off-diagonals. Paper presented at Amer. Psych. Assoc. 1964 Ann. Convention. *Amer. Psych.*, **19** (1964), 582.

45. BONNER, R. E. On some clustering techniques. *IBM J. of Res. & Dev.*, **8** (1964).

46. BORKO, H. A factor analytically derived classification system for psychological reports. *Perceptual and Motor Skills*, **20** (1965), 393–406.

47. BUHLER, ROALD. P-STAT: A system of statistical program for the 7090/7094. Programming notes, # 12 (1964). Princeton, N.J.: Princeton U. Computer Center.

48. BURNS, LELAND S., and ALVIN J. HARMAN. The complex metropolis, Part V of *Profile of the Los Angeles metropolis: Its people and its homes*. Los Angeles: U. of California Press, 1966.

49. BURROUGHS, G. E. R., and H. W. L. MILLER. The rotation of principal components. *BJ Stat. Psych.*, **14** (1961), 35–49.

50. BURT, CYRIL. Experimental tests of general intelligence. *BJP*, **3** (1909), 94–177.

51. ———. *The distribution and relations of educational abilities*. London: P. S. King & Son, 1917. Pp. xiii + 93.

52. ———. Correlations between persons. *BJP*, **28** (1937), 59–96.

53. ———. Methods of factor analysis with and without successive approximations. *BJEP*, **7** (1937), 172–95.

54. ———. The unit hierarchy and its properties. *Psych.*, **3** (1938), 151–68.

55. ———. The factorial analysis of emotional traits. *Character and Personality*, **7** (1939), 238–54, 285–99.

56. ———. *The factors of the mind: An introduction to factor analysis in psychology.* New York: MacMillan, 1941. Pp. xiv + 509.

57. ———. A comparison of factor analysis and analysis of variance. *BJP Stat. Sec.*, **1** (1947), 3–26.

58. ———. The factorial study of temperamental traits. *BJP Stat. Sec.*, **1** (1948), 178–203.

59. ———. Alternative methods of factor analysis and their relations to Pearson's method of "Principal axes." *BJP Stat. Sec.,* **2** (1949), 98–121.

60. ———. The structure of mind: A review of the results of factor analysis. *BJEP,* **19** (1949), 100–11, 176–99.

61. ———. Group factor analyses. *BJP Stat. Sec.,* **3** (1950), 40–75.

62. ———. Tests of significance in factor analysis. *BJP Stat. Sec.,* **5** (1952), 109–33.

63. BURT, C., and M. HOWARD. The multifactorial theory of inheritance and its application to intelligence. *BJ Stat. Psych.,* **9** (1956), 95–131.

64. BURT, CYRIL, and WILLIAM STEPHENSON. Alternative views on correlations between persons. *Psych.,* **4** (1939), 269–81.

65. BUTLER, JOHN M. Simplest data factors and simple structure in factor analysis. *Ed. Psych. Measurement,* **24** (1964), 755–63.

66. CADY, LEE D., MENARD M. GERTLER, LIDA G. GOTTSCH, and MAX A. WOODBURY. The factor structure of variables concerned with coronary artery disease. *Behavioral Science,* **6** (1961), 37–41.

67. CADY, LEE D., MENARD M. GERTLER, and LEWIS A. NOWITZ. Coronary disease factors. *Behavioral Science,* **9** (1964), 30–32.

68. CARLSON, HILDING B. A simple orthogonal multiple factor approximation procedure. *Psych.,* **10** (1945), 283–301.

69. CARROLL, JOHN B. An analytical solution for approximating simple structure in factor analysis. *Psych.,* **18** (1953), 23–38.

70. ———. Biquartimin criterion for rotation to oblique simple structure in factor analysis. *Science,* **126** (Nov. 29, 1957), 1114–15.

71. ———. IBM 704 program for generalized analytic rotation solution in factor analysis. Unpublished manuscript, Harvard University, 1960. Pp. 9.

72. CARROLL, JOHN B., and ROBERT F. SCHWEIKER. Factor analysis in educational research. *Rev. Ed. Res.,* **21** (1951), 368–88.

73. CATTELL, RAYMOND B. A note on factor invariance and the identification of factors. *BJP Stat. Sec.,* **2** (1949), 134–39.

74. ———. r_p and other coefficients of pattern similarity. *Psych.,* **14** (1949), 279–98.

75. ———. *Factor analysis.* New York: Harper & Bros., 1952. Pp. xiii + 462.

76. ———. *Personality and motivation structure and measurement.* Yonkers-on-Hudson, N.Y.: World Book Co., 1957. Pp. 948.

77. ———. Factor analysis: An introduction to essentials. *Biometrics,* **21** (1965), 190–215, 405–35.

78. CATTELL, R. B., H. BREUEL, and H. PARKER HARTMAN. An attempt at more refined definition of the cultural dimensions of syntality in modern nations. *Amer. Soc. Rev.,* **17** (1952), 408–21.

79. CATTELL, R. B., and A. K. S. CATTELL. Factor rotation for proportional profiles: Analytical solution and an example. *BJ Stat. Psych.,* **8** (1955), 83–91.

80. CATTELL, R. B., and K. DICKMAN. A dynamic model of physical influence demonstrating the necessity of oblique simple structure. *Psych. Bull.,* **59** (1962), 389–400.

443

81. CATTELL, R. B., and J. L. MUERLE. The "maxplane" program for factor rotation to oblique simple structure. *Ed. Psych. Measurement*, **20** (1960), 569–90.

82. CHRISTIAN, P., R. KROPF, and H. KURTH. Eine Faktorenanalyse der subjektiven Symptomatik vegetativer Herz- und Kreislaufstörungen. *Archiv für Kreislaufforschung*, **45** (1964), 171–94.

83. CLIFF, NORMAN. Analytic rotation to a functional relationship. *Psych.*, **27** (1962), 283–95.

84. ———. Orthogonal rotation to congruence. *Psych.*, **31** (1966), 33–42.

85. COMREY, ANDREW L. The minimum residual method of factor analysis. *Psych. Rep.*, **11** (1962), 15–18.

86. COOMBS, CLYDE H. A criterion for significant common factor variance. *Psych.*, **6** (1941), 267–72.

87. COOMBS, C. H., and R. C. KAO. Nonmetric factor analysis. *Bull. Dept. Engng. Res.*, No. 38 (1955). Ann Arbor: U. of Michigan. Pp. vii + 63.

88. ———. On a connection between factor analysis and multidimensional unfolding. *Psych.*, **25** (1960), 219–31.

89. COOMBS, CLYDE H., and GEORGE A. SATTER. A factorial approach to job families. *Psych.*, **14** (1949), 33–42.

90. CRAEGER, JOHN A. General resolution of correlation matrices into components and its utilization in multiple and partial regression. *Psych.*, **23** (1958), 1–8.

91. CURETON, EDWARD E. The principal compulsions of factor-analysts. *Harvard Educational Review*, **9** (1939), 287–95.

92. CURETON, T. K., and L. F. STERLING. Factor analyses of cardiovascular test variables. *J. of Sports Medicine and Physical Fitness*, **4** (1964), 1–24.

93. DANFORD, M. B. Factor analysis and related statistical techniques. Unpublished Ph.D. Thesis, North Carolina State College, 1953.

94. DARROCH, J. N. A set of inequalities in factor analysis. *Psych.*, **30** (1965), 449–53.

95. DAS, RHEA S. An application of factor and canonical analysis to multivariate data. *BJ Math. Stat. Psych.*, **18** (1965), 57–67.

96. DAVIS, F. B. The interpretation of principal-axis factors. *JEP*, **38** (1947), 471–81.

97. DICKMAN, K. W. Factorial validity of a rating instrument. Unpublished Ph.D. Thesis, U. of Illinois, 1960. Pp. 153.

98. ———. SSUPAC: Manual of computer programs for statistical analysis. Statistical Service Unit, U. of Illinois, 1964.

99. DICKMAN, K., and H. F. KAISER. Program for inverting a Gramian matrix. *Ed. Psych. Measurement*, **21** (1961), 721–27.

100. DICKSON, L. E. *First course in the theory of equations*. New York: John Wiley & Sons, Inc., 1922. Pp. vi + 168.

101. ———. *Modern algebraic theories*. New York: Benj. H. Sanborn & Co., 1930. Pp. ix + 276.

102. DODD, STUART C. On the sampling theory of intelligence. *BJP*, **19** (1929), 306–27.

103. DuBOIS, PHILIP H. An analysis of Guttman's Simplex. *Psych.*, **25** (1960), 173–82.

104. DURAIN, GENEVIEVE. L'analyse factorielle: Le colloque international de 1955. *Bull. Cent. Etud. Rech. Psychotech.*, **5** (1956), 79–89.

105. DURAND, DAVID. A note on matrix inversion by the square root method. *J. ASA*, **51** (1956), 288–92.

106. DWYER, PAUL S. The determination of the factor loadings of a given test from the known factor loadings of other tests. *Psych.*, **2** (1937), 173–78.

107. ———. The contribution of an orthogonal multiple factor solution to multiple correlation. *Psych.*, **4** (1939), 163–71.

108. ———. The evaluation of multiple and partial correlation coefficients from the factorial matrix. *Psych.*, **5** (1940), 211–32.

109. ———. A matrix presentation of least squares and correlation theory with matrix justification of improved methods of solution. *Ann. Math. Stat.*, **15** (1944), 82–89.

110. ———. The square root method and its use in correlation and regression. *J. ASA*, **40** (1945), 493–503.

111. ———. *Linear computations*. New York: John Wiley & Sons, Inc., 1951. Pp. xi + 344.

112. DWYER, PAUL S., and M. S. MACPHAIL. Symbolic matrix derivatives. *Ann. Math. Stat.*, **19** (1948), 517–34.

113. EBER, HERBERT W. Toward oblique simple structure: Maxplane. *Multivariate Behav. Res.*, **1** (1966), 112–25.

114. ECKART, C. and G. YOUNG. The approximation of one matrix by another of lower rank. *Psych.*, **1** (1936), 211–18.

115. ELFVING, G., R. SITGREAVES, and H. SOLOMON. Item selection procedures for item variables with a known factor structure. *Psych.*, **24** (1959), 189–205.

116. EMMETT, W. G. Sampling error and the two-factor theory. *BJP*, **26** (1936), 362–87.

117. ———. Factor analysis by Lawley's method of maximum likelihood. *BJP Stat. Sec.*, **2** (1949), 90–97.

118. ENGELHART, MAX D. The technique of path coefficients. *Psych.*, **1** (1936), 287–93.

119. EYSENCK, H. J. *Dimensions of personality*. New York: The Macmillan Co., 1949. Pp. 308.

120. ———. Criterion analysis—An application of the hypothetico-deductive method to factor analysis. *Psych. Rev.*, **57** (1950), 38–53.

121. ———. Uses and abuses of factor analysis. *Applied Stat.*, **1** (1952), 45–49.

122. ———. The logical basis of factor analysis. *Amer. Psychologist*, **8** (1953), 105–14.

123. FADDEEV, D. K., and V. N. FADDEEVA. *Computational methods of linear algebra*. San Francisco: W. H. Freeman & Company, 1963. Pp. 621.

124. FARRAR, DONALD EUGENE. *The investment decision under uncertainty*. Englewood Cliffs, N.J.: Prentice Hall, 1962. Pp. 90.

125. FERGUSON, GEORGE A. The factorial interpretation of test difficulty. *Psych.*, **6** (1941), 323–29.

126. ———. The concept of parsimony in factor analysis. *Psych.*, **19** (1954), 281–90.

127. FISHER, R. A. Frequency distribution of the values of the correlation coefficient in samples from an indefinitely large population. *Biom.,* **10** (1915), 507–21.

128. ———. On the mathematical foundations of theoretical statistics. *Phil. Trans. Roy. Soc.,* **222** (1922), 309–68.

129. ———. Theory of statistical estimation. *Proc. Camb. Phil. Soc.,* **22** (1925), 700–25.

130. ———. *The design of experiments.* Edinburgh: Oliver & Boyd, 1935, Pp. xi + 252.

131. ———. *Statistical methods for research workers.* 13th ed. New York: Hafner, 1958.

132. FLOOD, MERRILL M. A computational procedure for the method of principal components. *Psych.,* **5** (1940), 169–72.

133. FOOTE, R. J. A modified Doolittle approach for multiple and partial correlation and regression. *J. ASA,* **53** (1958), 133–43.

134. FORSYTH, A. R. *Geometry of four dimensions,* Vol. I. Cambridge: Cambridge University Press, 1930. Pp. xxix + 468.

135. FRENCH, J. W. The description of aptitude and achievement factors in terms of rotated factors. *Psychometric Monographs,* No. 5. Chicago: U. of Chicago Press, 1951. Pp. 278.

136. FRUCHTER, B. Orthogonal and oblique solutions to a battery of aptitude, achievement and background variables. *Ed. Psych. Measurement,* **12** (1952), 20–38.

137. ———. *Introduction to factor analysis.* New York: D. Van Nostrand Co., 1954. Pp. xii + 280.

138. FRUCHTER, BENJAMIN, and EDWIN NOVAK. A comparative study of three methods of rotation. *Psych.,* **23** (1958), 211–21.

139. FULLER, E. L., JR., and W. J. HEMMERLE. Robustness of the maximum-likelihood estimation procedure in factor analysis. *Psych.,* **31** (1966), 255–66.

140. GARNETT, J. C. M. On certain independent factors in mental measurement. *Proc. Roy. Soc. Lon.,* A, **96** (1919–20), 91–111.

141. GARRETT, HENRY E. The discriminant function and its use in psychology. *Psych.,* **8** (1943), 65–79.

142. GARRETT, H. E., and ANNE ANASTASI. The tetrad-difference criterion and the measurement of mental traits. *Ann. N.Y. Acad. Sci.,* **33** (1932), 235–82.

143. GENGERELLI, J. A. A simplified method for approximating multiple regression coefficients. *Psych.,* **13** (1948), 135–46.

144. GIBSON, W. A. Orthogonal and oblique simple structure. *Psych.,* **17** (1952), 317–23.

145. ———. Proportional profiles and latent structure. *Psych.,* **21** (1956), 135–44.

146. ———. Three multivariate models: Factor analysis, latent structure analysis, and latent profile analysis. *Psych.,* **24** (1959), 229–52.

147. ———. Nonlinear factors in two dimensions. *Psych.,* **25** (1960), 381–92.

148. ———. Orthogonal from oblique transformations. *Ed. Psych. Measurement,* **20** (1960), 713–21.

149. ———. An asymmetric approach to multiple-factor analysis. *BJ Stat. Psych.*, **14** (1961), 97–107.

150. ———. Latent structure and positive manifold. *BJ Stat. Psych.*, **15** (1962), 149–60.

151. ———. On the least-squares orthogonalization of an oblique transformation. *Psych.*, **27** (1962), 193–95.

152. ———. Factoring the circumplex. *Psych.*, **28** (1963), 87–92.

153. ———. On the symmetric treatment of an asymmetric approach to factor analysis. *Psych.*, **28** (1963), 423–26.

154. GINSBURG, NORTON (ed.). Essays in geography and economic development. Research paper, No. 62. Dept. of Geography, U. of Chicago, 1960.

155. GIRSHICK, M. A. Principal components. *J. ASA*, **31** (1936), 519–28.

156. ———. On the sampling theory of roots of determinantal equations. *Ann. Math. Stat.*, **10** (1939), 203–24.

157. GITTUS, ELIZABETH. The structure of urban areas: A new approach. *The Town Planning Rev.*, **35** (1964), 5–21.

158. GIVENS, WALLACE. *Numerical computation of the characteristic values of a real symmetric matrix.* Oak Ridge, Tenn.: Oak Ridge National Laboratory, 1954. Pp. 107.

159. GOLDSTINE, H. H., F. J. MURRAY, and J. VON NEUMANN. The Jacobi method for real symmetric matrices. *J. ACM*, **6** (1959), 59–96.

160. GOLUB, G. H. On the number of significant factors as determined by the method of maximum likelihood. Unpublished paper, U. of Illinois, 1954.

161. ———. Eigenvalues and eigenvectors of a real symmetric matrix. Computing programs J124 and J125 for the JOHNNIAC (1955). Santa Monica, Calif.: The RAND Corporation. Pp. 5.

162. GOSNELL, HAROLD F., and MARGARET SCHMIDT. Factorial and correlational analysis of the 1934 vote in Chicago. *J. ASA*, **31** (1936), 507–18.

163. GOULD, PETER, *et al.* Toward a geography of economic health: The case of New York State. *Annals Amer. Assoc. of Geographers*, **52** (1962), 1–20.

164. GREEN, BERT F. The orthogonal approximation of an oblique structure in factor analysis. *Psych.*, **17** (1952), 429–40.

165. GREGG, L. W., and R. G. PEARSON. Factorial structure of impact and damage variables in lightplane accidents. *Human Factors*, **3** (1961), 237–44.

166. GREVILLE, T. N. E. Some applications of the pseudoinverse of a matrix. *SIAM Rev.*, **2** (1960), 15–22.

167. GUILDFORD, J. P. The structure of intellect. *Psych. Bull.*, **53** (1956), 267–93.

168. GUILDFORD, J. P., and WILLIAM B. MICHAEL. Approaches to univocal factor scores. *Psych.*, **13** (1948), 1–22.

169. GUILDFORD, J. P., and W. S. ZIMMERMAN. Fourteen dimensions of temperament. *Psychological Monographs*, **70** (1956). Pp. 26.

170. GULLAHORN, JEANNE ERARD. A factorial study of international communication and professional consequences reported by Fulbright and Smith-Mundt grantees, 1947–1957. Unpublished Ph.D. Thesis, Michigan State U., 1964.

171. GULLIKSEN, H., and L. R. TUCKER. A mechanical model illustrating the scatter diagram with oblique test vectors. *Psych.*, **16** (1951), 233–38.

172. GUTTMAN, LOUIS. Multiple rectilinear prediction and the resolution into components. *Psych.*, **5** (1940), 75–99.

173. ———. General theory and methods for matrix factoring. *Psych.*, **9** (1944), 1–16.

174. ———. The principal components of scale analysis. Chapter in Samuel A. Stouffer, *et al.*, *Measurement and prediction.* Princeton, N.J.: Princeton U. Press, (1950), 312–61.

175. ———. Multiple group methods for common-factor analysis: Their basis, computation, and interpretation. *Psych.*, **17** (1952), 209–22.

176. ———. Image theory for the structure of quantitative variates. *Psych.*, **18** (1953), 277–96.

177. ———. Some necessary conditions for common-factor analysis. *Psych.*, **19** (1954), 149–61.

178. ———. A new approach to factor analysis: The Radex. Chapter in Paul F. Lazarsfeld (ed.), *Mathematical thinking in the social sciences.* New York: Columbia U. Press, (1954), 258–348.

179. ———. The determinacy of factor score matrices with implications for five other basic problems of common-factor theory. *BJ Stat. Psych.*, **8** (1955), 65–81.

180. ———. A generalized simplex for factor analysis. *Psych.*, **20** (1955), 173–92.

181. ———. "Best possible" systematic estimates of communalities. *Psych.*, **21** (1956), 273–85.

182. ———. Successive approximations for communalities. Research report, No. 12 (1957). Berkeley, Calif.: U. of California. Pp. 13.

183. ———. A necessary and sufficient formula for matrix factoring. *Psych.*, **22** (1957), 79–81.

184. ———. Simple proofs of relations between the communality problem and multiple correlation. *Psych.*, **22** (1957), 147–57.

185. ———. To what extent can communalities reduce rank? *Psych.*, **23** (1958), 297–308.

186. ———. What lies ahead for factor analysis? (Symposium: The future of factor analysis). *Ed. Psych. Measurement*, **18** (1958), 497–515.

187. ———. Metricising rank-ordered or unordered data for linear factor analysis. *Sankhya*, **21** (1959), 157–67.

188. ———. The matrices of linear least-squares image analysis. *BJ Stat. Psych.*, **13** (1960), 109–18.

189. GUTTMAN, LOUIS, and JOSEF COHEN. Multiple rectilinear prediction and the resolution into components: II. *Psych.*, **8** (1943), 169–83.

190. HADLEY, G. *Linear algebra.* Reading, Mass.: Addison-Wesley Publishing Co., 1961. Pp. 290.

191. HALL, D. M., E. L. WELKER, and I. CRAWFORD. Factor analysis calculations by tabulating machines. *Psych.*, **10** (1945), 93–125.

192. HAMILTON, MAX. An iterative method for computing inverse matrices. *BJP Stat. Sec.*, **5** (1952), 181–88.

193. ———. An experimental approach to the identification of factors. *BJ Stat. Psych.*, **11** (1958), 161–69.

194. HARMAN, HARRY H. Systems of regression equations for the estimation of factors. *JEP*, **29** (1938), 431–41.

195. ———. Extensions of factorial solutions. *Psych.*, **3** (1938), 75–84.

196. ———. Four aspects of factor analysis. *Proceedings of Educational Research Forum*, Endicott, N.Y., August 26–31, 1940. Published by IBM Corporation, New York, N.Y., **60–68**.

197. ———. On the rectilinear prediction of oblique factors. *Psych.*, **6** (1941), 29–35.

198. ———. The square root method and multiple group methods of factor analysis. *Psych.*, **19** (1954), 39–55.

199. ———. Some observations on factor analysis. Professional paper, P-710 (1955). Santa Monica, Calif.: The RAND Corporation. Pp. 8.

200. ———. Factor analysis. Chapter in H. S. Wilf and A. Ralston (eds.), *Mathematical methods for digital computers*. New York: John Wiley & Sons, Inc., (1960), 204–12.

201. ———. Transformation of coordinates. Professional paper, SP-733 (1962). Santa Monica, Calif.: System Development Corporation. Pp. 32.

202. ———. Direct oblimin program for the Philco 2000. Technical memorandum, TM-2956 (1966). Santa Monica, Calif.: System Development Corporation. Pp. 6.

203. ———. Program for the minres method of factor analysis. Technical memorandum, TM-2958 (1966). Santa Monica, Calif.: System Development Corporation. Pp. 8.

204. ———. Program for the maximum-likelihood method of factor analysis. Technical memorandum, TM-2960 (1966). Santa Monica, Calif.: System Development Corporation. Pp. 8.

205. HARMAN, HARRY H., and YOICHIRO FUKUDA. Resolution of the Heywood case in the minres solution. *Psych.*, **31** (1966), 563–71.

206. HARMAN, HARRY H., and BERTHA P. HARPER. AGO machines for test analysis. *Proceedings of the 1953 Invitational Conference on Testing Problems*. Princeton, N.J.: Educational Testing Service (1954), 154–57.

207. HARMAN, HARRY H., and WAYNE H. JONES. Factor analysis by minimizing residuals (Minres). *Psych.*, **31** (1966), 351–68.

208. HARRIS, CHESTER W. Direct rotation to primary structure. *JEP*, **39** (1948), 449–68.

209. ———. The symmetrical idempotent matrix in factor analysis. *J. Exp. Ed.*, **19** (1951), 238–46.

210. ———. Separation of data as a principle in factor analysis. *Psych.*, **20** (1955), 23–28.

211. ———. Characteristics of two measures of profile similarity. *Psych.*, **20** (1955), 289–97.

212. ———. Relationships between two systems of factor analysis. *Psych.*, **21** (1956), 185–90.

213. ———. Some Rao-Guttman relationships. *Psych.*, **27** (1962), 247–63.

214. ———. Some problems in the description of change. *Ed. Psych. Measurement*, **22** (1962), 303–19.

215. ——— (ed.). *Problems in measuring change.* Madison, Wisc.: U. of Wisconsin Press, 1963.

216. ———. Some recent developments in factor analysis. *Ed. Psych. Measurement*, **24** (1964), 193–206.

217. HARRIS, CHESTER W., and HENRY F. KAISER. Oblique factor analytic solutions by orthogonal transformations. *Psych.*, **29** (1964), 347–62.

218. HARRIS, CHESTER W., and DOROTHY M. KNOELL. The oblique solution in factor analysis. *JEP*, **39** (1948), 385–403.

219. HARRIS, C. W., and J. SCHMID, JR. Further application of the principles of direct rotation in factor analysis. *J. Exp. Psych.*, **18** (1950), 175–93.

220. HATTORI, K., KAGAYA, and S. INANAGA. The regional structure of surrounding areas of Tokyo. *Geographical Review of Japan*, (1960), 495–514.

221. HEERMANN, EMIL F. Univocal or orthogonal estimators of orthogonal factors. *Psych.*, **28** (1963), 161–72.

222. ———. The geometry of factorial indeterminacy. *Psych.*, **29** (1964), 371–81.

223. HEMMERLE, W. J. Obtaining maximum-likelihood estimates of factor loadings and communalities using an easily implemented iterative computer procedure. *Psych.*, **30** (1965), 291–302.

224. HENDRICKSON, ALAN E., and PAUL OWEN WHITE. PROMAX: A quick method for rotation to oblique simple structure. *BJ Stat. Psych.*, **17** (1964), 65–70.

225. HENRYSSON, STEN. The significance of factor loadings—Lawley's test examined by artificial samples. *BJP Stat. Sec.*, **3** (1950), 159–65.

226. ———. *Applicability of factor analysis in the behavioral sciences: A methodological study.* Stockholm: Almqvist & Wiksell, 1957. Pp. 156.

227. ———. The relation between factor loadings and biserial correlations in item analysis. *Psych.*, **27** (1962), 419–24.

228. HERDAN, G. The logical and analytical relationship between the theory of accidents and factor analysis. *J. Roy. Stat. Soc.*, **106** (1943), 125–42.

229. HEYWOOD, H. B. On finite sequences of real numbers. *Proc. Roy. Soc. Lon.*, **134** (1931), 486–501.

230. HOEL, PAUL G. A significance test for component analysis. *Ann. Math. Stat.*, **8** (1937), 149–58.

231. ———. A significance test for minimum rank in factor analysis. *Psych.*, **4** (1939), 245–53.

232. HOLZINGER, KARL J. *Statistical résumé of the Spearman two-factor theory.* Chicago: U. of Chicago Press, 1930. Pp. iv + 44.

233. ———. On factor theory. *Conference on Individual Differences in Special and General Abilities.* Washington: National Research Council, 1931.

234. ———. Preliminary reports on Spearman-Holzinger unitary trait study, Nos. 1–9 (1934–1936). Chicago: U. of Chicago, Statistical Laboratory, Dept. of Education.

235. ———. Why do people factor? *Psych.,* **7** (1942), 147–56.

236. ———. Factoring test scores and implications for the method of averages. *Psych.,* **9** (1944), 155–67.

237. ———. A simple method of factor analysis. *Psych.,* **9** (1944), 257–62.

238. ———. Interpretation of second-order factors. *Psych.,* **10** (1945), 21–25.

239. ———. Applications of the simple method of factor analysis. *JEP,* **40** (1949), 129–42.

240. HOLZINGER, KARL J., and HARRY H. HARMAN. Relationships between factors obtained from certain analyses. *JEP,* **28** (1937), 321–45.

241. ———. Comparison of two factorial analyses. *Psych.,* **3** (1938), 45–60.

242. ———. Factor analysis. *Rev. Ed. Res.,* **9** (1939), 528–31, 619–21.

243. ———. *Factor Analysis.* Chicago: U. of Chicago Press, 1941. Pp. xii + 417.

244. HOLZINGER, KARL J., and FRANCES SWINEFORD. The bi-factor method. *Psych.,* **2** (1937), 41–54.

245. ———. A study in factor analysis: The stability of a bi-factor solution. *Supplementary Educational Monographs,* No. 48. Chicago: Dept. of Educ., U. of Chicago, 1939. Pp. 91.

246. HOLZINGER, KARL J., assisted by FRANCES SWINEFORD and HARRY H. HARMAN. *Student manual of factor analysis.* Chicago: Dept. of Educ., U. of Chicago, 1937. Pp. vi + 102.

247. HORAN, L. G. Principal factor wave forms of thoraic QRS complex. *Circulation Research,* **15** (1964), 131–45.

248. HORN, J. L. An empirical comparison of various methods for estimating common factor scores. *Ed. Psych. Measurement,* **25** (1965), 313–22.

249. ———. A rationale and test for the number of factors in factor analysis. *Psych.,* **30** (1965), 179–85.

250. HORST, PAUL. A method of factor analysis by means of which all coordinates of the factor matrix are given simultaneously. *Psych.,* **2** (1937), 225–36.

251. ———. A non-graphical method for transforming an arbitrary factor matrix into a simple structure factor matrix. *Psych.,* **6** (1941), 79–99.

252. ———. Simplified computations for the multiple group method of factor analysis. *Ed. Psych. Measurement,* **16** (1956), 101–9.

253. ———. A simple method of rotating a centroid factor matrix to a simple structure hypothesis. *J. Exp. Ed.,* **24** (1956), 251–58.

254. ———. Relations among *m* sets of measures. *Psych.,* **26** (1961), 129–49.

255. ———. Generalized canonical correlations and their applications to experimental data. *J. Clin. Psych.,* Monograph Suppl. No. 14 (1961), 331–47.

256. ———. Matrix reduction and approximation to principal axes. *Psych.,* **27** (1962), 169–78.

257. ———. *Factor analysis of data matrices.* New York: Holt, Rinehart and Winston, 1965.

258. HORST, PAUL, and K. W. SCHAIE. The multiple group method of factor analysis and rotation to a simple structure hypothesis. *J. Exp. Ed.,* **24** (1956), 231–37.

259. HOTELLING, HAROLD. Analysis of a complex of statistical variables into principal components. *JEP,* **24** (1933), 417–41, 498–520.

260. ———. The most predictable criterion. *JEP,* **26** (1935), 139–42.

261. ———. Simplified calculation of principal components. *Psych.,* **1** (1936), 27–35.

262. ———. Relations between two sets of variates. *Biom.,* **28** (1936), 321–77.

263. ———. Some methods in matrix calculation. *Ann. Math. Stat.,* **14** (1943), 1–34.

264. ———. Practical problems of matrix calculation. *Proc. Berk. Symp. Math. Stat. Probl.,* U. of California Press (1949), 275–93.

265. ———. New light on the correlation coefficient and its transforms. *J. Roy. Stat. Soc.,* **15** (1953), 193–232.

266. ———. The relations of the newer multivariate statistical methods to factor analysis. *BJ Stat. Psych.,* **10** (1957), 69–79.

267. HOUSEHOLDER, A. S., and GALE YOUNG. Matrix approximation and latent roots. *AMM,* **45** (1938), 165–71.

268. HOWE, W. G. Some contributions to factor analysis. Report No. ORNL-1919. Oak Ridge, Tenn.: Oak Ridge National Laboratory, 1955. (Ph.D. Thesis, U. of North Carolina.)

269. HSÜ, E. H. Comparative study of factor patterns, physiologically and psychologically determined. *J. Gen. Psych.,* **47** (1952), 105–28.

270. HUMPHREYS, LLOYD G. Investigations of the Simplex. *Psych.,* **25** (1960), 313–23.

271. ———. Number of cases and number of factors: An example where N is very large. *Ed. Psych. Measurement,* **24** (1964), 457–66.

272. HURLEY, J. L., and R. C. CATTELL. The Procrustes program, producing direct rotation to test an hypothesized factor structure. *Behavioral Science,* **7** (1962), 258–62.

273. IMBRIE, JOHN, and TJEERD F. VAN ANDEL. Vector analysis of heavy-mineral data. *Geol. Soc. of Am. Bull.,* **75** (1964), 1131–56.

274. IRWIN, J. O. A critical discussion of the single-factor theory. *BJP,* **23** (1933), 371–81.

275. IRWIN, LARRY. A method for clustering eigenvalues. *Psych.,* **31** (1966), 11–16.

276. JACKSON, DUNHAM. The trigonometry of correlation. *AMM,* **31** (1924), 275–80.

277. ———. The relation of statistics to modern mathematical research. *Science,* **69** (January 18, 1929), 49–54.

278. JACOBI, C. G. J. Ueber ein leichtes Verfahren die in der Theorie der Saecularstoerungen vorkommenden Gleichungen numerisch aufzuloesen. *J. Reine Angewandte Mathematik,* **30** (1846), 51–94.

279. JENNRICH, R. I., and P. F. SAMPSON. Rotation for simple loadings. *Psych.,* **31** (1966), 313–23.

280. JOHNSON, RICHARD M. On a theorem stated by Eckart and Young. *Psych.*, **28** (1963), 259–63.

281. JONES, KENNETH J. The multivariate statistical analyzer. Mimeographed report, Harvard Univ., 1964.

282. JONES, WILLIAM B., and GLENN L. FOSTER. Determinants of duration of left ventricular ejection in normal young men. *J. Applied Physiology*, **19** (1964), 279–83.

283. JORDAN, CAMILLE. Essai sur la géométrie à *n* dimensions. *Bull. S. M. France*, **3** (1875), 103–74.

284. JÖRESKOG, K. G. On the statistical treatment of residuals in factor analysis. *Psych.*, **27** (1962), 335–54.

285. ———. *Statistical estimation in factor analysis*. Stockholm: Almqvist and Wiksell, 1963. Pp. 145.

286. ———. Testing a simple structure hypothesis in factor analysis. *Psych.*, **31** (1966), 165–78.

287. ———. Computer program for estimating and testing a simple structure hypothesis in factor analysis. Research memorandum, RM-65-3 (1965). Princeton, N.J.: Educational Testing Service. Pp. 21.

288. ———. Some contributions to maximum likelihood factor analysis. Research bulletin, RB-66-41 (1966). Princeton, N.J.: Educational Testing Service. Pp. 54.

289. KAISER, HENRY F. Solution for the communalities: A preliminary report. Research report, No. 5 (1956). Berkeley, Calif.: U. of California. Pp. 19.

290. ———. Note on Carroll's analytic simple structure. *Psych.*, **21** (1956), 89–92.

291. ———. The varimax method of factor analysis. Unpublished Ph.D. Thesis, U. of California, 1956.

292. ———. Further numerical investigation of the Tryon–Kaiser solution for the communalities. Research report, No. 14 (1957). Berkeley, Calif.: U. of California. Pp. 11.

293. ———. The varimax criterion for analytic rotation in factor analysis. *Psych.*, **23** (1958), 187–200.

294. ———. Computer program for varimax rotation in factor analysis. *Ed. Psych. Measurement*, **19** (1959), 413–420.

295. ———. A note on the Tryon–Kaiser solution for the communalities. *Psych.*, **24** (1959), 269–71.

296. ———. The application of electronic computers to factor analysis. *Ed. Psych. Measurement*, **20** (1960), 141–51.

297. ———. A note on Guttman's lower bound for the number of common factors. *BJ Stat. Psych.*, **14** (1961), 1–2.

298. ———. Formulas for component scores. *Psych.*, **27** (1962), 83–87.

299. ———. Scaling a simplex. *Psych.*, **27** (1962), 155–62.

300. ———. Image analysis. Chapter in C. W. Harris (ed.), *Problems in measuring change*. U. of Wisconsin Press, 1963.

301. ———. A method for determining eigenvalues. *J. SIAM*, **12** (1964), 238–48.

302. KAISER, HENRY F., and JOHN CAFFREY. Alpha factor analysis. *Psych.*, **30** (1965), 1–14.

303. KAISER, HENRY F., and KERN W. DICKMAN. Analytic determination of common factors. Unpublished manuscript, U. of Illinois, 1959. Pp. 7 + 12.

304. KELLER, J. B. Factorization of matrices by least squares. *Biom.*, **49** (1962), 239–42.

305. KELLEY, TRUMAN L. Essential traits of mental life. *Harvard Studies in Education*, **26** (1935). Cambridge, Mass.: Harvard U. Press. Pp. 146.

306. ———. Comment on Wilson and Worcester's "Note on factor analysis." *Psych.*, **5** (1940), 117–20.

307. ———. Talents and tasks: Their conjunction in a democracy for wholesome living and national defense. *Harvard Education Papers*, No. 1 (1940). Cambridge, Mass.: Grad. School of Ed., Harvard U. Pp. 48.

308. KELLOGG, CHESTER E. The problem of principal components: Derivation of Hotelling's method from Thurstone's. *JEP*, **27** (1936), 512–20.

309. KEMPTHORNE, O. The factorial approach to the weighting problems. *Ann. Math. Stat.*, **19** (1948), 238–45.

310. KENDALL, M. G. The analysis of economic time series. *J. Roy. Stat. Soc.*, A, **116** (1953), 11–34.

311. ———. Review of Uppsala symposium on psychological factor analysis. *J. Roy. Stat. Soc.*, A, **107** (1954), 462–83.

312. KENDALL, M. G., and B. BABINGTON-SMITH. Factor analysis. *J. Roy. Stat. Soc.*, B, **12** (1950), 60–94.

313. KENDALL, M. G., and D. N. LAWLEY. The principles of factor analysis. *J. Roy. Stat. Soc.*, A, **119** (1956), 83–84.

314. KESTELMAN, H. The fundamental equation of factor analysis. *BJP Stat. Sec.*, **5** (1952), 1–6.

315. KING, BENJAMIN F. The latent statistical structure of security price changes. Unpublished Ph.D. Thesis, U. of Chicago, 1964.

316. KLOEK, T., and L. B. M. MENNES. Simultaneous equations estimation based on principal components of predetermined variables. *Econometrica*, **28** (1960), 45–61.

317. KRUMBEIN, W. C., and JOHN IMBRIE. Stratigraphic factor maps. *Bull. of Amer. Assoc. of Petroleum Geologists*, **47** (1963), 698–701.

318. LADERMAN, J. The square root method for solving simultaneous linear equations. *Math. Tables and Other Aids to Computation*, **3** (1948), 13–16.

319. LANDAHL, H. D. Time scores and factor analysis. *Pysch.*, **5** (1940), 67–74.

320. LAWLEY, D. N. The estimation of factor loadings by the method of maximum likelihood. *Proc. Roy. Soc. Edin.*, **60** (1940), 64–82.

321. ———. Further investigations in factor estimation. *Proc. Roy. Soc. Edin.*, **61** (1942), 176–85.

322. ———. The application of the maximum likelihood method for factor analysis. *BJP*, **33** (1943), 172–75.

323. ———. Problems in factor analysis. *Proc. Roy. Soc. Edin.*, **62** (1949), 394–99.

324. ———. A modified method of estimation in factor analysis and some large sample results. *Uppsala Symposium on Psychological Factor Analysis.* Uppsala: Almqvist & Wiksell (1953), 35–42.

325. ———. A statistical examination of the centroid method. *Proc. Roy. Soc. Edin.,* **64** (1955), 175–89.

326. ———. Tests of significance for the latent roots of covariance and correlation matrices. *Biom.,* **43** (1956), 128–36.

327. ———. Estimation in factor analysis under various initial assumptions. *BJ Stat. Psych.,* **11** (1958), 1–12.

328. ———. Approximate methods in factor analysis. *BJ Stat. Psych.,* **13** (1960), 11–17.

329. LAWLEY, D. N., and A. E. MAXWELL. *Factor analysis as a statistical method.* London: Butterworth, 1963. Pp. viii + 117.

330. ———. Factor transformation methods. *BJ Stat. Psych.,* **17** (1964), 97–103.

331. LAWLEY, D. N., and Z. SWANSON. Tests of significance in a factor analysis of artificial data. *BJ Stat. Psych.,* **7** (1954), 75–79.

332. LAZARSFELD, PAUL F. The logical and mathematical foundation of latent structure analysis. Chapter in Samuel A. Stouffer, *et al., Measurement and prediction.* Princeton, N.J.: Princeton U. Press, (1950), 362–412.

333. LEDERMANN, WALTER. Some mathematical remarks concerning boundary conditions in the factorial analysis of ability. *Psych.,* **1** (1936), 165–74.

334. ———. On the rank of the reduced correlation matrix in multiple-factor analysis. *Psych.,* **2** (1937), 85–93.

335. ———. The orthogonal transformations of a factorial matrix into itself. *Psych.,* **3** (1938), 181–87.

336. ———. Shortened method of estimation of mental factors by regression. *Nature,* **141** (1938), 650.

337. ———. On a shortened method of estimation of mental factors by regression. *Psych.,* **4** (1939), 109–16.

338. ———. On a problem concerning matrices with variable diagonal elements. *Proc. Roy. Soc. Edin.,* **60** (1939).

339. LEV, JOSEPH. A note on factor analysis by the method of principal axes. *Psych.,* **1** (1936), 283–86.

340. LEVIN, JOSEPH. Simultaneous factor analysis of several Gramian matrices. *Psych.,* **31** (1966), 413–19.

341. LEYDEN, T. The identification and invariance of factors. *BJ Stat. Psych.,* **6** (1953), 119.

342. LORD, FREDERICK M. A study of speed factors in tests and academic grades. *Psych.,* **21** (1956), 31–50.

343. ———. Some relations between Guttman's principal components of scale analysis and other psychometric theory. *Psych.,* **23** (1958), 291–96.

344. LORGE, IRVING, and N. MORRISON. The reliability of principal components. *Science,* **87** (May 27, 1938), 491–92.

345. LORR, M., R. L. JENKINS, and F. F. MEDLAND. Direct versus obverse factor analysis: A comparison of results. *Ed. Psych. Measurement*, **15** (1955), 441–49.

346. LORR, M., and D. M. MCNAIR. Interview relationship in therapy. *J. Nervous and Mental Diseases*, **139** (1964).

347. LUBIN, A. A note on "Criterion analysis." *Psych. Rev.*, **57** (1950), 54–57.

348. LUBIN, A., and A. SUMMERFIELD. A square root method of selecting a minimum set of variables in multiple regression: II. A worked example. *Psych.*, **16** (1951), 425–37.

349. MACKIE, JOHN. The probable value of the tetrad difference on the sampling theory. *BJP*, **19** (1928), 65–76.

350. MACRAE, DUNCAN, JR. Direct factor analysis of sociometric data. *Sociometry*, **23** (1960), 360–70.

351. MADANSKY, ALBERT. Instrumental variables in factor analysis. *Psych.*, **29** (1964), 105–13.

352. ———. On admissible communalities in factor analysis. *Psych.*, **30** (1965), 455–58.

353. ———. Triangular decomposition program. Unpublished. Santa Monica, Calif.: The RAND Corp., 1965.

354. MAXWELL, A. E. Factor models. *JEP*, **47** (1956), 129–32.

355. ———. Statistical methods in factor analysis. *Psych. Bull.*, **56** (1959), 228–35.

356. ———. Recent trends in factor analysis. *J. Roy. Stat. Soc.*, A, **124** (1961), 49–59.

357. ———. Canonical variate analysis when the variables are dichotomous. *Ed. Psych. Measurement*, **21** (1961), 259–71.

358. ———. Calculating maximum-likelihood factor loadings. *J. Roy. Stat. Soc.*, A, **127** (1964), 238–41.

359. MCDONALD, RODERICK P. A general approach to nonlinear factor analysis. *Psych.*, **27** (1962), 397–415.

360. MCMAHON, JAMES. Hyperspherical goniometry; and its application to correlation theory for *n* variables. *Biom.*, **15** (1923), 173–208.

361. MCNAIR, D. M. Analysis of professed psycho-therapeutic techniques. *J. Consulting Psychology*, **28** (1964).

362. MCNEMAR, QUINN. On the sampling errors of factor loadings. *Psych.*, **6** (1941), 141–52.

363. ———. On the number of factors. *Psych.*, **7** (1942), 9–18.

364. MEDLAND, FRANCIS F. An empirical comparison of methods of communality estimation. *Psych.*, **12** (1947), 101–9.

365. MEREDITH, WILLIAM. Notes on factorial invariance. *Psych.*, **29** (1964), 177–85.

366. ———. Rotation to achieve factorial invariance. *Psych.*, **29** (1964), 187–206.

367. ———. A method for studying differences between groups. *Psych.*, **30** (1965), 15–29.

368. MERRIFIELD, PHILIP R., and NORMAN CLIFF. Factor analytic methodology. Chapter V in *Review of Educational Research*, **33** (1963).

369. MOOD, ALEXANDER M., and FRANKLIN A. GRAYBILL. *Introduction to the theory of statistics*. New York: McGraw-Hill Book Company, second edition, 1963. Pp. xv + 443.

370. MOORE, D. W., and JOHN ROSS. A fast principal components factor analysis program for the IBM 1620. *Ed. Psych. Measurement*, **24** (1964), 675–76.

371. MOSIER, CHARLES I. Influence of chance error on simple structure. *Psych.*, **4** (1939), 33–44.

372. ———. Determining a simple structure when loadings for certain tests are known. *Psych.*, **4** (1939), 149–62.

373. MOULTON, F. R. The velocity of light. *SM*, **48** (1939), 481–84.

374. MUIR, THOMAS. *A treatise on the theory of determinants*. New York: Privately published, 1930. Revised and enlarged by WILLIAM H. METZLER.

375. MULLEN, FRANCES. Factors in the growth of girls seven to seventeen years of age. Unpublished Ph.D. Thesis, Dept. of Education, U. of Chicago, 1939.

376. *National Bureau of Standards Applied Mathematics Series*, Nos. 29, 39, 49, 57 (on the solution of linear equations and the determination of eigenvalues). Washington, D.C.: Government Printing Office, 1953–60.

377. NEUHAUS, J. O. The quartimax method. Computing program for the CRC 102-A. Berkeley, Calif.: U. of California, 1956. Pp. 14.

378. ———. Tucker's rotational procedure. Computing program for the CRC 102-A. Berkeley, Calif.: U. of California, 1956. Pp. 21.

379. NEUHAUS, JACK O., and CHARLES WRIGLEY. The quartimax method: An analytical approach to orthogonal simple structure. *BJ Stat. Psych.*, **7** (1954), 81–91.

380. ORTEGA, J. M. An error analysis of Householder's method for the symmetric eigenvalue problem. Technical report, No. 18. Appl. Math. and Stat. Laboratory, Stanford U.

381. ORTEGA, JAMES M., and HENRY F. KAISER. The LL^T and QR methods for symmetric tridiagonal matrices. *Computer Journal*, **6** (1963), 99–101.

382. OVERALL, J. E., and L. E. HOLLISTER. Computer procedures for psychiatric classification. *J. AMA*, **187** (1964).

383. OVERALL, JOHN E., and JAMES L. PORTERFIELD. Powered vector method of factor analysis. *Psych.*, **28** (1963), 415–22.

384. OVERALL, JOHN E., and CLYDE M. WILLIAMS. Models for medical diagnosis: Factor analysis. Part One, theoretical. *Medical Documentation*, **5** (1961), 51–56.

385. PAIGE, LOWELL J., and J. DEAN SWIFT. *Elements of linear algebra*. Boston: Ginn & Company, 1961.

386. PEARSON, KARL. On lines and planes of closest fit to systems of points in space. *Phil. Mag.*, **6** (1901), 559–72.

387. PEARSON, KARL, and L. N. G. FILON. On the probable errors of frequency constants and on the influence of random selection on variation and correlation. *Phil. Trans. Roy. Soc.*, **191** (1898), 229–311.

388. PEARSON, K., and M. MOUL. The mathematics of intelligence. I. The sampling errors in the theory of a generalized factor. *Biom.*, **19** (1927), 246–92.

389. PETERSON, ROBERT J., S. S. KOMORITA, and HERBERT C. QUAY. Determinants of sociometric choices. *J. Soc. Psych.*, **62** (1964), 65–75.

390. PETRINOW, L., and C. HARDYCK. Behavioral changes in Parkinson patients following surgery—Factor analytic study. *J. Chronic Diseases*, **17** (1964).

391. PINNEAU, SAMUEL R., and ALBERT NEWHOUSE. Measures of invariance and comparability in factor analysis for fixed variables. *Psych.*, **29** (1964), 271–81.

392. PINZKA, C., and D. R. SAUNDERS. Analytic rotation to simple structure, II: Extension to an oblique solution. Research bulletin, RB-54-31 (1954). Princeton, N.J.: Educational Testing Service.

393. PITTS, FORREST R. (ed.). *Urban systems and economic development*. Eugene, Ore.: U. of Oregon, School of Business Administration, 1962. Pp. x + 126.

394. RAO, C. R. Estimation and tests of significance in factor analysis. *Psych.*, **20** (1955), 93–111.

395. ———. Some statistical methods for comparison of growth curves. *Biometrics*, **14** (1958), 1–17.

396. REIERSØL, OLAV. On the identifiability of parameters in Thurstone's multiple factor analysis. *Psych.*, **15** (1950), 121–49.

397. REUCHLIN, MAURICE. *Méthodes d'analyse factorielle à l'usage des psychologues*. Paris: Presse Universitaires de France, 1964. Pp. 418.

398. REYBURN, H. A., and M. J. RAATH. Simple structure: A critical examination. *BJP Stat. Sec.*, **2** (1949), 125–33.

399. REYBURN, H. A., and J. G. TAYLOR. On the interpretation of common factors: A criticism and a statement. *Psych.*, **8** (1943), 53–64.

400. RIMOLDI, H. J. A. The central intellective factor. *Psych.*, **16** (1951), 75–101.

401. RIPPE, D. D. Application of a large sampling criterion to some sampling problems in factor analysis. *Psych.*, **18** (1953), 191–205.

402. RODGERS, DAVID A. A fast approximate algebraic factor rotation method to maximize agreement between loadings and predetermined weights. *Psych.*, **22** (1957), 199–205.

403. ROFF, MERRILL. Some properties of the communality in multiple factor theory. *Psych.*, **1** (1936), 1–6.

404. ———. The relation between results obtainable with raw and corrected correlation coefficients in multiple factor analysis. *Psych.*, **2** (1937), 35–39.

405. ———. Linear dependence in multiple correlation work. *Psych.*, **5** (1940), 295–98.

406. ROHLF, F. JAMES. Multivariate methods in taxonomy. *Proc. IBM Scientific Computing Symposium on Statistics*. White Plains. N.Y.: IBM, Data Processing Division (1965), 3–14.

407. ROHLF, F. JAMES, and ROBERT R. SOKAL. The description of taxonomic relationships by factor analysis. *Systematic Zoology*, **11** (1962), 1–16.

408. ROSNER, BURT. An algebraic solution for the communalities. *Psych.*, **13** (1948), 181–84.

409. ROSS, JOHN. Informational coverage and correlational analysis. *Psych.*, **27** (1962), 297–306.

410. RUMMEL, RUDOLPH J. Dimensions of conflict behavior within and between nations. *General Systems*, Yearbook of the Soc. for the Adv. of General Systems Theory, **8** (1963), 1–50.

411. RUMMEL, RUDOLPH J., JACK SAWYER, HAROLD GUETZKOW, and RAYMOND TANTER. *Dimensions of nations*. In press.

412. SACKMAN, HAROLD, and J. B. MUNSON. Investigation of computer operating time and system capacity for man–machine digital systems. *J. ACM*, **11** (1964), 450–64.

413. SAUNDERS, D. R. Factor analysis II: A note concerning rotation of axes to simple structure. *Ed. Psych. Measurement*, **9** (1949), 753–56.

414. ———. Practical methods in the direct factor analysis of psychological score matrices. Unpublished Ph.D. Thesis, U. of Illinois, 1950.

415. ———. An analytic method for rotation to orthogonal simple structure. Research bulletin, RB 53-10 (1953). Princeton, N.J.: Educational Testing Service.

416. ———. A computer program to find the best-fitting orthogonal factors for a given hypothesis. *Psych.*, **25** (1960), 199–205.

417. ———. The rationale for an "oblimax" method of transformation in factor analysis. *Psych.*, **26** (1961), 317–24.

418. SAWANOBORI, Y. Characteristic roots and vectors. Computing program N.Y. CRV3 for the IBM 704 at SBC N.Y. Data Processing Center. International Business Machines Corporation, 1957. Pp. 20.

419. SCHER, A. M., A. C. YOUNG, and W. M. MEREDITH. Factor analysis of the electrocardiogram. *Circulation Research*, **8** (1960), 519–26.

420. SCHMID, J., and J. M. LEIMAN. The development of hierarchical factor solutions. *Psych.*, **22** (1957), 53–61.

421. SCHNORRE, L. F. The statistical measurement of urbanization and economic development. *Land Economics*, **37** (1961), 229–45.

422. ———. A generalized solution of the orthogonal procrustes problem. *Psych.*, **31** (1966), 1–10.

423. SCHÖNEMANN, P. H. Varisim: A new machine method for orthogonal rotation. *Psych.*, **31** (1966), 235–54.

424. SCHUBERT, GLENDON. The 1960 term of the Supreme Court: A psychological analysis. *Amer. Polit. Sci. Rev.*, **56** (1962), 90–113.

425. SEARS ROEBUCK AND CO. An investigation of the dimensions of executive morale. Unpublished manuscript, Psychological Research and Services Section, National Personnel Department, 1958. Pp. 89.

426. SEVIN, HANAN C. The effects of leadership climate on nonduty behavior of Army trainees. Microfilmed Ph.D. Thesis, No. 19,256, Columbia U., 1956.

427. SHAPIRO, MIRIAM S., and MAX GOLDSTEIN. A collection of mathematical computer routines. Mimeographed report, No. NYU-1480-14 (1965). New York: Courant Institute of Mathematical Sciences, New York University.

428. SHARE General Program Library. FORTRAN subroutine HOW. SHARE distribution No. 1321.

459

429. SLATER, PATRICK. The factor analysis of matrices of negative correlations. *BJ Stat. Psych.*, **6** (1953), 101–6.

430. SNYDER, VIRGIL, and C. H. SISAM. *Analytic geometry of space.* New York: Henry Holt & Co., 1914. Pp. xi + 289.

431. SOKAL, R. R. Quantification of systematic relationships and of phylogenetic trends. *Proc. 10th International Congress Entomology*, **2** (1956), 409–15.

432. ———. Thurstone's analytical method for simple structure and a mass modification thereof. *Psych.*, **23** (1958), 237–57.

433. SOKAL, ROBERT R., HOWELL V. DALY, and F. JAMES ROHLF. Factor analytical procedures in a biological model. *U. of Kansas Science Bull.*, **42** (1961), 1099–1121.

434. SOKAL, R. R., and P. H. SNEATH. *Principles of numerical taxonomy.* New York: Freeman, 1963.

435. SOLOMON, H. A survey of mathematical models in factor analysis, Part III. In Herbert Solomon (ed.), *Mathematical thinking in the measurement of behavior.* Glencoe, Ill.: Free Press (1960), 270–314.

436. SOLOMON, H., and B. ROSNER. Factor analysis. *Rev. Ed. Res.*, **24** (1954), 421–38.

437. SOMMERVILLE, D. M. Y. *An introduction to the geometry of N dimensions.* New York: Dover Publications, Inc., 1958.

438. SPEARMAN, CHARLES. General intelligence, objectively determined and measured. *AJP*, **15** (1904), 201–93.

439. ———. Correlations of sums and differences. *BJP*, **5** (1913), 417–26.

440. ———. *The abilities of man.* New York: Macmillan Co., 1927. Pp. vi + 416 + xxxiv.

441. ———. The factor theory and its troubles. V. Adequacy of proof. *JEP*, **25** (1934), 310–19.

442. ———. Abilities as sums of factors or as their products. *JEP*, **28** (1937), 629–31.

443. SPEARMAN, C., and K. J. HOLZINGER. The sampling error in the theory of two factors. *BJP*, **15** (1924), 17–19.

444. ———. Note on the sampling error of tetrad differences. *BJP*, **16** (1925), 86–89.

445. ———. Average value for the probable error of tetrad-difference. *BJP*, **20** (1929), 368–70.

446. STEPHENSON, W. Correlating persons instead of tests. *Character and Personality*, **4** (1935), 17–24.

447. ———. The inverted factor technique. *BJP*, **26** (1936), 344–61.

448. ———. The foundations of psychometry: Four factor systems. *Psych.*, **1** (1936), 195–209.

449. ———. *The study of behavior.* Chicago: U. of Chicago Press, 1953. Pp. ix + 376.

450. STEWART, FRANK M. *Introduction to linear algebra.* New York: D. Van Nostrand Company, 1963.

451. SUMMERFIELD, A., and A. LUBIN. A square root method of selecting a minimum set of variables in multiple regression: I. The method. *Psych.*, **16** (1951), 271–84.

452. SWINEFORD, FRANCES. Some comparisons of the multiple-factor and the bi-factor methods of analysis. *Psych.*, **6** (1941), 375–82.

453. TANTER, RAYMOND. Dimensions of conflict behavior within and between nations, 1958–1960. Unpublished Ph.D. Thesis, Northwestern University, 1964.

454. TENOPYR, MARY L., and WILLIAM B. MICHAEL. The development of a modification in the normal varimax method for use with correlation matrices containing a general factor. *Ed. Psych. Measurement*, **24** (1964), 677–99.

455. THOMPSON, J. R. Boundary conditions for correlation coefficients between three and four variables. *BJP*, **19** (1928), 77–94.

456. ———. The general expression for boundary conditions and the limits of correlation. *Proc. Roy. Soc. Edin.*, **49** (1929), 65–71.

457. THOMSON, G. H. A hierarchy without a general factor. *BJP*, **8** (1916), 271–81.

458. ———. The tetrad-difference criterion. *BJP*, **17** (1927), 235–55.

459. ———. Hotelling's method modified to give Spearman's g. *JEP*, **25** (1934), 366–74.

460. ———. On complete families of correlation coefficients, and their tendency to zero tetrad-differences: Including a statement of the sampling theory of abilities. *BJP*, **26** (1935), 63–92.

461. ———. Boundary conditions in the common-factor-space, in the factorial analysis of ability. *Psych.*, **1** (1936), 155–63.

462. ———. Methods of estimating mental factors. *Nature*, **141** (1938), 246.

463. ———. The estimation of specific and bi-factors. *JEP*, **29** (1938), 355–62.

464. ———. On estimating oblique factors. *BJP Stat. Sec.*, **2** (1949), 1–2.

465. ———. *The factorial analysis of human ability.* 5th ed. New York: Houghton Mifflin Co., 1951. Pp. xvi + 383.

466. THORNDIKE, ROBERT L. Factor analysis of social and abstract intelligence. *JEP*, **27** (1936), 231–33.

467. THURSTONE, L. L. Multiple factor analysis. *Psych. Rev.*, **38** (1931), 406–27.

468. ———. *The vectors of mind.* Chicago: U. of Chicago Press, 1935. Pp. xv + 266.

469. ———. The bounding hyperplanes of a configuration of traits. *Psych.*, **1** (1936), 61–68.

470. ———. The perceptual factor. *Psych.*, **3** (1938), 1–18.

471. ———. A new rotational method in factor analysis. *Psych.*, **3** (1938), 199–218.

472. ———. Primary mental abilities. *Psychometric Monographs*, No. 1 (1938). Chicago: U. of Chicago Press. Pp. 121.

473. ———. Second-order factors. *Psych.*, **9** (1944), 71–100.

474. ———. A multiple group method of factoring the correlation matrix. *Psych.*, **10** (1945), 73–78.

475. ———. The effects of selection in factor analysis. *Psych.*, **10** (1945), 165–98.

476. ———. A single plane method of rotation. *Psych.*, **11** (1946), 71–79.

477. ———. *Multiple factor analysis.* Chicago: U. of Chicago Press, 1947. Pp. xix + 535.

478. ———. An analytical method for simple structure. *Psych.*, **19** (1954), 173–82.

479. ———. A method of factoring without communalities. *1954 Invitational Conference on Testing Problems*. Princeton, N.J.: Education Testing Service (1955), 59–62, 64–66.

480. THURSTONE, L. L., and J. W. DEGAN. A factorial study of the Supreme Court. Research report, No. 64 (1951). Chicago: U. of Chicago Psychometric Laboratory.

481. TOPMILLER, DONALD A. A factor analytic approach to human engineering analysis and prediction of system maintainability. Research report, No. AMRL-TR-64-115 (1964). Behavioral Sciences Laboratory, Air Force Systems Command, Wright-Patterson Air Force Base, Ohio. Pp. 78.

482. TRYON, R. C. Multiple factors vs. two factors as determiners of abilities. *Psych. Rev.,* **39** (1932), 324–51.

483. ———. *Cluster analysis: Correlation profile and orthometric (factor) analysis for the isolation of unities in mind and personality.* Ann Arbor: Edwards Bros., 1939. Pp. 122.

484. ———. Communality of a variable: Formulation by cluster analysis. *Psych.,* **22** (1957), 241–60.

485. ———. Cumulative communality cluster analysis. *Ed. Psych. Measurement,* **18** (1958), 3–35.

486. ———. General dimensions of individual differences: Cluster vs. multiple factor analysis. *Ed. Psych. Measurement,* **18** (1958), 477–95.

487. TRYON, ROBERT C., and DANIEL E. BAILEY. The BC TRY computer system of cluster and factor analysis. *Multivariate Behav. Res.,* **1** (1966), 95–111.

488. TUCKER, LEDYARD R. The role of correlated factors in factor analysis. *Psych.,* **5** (1940), 141–52.

489. ———. A semi-analytical method of factorial rotation to simple structure. *Psych.,* **9** (1944), 43–68.

490. ———. The determination of successive principal components without computation of tables of residual correlation coefficients. *Psych.,* **9** (1944), 149–53.

491. ———. A method for synthesis of factor analysis studies. Personnel Research Section report, No. 984 (1951). Washington, D.C.: Dept of the Army. Pp. 120.

492. ———. A restatement of the equations for Lawley's maximum likelihood method of estimating factor loadings. Mimeographed report, Princeton U., 1953.

493. ———. The objective definition of simple structure in linear factor analysis. *Psych.,* **20** (1955), 209–25.

494. ———. An inter-battery method of factor analysis. *Psych.,* **23** (1958), 111–36.

495. ———. Implications of factor analysis of three-way matrices for measurement of change. Chapter in Chester W. Harris (ed.), *Problems in measuring change.* Madison, Wis.: U. of Wisconsin Press (1963), 122–37.

496. ———. Some mathematical notes on three-mode factor analysis. *Psych.,* **31** (1966), 279–311.

497. *Uppsala Symposium on Psychological Factor Analysis 17–19 March 1953.* Uppsala: Almqvist & Wicksell, 1953. Pp. 91.

498. VEBLEN, OSWALD, and J. H. C. WHITEHEAD. The foundations of differential geometry. *Cambridge Tracts in Mathematics and Mathematical Physics*, **29** (1932). Cambridge: University Press. Pp. ix + 97.

499. VERNON, P. E. *The structure of human abilities*. New York: John Wiley & Sons, 1951. Pp. 160.

500. VERSACE, JOHN. Factor analysis of roadway and accident data. *Highway Research Board Bulletin*, **240** (1960). Washington, D.C.: National Research Council, 24–32.

501. VINCENT, D. F. The origin and development of factor analysis. *Applied Stat.*, **2** (1953), 107–17.

502. VOIERS, W. D. Perceptual bases of speaker identity. *J. Acoustical Society of America*, **36** (1964), 1065–73.

503. VON HOLDT, R. E. An iterative procedure for the calculation of the eigenvalues and eigenvectors of a real symmetric matrix. *J. ACM*, **3** (1956), 223–38.

504. WALSH, JAMES A. An IBM 709 program for factor analyzing three-mode matrices. *Ed. Psych. Measurement*, **24** (1964), 669–73.

505. WARBURTON, F. W. The full factor analysis. *BJ Stat. Psych.*, **7** (1954), 101–6.

506. ———. Analytic methods of factor rotation. *BJ Stat. Psych.*, **16** (1963), 165–74.

507. WAUGH, FREDERICK V., and PAUL S. DWYER. Compact computation of the inverse of a matrix. *Ann. Math. Stat.*, **16** (1946), 259–71.

508. WENGER, M. A., KARL J. HOLZINGER, and HARRY H. HARMAN. The estimation of pupil ability by three factorial solutions. *U. of Calif. Publ. in Psych.*, **5** (1948), viii + 161–252.

509. WESTLEY, BRUCE H., and HARVEY K. JACOBSON. Dimensions of teachers' attitudes toward instructional television. *AV Communication Rev.*, **10** (1962), 179–85.

510. WESTLEY, BRUCE H., and MERVIN D. LYNCH. Multiple factor analysis of dichotomous audience data. *Journalism Quarterly*, **39** (1962), 369–72.

511. WHERRY, ROBERT J. A new iterative method for correcting erroneous communality estimates in factor analysis. *Psych.*, **14** (1949), 231–41.

512. ———. Hierarchical factor solutions without rotation. *Psych.*, **24** (1959), 45–51.

513. WHERRY, ROBERT J., and RICHARD H. GAYLORD. The concept of test and item reliability in relation to factor pattern. *Psych.*, **8** (1943), 247–64.

514. ———. Factor pattern of test items and tests as a function of the correlation coefficient: Content, difficulty, and constant error factors. *Psych.*, **9** (1944), 237–44.

515. WHERRY, ROBERT J., and BEN J. WINER. A method for factoring large numbers of items. *Psych.*, **18** (1953), 161–79.

516. WHITE, PAUL A. The computation of eigenvalues and eigenvectors of a matrix. *J. SIAM*, **6** (1958), 393–437.

517. WHITE, R. M., D. S. COOLEY, R. C. DERBY, and F. A. SEAVER. The development of efficient linear statistical operations for the prediction of sea-level pressure. *J. of Meteorology*, **15** (1958), 426–34.

518. WHITTAKER, SIR EDMUND, and G. ROBINSON. *The calculus of observations.* London: Blackie & Son, 1944.

519. WHITTLE, P. On principal components and least square methods of factor analysis. *Skand. Aktuar.*, **35** (1952), 223–39.

520. WILD, J. Factor analysis system (FAST). Computer program, No. UCSD-64-03 (1964). La Jolla, Calif.: Computer Center, U. of California, San Diego. Pp. 46.

521. WILKINSON, J. H. Householder's method for the solution of the algebraic eigenproblem. *Computer Journal*, **3** (1960), 23–27.

522. WILKS, S. S. Weighting systems for linear functions of correlated variables when there is no dependent variable. *Psych.*, **3** (1938), 23–40.

523. ———. The large-sample distribution of the likelihood ratio for testing composite hypotheses. *Ann. Math. Stat.*, **9** (1938), 60–62.

524. WILSON, E. B. On hierarchical correlation systems. *Proc. Nat. Acad. Sci.*, **14** (1928), 283–91.

525. WILSON, E. B., and JANE WORCESTER. Note on factor analysis. *Psych.*, **4** (1939), 133–48.

526. WISHART, J. The generalized product-moment distribution in samples from a normal multivariate population. *Biom.*, A, **20** (1928), 32–52.

527. ———. Sampling errors in the theory of two factors. *BJP*, **19** (1928), 180–87.

528. ———. Multivariate analysis. *Applied Stat.*, **4** (1955), 103–16.

529. WOLD, H. Some artificial experiments in factor analysis. *Nordisk Psykologi's Monogr.* No. 3 (1953), Uppsala.

530. WOLFLE, DAEL. Factor analysis to 1940. *Psychometric Monographs*, No. 3 (1940). Chicago: U. of Chicago Press. Pp. 69.

531. WOOD, K. R., R. L. McCORNACK, and L. T. VILLONE. Non-linear factor analysis program A-78A. Technical memorandum, TM-1764 (1964). Santa Monica, Calif.: System Development Corporation.

532. WOOD, ROBERT C. *1400 governments.* Cambridge. Mass.: Harvard U. Press, 1961. Pp. 267.

533. WOODBURY, MAX A., RICHARD C. CLELLAND, and RICHARD J. HICKEY. Applications of a factor-analytic model in the prediction of biological data. *Behavorial Science,* **8** (1963), 347–54.

534. WRIGHT, T. W., and J. F. HAYFORD. *The adjustment of observations.* New York: D. Van Nostrand Co., 1906. Pp. ix + 298.

535. WRIGLEY, CHARLES. The distinction between common and specific variance in factor theory. *BJ Stat. Psych.*, **10** (1957), 81–98.

536. ———. Objectivity in factor analysis. *Ed. Psych. Measurement*, **18** (1958), 463–76.

537. ———. The effect upon the communalities of changing the estimate of the number of factors. *BJ Stat. Psych.*, **12** (1959), 35–54.

538. ———. An empirical comparison of various methods for the estimation of communalities. Contract report, No. 1 (1956). Berkeley, Calif: U. of California. Pp. 27.

539. WRIGLEY, CHARLES, and JACK O. NEUHAUS. A re-factorization of the Burt-Pearson matrix with the ORDVAC electronic computer. *BJP Stat. Sec.*, **5** (1952), 105–8.

540. ———. The use of an electronic computer in principal axes factor analysis. *JEP*, **46** (1955), 31–41.

541. ———. The matching of two sets of factors. Contract report, No. A-32, Task A (1955). Urbana, Ill.: U. of Illinois. Pp. 13.

542. WRIGLEY, CHARLES, DAVID R. SAUNDERS, and JACK O. NEUHAUS. Application of the quartimax method of rotation to Thurstone's primary mental abilities study. *Psych.*, **23** (1958), 151–70.

543. YOUNG, GALE. Matrix approximation and subspace fitting. *Psych.*, **2** (1937), 21–26.

544. ———. Factor analysis and the index of clustering. *Psych.*, **4** (1939), 201–8.

545. ———. Maximum likelihood estimation and factor analysis. *Psych.*, **6** (1941), 49–53.

546. YOUNG, GALE, and A. S. HOUSEHOLDER. Factorial invariance and significance. *Psych.*, **5** (1940), 47–56.

547. YULE, G. U., and M. G. KENDALL. *An introduction to the theory of statistics.* 14th ed. New York: Hafner, 1958.

548. ZACHERT, V., and G. FRIEDMAN. The stability of the factorial pattern of air-crew classification tests in four analyses. *Psych.*, **18** (1953), 219–24.

549. ZIMMERMAN, WAYNE S. A simple graphical method for orthogonal rotation of axes. *Psych.*, **11** (1946), 51–55.

Index to Illustrative Examples

Variables[a]	Data[b]	Direct Solutions[c]	Derived Solutions[d]	Factor Measure-ments
5 Hypothetical	117	D: 117; Min: 391, 414–15; T-F: 117		
5 Psychological	116	M-L: 391–92, 416–17; T-F: 116		
5 Socio-economic	14, 397, 425–26	Min: 204, 391, 415; M-L: 229, 392, 417; PC: 137; PF: 161–63	D-Obl: 340, 398, 427; Obl-B: 396–97, 425; Obl-Q: 396, 425; Var: 309–10	349, 359–60, 398, 427
6 Hypothetical	43, 88, 89	D: 92; Min: 391, 415; PF: 390, 411	Subj: 394, 422	
8 Emotional	164	Min: 206–7; PF: 163–65		
8 Physical	80, 81, 147–54, 222, 357, 358, 386, 394, 395, 407, 422, 423–24	M-G: 393, 420–21; Min: 204–6; M-L: 222–29, 392–93, 419; PF: 146–55, 390, 412	D-Obl: 336; Obl-B: 328; Obl-C: 328; Obl-Q: 322, 328, 396–97, 425–26; Qmax: 302–3; Subj: 262–64, 277–88; Var: 307–9	355–57, 361, 365–68, 371–73, 398–400, 428–29
8 Political	165–66, 385, 407	PF: 165–66	Binorm: 332; D-Obl: 340; Obl-B: 332; Obl-C: 332; Obl-Q: 332, 395–96, 424; Qmax: 395, 423; Var: 395, 424	
9 Psychological	244	M-G: 244–46		
13 Psychological	178, 394, 422	C: 177–86; M-L: 230	Subj: 252, 264–67, 394, 422	
24 Psychological	124–5, 128, 130, 132–33, 330, 331, 339, 393–94, 421	BiF: 129; Min: 207–10; M-L: 231; PC: 167–68; PF: 168–70	D-Obl: 338; Obl-B: 329, 397, 426; Omax: 319; Qmax: 305, 311; Subj: 311; Var: 311	399, 428

[a] Problems and exercises are excluded, unless they are used in the text.

[b] Includes raw data, correlations, estimates of communality, and some other statistics that are not expressly part of a particular factor solution.

[c] *Code for direct solutions:*

BiF = Bi-factor
C = Centroid
D = Directly from factor model
M-G = Multiple-group
Min = Minres
M-L = Maximum-likelihood
PF = Principal-factor
PC = Principal components
T-F = Two-factor

[d] *Code for derived solutions:*

Binorm = Binormamin
D-Obl = Direct Oblimin
Obl-B = Biquartimin ⎫
Obl-C = Covarimin ⎬ Oblimin types
Obl-Q = Quartimin ⎭
Omax = Oblimax
Qmax = Quartimax
Subj = Subjective (graphical)
Var = Varimax

Index